# Foundations of
# physical education

*Works of R. Tait McKenzie. Courtesy Joseph Brown, School of Architecture, Princeton University.*

# Foundations of physical education

## Charles A. Bucher, A.B., M.A., Ed.D.
Director of Graduate Study in Physical Education and
Professor of Education, New York University,
New York, N. Y.

Fifth edition

With 330 illustrations

THE C. V. MOSBY COMPANY

Saint Louis  1968

To
our physical education colleagues
in other lands

# Preface

An author can revise a textbook in one of two ways. He can go through the text and make some superficial changes so that it doesn't require too much time and effort. Because of the pressures of one's routine professional duties and family and community responsibilities there is always a temptation to follow this procedure. However, a much more thorough and comprehensive revision has gone into the fifth edition of this book, *Foundations of Physical Education*. The goal has been to have a book that is up to date and that renders a contribution to the field of endeavor it serves. The author feels that this has been accomplished.

To perform this task has meant a careful analysis of the current edition; having talks with students, professors, and leaders in the field to get their reactions and suggestions; and holding conferences with the publisher to determine how he felt the text should be upgraded. Then came the task of going through each page and chapter of the text and spending hour after hour thinking, reading, researching, and writing the revised edition. The total task has required many hundreds of hours of great effort and work.

The fifth edition of the *Foundations* text has been thoroughly revised. It was the author's first book. It is also his favorite since it reaches so many of the new members who enter the ranks of physical education, as well as the many lay persons and leaders in the field. In performing this laborious task the author is deeply indebted to Miss Myra Goldman who helped immeasurably in the work that needed to be done. Her outstanding ability to contribute new ideas and material such as are found in the chapter on movement education, to analyze the old material, to organize the author's notes into meaningful statements, and to type the many additions the author prepared for this text is greatly appreciated.

A new chapter on the movement of education has been added; the international physical education chapter has been greatly expanded. The first chapter, Physical Education—An Emerging Profession, should be thought provoking for students majoring in this field. Projecting physical education into the future as a result of considerable research should be helpful to those persons planning for the years ahead; and an accurate analysis of the employment picture has been made and discussed. This constitutes only a small part of this revision. Each chapter has been changed to make it more meaningful and helpful to the reader.

*Charles A. Bucher*

# Preface to first edition

Since becoming a member of the physical education profession fifteen years ago, it has been the author's observation that there is a definite need for a book that presents the basic facts concerning the nature and scope of physical education. Therefore, this book has been written.

The author attempts to answer questions which would be raised by a student, teacher, administrator, parent, or other interested person, such as: What is the meaning and what are the objectives of physical education, what have been the changing attitudes toward this field of endeavor, and what are its relationships to allied areas? What are the biological, psychological, and sociological foundations of physical education? What preparation should physical educators have, what kind of work do they perform, where do they do it, and what is the need for their services? What qualifications are needed in their work, what problems and challenges will they meet on the job, and what does the future hold for their profession?

In the troubled times through which the world is passing, many opportunities are presenting themselves to the field of physical education. Through well-organized physical education programs individuals can be made more physically and mentally fit for the arduous duties they are being required to perform. Furthermore, the importance of democratic principles in day-to-day living can be more fully realized. It is hoped that in some measure this book will help the profession of physical education to realize its potentialities.

The author wishes to express his appreciation to the many authors, professional organizations, and publishing firms for permission to use quotations, illustrations, and other material. The writer also wishes to thank the many educators, state directors of physical education, officers of the American Association for Health, Physical Education, and Recreation, chairmen of departments of physical education, presidents of professional organizations, and others who supplied material for this book.

The author is particularly indebted to his wife, Jacqueline D. Bucher, whose constant cooperation, assistance, and encouragement made this book possible. Literally hundreds of hours were spent by her in editing and typing the manuscript and in discussing various problems concerned with publication.

The writer wishes to thank Dr. Jay B. Nash, Chairman, Department of Physical Education, Health and Recreation, New York University, for his guidance, help, conferences, and encouragement. His willingness to confer with the author at any time, his comments and suggestions after reading the manuscript, and his offer to write the introduction which so aptly presents the problems to be discussed in this book have been greatly appreciated.

Acknowledgment is also made to Dr. Leslie W. Irwin of Boston University for his suggestions and guidance and to Dr. T. Erwin Blesh of Yale University for his help.

*Charles A. Bucher*
NEW YORK, N. Y.

# Contents

**PART THREE**

# Relationship of physical education to health, recreation, camping, and outdoor education

**PART FOUR**

# Changing concepts of physical education

**PART FIVE**

# Scientific foundations of physical education

Chapter **20** Duties of physical education personnel, 607

Chapter **21** Professional preparation in physical education, 629

## PART SEVEN

# The profession

Chapter **22** Professional organizations, 669

Chapter **23** Certification requirements for employment in physical education, 702

The onslaught

*Works of R. Tait McKenzie.*
*Courtesy Joseph Brown, School of Architecture, Princeton University.*

**PART ONE**

# Nature and scope of physical education

# Chapter 1

# Physical education as an emerging profession

Many occupations, trades, crafts, and other fields of endeavor constantly strive to achieve professional status. Library workers, pharmacy specialists, social workers, business management people, and physical educators, to name a few, hope to eventually receive the accolade of the status of a profession. At the present time these fields of endeavor are not members of the family of professions in the same sense that medicine and law are, but they are constantly working toward that goal.

Although some vocations call themselves professions, this does not mean it is necessarily true. They may have satisfied some of the requirements but have failed to achieve full-fledged professional status. Physical education is at times labeled a profession by some of its practitioners and leaders. Most of us use the term rather loosely and, in so doing, mean that we who perform this valuable service are bound together by close ties that have been developed through training and experience. We are dedicated to our work and contribute to the good of society, and therefore we feel we rate the status of a profession. In fact, the reader will find physical education referred to as a profession in this light throughout this book. However, in a strict interpretation of the term "profession," it can be stated more accurately that physical education is emerging as a profession rather than having achieved the professional status of medicine, law, or theology.

We who associate ourselves with the field of physical education want to see it become a strong profession and be widely accepted by educators and the public in general. We feel strongly about the importance of our work and the service it renders to education and humanity. At the same time we recognize that we must earn the right to the professional label, and therefore we are working hard to see that this becomes a reality. We recognize there are certain benefits associated with being called a profession. As physical educators, we want to achieve these benefits for ourselves and our colleagues.

## WHY BE A PROFESSION?

Some of the benefits associated with achieving full professional status are the following:

1. *A profession has public recognition.* The doctor or lawyer is a person who is engaged in a highly respected type of work. The public trusts his judgment and skill. His profession rates high with the

**3**

rank and file of the entire population. The doctor or lawyer in the public's eyes is rendering an outstanding service to humanity—one that society cannot readily do without, one that the lay person cannot perform for himself. The diagnosis of disease and the accurate interpretation of the legal statutes is beyond the untrained person's grasp and, therefore, he seeks the services of the professional to help him solve his problems.

2. *A profession is more selective as to whom it permits to practice in its specialty.* Not everyone can belong to the profession of medicine or law. Just because a student may have graduated from high school and gained college admittance does not mean that he is eligible to become a member of the medical or legal fraternity. He may rank high in his class, be an All-American football player, and an outstanding debater, but this is not enough to open the gates to the profession. There are other qualifications that must be met

—stringent requirements that very few persons are successful in meeting. Because of the selective procedures that are followed there is usually a shortage of such professionals, and therefore the demand is great and the services are sought after very intensely. The result: *It is an honor* for a young person to belong to such a select group. Many want to be admitted but few are chosen.

3. *A profession permits its practitioners more freedom in rendering their services to society.* The doctor or lawyer is not in a position where he is told what to do and how to do it by a lay person, a person who has little specialized knowledge about the field, service, or practice. The members of the medical and legal professions have a degree of autonomy that enables them to decide important questions about their specialty for themselves. They have freedom to decide what to do on their own as a result of their own knowledge, skill, and experience. They do

not have to punch clocks or conform to the wishes of the uninformed. Furthermore, only the professional himself can say when his colleague makes a mistake.

4. *The future belongs to the professionals.* The members of the professions possess the knowledge, skill, and render the services needed in the space age. This is why a large percentage of the gross national product is spent each year on the training of professionals. This is why highschool students and those going on to college are profession oriented. This is why many college graduates are planning to do graduate work that will admit them to one of the professions. This is why industry has become more dependent upon the services of the professions. This is why there are great expansion plans for the traditional professions and the nation is giving birth to many new professions.

It is the hope of each one of us who believes in the field of physical education that it will become one of the new professions to emerge in the future. Whether or not this becomes a reality will depend upon each major student studying in the nation's colleges and universities, and upon each leader practicing his art in the nation's institutions of learning and other settings, wherever they may exist. Physical educators will determine their own destiny as they meet the requirements for professional status.

## WHAT REQUIREMENTS MUST PHYSICAL EDUCATION MEET IN ORDER TO ACHIEVE PROFESSIONAL STATUS?

Although many authors and organizations have set forth what they believe to be the requirements of a profession, none have been more widely accepted than those of Myron Lieberman.* His eight

*Lieberman, Myron: Education as a profession, Englewood Cliffs, N. J., 1956, Prentice-Hall, Inc.

characteristics of a profession are presented here in terms of the requirements that physical education must meet if it is to achieve professional status. In addition, the author lists some questions for the reader to think about and answer for himself.

1. *To be a profession physical education must perform a unique and essential service.* The service must be identified clearly, be specific, and be essential. The group that performs the service must be clearly discernible from other groups in the population, as being qualified and capable of performing this valuable and unique service for all people. The service has outstanding social significance and serves practical and definite ends.

**Question 1:** Are physical educators clearly discernible from other groups in our society as individuals who help human beings understand and benefit from the contribution that physical activity makes to physical, mental, and social development?

**Question 2:** Are physical educators sometimes confused with other groups of individuals such as professional athletes, slenderizing salon operators, and physical-fitness faddists, in rendering a service supposedly uniquely associated with physical education?

2. *To be a profession the field of physical education must be so constituted that there is an emphasis upon intellectual techniques in the performance of the service.* The unique service that is performed by the group must be intellectually oriented. It must be based on science and learning. It must be based upon knowledge, logic, and sound judgment, as contrasted to mere manual skill. When manual skills are a part of the service, then the skills must depend upon high-level intellectual controls.

**Question 1:** Is the service rendered by physical educators intellectually oriented?

**Question 2:** Are the skills involved in

physical education guided by high-level intellectual controls?

3. *To be a profession physical education must require a long period of training for its members.* Since the service rendered by a profession is based upon a high-level intellectual orientation, there is a need to provide an extended period of professional preparation, in order to impart the specialized knowledge, mental skills, and other scientific foundations which are essential to the adequate performance of the service.

**Question 1:** Does the period of professional preparation in physical education provide adequate time for laying the necessary foundations which are essential for the performance of the service?

**Question 2:** Is the length and depth of professional preparation in such areas as foundational sciences, human growth and development, skills, movement analysis, philosophy, measurement and evaluation, and methodology, sufficient to provide the training that is needed to effectively perform this unique service?

4. *To be a profession physical education must have considerable autonomy for both its practitioners and the members of the group as a whole.* The nature of a professional service is so technical that the persons rendering the service are granted a great measure of autonomy in deciding the nature of the service, how it should be performed, and the choice of the individuals who are permitted to render this important contribution to society. Furthermore, the members of the profession are granted considerable freedom in carrying out this service, free from supervision.

**Question 1:** Are physical educators permitted to determine who will become duly licensed members of their group and who are thereby permitted to perform this valuable service?

**Question 2:** Are physical educators who teach at the various educational levels permitted to act on their own and make important decisions for themselves?

5. *To be a profession physical educators must accept responsibility for their behavior and judgments, within the scope of*

*their professional autonomy.* While physical educators are in the gymnasium teaching classes, conducting their intramurals, coaching athletic teams, and performing the myriad of other responsibilities they are assigned to carry out, they must accept responsibility for the autonomy they are given and for the freedom they enjoy as members of a profession.

**Question 1:** Do physical educators in order to make wise judgments keep themselves well-informed by reading the latest professional literature so that they can render their professional service in the best manner possible?

**Question 2:** Are physical educators inwardly motivated to discover and implement the best teaching techniques, to make the most valuable use of each teaching period, and to render this valuable professional service to each student, in accordance with his needs?

6. *To be a profession physical educators must recognize that the service rendered is more important than the economic gain derived.* The service rendered is so essential to society that it must be rendered regardless of economic gain. This does not mean there are no economic rewards for performing the service. However, it does mean that the practitioner is obligated to consider the service before the reward. On some occasions he may even be required to perform the service without any economic gain whatsoever. The spirit of public service pervades each member of the group.

**Question 1:** Are physical educators interested more in professional service than personal profit?

**Question 2:** Are physical educators able to control the market for their services in the same way that doctors and lawyers are, and can they thereby affect their economic position?

7. *To be a profession physical educators must have a self-governing, professional organization of their practitioners.* A pro-

fessional organization of the practitioners is needed to control, police, upgrade, and insure a continuous flow of well-prepared members to its ranks, thus extending its public acceptance.

**Question 1:** What is the self-governing organization of physical educators?

**Question 2:** In what specific ways are physical educators controlled, policed, and upgraded by their professional associations? How are only well-prepared members recruited and permitted to enter the ranks by these professional organizations?

8. *To be a profession physical educators must have a code of ethics that has been reinforced and interpreted by concrete cases that have been reviewed under the conditions of the "Code."* The individual practitioner is expected to guide himself by the professional code of ethics that has been developed by the organization for the good of the profession. The code reflects a primary orientation to the community interest rather than to individual self-interest.

**Question 1:** Do physical educators have a code of ethics? What is it?

**Question 2:** Do physical educators have a way of summoning the moral force of their professional group against the malpractices of members of their group?

## PROBLEMS AND STEPS BEING TAKEN BY OCCUPATIONS TO ACHIEVE PROFESSIONAL STATUS

Occupations desiring to become professions follow many steps in order to achieve the coveted status. For example, they try to find an intellectual base for their work. The YMCA secretary wants to be recognized for more than the help he gives to young people looking for the right path to a meaningful life. Therefore, he points out, there is an intellectual base to his work. This consists of a knowledge of human growth and development, of human behavior, and of the nature of life in the community. The school administrator is busy trying to develop a science of administration, as is the specialist in business management. The librarian is trying to be recognized as an expert on the effects of reading on human beings, and also in certain areas of communications. Therefore, it can be seen that occupations desiring to become professions establish a rationale, a system of knowledge, which forms the intellectual foundation of the field of endeavor. Furthermore, since members of the special group are not uniformly inculcated with this knowledge, the group attempts to see that the selection and training of the members make such a goal possible. The leaders in the group take the initiative in pushing for such achievement.

Occupations desiring to become professions try to show they are rendering a service rather than working entirely for profit. This is why insurance agents say they are not selling, but that they are instead rendering a service by giving people expert, specialized advice on risks they face from day to day in their lives, and telling them how to protect themselves from these risks. There is a concerted effort on the part of the group seeking professional status to establish the fact that the profit motive is not the basis for their operation, but instead, it is a concern for the welfare of society and the need for human betterment.

Occupations desiring to become professions have courses established in undergraduate and graduate schools for training in their fields of work. In so doing, they show that an extended period of preparation is needed to effectively perform their service. Furthermore, since more special knowledge is needed for the more elite positions in their occupational structures, the advanced work frequently related to a master's or doctorate degree is an indication that the individual has mastered the advanced knowledge, and is thereby eligible for a higher position.

Occupations desiring to become professions seek more independence, more recognition, and a clear delineation of their service, as related to other outside groups that perform similar services. This step requires a careful delineation of the training required and service performed by the occupational group, in order to clarify and show how their membership differs from others who claim to perform similar services for society. The problem is not only establishing the rationale involved for such reasoning, but also communicating effectively this line of reasoning to the public in general.

Occupations desiring to become professions seek to establish requirements for entry into their professions. Furthermore, they try to police the profession with the result that in some cases charlatans and quacks are expelled from the organizations. There is keen competition on the part of the group to attract to its fold the most qualified trainees possible. Once they have in their ranks the most eligible candidates, they shepherd them with great care, impressing upon them their commitment to their field of endeavor.

Occupations desiring to become professions become more sensitive to public opinion, and therefore public relations becomes a necessity in conveying to outsiders the esoteric service that is being rendered by this important group of individuals.

Occupations desiring to become professions construct codes of ethics to guide the behavior of the members of the group. However, in many cases, the members find that these codes are too general in nature and quite difficult to identify with. Very often the machinery for enforcement of the codes is inadequate and ineffective.

Finally, the leaders and intellectuals in the occupational group recognize the weaknesses and inadequacies of their membership, and the difficulties in striving for the status of a profession. In justifying

Physical education demonstration in Japan.

this problem, however, they point to the fact that many of the traditional professions experienced the same growing difficulties and problems that they are experiencing, and that with time they will erase these weaknesses. Thus, as one leader of the American Management Association pointed out: "It's something like medicine years ago, when the doctors came to the realization that working in a drugstore was not sufficient training for their profession. Now management is going through a similar transition."*

Physical education as an emerging profession is facing problems that many occupational groups have faced in trying to achieve their goals. A field of endeavor does not receive the status of a profession in one quick step or in a short period of time. This takes many years to accomplish, and requires outstanding leadership, sound thinking, a great deal of research,

*The New York Times, December 27, 1957.

and a dedicated membership. Physical education as we know it today is comparatively young. The American Association for Health, Physical Education, and Recreation (AAHPER) was established in 1885. We have come a long way. We are emerging as a profession. We should stride forward with great vigor to insure that we become a strong profession.

## CURRENT STATUS OF PHYSICAL EDUCATION

Thus far in this chapter we have seen the benefits associated with the status of a profession, the criteria that must be met to achieve such status, some of the problems encountered, and steps being taken by other occupations to achieve this status. Now we turn to the present status of physical education, and finally, to some specific steps that physical education needs to take to achieve true professional status.

## What students think about physical education

With the help of my students, I have surveyed the thinking of many pupils in our elementary and secondary schools to find out what they think about physical education. Following is a partial list of what boys and girls feel are some of the values and strengths and weaknesses of physical education. These findings are listed to help the reader more clearly understand what other people think is the meaning of physical education.

### Some of the values pupils found in physical education

1. Learned to play well
2. Learned how to get along with others
3. Had fun
4. Exercised
5. Helped in becoming a healthy person
6. Learned not to cheat
7. Improved physical skills
8. Developed sportsmanship qualities
9. Developed teamwork
10. Released excess energy
11. Trained the body
12. Provided a necessary and healthy balance for mental activities
13. Developed a stronger body
14. Became better coordinated
15. Relaxed
16. Learned how to express self through use of the body
17. Learned rules of games and sports
18. Developed good attitudes
19. Made new friends
20. Learned to assume responsibility
21. Developed poise
22. Helped to keep weight down
23. Developed skills for later life
24. Learned to follow directions
25. Developed self-confidence
26. Learned to give and take
27. Developed feeling of accomplishment
28. Became physically fit
29. Found outlet for mental frustration

*Cornell College, Mount Vernon, Iowa.*

One value of physical education is learning how to express oneself through use of the body.

30. Developed socially
31. Developed proper posture
32. Developed interest in national and international sports
33. Developed leadership qualities
34. Developed character
35. Improved personality
36. Developed such qualities as courage and self-discipline
37. Developed will power

## Some strengths of physical education programs listed by pupils

1. Good instructors
2. Variety of activities
3. Good facilities
4. Excellent after-school program
5. Vigorous exercise
6. Well-organized program
7. Leaders' club
8. Five-day-a-week program
9. Sports and skills taught thoroughly
10. Physical fitness made interesting
11. Exercises given daily
12. Gymnasiums open before and after school for exercising
13. Awards provide motivation
14. After-school activities are an outgrowth of the regular program

## Some weaknesses of physical education programs listed by pupils

1. Poor instructors
2. Lack of planning and organization
3. Insufficient variety of activity
4. Crowded classes
5. Poor facilities
6. Individual instruction lacking
7. Easy tests
8. Lack of motivation
9. Periods too short
10. Insufficient calisthenics
11. No adapted program
12. Too much exercise—no time for sports
13. No defined program
14. Too competitive

## Place of physical activity in the lives of educators, parents, and general public

A survey of one hundred teachers, professors, parents, representatives of the general public, superintendents and principals of schools, and directors of physical education was conducted to determine what role physical activity played in their day-to-day routines.

**Question 1:** How much time do you spend on the average in physical activity each day?

The majority of the persons interviewed (87%) spent more than one-half hour per day in some type of physical activity. For some of these persons it was part of their job, but most persons surveyed indicated that they engaged in physical activity outside of their working hours. Some types of activity engaged in were walking, calisthenics, running, team sports, and individual sports. Educators were the only group surveyed where the majority indicated they spent less than half an hour per day in physical activity outside of work hours, whereas the other groups surveyed indicated they spent more than half an hour in physical activity outside of working hours.

**Question 2:** How much time should you spend in physical activity each day?

Ninety-seven per cent of the persons surveyed felt that at least one-half hour of physical activity should be engaged in each day. Those surveyed indicated that it is important to exercise but that daily professional tasks often prevented such a practice.

**Question 3:** What type of physical activity do you engage in most frequently?

Sixty-three per cent of the persons surveyed participated in some form of individual sports, 11% participated in team sports, and 49% engaged in some type of calisthenic exercise during out-of-work hours.

**Question 4:** Would physical activity be beneficial to competence in your position?

A group of 126 students were included as part of the survey in respect to this question. These students as a group did not see the value of physical activity as a means of helping them with their school work.

The adults who were surveyed indicated that physical activity was beneficial to their work. They listed such factors as the following: it helped them to feel better, they were more alert, they could work longer without fatigue, it provided relief from nervous tension, they did not tire so easily, and it contributed to their appearance.

**Question 5:** Does physical activity have a beneficial effect on general health?

All persons surveyed indicated that they felt there was a positive correlation between physical activity and general health. Some factors they listed included: weight kept under control, waste eliminated from the system, muscle tonus increased, relaxation furthered, and cardiorespiratory development enhanced.

**Question 6:** Does physical activity have a healthful effect on physical development?

All persons surveyed felt that physical activity contributed to physical development. They indicated that the human body needs physical activity for its normal development and best functioning. They did mention, however, that exercise might be harmful to some persons.

**Question 7:** Does the viewing of professional sports on television enhance the nation's desire for participation in physical activity?

The majority of the persons surveyed felt that it could possibly have some effect on the nation's physical activity participation, but most persons surveyed had grave doubts. Some of the factors listed included: "It might help in certain sports such as tennis, golf, and bowling." "Small children might idolize the professionals and this could motivate them to participate." "Watching sports will only make the person more adept at watching and will not aid in getting him to participate."

"Watching will make the person more passive toward physical activity."

## Attitude of educators, parents, and general public regarding role of physical education in schools and colleges

The same one hundred persons surveyed concerning the place of physical activity in their lives were also asked the question about the role of physical education in the schools. The questions and the reactions of the persons surveyed are as follows:

**Question 1:** Is physical education essential to a well-balanced educational program?

Eighty-nine per cent of the persons surveyed indicated overwhelming support for physical education as a part of the educational program. The exact role that physical education should play in general education was not clear, but the need for such a program was recognized by most persons surveyed.

**Question 2:** Do you feel that physical education classes should be similar in scope and objectives to all phases of the educational program?

The response to this question ranged from a question being raised to a "Yes" answer. In general, the persons surveyed (59%) felt there was a positive correlation between what physical education is trying to do and what other aspects of the program are attempting to accomplish. The most prevalent question raised the point as to whether physical education should be concerned with a mental objective in the same way that other subjects are. Some persons seemed to feel that physical education should be concerned only with education of the physical.

**Question 3:** Which of the following terms best defines physical education? (Athletics, Calisthenics, Movement, Physical Fitness, Skill Development, All of the terms collectively.) A space was also provided to list any other terms that define physical education.

The majority of the persons surveyed (52%) indicated that all the terms that were cited should be included in a definition of physical education. The term "physical fitness" was thought by many (27%) to be the term that should be used.

**Question 4:** How much time should be devoted to physical education in the school program each week? (1 period per day, 3 times per week, 2 times per week, other).

Sixty-one per cent of the persons surveyed felt that physical education should be taught once a day. Only two groups, the professors and the parents, indicated they might possibly be more in favor of three times a week. One principal made an interesting comment: "Physical education should be conducted at the close of school and required for all students. Those on athletic teams would practice at this time and the others would have regular physical education classes."

**Question 5:** Which type of activities should be most emphasized in physical education? (Team Sports, Carry-over Activities, Individual Sports, General Exercises, Recreational Activities, Other.)

Most of the persons surveyed felt that all types of activities should be given in physical education, although there was some feeling that recreational activities should not be a part of physical education. Some persons stressed that the type of program would depend upon the student's needs, age, facilities, and teachers available.

**Question 6:** What should be the average size of the physical education class?

Principals and superintendents as a group seemed to feel that the physical education class should be larger than the size of classes for the academic subjects.

They were the only group that felt this way. It was pointed out by several persons surveyed that many times the answer would be dependent upon the size of the school, activity involved, facilities, and number of teachers available.

**Question 7:** What should be the basis for grading in physical education classes?

The majority of the persons surveyed felt that physical education grades should be done on a separate report from the other educational offerings. School administrators and professors were the only groups to feel that it should correspond with the marking in other subjects. Some comments made by the persons surveyed included: "It should be based upon the improvement the student makes in class." "Unsatisfactory and Satisfactory are sufficient grades for students in physical education." "It depends upon the objectives of the school." "Marking in physical education is so subjective that it cannot be done properly."

## PHYSICAL EDUCATION DEFINED

Physical education as a career offers many opportunities to the individual who likes to work with children and adults, likes a large variety of games and sports, enjoys working in the out-of-doors and in the gymnasium or swimming pool, and is interested in rendering a service to mankind, as well as leading a vigorous and interesting life. Each potential and active member of the physical education profession should understand clearly such things as the meaning of the name given to this field of endeavor, the activities that comprise this field, the qualifications necessary for an individual performing this type of work, the opportunities available, the preparation required, and the responsibilities involved. Such information will help the individual to become more fully aware of the part he or she can play in physical education.

Some individuals think physical education is concerned only with varsity sports; some think of it as muscles and perspiration; to others it means "arms and legs and good intentions"; to others it means body building; and to others it is calisthenics done to the shouting in cadence of "1, 2, 3, 4." Because of the confusion that exists in regard to physical education, and because of the numerous definitions that have come down through history, first, it seems imperative to clarify what is meant by education; second, what is meant by physical education as applied to education; and third, what is meant by such terminology as hygiene, physical culture, gymnastics, physical training, athletics, and physical education.

**Meaning of the term "education"**

The term *education* means different things to different individuals. One individual will define it as a training process that comes about through study and instruction; another person will say it is a series of experiences that enables a person to better understand new experiences; and to others it means growth and adjustment. John Dewey, an educator who has most profoundly influenced present-day education, defines education as the reconstruction of events that compose the lives of individuals so that new happenings and new events become more purposeful and more meaningful. Furthermore, through education, individuals will be better able to regulate the direction of ensuing experience. Dewey's interpretation, it seems, sums up in a few words what is meant by education. It means that a person thinks in terms of his previous experiences. It further means that the individual's education consists of everything he does from birth until death. Education is a "doing" phenomenon. You learn through doing. Education takes place in the classroom, in the library, on the playground, in the gymnasium, on trips, and at home. It is not confined to a school or a church

but takes place wherever individuals congregate.

The problem now arises as to what experiences will best result in a happy and rich life. The solution seems to be in the provision of experiences that will have a practical value in the lives of individuals as they live from day to day. Worthwhile experiences will enable a person to live a more purposeful, a more interesting, and a more vigorous life. The aim or goals of education, therefore, should receive consideration if a person is to know in what direction educational experiences are to be guided. The Educational Policies Commission, in discussing policies for education in American democracy, states the following as the purpose of education:

. . . The primary business of education, in effecting the promises of American democracy, is to guard, cherish, advance, and make available in the life of coming generations the funded and growing wisdom, knowledge, and aspirations of the race. This involves the dissemination of knowledge, the liberation of minds, the development of skills, the promotion of free inquiries, the encouragement of the creative or inventive spirit, and the establishment of wholesome attitudes toward order and change—all useful in the good life for each person, in the practical arts, and in the maintenance and improvement of American society, as our society, in the world of nations. So conceived, education seems to transcend our poor powers of accomplishment. It does in fact, if perfection be expected; but such is the primary business of public education in the United States; theory supports it; practice inadequately illustrates and confirms it.*

It is of interest to note, while reflecting on this statement of the purpose of education, that knowledge in itself is not enough. In addition, such a thing as ethics is also indispensable. As this report points out, "The nature of the knowledge

---

*Educational Policies Commission: Policies for education in American democracy, Washington, D. C., 1946, National Education Association and American Association of School Administrators, p. 60.

to be disseminated is qualified by the condition, 'useful in the good life and in the maintenance and improvement of American society.' Both ethics and the nature of American civilization are drawn into immediate and inescapable consideration."*

The Commission further points out that education is as much concerned with the training of the body and spirit as with the transmission of knowledge.

It is not merely with the transmission of knowledge that education is deeply concerned. The functions of the schools are not fully described by a summary of programs, curriculum, and methods. No written or spoken words do, or can, completely convey the meaning of education as the day-to-day living force that it is in fact and may be—in the transactions of the classroom, in the relations of teacher and pupil, in the associations of pupil and pupil, and in the experiences of the library and athletic field. Here are exchanges, bearings, and influences too subtle for logical expression and exact measurement. Yet we cannot doubt their existence, at least those of us who recall our own educational experiences and see teachers at work. Here, in the classroom, the auditorium, laboratory, and gymnasium, are in constant operation moral and cultural forces just as indispensable to civilization as knowledge or any material elements—indeed primordial in nature and the pre-conditions for the civilized uses of material things.†

It can readily be seen that physical education, with its emphasis on building a physically, emotionally, mentally, and socially fit society, definitely plays an important role in modern-day education. The mind and body represent a unity in man. One gives strength to the other, one supports the other, and both function harmoniously in the educated person.

The Educational Policies Commission also points out four groups of objectives in discussing the purpose of education. These purposes are the objectives of (1) self-realization, (2) human relationship, (3) economic efficiency, and (4) civic responsibility.

The objectives of self-realization concern themselves with such important items as the desire for learning; the ability to speak, read, and write effectively; an acquisition of knowledge and habits concerned with healthful living; and the ability to use leisure time in a wholesome and satisfying manner.

The objectives of human relationship are concerned with such things as an appreciation of the home, friendships, courtesy, the value of human welfare, and the ability to work harmoniously with one's fellowmen.

The objectives of economic efficiency pertain to producer and consumer education. On the one hand, this stresses such things as the importance of good workmanship, selecting one's vocation carefully, and occupational adjustment, appreciation, and efficiency; and on the other hand, it stresses such things as consumer judgment, buying, and protection.

The objectives of civic responsibility apply to such things as the citizen's responsibility to his fellowmen, to his country, and to the world; his responsibility for developing a tolerant, scientific, critical, sympathetic, and cooperative attitude within himself; and his responsibility for developing an unswerving loyalty to the democratic way of life.

A heavy responsibility rests upon the shoulders of those who spend a large share of their time with the youth of today. If experiences are provided that are satisfying, successful, and directed toward enriching an individual's life, these pur-

---

*Educational Policies Commission: Policies for education in American democracy, Washington, D. C., 1946, National Education Association and American Association of School Administrators, p. 62.

†Educational Policies Commission: Policies for education in American democracy, Washington, D. C., 1946, National Education Association and American Association of School Administrators, p. 64.

Attention in education should be focused on the child.

poses of education will be accomplished. However, if there is a shunning of this responsibility, if an indifferent attitude is assumed, if attention is not focused on the child, if children are allowed to grow up without having experiences that build for the good life, then education, as provided through organized institutions, is not realizing its potentialities. Every teacher has within his or her power the ability to aid in the fulfillment of the objectives of self-realization, human relationship, economic efficiency, and civic responsibility in each individual. The education that takes place on the playground, in the swimming pool, and in the gymnasium can help considerably in accomplishing these purposes.

## Physical education as applied to education

The term *physical education* takes on a new meaning after a consideration of the word *education*. The word *physical* refers to the body. It is often used in reference to various bodily characteristics such as physical strength, physical development, physical prowess, physical health, and physical appearance. It refers to the body as contrasted to the mind. Therefore, when you add the word *education* to the word *physical* and use the words *physical education,* you are referring to the process of education that goes on when activities that develop and maintain the human body are concerned. When an individual is playing a game, swimming, marching, working out on the parallel bars, skating, or performing in any one of the gamut of physical education activities that aid in the development and maintenance of his body, education is taking place at the same time. This education may be conducive to the enrichment of the individual's life or it may be detrimental. It may be a satisfying experience or it may be an unhappy one. It may help in the building of a strong and cohesive society or it may result in antisocial outcomes on the part of the participant. Whether or not physical education helps or inhibits the attainment of educational objectives will depend to a great extent upon the leadership that is responsible for its direction.

Physical education is a very important part of the educational process. It is not a "frill" or an "ornament" that has been tacked on to the school program as a means of keeping children busy. It is, instead, a vital part of education. Through a well-directed physical education program, children develop skills for the worthy use of leisure time, engage in activities that are conducive to healthful living, develop socially, and contribute to their physical and mental health.

A study of history reveals that other civilizations have recognized the important place of physical education in the training of their youth. In ancient Athens, for example, three main studies were followed by every Athenian: gymnastics, grammar, and music. Here in America the contributions of physical education in the educational program have been recognized for many years. In 1918 the National Educational Association set forth its well-known *Cardinal Principles of Secondary Education* which listed seven objectives of education: health, command of fundamental processes, worthy home membership, vocation, citizenship, worthy use of leisure, and ethical character. Physical education is playing a very important part in achieving these objectives. Through such contributions as the benefits of exercise to physical health, the fundamental physical skills which make for a more interesting, efficient, and vigorous life and the social education that contributes to the development of character and good human relations, these cardinal principles are brought nearer to realization.

## Terminology

The multiplicity of terms that are sometimes used synonymously for physical education makes it imperative that the meaning of these various terms be clarified.

**Hygiene.** Hygiene comes from the Greek word *hygieinos,* meaning healthful. This refers to the science of preserving one's health. It often refers to rules or principles that are prescribed for the purpose of developing and maintaining health. In past years many school physical education departments were known as departments of hygiene. A few still use this term. It appears that this term became popular as a result of legislation in various states that sought to have the effects of tobacco and alcohol brought to the attention of all students through a course that was often known by the name of hygiene. There are still many laws on the statute books prescribing such instruction. Since World War I this term has become more or less obsolete. Newer terminology is being used, such as health education and personal and community health.

**Physical culture.** The term *physical culture* is an obsolete term in education, having been used in the late nineteenth century to parallel the use of other names of courses that at times were called religious culture, social culture, and intellectual culture. This term is still used by some faddists in commercial ventures to popularize the beneficial effects of exercise. Such men as the late Bernarr Macfadden have, through their publications and business enterprises, done a great deal to spread the use of such terminology. Physical culture has been used synonymously for physical training. It implies that through various physical activities health may be promoted. It is a term, however, that is not in use today in our institutions of learning.

**Gymnastics.** The word *gymnastics* refers to exercises that are adaptable to or are performed in a gymnasium. It is the art of performing various types of physical exercises and feats of skill. The term has been and still is used extensively in the various physical education programs on the continent of Europe. Anyone trained in physical education has heard mention of such programs as the German and Swedish systems of gymnastics. Formal drills such as calisthenics were until recently utilized extensively in many physical education programs in the United States. Today, when one thinks of gymnastics, formal drills come to mind which are conducted either with or without the use of apparatus. Americans do not use the term synonymously with physical education but, instead, with just that phase of the physical education program concerned with formal drills. Physical education programs today are more concerned with allowing the individual to express himself in various types of games rather than through formal drill. This is believed to be more in keeping with the democratic way of life.

**Physical training.** The term *physical training* to many individuals has a military tinge. It is a term that has been used in school programs of physical activity and also a term that has been used in the armed forces. Hetherington used the term to connote big-muscle activity in the school program of physical education. On the other hand, both during World War II and at the present time its use refers to the entire program of physical conditioning that the armed forces require men to go through as preparation for their rigorous duties. Most individuals agree that because of the military connection the term is used to imply training. This term has become rather outmoded for the modern-day physical education programs that are found in the public schools. Today, physical education programs realize outcomes other than just those that are concerned with the physical aspects. For example, there are sociological outcomes that result in an individual's better adaptation to group living. The term *physical education* also implies that physical activity serves the field of education in a much broader sense than physical training does.

**Fitness and physical fitness.** A group of members of the American Association for Health, Physical Education, and Recreation approved the following definition of fitness: "That state which characterizes the degree to which the person is able to function." In other words, it represents the individual's capacity to live most vig-

*Courtesy Public Relations Department, Thailand.*

Calisthenics demonstration by cadet academy students at Asian games.

orously and effectively with his own resources. Physical fitness refers primarily to
bodily aspects of fitness. It implies such
abilities as that of resisting fatigue, performing with an acceptable degree of
motor ability, and being able to adapt to
muscular stress.

**Health.** Health, according to the World
Health Organization, refers to such qualities as physical, mental, emotional, and
social health. It is not limited to the mere
absence of disease and infirmity. It means
total fitness.

**Recreation.** Recreation is concerned
with those activities performed by an individual during hours not at work. It is
frequently referred to as leisure-time activity. Recreation education is aimed at
educating people to utilize their leisure
hours in a constructive manner. This implies a careful selection of activities.

**Athletics.** The term *athletics* refers to
the games or sports that are usually engaged in by individuals who are strong,

robust, skilled, and able to participate in
vigorous exertions. The interest in athletics in the United States has been
largely inherited from Great Britain. With
the introduction of athletics into colleges
and universities, there has been a rapid
growth in all sports engaged in on an intercollegiate basis. The first intercollegiate meet was a boat race in 1852 between
the crews of Harvard University and Yale
University. The first intercollegiate football game is believed to have been played
between Rutgers University and Princeton University in 1869. These rivalries
still exist today.

Many lay persons frequently think of
athletics and physical education as being
similar in meaning. However, most physical education personnel think of athletics
as one phase of a broad physical education program—that division of the program concerned with interscholastic or
intercollegiate sports competition. A director of athletics in a school has as his

primary responsibility the direction of this competitive program.

**Physical education.** The term *physical education* is much broader and much more meaningful for day-to-day living than many of those terms that have been discussed previously. It is more closely allied to the larger area of education, of which it is a vital part. It implies that its program consists of something other than mere exercises done at command. A physical education program under qualified leadership aids in the enrichment of an individual's life.

Before formulating a definition of physical education it is interesting to note how three former leaders in the field of physical education defined this term.

Hetherington listed two things with which physical education is concerned.

First, physical education is concerned with big-muscle activity and the benefits that may be derived therefrom and, second, with its contribution to the health and growth of the child so that he may realize as much as possible from the educational process without having growth handicaps.

Nash pointed out that physical education is one phase of the total education process and that it utilizes activity drives that are inherent in each individual to develop a person organically, neuromuscularly, intellectually, and emotionally. These outcomes are realized whenever physical education activities are conducted in such places as the playground, gymnasium, and swimming pool.

Sharman pointed out that physical education is that part of education which takes place through activities that involve

*Louis C. Kingscott and Associates, Inc.*

Physical education class at West High School, Davenport, Iowa. Physical educators should offer a program of activities in which participants will realize results beneficial to their growth and development.

the motor mechanism of the human body and that results in the individual's formulating behavior patterns.

From these various definitions of physical education, it can be seen that any definition of the term should incorporate such concepts as selected physical activities and related learnings that are realized through participation in these activities, and should show that it is a part of the educational process.

I propose the following as a definition of physical education: *Physical education, an integral part of the total education process, is a field of endeavor that has as its aim the development of physically, mentally, emotionally, and socially fit citizens through the medium of physical activities that have been selected with a view to realizing these outcomes.*

In a larger sense, this definition of physical education means that the leaders in this field must develop a program of activities in which participants will realize results beneficial to their growth and development; that they will develop, through participation, such physical characteristics as endurance, strength, and the ability to resist and recover from fatigue; that neuromuscular skill will become a part of their motor mechanism so that they may have proficiency in performing physical acts; that socially they will become educated to play an effective part in democratic group living; and that they will be better able to interpret new situations in a more meaningful and purposeful manner as a result of these physical education experiences.

## GOALS TO BE ACHIEVED IN MAKING PHYSICAL EDUCATION A STRONG PROFESSION

Some suggestions for making physical education a strong profession are as follows:

1. *Physical education must have members within its ranks who are well pre-* *pared for their work.* Physical educators must have a liberal education. There needs to be a recognition that they are, first, educators and, second, specialists. This means being well versed in such subject matter areas as English, history, science, mathematics, foreign language, art, and music. Physical educators must have intensive training in psychology, philosophy, teaching methods, values, tests and measurements, and other disciplines that are frequently called educational theory and applied techniques. Finally, physical educators need good preparation in their own specialty—the scientific foundations and the tools of their trade. They must be specialists to whom the public looks for guidance, help, and professional direction in the fields of sports, physical fitness, and allied areas. As the public looks to the lawyer for guidance in matters concerning litigation and law, so they should look to physical educators for direction in matters concerning physical activities. Physical educators should stand out above the rank and file of the general population as being expertly equipped, trained, and prepared in their specialized area. Such preparation is essential to being recognized as one who belongs to a profession.

2. *Physical education must have members within its ranks who wish to render a service to mankind.* The idea of service must be predominant in the minds of physical education practitioners. The consuming idea must not be what the profession can do for them but rather what they can do for the profession—the services they can render to human beings in helping them to live happier, healthier, and more vigorous and interesting lives. Physical education, as well as all subjects that comprise the educational program, must be designed and constituted so that it educates and prepares people to become all they are capable of becoming. Such qualities as physical fitness and good human relations are worthy goals of accomplish-

ment and will make for a better world. A member of any profession who is concerned with human beings and is determined to leave this earth a little better for his or her having been here is the kind of individual who will contribute to making his profession a dynamic and important one.

3. *Physical education must have members within its ranks who believe in and practice excellent performance.* Whether it is preparing for class, developing a skill, gaining knowledge of an effective teaching technique, planning a lesson, teaching a class, coaching a team, or engaging in any other activity that is a part of the physical education profession, the performance should be characterized by excellence. Each practitioner should strive at all times to do his or her best. Since the principle of individual differences will operate, the quality of performance will vary from individual to individual;

nevertheless, each one strives to do the best within his or her own abilities. Members giving their best for their profession will bring rich dividends to themselves as well as to their chosen field of endeavor.

4. *Physical education must have members within its ranks who have formulated a sound philosophy of physical education and are articulate in communicating this philosophy to others.* It has been my experience that some physical educators have not given careful thought to the worth of their subject within the broad field of education. Consequently, they find it difficult to interpret meaningfully the importance and place of their field of work in schools, colleges, and youth-serving agencies. A person without a clear-cut, soundly based philosophy is like a ship without a rudder. Vacillation, indifference, indirection and ineffective performance will be reflected in his or her actions. Physical educators should study

Physical education must have members within its ranks who believe in and practice excellent performance. Small-group instruction in physical education.

carefully such disciplines as biology, psychology, and sociology, from which physical education derives its scientific foundations, and then they should formulate what they believe to be a sound philosophy that has worth and that can be clearly communicated to colleagues, parents, students, and the public in general. A person who is going to devote a lifetime to a career should want to be able to clearly interpret the value of his chosen field to others.

5. *Physical education must have members within its ranks who have high standards of ethical conduct.* It is common knowledge that most people would "rather see a sermon than hear one any day." Members of outstanding professions attempt to translate their sermons into action. The members are living examples of that which they proclaim to be good for others. Most of us would not be impressed if a minister had the habit of swearing, a banker spent his money foolishly, or a businessman cheated his clients. Neither will the public be impressed by the physical education profession unless the members themselves believe in it to the extent that they feel that what they advocate for others is also good for themselves. This means that they will be in good physical condition, practice good health habits, have wholesome attitudes, set a good example for students, and be active in professional associations. The American Association for Health, Physical Education, and Recreation has a *Code of Ethics* for its membership. It might be useful for each member to review this code once each year.

6. *Physical education must have members within its ranks who play an active part in professional organizations.* Professions prosper and contribute only as their members band together to improve themselves, upgrade their services, solve knotty problems, enhance working conditions, and in general make their fields continu-

ally better vocations with which to be associated. Such professional endeavors require much time and effort on the part of members. Time and effort must be given unselfishly, without pay and personal gain and primarily for the purpose of improving and contributing to a better society. Unfortunately, too few members are professionally active in their associations at the present time. Members are not assuming their rightful responsibility. Some persons are living off the efforts, enjoying the privileges, and benefiting from the work expended by a few dedicated members. In a sense these people are parasites. Members of a profession should be professionally active from the time they are students in a college or university to the time they are separated from the profession.

Some professional leaders believe a member has his first loyalty to his local and state associations and then to the district and the national associations. This is a question that each person will have to answer for himself.

7. *Physical education must formulate a body of knowledge that clearly establishes the fact that this field of endeavor involves a highly specialized intellectual technique.* Physical education needs a well-defined intellectual foundation. A theory and body of knowledge must be clearly stated that shows we are engaged in physical education, not just physical training. Research in physical education must be directed toward the identification of basic concepts that serve as threads of knowledge common to physical education work. Abernathy* identifies six points that perhaps offer clues to the theory and body of knowledge, underlying physical education. These include the empirical study of successful and unsuccessful ex-

---

*Abernathy, Ruth: The search for significant persistent themes in physical education, Journal of Health, Physical Education, and Recreation 36:26, March, 1965.

perience, a study of methodology, the kinesiologic approach aimed at the anatomical basis of activities, human behavior and action systems, motor learning, perception, motivation, and a mathematical approach where accurate models and formulas exist to describe the field of endeavor.

Several leaders in the profession have advocated human movement as the basis for the intellectual orientation, providing knowledge as to its nature, determinants, and role in the growth, development, and education of human beings.*

There should be considerable thought, research, and discussion on the intellectual basis for physical education. Physical education cannot achieve professional status without such a rationale.

8. *Physical education must clearly show that the service it renders is unique to this field and capable of being effectively performed only by its qualified members.* There are many impostors who claim to render a service similar to that with which physical education is identified. The physical fitness movement has attracted hundreds of quacks and charlatans who claim to build strength, take off weight, and make women beautiful. These impostors are using the term physical education, and many times claiming to be physical educators themselves. Such inroads by misfits act as a strong deterrent to the achievement of professional status, and result in loss of public confidence. The persons who are not trained do not belong, and should be expelled. Stringent regulations must be adopted for membership and strong disciplinary action taken when professional standards are swept aside.

## NEED FOR UNDERSTANDING TRUE MEANING OF PHYSICAL EDUCATION

Indications that the public does not appreciate the value of physical education

*See Chapter 13.

include lack of facilities, insufficient time allotted to physical education in the schools, failure to give credit for physical education in school programs, frequent emphasis on a few gifted athletes at the expense of all the students, haphazard scheduling of classes, indifference on the part of many administrators, poor financial backing, poorly planned programs, and the inadequate training programs in many teacher-education institutions. If the true meaning of physical education were understood by all, these conditions would not exist, and instead of encountering opposition to the establishment of acceptable physical education programs, they would be welcomed with open arms because their values and contributions to enriched living would be recognized.

A member of the physical education profession has the potentialities for making a great contribution to a healthy and physically fit America. This contribution can be made by developing a sound philosophy with respect to what physical education is, what the objectives of the profession are, what contributions it can make to enriched living, and then by zealously attempting to spread this philosophy to as many others as possible, by being a living example of one's preachments, and by providing the leadership for programs that yield benefits that cannot be denied by anyone. In order to make this contribution, however, the true meaning of physical education must be understood. This book has been written for the express purpose of helping the student and teacher to understand better and to formulate and develop more clearly a sound philosophy of physical education.

### QUESTIONS AND EXERCISES

1. What are some of the essential facts that every member of the physical education field of endeavor should know in regard to his specialty?
2. What are some of the erroneous concep-

tions of physical education that exist in the minds of many individuals?

3. Do you feel that John Dewey would be in favor of physical education? Why?

4. Define the term *education*. What in your own thinking would be an acceptable definition of an educated person? What are the advantages of being an educated person in light of your definition? Why do you feel that you are or are not an educated person?

5. Why would an individual who had training only in the accumulation of facts not be an educated person?

6. What is meant by each of the following terms: hygiene, physical culture, gymnastics, physical fitness, health, recreation, physical training, and athletics? What is the relation of each to physical education?

7. What is an acceptable definition of physical education? From your personal observations and experiences why do you feel that members of this field of endeavor are or are not interpreting physical education correctly?

8. Why is physical education an integral part of any educational program?

9. To what extent did the physical education program in which you participated in elementary and high school contribute to your physical, social, mental, and emotional welfare? Where and how do you feel that it could have made a greater contribution?

10. Why is there a great need for understanding the true meaning of physical education? What are your responsibilities as a member of the physical education specialty to interpret your work correctly?

## SELECTED REFERENCES

Abernathy, Ruth: The search for significant persistent themes in physical education, Journal of Health, Physical Education, and Recreation 36:26, March, 1965.

American Association for Health, Physical Education, and Recreation, This is physical education, Washington, D. C., 1965, The Association.

Brown, Camille, and Cassidy, Rosalind: Theory in physical education, Philadelphia, 1963, Lea & Febiger.

Bucher, Charles A., editor: Methods and materials in physical education and recreation, St. Louis, 1954, The C. V. Mosby Co.

Bucher, Charles A.: Administration of school health and physical education programs, St. Louis, 1967, the C. V. Mosby Co.

Bucher, Charles A.: Fitness and health (editorial), Educational Leadership 20:356, March, 1963.

Bucher, Charles A., Koenig, Constance, and Barnhard, Milton: Methods and materials for secondary school physical education, St. Louis, 1965, The C. V. Mosby Co.

Bucher, Charles A., and Reade, Evelyn M.: Physical education in the modern elementary school, New York, 1964, The Macmillan Co.

Cowell, Charles C.: Scientific foundations of physical education, New York, 1953, Harper & Brothers.

Davis, E. C.: The philosophic process in physical education, Philadelphia, 1961, Lea & Febiger.

Dewey, John: Democracy and education, New York, 1929, The Macmillan Co.

Educational Policies Commission: Policies for education in American democracy, Washington, D. C., 1946, National Education Association and American Association of School Administrators, book III.

Hetherington, Clark W.: School program in physical education, New York, 1922, World Book Co., part III.

Journal of the American Academy of Arts and Sciences, Daedalus 92:647, Fall, 1963.

Kaufman, Earl: A critical evaluation of the components basic to certain selected professions with a view to establishing recreation as a profession, Doctoral thesis, 1949, New York University.

Lieberman, Myron: Education as a profession, Englewood Cliffs, N. J., 1956, Prentice-Hall, Inc.

Morris, Van Cleve, and others: Becoming an educator, New York, 1963, Houghton Mifflin Company.

Nash, Jay B.: Physical education: interpretations and objectives, New York, 1948, A. S. Barnes & Co.

Rice, Emmett A., Hutchinson, John L., and Lee, Mabel: A brief history of physical education, New York, 1958, The Ronald Press Co.

Sharman, Jackson R.: The teaching of physical education, New York, 1936, A. S. Barnes & Co.

VanDalen, Deobold B., Mitchell, E. D., and Bennett, B. L.: World History of physical education, New York, 1953, Prentice-Hall, Inc.

Weston, Arthur: The making of American physical education, New York, 1962, Appleton-Century-Crofts.

# Chapter 2

# Services rendered by physical educators

To be a profession physical education must render a service that is essential to society. The practitioner regards the rendering of this service as being more important than the economic gain derived, and renders it in a manner that will benefit the entire populace, whether young or old, male or female, rich or poor. This chapter is concerned with identifying the services that physical educators perform in utilizing physical activity as a medium for contributing to the physical, mental, and social well-being of human beings.

Physical education is a rapidly expanding profession. There are more than 700 institutions training personnel for some phase of this specialized field of endeavor. It has been estimated that there are over 200,000 men and women in the United States who perform physical education duties that are related to the field of education. There are 50,000 members in the American Association for Health, Physical Education, and Recreation, an organization that is very active in furthering the profession of physical education. The different games and sports played are innumerable. Menke gives the history of more than seventy in his encyclopedia. These include a variety of sports and games such as paddle tennis, squash, water polo, archery, tug of war, yachting, lacrosse, tennis, golf, basketball, skeet, skiing, polo, backgammon, birling, fencing, jai alai, jujitsu, bowling, volleyball, and badminton. These physical education activities are conducted in the smallest hamlet and in the largest city; in back yards and in public sport palaces; in public school classrooms, gymnasiums, and swimming pools; in the YMCA, YWCA, YMHA, and YWHA; in industrial plants and in athletic clubs; in settlement houses and in public playgrounds; in boys' and girls' clubs and adult recreation centers; in hospitals and in penal institutions.

The nature and scope of physical education includes not only the teaching and coaching of games and sports but also such activities as dancing, correctives, rehabilitation, and camping. The picture of physical education may be portrayed to the prospective teacher by describing the nature and scope of physical education, first, as services provided by physical educators, which will be considered in this chapter, and, second, as settings where these services are rendered (Chapter 3).

The services performed by three physical education teachers, as shown on page

*Shaker Heights High School, Cleveland, Ohio.*

To be a profession physical education must render a service that is essential to society.

29, provide a picture of some of the responsibilities and contributions made by physical educators in two schools and one university. One can readily see that a physical educator is busy from morning until night rendering services to students and to the community and public in general.

The services rendered by physical education personnel may be divided into the following for purposes of convenience:

1. Counseling
2. Providing movement experiences
3. Teaching games and other selected physical education activities
4. Teaching dance
5. Physically educating the atypical individual
6. Coaching sports
7. Building physical fitness
8. Conducting research
9. Preparing professional leaders
10. Administering programs
11. Conducting and supervising intramural, extramural, and interscholastic and intercollegiate athletic programs, clubs, and other activities
12. Working in international exchange programs
13. Teaching health
14. Conducting safety and driver education programs
15. Working in recreation programs
16. Working in camping and outdoor education programs

## COUNSELING

The teacher of physical education plays a unique role in the life of each student with whom he comes in contact. One of the greatest services that can be rendered is that of counseling boys and girls concerning matters that affect their physical selves and the development of their personalities. Boys and girls are concerned with their body image, how to build physical fitness, the way to gain strength, how to become skilled in their favorite physical activities, suggestions for developing poise, how to maintain weight control, finding the path to a beautiful body, and a host of other desires and interests. They want to sit down and discuss face to face some of the physical changes that are taking place in their bodies and what they mean and what they should do about them. Young people desire accurate and objective information in regard to the role of sex in their lives. They want to know what it means if they smoke and drink or use drugs. They want to have information on why they are required to attend physical education class, learn skills, and know certain physiological facts.

In order to be an effective counselor, the physical education teacher must have a sincere desire to help young people. He must recognize that this is an important service to render if he is to be worthy of membership in his specialty. He must want to render this service and be prepared to render it most effectively. Furthermore, he needs to provide the time in his schedule when students and other persons will have the opportunity to utilize this service.

In order to be an effective counselor, the physical education teacher must be acquainted with how boys and girls grow and develop, their developmental tasks, and the problems they experience. He must be able to clarify their problems, give encouragement, offer friendship, and provide a feeling of belonging.

The effective counselor will get as much information as possible about the person needing advice. In so doing, he will talk with parents, use school records, and know other sources of help when referral becomes necessary. He will work closely in a school situation with the guidance officer and the personnel in this area.

The physical educator can render a valuable counseling service to all persons who are interested in and have problems that relate to his specialty. This service can go beyond the students in the school, to men and women in the community who want accurate information that will help them solve their problems.

## PROVIDING MOVEMENT EXPERIENCES

A service that represents the heart of physical education is that of providing meaningful movement experiences. Movement cuts across games, skills, gymnastics, dance, and other activities that are taught in this field of endeavor. The factors of time, space, force, and flow can be explored as the student or other person engaging in the physical education experience learns to understand how his body relates to these various factors. The individual learns about his body and how it functions under various conditions where physical activity is involved. The teacher acts as a guide in helping the person to better understand his body and its performance capabilities. He develops understanding about and appreciation for human movement. He learns about the

*Toledo Public Schools, Toledo, Ohio.*

Movement education—an important service rendered by physical educators.

important place of movement in all of life's activities. He gains an awareness of his body.

A significant group of professional physical educators feel that movement is an educational discipline. It is a science. It has a subject matter—a body of knowledge. There are principles and laws involved in the efficient performance of movement. And when these knowledges, principles, and laws are brought into play, contributions can be made to the physical, mental, social, and emotional growth of the individual.

There are different schools of thought and approaches to movement within the field of physical education. Some leaders subscribe to definite units or courses de-

| Services of Mrs. Jones, teacher of physical education in Midwest | Services of Mr. Smith, teacher of physical education in East |
|---|---|
| Teaches six classes of games and other physical education activities each day | Teaches six classes of physical education each day |
| Gives tests over subject matter pertaining to rules, courts, and skill tests | Supervises the noon lunch period in the gymnasium |
| Engages in individual work with students on rhythm activities | Prepares equipment lists for physical education classes, six interscholastic sports, and all intramural activities |
| Teaches activities before school from 7:50 to 8:25 A.M., including tap dancing, soft-shoe dancing, and attending committee meetings with special dance groups and gymnasium leaders | Arranges transportation for after-school sports activities |
| Supervises after-school activities, including Can Can dance class, modern dance group, as well as giving advice to future Nurses' Club | Secures officials for athletic activities |
| | Serves on various community and school committees, including buildings and grounds committee, Boosters' club, curriculum committee |
| Engages in after-dinner activities, including chaperoning school dances, ushering at football and basketball games, helping with such special programs or events as homecoming, Christmas plays, and dance rehearsals for school variety show | Conducts coaching and staff meetings |
| | Attends all athletic contests at home and away |
| | Chaperons school functions such as dances |
| | Inspects and determines what equipment should be reconditioned and discarded |
| | Attends league athletic meetings |
| | Arranges for all details in respect to game and athletic management |

| Services of Professor Brown, Division of Physical Education, Health and Recreation, in a large state university in the Far West | |
|---|---|
| Teaches a course in the history and principles of physical education to undergraduate students three hours per week | Chaperons one undergraduate function, such as a dance or a club activity, once every two weeks |
| Teaches activity courses in team sports and also gymnastics twice a week to nonmajor freshman students | Keeps office hours for students and sees students four hours per week |
| Attends faculty meeting or committee meeting two hours per week | Spends two hours in preparation for each class taught each week |
| Teaches course in Methods and Materials for Teaching Games of Low Organization to major students three times per week | Works regularly on proposal to obtain research grant |
| | Spends ten hours per week on research project |
| | Teaches administration of physical education course three times per week |

voted to movement, whereas others feel that movement education constitutes the whole, encompassing physical education (see Chapter 13 for a fuller discussion of movement). There are those persons who advocate movement as an academic discipline and those who advocate it as an educational process.

Regardless of which school of thought a physical educator subscribes to, a valuable service can be rendered by physical educators through the principles underlying the movement. It is an attempt to enrich the total life of the individual through selected experiences that relate to physical activity.

Furthermore, it is apparent that movement education as such is only in its embryo stage and that as our knowledge and understanding of this phenomenon increase and our thinking is clarified, the service that we will be able to render to human beings will be increased. It is up to each physical educator to study the

various theories that are being advocated in regard to movement, and to investigate on his own what form movement should play in his program. In so doing, he will better understand its possibilities for improving his physical education program, and the contributions it can make to human beings.

## TEACHING GAMES AND OTHER SELECTED PHYSICAL EDUCATION ACTIVITIES

Games are a popular pastime for the young and the old, for boys and girls, and for men and women. They offer an opportunity for all to obtain exercise, fun, and relaxation.

Games are one of the main components of any physical education program; therefore the physical educator must be familiar with many of them. He should know the essential features of the various games, rules, methods of organization, values received from participation, equip-

*Detroit Public Schools, Detroit, Mich.*

Games are one of the main components of any physical education program.

ment and facilities needed, and ways of motivating the participants. He should also have motor skill in as many of these activities as possible. It has been proved time and time again that the ability to demonstrate a particular skill aids greatly in the teaching process and also increases the prestige of the teacher in the eyes of the students.

Some of the games and other related physical education activities with which every person in physical education should be familiar are listed:

*Team games*

1. Softball
2. Baseball
3. Basketball
4. Football (men only)
5. Touch football
6. Volleyball
7. Soccer
8. Speedball
9. Field hockey
10. Water polo
11. Ice hockey (men only)

*Dual and individual sports*

1. Track
2. Deck tennis
3. Table tennis
4. Shuffleboard
5. Bowling
6. Wrestling (men only)
7. Golf
8. Squash
9. Darts
10. Badminton
11. Horseshoes
12. Handball
13. Archery
14. Fencing
15. Tennis

*Formal activities*

1. Calisthenics
2. Marching

*Aquatics*

1. Swimming
2. Diving
3. Lifesaving
4. Canoeing
5. Rowing
6. Water games

*Outdoor winter activities*

1. Skating
2. Snow games
3. Skiing
4. Tobogganing
5. Hiking

*Self-testing activities*

1. Running
2. Jumping
3. Climbing
4. Hanging
5. Chinning
6. Sit-up
7. Forward roll
8. Stunts
9. Knee dip
10. Push-up

*Games of low organization*

1. Dodge ball
2. Hopscotch
3. Rope jumping
4. Two deep
5. Under leg
6. Ring games
7. "Tag" and "It" games

*Gymnastic activities*

1. Tumbling
2. Pyramid building
3. Apparatus
4. Acrobatics
5. Obstacle course
6. Rope climb

*Relays*

1. Potato relay
2. Over and under relay
3. Jump the stick relay
4. Sack relay
5. Hopping relay

## TEACHING DANCE

Dancing is one of the oldest arts and should be an important part of every physical education program from the primary grades through college. As far back as one can go into history, it is possible to find that dancing was a prominent pastime in the lives of all peoples. Early savages danced periodically in their religious festivals, in preparing for combat, and for amusement. It has come down through the ages, bringing with it an account of the way people lived in other lands. It is a means of communication. Through the dance one may creatively express how he feels about people, forces of nature, and other phases of our culture. It provides enjoyment, a means of emotional release, and enables one to express desires in action. It results in beneficial physiological effects by stimulating the various organic systems of the body. It helps to develop balance, control, and poise and provides the opportunity to respond to music through movement.

The dance program consists of *fundamental rhythms,* such as running, walking, skipping, jumping, hopping, and the imitation of real and imaginary characters through rhythmic activities; *folk*

*George Peabody College, Nashville, Tenn.*

Dancing is one of the oldest arts.

*dances* and *singing games,* such as "Farmer in the Dell," "Csebogar," "Pop Goes the Weasel," "Norwegian Mountain March," and "Schottische"; *athletic* or *gymnastic dancing,* which is dancing done with vigor and which includes such acts as cartwheels, rolls, running, and skipping; *tap* and *clog dancing,* which provides for greater coordination of the body's muscular and nervous systems; *social* or *ballroom dancing,* which is rapidly being included in many physical education programs for its social value; and *modern dancing,* which is a medium of expressing oneself creatively and aesthetically through movement.

The elementary-school program in rhythms and dance should, according to some experts in elementary-school work, include fundamental rhythms, pantomimic and dramatic dances, dramatic and singing games, folk dances, national dances, clog and athletic dances, and character dances. It is quite generally agreed that in the elementary school these make up from 20 to 40% of the entire physical education program.

In the junior high school, the more popular phases of the dance program for boys deal with clog and tap dancing and social dancing, and for girls, folk, clog and tap, and social dancing are popular.

In the senior high school, clog and tap, athletic, and social dancing are popular in boys' programs, and clog and tap, folk, social, and modern dancing are popular in girls' programs.

At the college and university level, folk, square, ballroom, modern, and tap dance are frequently included in the curriculum. In addition, such courses as the history and philosophy of dance, methods of teaching various forms of dance, dance production, and cultural concepts of dance are offered.

Dance is becoming a popular and rewarding career for those physical educators who wish to render a service helping young persons to better understand their bodies and express themselves through rhythmic activity. Although many opportunities present themselves in elementary and secondary schools and also in dance studios and community agencies and recreation programs, the college and university levels, where more often than not dance teachers work in departments, divisions, or schools of physical education, also offer many opportunities to serve. There has been considerable expansion of dance programs in recent years in institutions of higher learning. Liberal arts colleges are offering expanded programs of dance experiences for their students, professional preparing programs are training teachers of physical education with an emphasis in the area of the dance, and other institutions are providing instruction in modern, ballroom, or folk dance for the general student body.

The dancing program in schools and colleges seems to be receiving more and more emphasis as it becomes increasingly popular. As a result, there is a demand for teachers of physical education who are specialists in the various phases of dance. One of the leaders in the field of physical education, and chairman of one of the largest physical education departments in the country, recently made the remark that the demand for teachers of dance was much greater than the supply, and that as a result many jobs were still waiting for prospective teachers. It should be remembered, however, that prospective teachers interested in the dance should also prepare themselves to teach the other activities in the physical education program equally well. The opportunities for teaching dance alone are limited.

## PHYSICALLY EDUCATING THE ATYPICAL INDIVIDUAL

Another valuable service that can be rendered by physical educators is the individualization of the program to fit the needs of each person. Blanket programs of physical education are not suitable. There are many students who have some atypical physical condition and physical educators should try to alleviate or eliminate these atypical conditions. One medical doctor told the author that physical educators do a fine job helping the healthy and gifted student to become healthier or more skilled, but do a poor job in helping the unhealthy or atypical person

to develop to his optimum capacity. Whether or not this medical doctor's observation is correct is beside the point. A valuable service can and should be performed by physical educators in the adapted physical education program. Physical education programs that help the atypical person are quite frequently referred to by such terms as corrective physical education, individual physical education, posture training, reconstructive physical education, physical education for the atypical child, and body building.

Since there is considerable emphasis today on educating the atypical individual, this subject is treated at length in this chapter.

### The mentally retarded

The mentally retarded child needs physical education. Yet in many schools throughout the United States, there is no provision made for meeting this need. It has been estimated that there are now about six million mentally retarded children and adults in the United States, and by 1970, the number will probably exceed seven million. Approximately 126,000 mentally retarded babies are born in this country every year.

Mental retardation is a major problem to which the field of physical education is at present giving comparatively little internal emphasis. There has been only a smattering of research conducted in the area of mental retardation by physical educators. Although federal funds have been made available for research concerned with the mentally retarded, only small amounts have been requested by physical educators. At present, there are few, if any, professional preparation programs in physical education that train teachers of the mentally retarded, although some schools offer a course in this area within their professional programs. Yet by 1971, the United States will need more than 1,000 physical educators with specific preparation in teaching the mentally retarded.

The Joseph P. Kennedy, Jr. Foundation is presently the prime organization concerned with all phases of research on, and education for, the mentally retarded. As recently as 1964, the Kennedy Foundation was the only group providing summer camp experiences and recreation programs for the mentally retarded. In 1966, the Kennedy Foundation sponsored a series of regional seminars for physical educators to acquaint them with the physical education needs of the retarded.

The mentally retarded boys and girls that attend public schools benefit from a program of physical activity that is carefully tailored to their needs. These children show a wide range of intellectual ability and, in general, are below average in physical performance and capacity. While some mentally retarded boys and girls are skilled enough to participate in a regular program of physical education, the vast majority are physically two to four years behind normal youngsters of the same age. The mentally retarded are not as physically strong, lack endurance, and tend to be overweight. While their physical development is slower, they seem to mature physically at an earlier age than do most boys and girls. In general, the retarded have poor motor coordination, lack physical and organic fitness, and have poor posture. Some mentally retarded children have physical handicaps, and some also have personality disturbances.

Several recent research reports published in England and the United States have drawn similar conclusions concerning the effect of a well-balanced program of physical education. The researchers have pointed out that while normal boys and girls attain high scores on physical performance tests, the mentally retarded received scores almost as high following exposure to a physical education program designed to meet their specific needs. One of the measures that researchers have used most consistently has been the AAHPER Youth Fitness Test. Other researchers have said that the difference in motor performance between the mentally retarded and the normal is based on the differences in mental ability rather than on any significant difference in natural motor ability.

Still other researchers have pointed out that the mentally retarded have been denied planned programs in physical education. Often, they are placed in regular physical education classes without regard to their unique needs. Surveys have indicated that most of the mentally retarded spend their leisure time in sedentary pursuits. Most have little interest in hobbies, and they have not been encouraged to be active. Most are given little opportunity to participate in organized, leisure-time physical education or recreation programs. Because they have not had a strong background of play experience, the mentally retarded must be taught how to play.

The physical education teacher who is responsible for teaching a group of mentally retarded children cannot proceed as he would with a group of normal children. The mentally retarded need to be successful, they need to achieve. Thus, any goals that are set must be reachable ones. The mentally retarded often lack confidence and pride. They need a patient teacher who will praise the smallest effort or improvement. Continued frustration at failure to reach a skill level that is too high, and lack of recognition often lead to aggressive or asocial behavior. The mentally retarded make slow progress in skill development, and have great difficulty in abstract thinking. Their program of physical education must be a varied and interesting one. Skills must be taught by demonstration. Because the attention span

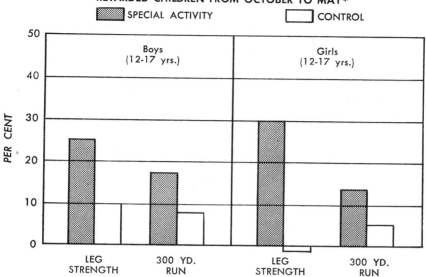

AVERAGE PER CENT IMPROVEMENT IN THE STRENGTH AND ENDURANCE OF RETARDED CHILDREN FROM OCTOBER TO MAY*

*These are examples of measured improvements produced by an intensive organic fitness program. The special activity consisted of running activities engaged in twice weekly.

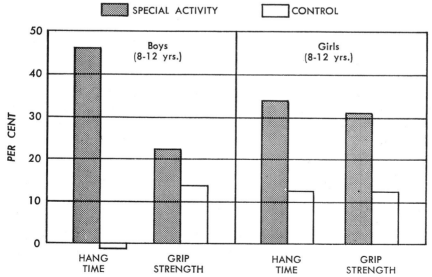

AVERAGE PER CENT IMPROVEMENT IN THE MUSCULAR FITNESS OF RETARDED CHILDREN FROM OCTOBER TO MAY*

*These are examples of measured improvements produced by intensive muscular activity involving the arms and shoulders. The special activity consisted of medicine ball games, engaged in twice weekly.

From Hayden, Frank J.: Physical fitness for the mentally retarded, London, Ontario, Canada, 1964. Copyright by Frank Hayden.

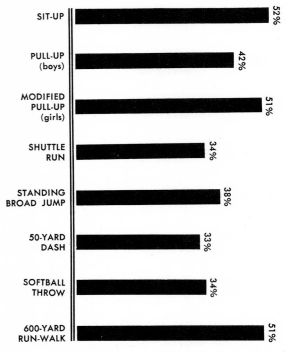

*American Association for Health, Physical Education
and Recreation: Recreation and fitness for the mentally
retarded, The Association, 1965.*

The mean percentile scores on the AAHPER Youth Fitness Test of 270 educable mentally retarded boys and girls, ages 10-17, in the St. Louis County (Missouri) Special School District for the Education and Training of Handicapped Children.

of a mentally retarded child is short, and because he tires easily, the program must be designed to maintain his interest and involve him personally.

Those who have extensively taught the mentally retarded find that they enjoy swimming, tumbling, rhythmics, climbing over obstacles, lead-up games, and trampolining. They point out that the concept of team play is too abstract, and that the retarded at times have difficulty in following directions. Thus, lead-up games present the needed challenge and competition, and prevent the frustration encountered in the more highly organized team sports. Movement education seems almost ideally suited to programs for the mentally retarded.

Physical education is essential to the mental and physical development of the retarded. A well-planned program will help these youngsters to develop the fitness and endurance they need. Physical education adds to their physical and mental well-being, and gives them an opportunity to experience success and achievement.

### The culturally disadvantaged

The culturally disadvantaged are of many races and colors. They live in the slums of the large cities, or in rural poverty pockets in all areas of the country. Their numbers are constantly on the increase, particularly in the large cities. Estimates made by the Ford Foundation classified one out of every three city children as culturally disadvantaged. By

1970, the Foundation expects that 50% of the children who live in large cities will fall into this classification.

The culturally disadvantaged child does not resemble his middle or upperclass peers in home and neighborhood environment, economic level, scholastic achievement, motivation, or aspiration level. These differences set the culturally disadvantaged child apart, and are, in fact, the causes of his deprivation and resulting scholastic and personal adjustment problems.

The culturally disadvantaged child often reflects in a school situation the negative influences of his home and neighborhood environment. The cultural standards of these environments are frequently inconsistent. Because the home is often neither a place where conversation is stimulated nor reading encouraged, the child enters school ill-equipped to communicate easily, or to adapt to the learning environment as readily as does the more advantaged child. Furthermore, the disadvantaged family is frequently a transient one, moving from city to city in search of better-paying jobs or other advantages. The culturally disadvantaged child thus moves from school to school, making adjustment more difficult with each change.

The culturally disadvantaged often resent the school, the teachers, and its administrators because each represents the unattainable middle-class image of society at large. Education is viewed as valuable, but the values are quite different in context from those sought or defined by the advantaged segment of society.

The culturally disadvantaged child does not feel that he is a part of the society in which he lives. In a classroom situation, he is unable to compete. He is unstable emotionally, and his excitability and restlessness contribute to a short attention span. He cannot think in the abstract, form concepts, use logic, or communicate well verbally. Thus, he falls behind grade level in achievement, and attains low scores on intelligence and standardized tests. These failures contribute to a lack of motivation, a low level of aspiration, and lack of ambition. The final result of years of failure is a negative self-image expressed by hostile, aggressive, and nonconforming behavior.

Education must be adapted to the specific needs of the culturally disadvantaged child. What motivation he does possess, what creativity he has, what abilities he shows, must be fostered and encouraged rather than suppressed. Understanding teachers, and a classroom climate geared to the specific needs of this child are of the utmost importance. This child needs an opportunity to change his negative image of himself to a positive one. A chance to succeed on his own level, rather than imposed levels will aid not only in building a more positive image, but in increasing his self-respect, his poise, and his confidence.

Physical education can contribute to the culturally disadvantaged in a very positive manner. Often, the disadvantaged child has no recreational facility available to him. He must use streets or littered lots, and his games and sports are unsupervised. Within the environment of the school, the disadvantaged child can be given a worthwhile physical education experience geared to him. A small class size will allow the instructor to give each student the attention, help, encouragement and praise he needs. Within a relaxed, low-pressure, and informal environment, discipline will be easier to learn and maintain. Skill learnings will accrue more readily. Careful progressions in the skills that are offered will increase the opportunities to achieve success, and give a measure of personal satisfaction. The instructor must strive to develop rapport with these students, and he must be able to understand and respect them. He must provide the experiences and learnings that they need to cope with their immediate and future recreational pursuits.

The physical education program for the culturally disadvantaged must be designed to allow for the release of tension; to foster creativity; to answer the need to exert leadership; to instill knowledge of hygiene; to allow for social interaction; to provide competition of a worthwhile nature; and to give a background of lifetime sports. Above all, the physical education program must be an *activity* program that stresses and values the individual.

Team, dual, and individual sports all have their place in a physical education program for the culturally disadvantaged. On the elementary school level, movement education and its jumping, running, throwing, and other activities natural to childhood will help encourage creativity, the ability to abstract, and provide the child with the self-expression and activity that are needed. For the older child, such activities as bowling, skating, swimming, archery, rhythmics, and self-testing activities not only provide constant activity, but also offer a broad exposure to those skills from which the individual can gain confidence as he achieves higher skill levels. Team sports provide an invaluable opportunity to compete and to let off steam in an acceptable manner, and to learn the give-and-take that these sports help to teach. After school hours, the physical education program can do invaluable service to the culturally disadvantaged by organizing intramurals and supervised leagues in various sports.

## The physically handicapped

The physically handicapped, such as the blind, the deaf, and other children who are permanently or temporarily disabled, cannot be denied a chance to participate in a physical education program. These children need activity, they need to build strengths, and they need to achieve success. They also need the give-and-take of active sports and games.

While the permanently disabled often must be placed in an adapted program, blind or deaf children frequently can enter a regular physical education class along with their peers who have normal sight and hearing.

Little modification of normal teaching methods is needed to assist the deaf child. He or she can lip-read and make use of other visual stimuli. With safety a primary concern, these children can participate in the full physical education program.

The blind child requires some modification of method and equipment. Explanations must be clear and concise. In games where balls are used, aural cues must be given, both by the teacher and by other players. Several sporting goods manufacturers have developed hockey, soccer, and basketballs with bells inside them, especially for use with the visually handicapped. The blind can enjoy stunts and tumbling, dance, gymnastics, trampolining, swimming, and other activities, including many of the other team and individual sports, such as track and field. They have been found to adjust readily, and to be able to perform well in an atmosphere where their needs are taken into consideration.

## The body mechanics and remedial program

Poor body mechanics is a physically handicapping condition and under the right circumstances special exercises help in the elimination or alleviation of certain functional conditions of poor posture. For example, in pes planus (flat feet) or scoliosis (lateral curvature of the spine) it is possible to alleviate conditions through various prescribed exercises. Most programs are also concerned with other phases of poor development that are caused by such conditions as poor nutrition.

*Nathan Hale High School,*
*Seattle Public Schools, Seattle, Wash.*

Girls' body mechanics and adaptive class.

In respect to the body mechanics program, the greatest emphasis is on posture. This emphasis on posture is nothing new, however, in that it has been stressed since early times when the Greeks recognized its importance to bodily appearance and proper organic functioning. However, the main objective of early peoples was the aesthetic value. The term *body mechanics* is believed to have had its origin in Boston, Massachusetts, where it was associated with the work of Dr. Lloyd Brown and Dr. Roger Lee. For many years programs were designated and designed to utilize the word *posture* as the key word to connote what was to be accomplished. However, it is now believed that *posture* is a word that is inadequate for describing the work that is being done, and so the term *body mechanics* is being used more and more frequently because it is believed to be much more descriptive. Correct body mechanics permits the various organs of the body to function at their highest efficiency. In order to achieve this peak efficiency, such things as distribution of body weight, pull of gravity, pelvic tilt, and position of the chest, shoulders, and head must be taken into consideration.

Approximately 75% of all the youth in the United States can be classified as having varying degrees of poor body mechanics. This shows to some extent the need that exists for a sound body mechanics program. It is possible and desirable to impress upon children what is good and what is bad posture, and they can be motivated to work on improving defective body alignment. The program, however, must be practical and functional and so it must be a "doing" thing. Children must be encouraged to improve their posture through their daily routine activities, physical activity, and better health practices. Such causes of poor body mechanics as muscular insufficiency, poor organic development, bad habits, injuries, and factors concerned with general hygiene will not be alleviated through mere talking about good body mechanics. If it is not a "doing" program, such effects from bad posture as impaired efficiency of the body, poor appearance, and impaired organic function will remain with the individual.

One of the main handicapping influences today to the development of a sound body mechanics program is the lack of

*Los Angeles Public Schools, Los Angeles, Calif.*

A class in body mechanics.

adequately trained personnel. All teachers and individuals working with young people should be versed in factors conducive to the developmental and preventive program of body mechanics. The physical educator can help by developing a specialized program of his own, and at the same time assisting other members of the staff to become familiar with their part in the total program. In this way much can be done to eliminate the high percentage of persons that fall into the poor body mechanics group. Teachers should be encouraged to motivate children to emphasize their height, to relax, and to avoid strain on joints and muscles.

The emphasis in body mechanics should not only be on "static" posture, as when one is sitting or standing, but also on good body mechanics when the body is in mo-

tion. In the past the stress has been too much in favor of the static posture, with little or no emphasis on alignment when the body is in action. This has proved to be wrong. Regardless of whether an individual is running to catch a bus or riding in one or watching a ball game on television or participating, the principles of good body mechanics should be observed.

One consideration should be made clear in regard to the remedial program. This program should be conducted in very close association with the medical profession. Physical educators must realize where the work of the physical education teacher ends and where the work of the physician starts. In many cases of functional and structural disorders, the orthopedic specialist is needed. The average physical education teacher does not have sufficient training in such areas as orthopedics and pediatrics to direct and carry out an extensive corrective program.

Any prospective student interested in these areas of physical education as possible phases for specialization would be interested in the qualifications for an instructor as described by Rathbone, a recognized expert. She points out that a trained person in these areas should know the fundamentals of good teaching; should have an adequate background of anatomy and kinesiology; should know the principles underlying mechanical adjustment, muscular activity, and support; should understand the role of physical therapy in treatment; and should be well versed in mental hygiene.

Every individual has a greater chance of realizing happiness if his body functions correctly and if he is physically fit. Although the need for good body mechanics and remedial work has been recognized, it should be realized that because of facilities, personnel, and time, few schools are able to develop adequate programs. Furthermore, the stress in remedial physical education is changing from therapy to education. The trend is toward emphasizing the use of physical education sports and activities in the program. In this way the atypical child may have the opportunity in regular physical education classes and not as a separate group to develop skills, knowledge, emotional stability, and social adjustment, which will enable him to develop to his optimum capacity.

The same comment that was made in respect to physical educators who were interested in specializing in dance also holds true for the adapted physical education program. The prospects for employment as a specialist with duties pertaining only to this area are limited. Therefore the student who is interested in this type of work should, in addition to special preparation in one of these areas, also be prepared to teach other physical education activities.

## Rehabilitation program

The so-called rehabilitation program is also concerned with the atypical individual and therefore is also included in this section.

The rehabilitation programs in the armed forces played an important part in World War II, and they have been continued in veterans' hospitals with marked success. This has resulted in a renewed emphasis on this phase of physical education. In the armed forces and the veterans' hospitals these programs deal with those individuals who have been injured in the line of duty and have suffered some handicapping condition. They are also concerned with psychopathic patients who could not stand the strain of army routine and combat. These individuals need rehabilitation or reeducation in order for them to follow a vocation successfully and become once again useful citizens in our society. This program is similar to the remedial program in the schools in that it is concerned with handicapped individuals.

Rehabilitation might be interpreted to include the reeducation of the whole gamut of handicapped individuals. This would include the crippled, those with speech defects, sight defects, and hearing defects, the mentally and emotionally maladjusted, the mentally deficient, and the psychopathic. Through illness and injury alone, 250,000 men and women become disabled each year. When the word *rehabilitation* is used in physical education, however, it is concerned with those who need physical rehabilitation or physical reconditioning. These individuals, through adapted physical activities, may have their condition alleviated, whether it be a limiting physical condition or a mental

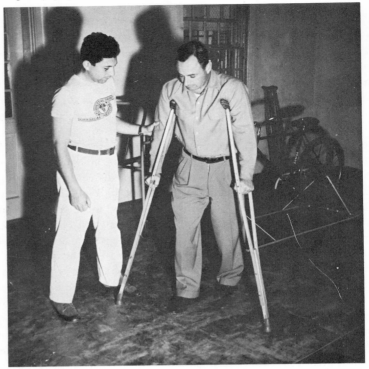

*Veterans Administration Hospital, Corrective Therapy Department,*
*Sepulveda, Calif.*

Gait training, neuromuscular coordination, and strengthening exercises are prescribed for general medical, neurological, and orthopedic patients.

condition. It has been proved time and time again that if an individual has a stiff elbow or a stiff knee, for example, the condition may be helped through adapted physical activities. Furthermore, the individual who is mentally disturbed and emotionally upset may, through physical activity, become so engrossed in this wholesome pastime that he will forget all about his worries or afflictions, and as a result his condition will improve.

Today, many physical educators trained in rehabilitation work are located in veterans' hospitals where physical reconditioning programs play a major part in the rehabilitation process. Any physical educator going into this type of program should realize that in many respects this work is more demanding than working with physically perfect human beings. In many cases it means working with an individual who has lost an arm or a leg, suffered paralysis, or received some other serious injury. It means hard work and not too many thanks. The individuals one works with are often disgruntled and mentally upset because of their condition. The satisfaction comes, however, when a human being is restored to useful service.

The program in physical reconditioning attempts to restore muscular strength and endurance to adequate levels. This phase of the program of physical education is for individuals who have been hospitalized for long periods, patients who are convalescing, and individuals whose diagnosis shows a mental condition that would benefit from such treatment.

## COACHING SPORTS

One of the most popular services that physical educators perform is that of coaching. A great many students who show exceptional skill in some interscholastic sport such as basketball, baseball, or football feel that they would like to become members of the physical education profession so that they may coach. They feel that since they have proved themselves athletes in high school they will be successful in coaching. This, however, is not necessarily true. It may seem paradoxical to the layman, but there is insufficient evidence to show that exceptional skill in any activity necessarily guarantees that one can be a good teacher of that activity. Many other factors such as personality, interest in youth, psychology of learning, intelligence, integrity, leadership, character, and a sympathetic attitude carry as much or more weight in coaching success.

Coaching should be recognized as teaching. Because of the nature of his position, a coach may be in a more favorable position to teach concepts that make for effective daily living than any other member of a school faculty, YMCA staff, or community center staff. Youth, with an inherent drive for activity and action and quest of excitement and competition which are found in sports, look up to the coach and in many cases feel that he is the type of individual to be emulated. Therefore, the prospective coach should recognize the influence he has over youth and see the value of such attributes as character, personality, and integrity. Although a coach must know thoroughly the game he is coaching, these other characteristics are of equal importance. The coach of an athletic team has within him the power to build future citizens with traits that are desirable and acceptable to society or citizens who have a false concept as to what is right and proper. Incidents that occur at many sports events throughout the country show that some of the leadership provided in athletics today is working to the detriment of acceptable character and moral outcomes. The coach is often tempted, due to the insecurity of his position, the emphasis on winning teams, student and alumni pressure, the desire for lucrative gate receipts, and the publicity that goes with winning teams, to seek outcomes not educational in nature. Unless the coach is an individual of strong character and willing to follow an unswerving course in the direction of what he knows to be right, many evils will enter the picture, and as a result the outcomes that are derived from competition in athletic events will inhibit rather than contribute to the building of good citizenship in youth.

The question is often raised as to whether it is necessary for a coach to have skill in the activity he coaches. There are many coaches today who sat on the bench for four years during their college football, basketball, baseball, tennis, or swimming days. There are many who excelled in the particular sport they are now coaching. There are others who never competed in the activity. Although exceptional skill in an activity is definitely desirable, it would be a fallacy to say that it should be a requirement for coaching. Through study and as a result of interest in an activity, many individuals have developed themselves to a point where they have been able to do a superior job in this area.

Any student of physical education planning to enter the coaching profession should recognize the uncertainty of tenure that is associated with this work. Pressure from alumni, sports writers, students, and the public can cause him to lose his job when the number of games in the "won" column does not meet with their approval. Many coaches have done commendable work and yet have been forced to leave their jobs because the material

*Colorado Springs Public Schools,*
*Colorado Springs, Colo.*

Coaching varsity sports offers an interesting career for many individuals. Varsity hurdlers in action.

with which they had to work was not of championship caliber. Hughes and Williams have pointed out some significant facts in respect to this malady associated with coaching:

> Whereas no Professor of English is judged by the number of Miltons, Stevensons, Shakespeares or Howells he graduates from his courses, the coach is judged by his team's scores. Regardless of whether or not his team plays well, knows the game, conducts itself as gentlemen, is alert, reliable, and resourceful, the measure of winning still remains the sole criterion of success.*

Coaching on the secondary school level can prove just as insecure as on the college level—much depends upon the school, community, and the school administration. Coaching offers an interesting and profitable career to many individuals. However, a coach should recognize the possibility

of becoming located in a school where the pressure may be so great as to cause unhappiness, insecurity, and even the loss of a job.

It should be understood very clearly that coaching is only one phase of the physical education profession and that coaching is teaching. Because of this close relationship with physical education and the education field in general, it should be recognized that a prospective coach should be qualified in certain phases of physical education. He should have a background in physical and biological science, skills, social sciences, education, humanities, and certain physical education subject matter. Only in this way will it be possible for the coach to best serve the youth of this country.

## BUILDING PHYSICAL FITNESS

During the last decade there has been much emphasis upon physical fitness. Ever since tests revealed that American children and youth were physically inept

---

*Hughes, William Leonard, and Williams, Jesse Feiring: Sports, their organization and administration, New York, 1944, A. S. Barnes & Co., p. 76.

*Youth Services Section, Los Angeles City Schools, Los Angeles, Calif.*

Weight training as a means of developing physical fitness.

compared to the young people in other countries, there has been much concern in school, college, agency, and community programs to upgrade the physical fitness of the American population.

Physical educators recognize the necessity of developing physical fitness in human beings and organize their programs to accomplish this objective and render this service to their constituency (see also Chapters 15 and 16).

The building of physical fitness involves many essentials other than physical activity, such as nutrition, rest, sleep, relaxation, and proper medical care. However, research has indicated that physical exercise is an important ingredient. Therefore,

physical educators can render a valuable service by organizing programs that include opportunities for individuals to engage in physical activity and also to learn something about the scientific foundations underlying the development and maintenance of physical fitness. Such programs should motivate students to apply during their school years and also throughout life, not only the physical skills they have learned but also the knowledge and understanding that have provided insights into the importance of being physically fit.

One further point should be mentioned. Physical education is concerned with other services in addition to the development of physical fitness in its constituency.

Therefore, proper balance in the allocation of time, facilities, personnel, and budget appropriations should be given to physical fitness, so that it will also be possible for the physical educator to render the other services that are a part of his field of endeavor.

## CONDUCTING RESEARCH

The purpose of research in any field is to push back the frontiers of knowledge. Physical education has lagged behind other fields in both its production and its use of research. Physical education has tended to rely heavily on research done in related fields. This may be one of the reasons why physical education is not considered an academic subject with academic status.

The major physical education research publication, *Research Quarterly,* has made a concerted effort in recent years to improve and stimulate the quality of research. Considerable physical education research is being done by graduate students who publish their theses and dissertations in *Research Quarterly.*

Recently, funds for research in physical education have been made available by the United States Office of Education, the National Institutes of Health, and the Department of Defense. Many leading colleges and universities have built, or are building, research laboratories. Most graduate programs on the master's and doctoral level require the completion of a course in research, but some schools do not require the writing of a scholarly paper for advanced degrees.

The tools of research in physical education include both the tried and tested and the newer, more sophisticated devices. Dynamometers, ergometers, treadmills, tensiometers, goniometers, fleximeters, silhouettographs, reaction timers, and the techniques of slow- and stop-motion cameras, special projection devices, and other means are used to measure the range of the body's abilities and reactions. Various attitude and personality tests are frequently correlated with the results of physical tests. The results of these tests are converted to statistics, charts, and tables. A recent criticism of research in physical education was that it depended too heavily on statistical analysis, and disguised the true meaning of results, and the possible applications of the results.

The most recent trend in physical education research has been in the area of physical fitness, although the mechanics of movement in various sports skills have also been intensively scrutinized.

In spite of the recent advances, much research remains to be done in the areas of motor learning, movement education, skill testing, physical fitness and physical ability, teaching methods, and curriculum.

Any occupation that desires to achieve the status of a profession must continually be pioneering, on the cutting edge of new developments, uncovering new knowledge, supporting hypothesis that have been formulated, and determining new truths pertinent to its field. Therefore, physical educators recognize the importance of conducting research in order to achieve this status and accomplish these objectives. Some of the research that has been conducted by physical educators in the past has not been significant and has not been conducted according to sound scientific procedures. However, with the renewed emphasis upon this service, the increased recognition of its significance and value in advancing physical education, and the various services that physical educators perform, more scholarly research is gradually being accomplished.

Physical educators who desire to render a service in the field of research should become well grounded in such areas as the sciences, research methodology, and the organization and conduct of research studies. These competencies take considerable time to develop and usually require many years of graduate work, including pursuing programs leading to masters and doctoral degrees. For those persons who have the interest and develop the competencies, however, there are many opportunities for rendering a valuable professional service. Approximately thirty colleges and universities engaged in physical education work now have research laboratories where research experimentation is carried on. There are job opportunities open to the qualified physical educator for conducting research on a full-time basis, carrying on research in addition to his teaching responsibilities, and serving as a laboratory and research assistant. In addition, there are research opportunities available in voluntary agencies, industry, and other settings.

There is a trend today toward interdisciplinary research, with a team approach being utilized. In such cases, the physical educator–researcher and a psychologist or sociologist, for example, work together, combining their knowledge and skills on problems that cut across both their fields of endeavor.

Most of the research being conducted today in physical education appears to be in the area of exercise physiology. However, there are an increasing number of studies being devoted to the relation of physical activity to psychological and sociological development of human beings.

## The ten most significant lines of educational research in the last decade

Ten of the most significant lines of educational research dating from 1957 were outlined by Daniel E. Griffiths* in a speech delivered to the convention of the American Association of School Admin-

istrators. These research findings are presented here in adapted form.

The first study* was concerned with an analysis of the rate of growth, and the changes in certain human characteristics over a specified length of time. The characteristics studied included: height, general intelligence, male aggressiveness, female dependence, male and female intellectuality, and general school achievement. The researcher developed two hypotheses: (1) environment affects the changes in human characteristics, and has its strongest effect when the change is taking place most · rapidly, and (2) the relevant factors in the environment are highly correlated with the changes that take place. The implications of the study for general education include the following: that primary education is extremely important, and deserves more consideration in regard to highly qualified teaching personnel, smaller class size, in-service teacher training, increased budget allocations, diagnostic services for pupils, and increased use of psychologists, and specialists in testing, evaluation, reading, and languages.

The second study† was concerned with the analysis of human intelligence. Primary intellectual abilities were classified by the use of special tests, and placed into three groups. The first group, basic processes, included five factors: cognition, memory, convergent thinking, divergent thinking, and evaluation. The second group, content, included four factors: figural, symbolic, semantic, and social. The third classification, products, included six factors: units, classes, relations, systems, transformations, and implications. The researcher concluded that one of the many implications of his study dealt directly

*Griffiths, Daniel E.: The ten most significant educational research findings in the past ten years, Executive Action Letter, 6:10, May, 1967. Publication of the Croft Educational Services, New London, Conn.

*Bloom, Benjamin S.: Stability and change in human characteristics, New York, 1964, John Wiley & Sons, Inc.

†Guilford, J. P.: Three faces of intellect, American Psychologist 14:469, Aug., 1959.

with education. In regard to education, he said that the concept of the learner and the learning process is subject to change, and that "learning is the discovery of information, not merely the formation of associations." This particular implication has influenced the new curriculums in many academic areas.

The third study* discussed the use of computer technology in studying theories of learning. The use of computers in a learning laboratory allows researchers to study and analyze more effectively the rate of learning of each individual, and differences in learning rates between individuals. Computers can also help, according to the findings of this study, to reinforce correct responses immediately, or correct wrong responses; facilitate the transfer of learning concepts from subject to subject; and aid in the determination of the best way to present and organize material to be learned.

The fourth study† was concerned with the effect of the environment on individual development. The results indicated that for the first and fifth grade students in this study, the more disadvantaged children were significantly lower generally in verbal and conceptual measures than were more advantaged youngsters. The researchers pointed out that the disadvantaged tend to decrease in intellectual performance unless they are exposed to specialized programs.

The fifth study‡ also dealt with individual development and is based largely on the theory and work of the Swiss psychologist Piaget. This study pointed out that the individual develops by sequential stages, but the appearance of each developmental stage varies with the individual, and among individuals. Nervous maturation, experience, social transmission, and autoregulation help to control individual development. This study implied that the individual must determine his own readiness to learn, and is best suited to guide his own learning.

The sixth study* was concerned with the characteristics of administrators and their styles of administering. The activities and styles of 232 elementary school principles were scored and analyzed in a simulated school created for this study. Eight different administrative methods and personalities were identified and their relationship shown to basic mental ability, basic personality factors, interests, job performance values, group instruction, superior's ratings, teacher ratings, professional and general knowledge, and biographical data.

The seventh study† discussed Project Talent, which was developed to investigate interests, career plans, and the relationship of high-school courses to the life objectives of approximately 440,000 students in public and private high schools. Their responses to a battery of tests were analyzed, along with other data. Follow-up studies will be conducted on these same students at intervals of one, five, ten, and twenty years after they complete high school. The hoped-for out-

---

*Suppes, Patrick: Modern learning theory and the elementary school curriculum, American Educational Research Journal 1:2, March, 1964.

†Annual Report 1965, Institute for Developmental Studies, School of Education, New York University.

‡Ripple, Richard E., and Rockcastle, Verne N., editors: Piaget rediscovered, New York, 1964, School of Education, Cornell University.

---

*Hemphill, John, Griffiths, Daniel E., and Frederiksen, Norman: Administrative performance and personality, New York, 1962, Teachers College Press.

†Flanagan, John C.: Maximizing human talents, The Journal of Teacher Education **13:** 209, June, 1962.

Flanagan, John C., and others: The identification, development, and utilization of human talents: the American high school student, Cooperative Research Project No. 635, 1964, University of Pittsburgh.

comes include: a comprehensive youth-talent inventory; improved standards of measurement and evaluation; an understanding of career choice; and evaluation of the relationship of education to career.

The eighth line of research* was devoted to the results of curriculum revision projects such as the "new math," and their influence on modern learning concepts, the structuring of knowledge, and emphasis on laboratory methods in the teaching of sciences.

The ninth line of research† discussed the Conant reports on various phases of American education, and pointed out the significance of Conant's recommendations for education.

The final line of research‡ discussed the biological bases for memory and learning and the role of deoxyribonucleic acid and ribonucleic acid in such processes.

The study discussed by Griffiths indicated that while no positive conclusions can be drawn from the research to date, important findings would probably be evidenced within the succeeding ten-year period.

## PREPARING PROFESSIONAL LEADERS FOR PHYSICAL EDUCATION WORK

For those physical educators who aspire to the college and university level, and who are interested in helping to shape the future of their field of endeavor by contributing to the preparation of future

*Ripple, Richard E., and Rockcastle, Verne N., editors: Piaget rediscovered, New York, 1964, School of Education, Cornell University.

†Conant, James Bryant: The American high school today, New York, 1959, McGraw-Hill Publishing Co.; Education in the junior high school years, Princeton; 1959, Educational Testing Service; Slums and suburbs, New York; 1961, McGraw-Hill Publishing Co.; The education of American teachers, New York, 1963, McGraw-Hill Publishing Co.

‡Gaito, John, DNA and RNA as memory molecules, Psychological Review **70**:471, Sept., 1963.

leaders of their field, there are many opportunities to render this valuable service in the more than 700 institutions that have such programs.

The qualifications for teaching in professional preparation programs include advanced degrees, a high academic record, an interest in and understanding of college students, a broad view of educational problems, and many times, previous experience at elementary or secondary school levels. The college teacher must be particularly well versed and competent in his field and have a desirable personality and nonacademic traits, such as good character. The teacher that is sought after is also one that can be characterized as truth seeking, humble, steadfast, and possessing a sympathetic understanding for human beings.

A professor in a professional preparation program might render a variety of services, including teaching such courses as history and philosophy of physical education, tests and measurements, methods, skills, organization and administration, programs for the atypical individual, and health observation. In addition, there might be research activities, committee service, advice and counsel of students, writing, community service, consulting, and participating in the work of professional associations.

A college or university staff usually includes various instructional ranks, including that of instructor, assistant professor, associate professor, and professor. In some cases there are distinguished professors. Furthermore, there is usually a head or chairman of the department, division, and in some cases, a dean of a school or college of physical education, health, and recreation.

The services that are rendered by physical educators in professional preparation programs can be very rewarding. By providing experiences that will help to develop those qualities, competencies, and attributes in students preparing to become leaders in the field, and doing an outstanding job in this training experience, a teacher's work will live on forever in the lives of his students and other leaders of future generations.

## ADMINISTERING PROGRAMS

A valuable service is rendered by those physical educators who administer programs in schools, colleges, governmental agencies and other programs, wherever they exist. Such work requires special qualifications if one is to perform the service well. Such qualifications would include a knowledge of the theory of administration, integrity, administrative mind, ability to instill good human relations, ability to make decisions, health and fitness for the job, willingness to accept responsibility, understanding of work, command of administrative technique, and intellectual capacity.

It is being recognized increasingly that administration is not a matter of hit or miss, trial and error, or expediency. Instead, a theory of administration is emerging. It is further recognized that from a study of this administrative theory one will gain insights into how to administer and how human beings work most effectively. Administrative theory will also help in the identification of problems that need to be solved if an effective working organization is to exist. Although some educators oppose the idea that a framework of theory can be established, it seems assured that administration is rapidly becoming a science, and is thereby characterized by more objectivity, reliability, and a systematic structure of substance. Such theory is explaining what administration is, and is providing guides to administrative action.

Those students who aspire to administrative positions in physical education, in addition to mastering the theory of administration, should also recognize that

one of the most important services they render is to human beings. Although some functions and areas can be somewhat mechanical, such as office management, budget making and financial accounting, purchase and care of supplies and equipment, legal liability, insurance management, curriculum planning, public relations, teacher and program evaluation, and facility management, relations with the staff, colleagues, and the public in general, can never become mechanical and routine. The administrator must always be sympathetic and understanding, friendly and considerate, honest and fair. In other words, he must be an expert in the area of human relations.

One further point should be mentioned. There is a trend for both men and women to be hired as administrators. In the past, when an administrative opportunity opened, the man was always the first to be considered. Although the odds in most situations are still in favor of the man, they have been reduced considerably. Sex is no longer the important factor it was years ago in the selection of an administrator. Many outstanding women administrators have proved they are competent to perform such a service.

## CONDUCTING AND SUPERVISING VARIOUS PROGRAMS, CLUBS, AND OTHER ACTIVITIES

Most schools and colleges have intramural, interscholastic, and intercollegiate athletic programs. Interscholastic and intercollegiate athletics are phases of the total physical education program. They are for those students who are skilled in sports and desire to compete against players from other schools and colleges in such activities as football, basketball, swimming, baseball, field hockey, volleyball, and track and field. Intramural athletics are usually open to all students and provide competition in various sports and activities within the same school situation.

In addition to interscholastic, intercollegiate and intramural athletics, clubs and other physical education activities are usually sponsored by most schools and colleges. These may take the form of boosters' clubs, cheerleading clubs, varsity clubs, and physical fitness clubs, as well as such activities as sports clinics and noon-hour recreation programs.

It is important to point out also that at the precollege level the physical educator is frequently called upon to monitor study halls, before-school and after-school student activities, and homerooms; to serve on curriculum, athletic, and other committees; and to participate in community programs when his or her talents can be of assistance.

## WORKING IN INTERNATIONAL EXCHANGE PROGRAMS

The shrinking world and the space age have brought about a vast interchange of specialists in all forms of endeavor. Physical educators, because of their special services, have been able to render a valuable service in many parts of the world. Operation Crossroads, The Peace Corps,

the American Specialist Program, and other programs carried on by the U. S. State Department and others have resulted in physical educators rendering services in such countries as Japan, Taiwan, Nepal, Nigeria, Pakistan, Peru, Senegal, Thailand, Turkey, Venezuela, Korea, the Philippines, and many other nations. These specialists have taught basketball, football, dodgeball, dance, and other sport and activity skills, coached athletic teams, organized recreation programs, lectured to civic groups and college students, attended and participated in conferences, and performed other outstanding services wherever they have gone.

Sports and physical education activities have great appeal for people in all countries. Since the United States has succeeded in many types of international sports competitions, and developed physical education programs in its schools and colleges that have achieved prominence in world circles, the physical education specialist has been in increasing demand by other governments and professional groups as a consultant, organizer, and teacher.

Japanese physical education class.

During an age when international strife is prevalent in many parts of the globe, where peace is a constant goal of humanity, when better understanding among the peoples of the world is a desperate need, when international education is an urgent necessity, and when emerging nations need assistance, physical educators can render a valuable service in utilizing their skills to help those in need. Furthermore, this service can be rendered here at home with our many international citizens, as well as abroad.

## TEACHING HEALTH

Surveys indicate that many physical educators teach concentrated health courses in the nation's schools. In some cases physical education personnel have been qualified to assume this responsibility and in other cases they have not. The teaching of health* as a subject-matter area should be done by a person who has training and experience to do the job effectively. However, there are many areas of health teaching, not involved in a concentrated health course, where all physical educators should be active. Physical educators should be concerned with emphasizing good health practices in their various activities; in stressing proper sanitary procedures conducive to a healthful environment; in pointing out to students the importance of such things as nutrition, rest, sleep, and medical examinations, to physical fitness; in showing the need to abstain from using tobacco, alcohol, and drugs; and in capitalizing on many other opportunities to impart knowledge and help in the development of wholesome health attitudes and practices in the physical education program. In these various ways physical educators can render a valuable service.

Health within the school structure consists of health education,* health services, and healthful school living. In the area of health education scientific knowledge is imparted and experiences are provided so that students may better understand the importance of developing good attitudes and health practices. Information concerning such topics as nutrition, communicable disease, rest, exercise, sanitation, first aid, and safety is presented. On the elementary level the responsibility for such health education rests on the shoulders of the classroom teacher, although in some school systems trained specialists are provided as resource persons. On the secondary level it is recommended that individuals who have had special training in health education be responsible for concentrated health instruction. This is not always the case. Sometimes in the absence of a trained specialist the teacher of physical education, home economics, science, or some other subject is given the responsibility. It should be reiterated that if a physical educator teaches health he should be qualified to perform this service.

Other phases of the school health program include health services and healthful school living. The health services include health appraisal, health counseling, correction of defects, provision for the exceptional child, prevention and control of communicable disease, and emergency care of injuries. Healthful school living refers to the physical and emotional environment in which the child lives while at school.

A significant study in the field of health education conducted in recent years is the School Health Education Study, which was initiated in September, 1961, under a grant from the Samuel Bronfman Foundation of New York City. This study has included to date a synthesis of research in selected areas of health instruction, a

*Sometimes referred to as health instruction or health science.

*See also Chapter 8.

national study of health instruction in the public schools, and the development of a concept approach to the teaching of health, which identifies the key concepts to be taught, conceptual statements for organizing the curriculum, and substantive elements that delineate the subject matter content. All of these concepts are directed at certain behavioral outcomes that are deemed desirable for the student. This study has determined the nature and scope of health education in the public schools of the United States, the kind of instruction students receive, how much boys and girls know about health matters, who teaches these pupils, how the subject is organized and scheduled in the school program, the health content areas that are emphasized, and many other factors

of importance to all educators and persons interested in health. The study is now giving special concern to the development of experimental curriculum materials.

## CONDUCTING SAFETY AND DRIVER EDUCATION PROGRAM

Closely allied with health is the program of safety and driver education. This important field of work gained divisional status in the American Association for Health, Physical Education, and Recreation on March 31, 1959. It is concerned with promoting active and effective programs in all forms of safety and driver education including recreational safety, home and community safety, driver and traffic safety, safety in physical education

*Shaker Heights High School, Cleveland, Ohio.*

Teaching life-saving techniques in physical education class.

and athletics, and safety throughout the school environment. Schools are being urged to hire qualified personnel to conduct and supervise the safety and driver education program. Where such programs have been initiated, the safety record has been considerably improved.

Many physical educators are being assigned duties and responsibilities in safety and driver-education programs. It is recommended that those physical educators who desire to participate in such programs should qualify themselves accordingly.

For persons trained in safety education opportunities are available in the schools as supervisors of safety education and as teachers of driver education, in industry and government as safety supervisors and safety directors, in communities as supervisors and consultants in community safety and as safety education officers, and in colleges and universities as teachers of safety and driver education, and directors of college campus safety activities.

Qualifications for safety positions include being able to work with people, having a knowledge of the field of safety, demonstrating effectiveness in group dynamics, possessing intellectual curiosity, and desirable safety skills and attitudes.

## WORKING IN A RECREATION PROGRAM*

Recreation programs in schools, communities, youth-serving agencies, industry, hospitals, and other organizations are growing rapidly. These programs are designed to provide young and old alike with profitable activities in which they can engage during their leisure hours. Special skills are needed for physical educators working in such programs. Such activities as games, sports, dance, and rhythms, play an important role in many

communities. It is a common practice for physical educators in our schools to find supplementary work in the recreation programs of their communities.

Various personal attributes are important for the physical educator desiring to perform services in recreation programs. These include such characteristics as integrity, friendly personality, enthusiasm, initiative, organizing ability, and other qualifications that will aid in the achievement of recreation objectives. It is especially important that the person working in recreation understands and appreciates human beings. He or she must have respect for the human personality; a broad social viewpoint; the desire to inculcate a high standard of moral and spiritual values; a recognition of the needs, interests, and desires of individuals; an appreciation of the part that recreation can play in meeting these needs and interests; and a desire to serve humanity. There is also a special need for recreators to have an understanding and appreciation of community structure and the place of recreation at the "grass roots" level of this structure.

## CAMPING AND OUTDOOR EDUCATION PROGRAMS*

Many physical educators render services in camping and outdoor education programs. These programs are recognized as having an educational value that should be experienced by every boy and girl. Although there are comparatively few camps throughout the United States that are associated with school systems, the trend seems to be in the direction of camping as part of the educational experience provided by the public schools. Outdoor education programs in camps and other settings are also becoming popular.

Outside the field of education, camps

are sponsored by state, county, and municipal governments and by such organizations as churches, Boy Scouts and Girl Scouts, YMCA, YWCA, YMHA, and YWHA groups, 4-H clubs, and private corporations.

Many educational institutions preparing teachers of physical education recognize the value of camping and its importance in education. Prospective teachers of physical education in some training programs are required to spend one or more sessions at a camp. This experience orients the student in camp living and in the organization and administration of a camp, and it emphasizes the value of outdoor education.

Camping should be included in the educational experience of every boy and girl because of the many values that it offers. In the camp situation individuals learn how to live together cooperatively and democratically. Regardless of whether a camper comes from a rich or a poor home, is white or Negro, is Jewish or Protestant, he shares camp responsibilities and lives peacefully with others. Campers live in the fresh air twenty-four hours a day, and engage in activities that are conducive to both mental and physical health. In the camp situation they are free from the tensions caused by irritating noises, bright lights, and crowded conditions of urban life. They develop an appreciation of nature. They experience adventure. They learn skills.

The program in most camps consists of such sports activities as swimming, boating, fishing, horseback riding, tennis, badminton, hiking, horseshoes, basketball, and softball; such social activities as campfires, frankfurter and marshmallow roasts, dancing, mixers, and cookouts; and opportunities to develop skills and an appreciation in arts and crafts, photography, Indian lore, drama, music, and nature study.

Some states have passed legislation mak-

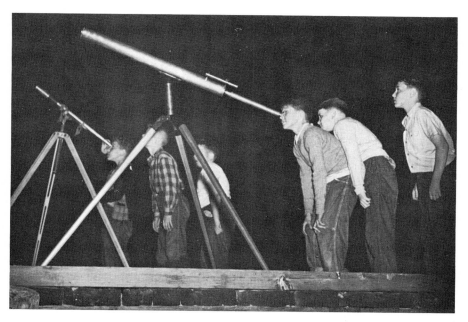

*Glencoe Public Schools, Glencoe, Ill.*

Camping out overnight offers opportunities to study and observe some of the celestial wonders of the universe.

ing tax money available to the schools who provide camping for the public school children. This trend in state-level provision for camping in the public schools means that more and more opportunities are going to be made available for children to have this worthwhile experience. Two of the states that have made legislative provision for school camping are Michigan and New York.

In the state of Michigan a bill was passed in 1945 which provided that boards of education, with the exception of those in primary school districts, could operate camps independently or jointly with other boards of education or governing bodies for purposes of recreation and instruction. Provision was made for the charging of fees, if necessary, to cover expenses incurred in maintaining the camp. However, these camps are to be run on a nonprofit basis. Provisions were also made for boards of education to employ personnel to operate these camps, to maintain essential facilities, and to locate camps on property other than that owned by the board of education, provided that the consent of the owner of said property had been secured. Finally,

a provision was made stipulating that the cost of operating a school camp should not be included in the determination of per capita costs of the regular school program.

In the state of New York legislation has provided that boards of education may operate camps on land secured by the school district for camp purposes. In 1944 the legislature of the state of New York passed the Desmond School Camp Bill, which makes it possible for school districts to appropriate funds for instructional programs deemed advisable for school children. Camping is one experience that is being recognized more and more as being essential for all children of school age.

Any individual trained in physical education may play a major part in the organization and administration of any school camp. Through his training in education, through his specialized skills which make up a great part of the program of any camp, and through his experiences in working with others in a camp situation, he is in a most important position to play a major role in this trend back to nature.

Outdoor education is not the same as camping, although it may and frequently

*State of Michigan.*

High school campers plant shrubs for erosion control and game management.

does take place in a camp setting. Outdoor education refers to the use of nature's classroom as a learning situation. This does not necessarily have to be a camp setting. It can take place on a hike, an overnight trip, a visit to the museum or zoo, or anywhere that the wonders of the out-of-doors are utilized. In this setting it is possible to do such things as discover how plants grow, study the stars, use a map and compass, discover the meaning of "contour," collect native craft materials, build outdoor shelters, experience the beauty of nature, engage in conservation projects, plant trees, care for animals and pets, and learn safe use of simple hand tools. Science, art, social studies, and other student groups will find many materials that they can study and experiences that will broaden their knowledge.

## QUESTIONS AND EXERCISES

1. In approximately 250 words describe the nature and scope of the services performed by physical educators.
2. List as many games and other related physical education activities as possible with which every person in physical education should be familiar.
3. What are the advantages and disadvantages of coaching?
4. Describe what you would consider to be the ideal coach.
5. What part does dance play in the physical education program? Why should men as well as women physical educators be trained in the field of the dance?
6. Discuss the contributions of camping and outdoor education to child growth and development.
7. What values can be derived from a camp experience that could not be gained from a formal classroom environment?
8. Describe a camping or outdoor educational experience in which you have engaged. What values did you receive from such an experience?
9. What are the essentials of good posture?
10. What are the advantages of observing good body mechanics?
11. What evidence is available to support the premise that good body mechanics should be stressed by parents and the school?
12. Describe the meaning inherent in the slogan "Out of Bed Into Action."
13. What are the qualifications needed to be an administrator? Researcher? Teacher of health?

## SELECTED REFERENCES

American Association for Health, Physical Education, and Recreation: The growing years —adolescence, Washington, D. C., 1962, The Association.

American Association for Health, Physical Education, and Recreation: This is physical education, Washington, D. C., 1965, The Association.

American Association for Health, Physical Education, and Recreation: Recreation and fitness for the mentally retarded, Challenge 1:2, March, 1966.

American Association for Health, Physical Education, and Recreation: Activity programs for the mentally retarded, Journal of Health, Physical Education, and Recreation, April, 1966.

Asbell, Bernard: Not like other children, Redbook, Oct., 1963.

A Symposium by Selected Physical Educators: Dance as an art form in physical education, Journal of Health, Physical Education, and Recreation 35:19, Jan., 1964.

Bucher, Charles A., editor: Methods and materials in physical education and recreation, St. Louis, 1954, The C. V. Mosby Co.

Bucher, Charles A.: Health, physical education, and academic achievement, NEA Journal 54:5, May, 1965.

Bucher, Charles A.: Administration of school health and physical education programs, St. Louis, 1967, The C. V. Mosby Co.

Bucher, Charles A., Koening, Constance, and Barnhard, Milton: Methods and materials for secondary school physical education, St. Louis, 1965, The C. V. Mosby Co.

Bucher, Charles A., and Reade, Evelyn M.: Physical education in the modern elementary school, New York, 1964, The Macmillan Co.

Carlton, Lessie, and Moore, Robert H.: Culturally disadvantaged children can be helped, NEA Journal 55:13, Sept., 1966.

Christaldi, Josephine, and Mueller, Grover W.: Let's do something about posture education, Journal of Health, Physical Education, and Recreation 34:14, Jan., 1963.

Committee on Standards, Safety Education

Supervisors Section, National Safety Council: A job analysis for safety education supervisors, Journal of Health, Physical Education, and Recreation 31:20, Jan., 1960.

Conant, James B.: Slums and suburbs, New York, 1964, New American Library.

Cureton, Thomas Kirk: Research in physical education in the United States, Physical Education Journal, Australian Physical Education Assn. No. 9, Feb.-March, 1957, p. 11.

Daniels, Arthur S., and Davies, Evelyn A.: Adapted physical education, New York, 1965, Harper & Brothers.

DeAngelis, Edith G.: Report on the seminar in physical education for the mentally retarded, Massachusetts Association for Health, Physical Education, and Recreation Newsletter 12:1, Fall, 1966.

Division of Safety and Driver Education, American Association for Health, Physical Education, and Recreation, Journal of Health, Physical Education, and Recreation 30:38, Sept., 1959.

Esslinger, Arthur A., and Clarke, H. Harrison: Graduate study and research as related to physical education, California Association for Health, Physical Education, and Recreation Journal 28:2, Nov.–Dec., 1965.

Fischer, J. A.: Helping to solve the social and psychological adjustment problems of the handicapped, Journal of Health, Physical Education, and Recreation 31:35, Feb., 1960.

Harrington, Michael: The other America, New York, 1962, The Macmillan Company.

Hayden, Frank J.: Physical fitness for the mentally retarded, Toronto, Canada, 1964, Rotary Clubs.

Hooley, Agnes M.: We can serve the students with disabilities, Journal of Health, Physical Education, and Recreation 30:45, March, 1959.

Ingram, Anne Gayle: The dancer-teacher . . . , Journal of Health, Physical Education, and Recreation 36:29, March, 1965.

Joint Committee on Health Problems in Education, National Education Association and the American Medical Association: Health education, Washington, D. C., 1961, National Education Association.

Jones, George W.: Compensatory education for the disadvantaged, NEA Journal 56:21, April, 1967.

Kroll, Walter: Graduate education: teacher versus researcher?, The Physical Educator 22:15, March, 1965.

Lee, Mabel, and Wagner, Miriam M.: Fundamentals of body mechanics and conditioning, Philadelphia, 1949, W. B. Saunders Co.

Masters, Hugh B.: Values of school camping, Journal of Health, Physical Education, and Recreation 22:14, Jan., 1951.

Moseley, M. Louise: And—why not, MAHPER Newsletter 12:1, Fall, 1966.

Nixon, John E., and others: An introduction to physical education, ed. 6, Philadelphia, 1964, W. B. Saunders Company.

Physical education and recreation for the retarded, Physical Education Newsletter 9:19, June, 1965.

Riessman, Frank: The culturally deprived child, New York, 1962, Harper and Row.

Smith, Julian W.: The Michigan story of camping and outdoor education, Journal of Educational Sociology 23:508, May, 1950.

Smith, Julian W.: Outdoor education for American youth, Washington, D. C., 1957, American Association for Health, Physical Education, and Recreation.

Smith, Kermit: A place for the physically handicapped, Tennessee Health and Physical Education Journal 5:1, September, 1966.

Staton, Wesley M.: Physical education or physical medicine, Education 70:75, Oct., 1949.

Stein, Julian U.: A practical guide to adapted physical education for the educable mentally handicapped, Journal of Health, Physical Education, and Recreation 33:30, Dec., 1962.

Wienke, Phoebe: Blind children in an integrated physical education program, The New Outlook for the Blind 60:3, March, 1966.

# Chapter 3

# Settings for physical education activities

The services that physical educators render to children, youth, and adults are an important consideration for young people who are preparing for a professional career in physical education, and also for those individuals who are already on the job in communities throughout the country. However, services cannot be considered in a meaningful manner by themselves. They must be considered in relation to the settings where they are performed.

## CONSIDERATIONS FOR PHYSICAL EDUCATORS IN SELECTING A SETTING IN WHICH TO WORK

In this chapter many settings in which physical education activities are administered, supervised, taught, coached, performed, and carried out as parts of school and other organizational programs will be discussed. Physical educators will be interested in seeking job opportunities and in performing services in one of these settings, depending on pertinent factors relating to their qualifications for the job and their ability to perform effectively. A few considerations in selecting the setting are professional preparation, abilities, interests, and job availability.

### Professional preparation

The preparation an individual has had in respect to general education, and such courses and experiences as psychology, methodology, skills, student teaching, and other aspects of training programs will play a part in the selection of a setting. A person who has prepared for elementary school teaching will obviously be interested in teaching at that educational level just as the person who has prepared for college teaching wants to be situated in an institution of higher learning. Such preparation has oriented the individual to a particular setting and provided knowledge, understanding, and skill to do an effective job in that location. Therefore professional preparation plays an important part in determining the setting in which the individual will work.

### Abilities

It is important to match personal abilities with the job and setting. At an early age Einstein showed an uncanny aptitude with figures, and Henry Ford showed superior ability working with machines and gadgets. These great leaders had abilities that helped them to be successful in their work. Some people have greater ability than others in the area of research which might better qualify them for college work. Others may demonstrate ability in working with children, which might better qualify them for elementary school work, or skill in golf, which might better qualify them for a professional job in a country club. Each person should match his or her abilities against several settings as a means of arriving at the right decision for a successful career. Strong preference should be given to those settings where there is tangible evidence that outstanding ability exists.

### Interests

Other things being equal, the setting where there is greatest interest should offer a better chance for success because the person will be doing what he or she wants to do. However, if other factors such as abilities are not taken into consideration, it may mean the job will not be done well. There are people with exceptional interest in golf but who score well over 100 for a round of eighteen holes.

Since interests may change, it is also important to carefully evaluate them in order to cement realistic desires and rule out passing fancies.

### Job availability

Professional preparation, abilities, and interests are important, but at the same time there is a practical consideration—job availability. After a person spends four or five years preparing for a career, he or she naturally wants to find a job in his field. It may be that the chances of obtaining employment in one setting may be brighter than in another. Therefore, availability of work is a consideration that cannot be overlooked.

### Settings

Physical education activities are conducted in many and varied settings. The most popular and prominent settings at the present time are as follows:

1. Public and private schools and colleges
2. Service organizations
3. Industrial concerns
4. Youth organizations
5. Recreational areas
6. Athletic clubs and other sport organizations
7. Professional and commercial areas
8. Camps
9. Governmental and welfare agencies
10. Churches
11. Hospitals
12. Penal institutions
13. Other countries

## PUBLIC AND PRIVATE SCHOOLS AND COLLEGES

Physical education activities play an important part in schools and colleges. The nation's schools and colleges may be categorized as nursery schools, kindergarten, primary grades, upper elementary grades, junior high school, senior high school, junior college, college, and university.

The nation's schools and colleges in the years to come will continue to be the settings where most physical educators will find work. The reason for this is the rapid growth of the school and college population and the continued demand for teachers in these institutions. Through 1970 the demand each year for additional teachers for public elementary schools alone will be approximately 100,000. At the present annual rate, only 75,000–80,000 college graduates are prepared to teach in the elementary schools. At the high school level, there is a shortage in most teaching fields. Physical education for men and social studies at present are exceptions since they are oversupplied in some parts of the country. There is an urgent need for teachers who are qualified to teach at the college level.

Today, the public and private school enrollment in all institutions from kindergarten to graduate school is nearly sixty

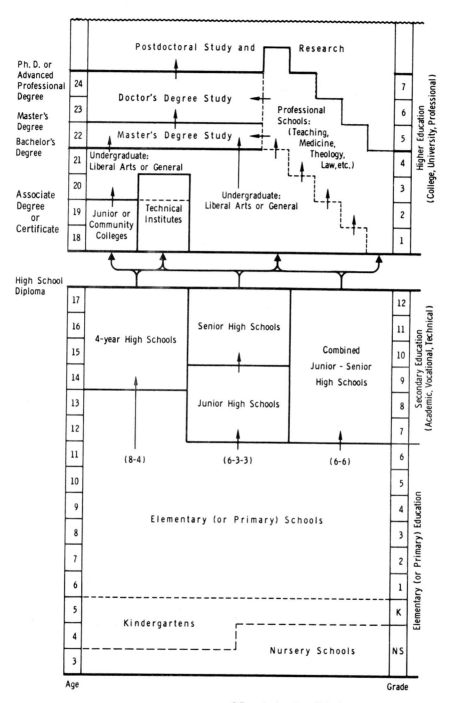

*Office of education, U.S. Department of Health,*
*Education, and Welfare: Digest of educational statistics, 1966,*
*Washington, D. C.*

The structure of education in the United States.

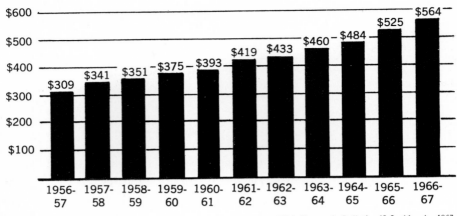

*NEA Research Bulletin 45:5, March, 1967.*

Current expenditure per pupil in average daily attendance at public elementary and secondary schools.

million—over six million in higher education alone. Ten years ago school and college enrollments were under forty million. The United States Office of Education foresees enrollments of sixty-two million by 1973. Two-year college enrollments have jumped from less than 300,000 students in 1954 to more than one million, and it is growing at the rate of 20% each year. About fifty new community colleges are being opened each September.

More men are entering the teaching profession. In 1966, there was a growth of 4.1% in the number of men entering teaching as compared with an increase of 3.5% in the number of women teachers. Ten years ago the men made up approximately 26% of the nation's teaching staff. Today, the figure is 32%. In the elementary and high schools today, there are approximately 557,000 men teachers and 1,202,000 women. Some facts about teachers in the schools are as follows:

*Average age:*
  Average is between 41 and 42 years of age; women teachers on the average are almost eight years older than men teachers.
*Marital status:*
  About 78% of the public school teachers are or have been married.

*Experience:*
  Median teacher has 11 years of teaching experience; women teachers on the average have been teaching twice as long as men.

**Elementary school**

The objectives of elementary school education have been well stated by a group of teachers in Winnetka, Illinois.* These objectives are presented here in adapted form. The elementary schools should be designed to (1) encourage intellectual growth, (2) develop basic skills, (3) give consideration to the child as a total human being, (4) help children develop attitudes, habits, values, appreciations, and understandings which will insure a constructive adult life, (5) discover and meet the special talents and needs of all children, (6) develop habits of rational thinking and problem-solving, (7) foster physical and mental health, (8) establish a setting that furthers social and aesthetic development, (9) inculcate an appreciation of hard work, and (10) stress moral and spiritual values.

Some reasons given by physical educa-

---

*Beliefs and objectives of the Winnetka public schools, Winnetka, Ill., 1961, The Board of Education.

tors as to why they like teaching in the elementary schools include the following:

1. It offers a combination of opportunity, reward, challenge, and deep gratification for services performed.
2. Pupils are motivated, eager, enthusiastic, and take pride in their progress.
3. The child has a natural craving for activity which makes work a pleasure.
4. At the elementary level it is possible to witness rapid, visible advancement of pupils.
5. It is a joy to work with happy youngsters.
6. There is a great challenge in working with a child during his most impressionable and formative years.
7. There are more job openings at the elementary level.
8. The personal satisfaction is great when a small hand slips into yours and a voice says, "I like you."

In elementary schools the program consists mainly of movement experiences, including rhythmical activities, story plays, creative activities, self-testing activities, relays, hunting games, aquatics, and winter sports. These activities are largely conducted by the classroom teacher. Many educators feel that, since the elementary school teacher teaches a variety of school activities to children all day, she should also teach them physical education. At the same time, however, many educators feel that the physical education program in the elementary school should be directed by specialized personnel because it is recognized that physical education at this level is one of the most important subjects due to the activity drive in children, the necessity for "big-muscle" activity, and the need for developing a broad foundation of physical skills for future use. A sound foundation of physical education skills in the early years will help to guarantee the pursuit of physical activity in the later years and will motivate individuals into activity on their own initiative.

To provide qualified leadership in physical education on the elementary level,

different procedures are followed. Supervisors of physical education are provided in many school systems to aid the classroom teachers in developing a sound program. Some systems have "demonstration" teachers who are on call, and any classroom teacher may request their services if they are interested in having some particular game, rhythmic activity, or relay demonstrated or discussed. There is also developing what is known as a "resource" teacher in physical education on the elementary level. This individual is a specialist in physical education and is relieved of many routine classroom duties to coordinate the physical education program in a particular elementary school. Some teacher-training institutions are certifying teachers with a double major, one in physical education and one in elementary education. This enables the prospective teacher to accept a position in the elementary school where part of the time will be utilized to coordinate the physical education program. With stress being placed on physical education in the elementary school, it is hoped that throughout the country more personnel qualified in physical education will be added to school faculties.

## Secondary school level

The secondary school level refers to those grades that follow elementary school, starting with grade seven and continuing to the college years. Secondary schools are organized according to various administrative patterns. Some of the more prevalent patterns are: the traditional high school or 8-4 system, the combined junior and senior high school or 6-6- or 7-5 plan, the 6-3-3 system where the junior high school is grouped separately, and the 6-2-4 system with the four-year high school.

The purposes of the secondary school have been stated by many educational groups (see Chapter 7 for a discussion

*Text continued on p. 68.*

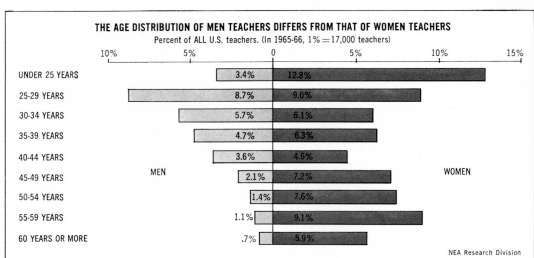

### THE AGE DISTRIBUTION OF MEN TEACHERS DIFFERS FROM THAT OF WOMEN TEACHERS
Percent of ALL U.S. teachers. (In 1965-66, 1% = 17,000 teachers)

| Age group | MEN | WOMEN |
|---|---|---|
| UNDER 25 YEARS | 3.4% | 12.8% |
| 25-29 YEARS | 8.7% | 9.0% |
| 30-34 YEARS | 5.7% | 6.1% |
| 35-39 YEARS | 4.7% | 6.3% |
| 40-44 YEARS | 3.6% | 4.6% |
| 45-49 YEARS | 2.1% | 7.2% |
| 50-54 YEARS | 1.4% | 7.6% |
| 55-59 YEARS | 1.1% | 9.1% |
| 60 YEARS OR MORE | .7% | 5.9% |

NEA Research Division

Thirty-one percent of the teachers in 1965-66 were men; 69 percent were women.

For all teachers, the median age was 36 years. It was 33 years for men and 40 years for women.

The men were heavily concentrated in one age group—25-29 years. Women, however, were in a bi-modal distribution, with peaks in the group under 25 years and in the 55-59 year group. At ages 30-34, the number of men was nearly as large as the number of women.

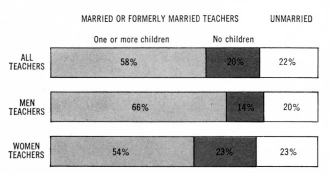

### A MAJORITY OF TEACHERS ARE MARRIED AND ARE PARENTS

MARRIED OR FORMERLY MARRIED TEACHERS     UNMARRIED

One or more children     No children

| | One or more children | No children | Unmarried |
|---|---|---|---|
| ALL TEACHERS | 58% | 20% | 22% |
| MEN TEACHERS | 66% | 14% | 20% |
| WOMEN TEACHERS | 54% | 23% | 23% |

NEA Research Division

Of the teachers who are married or have been formerly married, 22 percent of the men and 20 percent of the women have only one child; 31 percent of the men and 23 percent of the women have three or more children.

### THE TEACHER IS A VOTING CITIZEN

Percent voting in 1964 national election

GENERAL POPULATION OF VOTING AGE
69%

PUBLIC SCHOOL CLASSROOM TEACHERS
89%

NEA Research Division

Twenty-two percent of the teachers are members of a political party organization; 12 percent gave funds to their political party; 9 percent served as party workers in the 1964 election and 3 percent have themselves been candidates for public office.

*Hazel Davis: Profile of the American public school teacher, 1966, NEA Journal 56:11, May, 1967.*

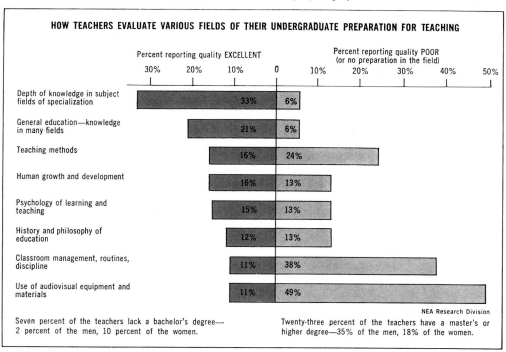

## HOW TEACHERS EVALUATE VARIOUS FIELDS OF THEIR UNDERGRADUATE PREPARATION FOR TEACHING

Percent reporting quality EXCELLENT

Percent reporting quality POOR
(or no preparation in the field)

| | EXCELLENT | POOR |
|---|---|---|
| Depth of knowledge in subject fields of specialization | 33% | 6% |
| General education—knowledge in many fields | 21% | 6% |
| Teaching methods | 16% | 24% |
| Human growth and development | 16% | 13% |
| Psychology of learning and teaching | 15% | 13% |
| History and philosophy of education | 12% | 13% |
| Classroom management, routines, discipline | 11% | 38% |
| Use of audiovisual equipment and materials | 11% | 49% |

NEA Research Division

Seven percent of the teachers lack a bachelor's degree—2 percent of the men, 10 percent of the women.

Twenty-three percent of the teachers have a master's or higher degree—35% of the men, 18% of the women.

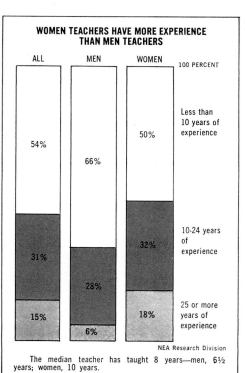

## WOMEN TEACHERS HAVE MORE EXPERIENCE THAN MEN TEACHERS

| ALL | MEN | WOMEN | 100 PERCENT |
|---|---|---|---|
| 54% | 50% (MEN 66%) | | Less than 10 years of experience |
| 31% | 28% | 32% | 10-24 years of experience |
| 15% | 6% | 18% | 25 or more years of experience |

NEA Research Division

The median teacher has taught 8 years—men, 6½ years; women, 10 years.

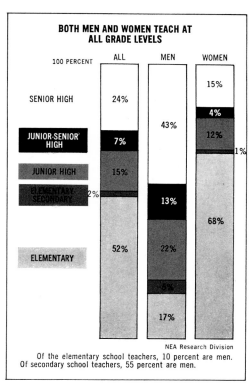

## BOTH MEN AND WOMEN TEACH AT ALL GRADE LEVELS

100 PERCENT

| | ALL | MEN | WOMEN |
|---|---|---|---|
| SENIOR HIGH | 24% | 43% | 15% |
| JUNIOR-SENIOR HIGH | 7% | | 4% |
| JUNIOR HIGH | 15% | | 12% |
| ELEMENTARY-SECONDARY | 2% | 13% | 1% |
| | | 22% | 68% |
| ELEMENTARY | 52% | 5% | |
| | | 17% | |

NEA Research Division

Of the elementary school teachers, 10 percent are men. Of secondary school teachers, 55 percent are men.

*Hazel Davis: Profile of the American public school teacher, 1966, NEA Journal 56:11, May, 1967.*

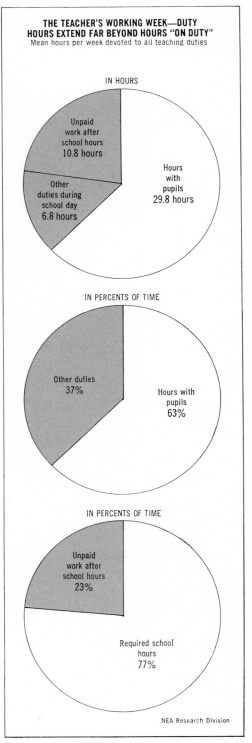

**WHAT THE SECONDARY SCHOOL TEACHERS TEACH**

100 percent of teachers

ART (2.0%), AGRICULTURE (1.6%), OTHER (2.3%)

MUSIC (4.7%)

INDUSTRIAL ARTS (5.1%)

HOME ECONOMICS (5.9%)

FOREIGN LANGUAGE (6.4%)

HEALTH AND PHYSICAL EDUCATION (6.9%)

BUSINESS EDUCATION (7.0%)

SCIENCE (10.8%)

MATHEMATICS (13.9%)

SOCIAL STUDIES (15.3%)

ENGLISH (18.1%)

NEA Research Division

**THE TEACHER'S WORKING WEEK—DUTY HOURS EXTEND FAR BEYOND HOURS "ON DUTY"**

Mean hours per week devoted to all teaching duties

IN HOURS

Unpaid work after school hours 10.8 hours

Other duties during school day 6.8 hours

Hours with pupils 29.8 hours

IN PERCENTS OF TIME

Other duties 37%

Hours with pupils 63%

IN PERCENTS OF TIME

Unpaid work after school hours 23%

Required school hours 77%

NEA Research Division

*Hazel Davis: Profile of the American public school teacher, 1966, NEA Journal 56:11, May, 1967.*

*Toledo Public Schools, Toledo, Ohio.*

Physical education at the elementary school level.

*Educational Facilities Laboratories, Inc., New York, N. Y.*

Facilities are constantly changing to meet the needs of modern-day physical education programs as shown in Holland High School, Holland, Mich.

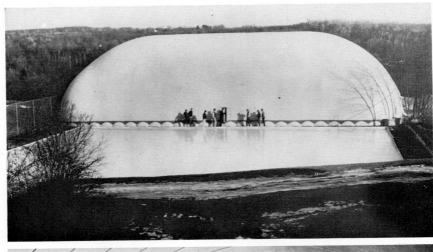

*Educational Facilities Laboratories, Inc., New York, N. Y.*

Air-supported structure for physical education activities at Forman School, Litchfield, Conn.

of such objectives). The primary functions allocated to the secondary school include promoting the total development of the pupil, including his intellectual powers, a basic knowledge of major fields of study, and his unique talents, whatever they may be. A second purpose is to help the pupil achieve a better understanding of his abilities, interests, and potentialities. A third purpose is to orient the pupil in various fields of work so that he may learn how his abilities and interests relate to these areas of endeavor. A fourth purpose is to help each student develop a sound system of values. A fifth purpose is to help the pupil develop a philosophy of life together with the skills, health, interests, appreciations,

*Detroit Public Schools, Detroit, Mich.*

Physical education carries its own drive.

and social attributes that are essential to a good life. Finally, a sixth purpose is to develop an understanding of the democratic process and the role of the student in furthering this way of life.

Some reasons given by physical educators as to why they like teaching at the secondary school level include the following:

1. Love of team sports
2. Excitement of and interest in coaching sports
3. The compartmentalization of subject matter
4. An interesting group of students with whom to work
5. Satisfaction derived in seeing students transfer skills from physical education class to after-school intramurals and recreation
6. The challenge of guiding students through the awkward, transitional period of unrest and uncertainty of the junior high school years
7. The inspiration derived in working on a staff with other professional colleagues

8. Love of more highly organized games and activities

### Junior high school

In junior high schools the physical education program includes aquatics, posture work, dual and individual sports, self-testing activities, formal activities, games and relays, sports of higher organization, rhythmics and dancing, contests, apparatus, and tumbling and stunts. Many of the activities for both boys and girls are very similar at this level, but it is desirable that they be separated for a large part of their work. The activities must be selected with care because of the anatomical and physiological nature of this age group. Pupils at this level are susceptible to fatigue, are in a period of rapid growth, and find it difficult to coordinate their actions, which results in awkwardness. There must be careful supervision by qualified personnel of all physical education activities in

Physical education on the junior high school level.

order that the student may experience optimum development. In some school systems the physical education programs in the junior high school grades (seventh, eighth, and ninth) are administered in much the same way as the first six grades. The classroom teachers handle the physical education programs for their respective grades. In other school systems the junior high school is separate from the elementary and the senior high schools. In this particular type of setup it is common to find trained physical education men and women handling the classes in physical education. In still other school systems, one or more grades of the junior high school are included in the senior high school building, where trained physical education personnel usually handle the classes. The teachers on the junior high school level should be specialists in physical education. They should be sympathetic to the problems of boys and girls and should be able to guide children successfully during this formative period. They should understand the needs of chil-

dren and their interests and capacities and should realize that they may be of exceptional service to the student during this time when he is planning his future.

### Senior high school

The senior high school physical education program should be the responsibility of specialized persons. During high school more stress is placed on the team games of higher organization and on dual and individual games. It is also during this period that the student should develop sufficient skill so that when he leaves school he will have the necessary fundamental skill, the desire, and the knowledge to participate successfully and enjoyably. Because many students do not go on to college, it is essential that they acquire this skill, knowledge, and interest before they leave school. The competitive element is very prominent in high school students; and the more highly organized games, intramural and interscholastic sports, and field and play days offer an

Pikeville High School, Pikeville, Ky.

Girls' tumbling and gymnastics class on the high school level.

opportunity for the students to give vent to this instinct. However, the physical education teacher, through careful supervision and guidance, must ensure that the activity is not too strenuous and that excessive demands are not placed on the participant. Girls are frequently as interested in sports as boys, and many activities may be modified in order to provide a corecreational program.

The program of activities in the high school should include a core and an elective program both for boys and for girls. The program includes such activitities as basketball, formal activities, field hockey, advanced rhythms, volleyball, tumbling, track and field, touch football, swimming, softball, soccer, archery, badminton, bowling, tennis, dance, winter activities, handball, golf, camping, and corrective activities.

Because of the differences in strength, interests, and skill, the boys' and girls'

physical education programs are usually separate on the senior high school level. This necessitates at least one specialist for the girls and one for the boys. Furthermore, in larger schools there are frequently additional personnel for such phases of the program as coaching and corrective work. It has been recommended that classes in physical education be limited in number of students to not more than thirty-five to forty. If this becomes standard practice, more physical educators will be needed. As it is, the senior high school level is one of the most popular and important settings for physical education personnel in the national education setup.

The preparatory school and private school have much the same type of program as is found in the senior high school. In many of these schools, however, the advantages for a well-rounded and successful physical education program are much greater. Because of small enrollments, beautiful athletic fields, spacious gymnasiums, and swimming pools, these schools may offer a program that is in many ways superior to those found in many public schools, colleges, and universities.

### College and university

There are many types of colleges including public and private; large and small; resident and nonresident; urban and rural; secular or sectarian; liberal, technical, or professional; two-year or four-year; coeducational or for a single sex; or a combination of the above.

Colleges and universities take their goals and direction from many sources. The founders, faculty, trustees, donors, alumni, or administration of a college or university might indicate that it is to devote its endeavors to agriculture or to the liberal arts, to training teachers or to preparing architects, to ensuring social com-

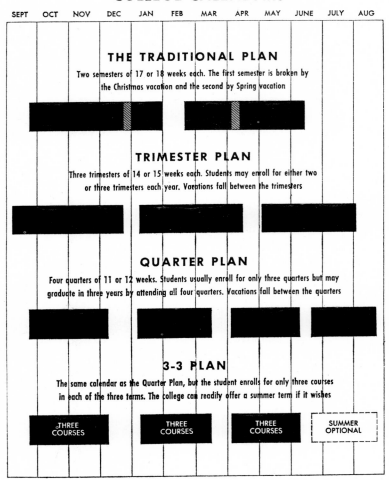

## COLLEGE CALENDARS

SEPT   OCT   NOV   DEC   JAN   FEB   MAR   APR   MAY   JUNE   JULY   AUG

### THE TRADITIONAL PLAN
Two semesters of 17 or 18 weeks each. The first semester is broken by the Christmas vacation and the second by Spring vacation

### TRIMESTER PLAN
Three trimesters of 14 or 15 weeks each. Students may enroll for either two or three trimesters each year. Vacations fall between the trimesters

### QUARTER PLAN
Four quarters of 11 or 12 weeks. Students usually enroll for only three quarters but may graduate in three years by attending all four quarters. Vacations fall between the quarters

### 3-3 PLAN
The same calendar as the Quarter Plan, but the student enrolls for only three courses in each of the three terms. The college can readily offer a summer term if it wishes

THREE COURSES    THREE COURSES    THREE COURSES    SUMMER OPTIONAL

*Saturday Review, Dec. 15, 1962.*

College calendars.

petence or intellectual growth, to preparing for a profession or to getting a general education, or a combination of these purposes. In other words, the purposes of colleges are varied—all do not have the same goals.

Some reasons given by physical educators as to why they like teaching at the college level include the following:

1. Students are more mature.
2. The instructor and professor have more freedom.
3. Professional preparatory programs offer opportunities to train future professional leaders.
4. Campus living is satisfying as is college life in general.
5. There is more prestige in teaching at the college level.
6. There are more opportunities to participate in work of professional associations.
7. Opportunities to improve one's own educational background by taking graduate work are greater.

### The two-year college

The average enrollment for a junior college is approximately 1,600–2,000 students. Most of the two-year colleges require physical education for approximately two hours a week for each of the two years. In a few colleges physical education is required the first year and is made elective the second year. The activities offered in the first year are predominantly team sports. The activities offered in the second year include individual, dual, and carry-over sports, along with team sports. The most common activities offered in the two-year colleges include basketball, gymnastics, track and field, volleyball, tennis, touch football, soccer, golf, archery, bowling, weight lifting, wrestling, swimming, field hockey, badminton, and dancing.

Some colleges require a textbook as part of the physical education experience. Many two-year colleges require health courses for their students which are frequently taught by physical education professors. A majority of the two-year colleges have a director of physical education who frequently is also the athletic director.

Since the two-year college is comparatively new on the American scene, programs are varied from state to state and college to college. In the future it would

Full-time teaching staff working in junior colleges with salary schedules based on professorial ranks:

| | | |
|---|---|---|
| ■ Instructors | 1,701 | 9.7% |
| ▨ Assistant professors | 1,587 | 9.0 |
| ▥ Associate professors | 749 | 4.2 |
| ☐ Professors | 312 | 1.8 |
| | 4,349 | 24.7% |

■ Instructors working in junior colleges with salary schedules based on preparation levels, 13,252 or 75.3%.

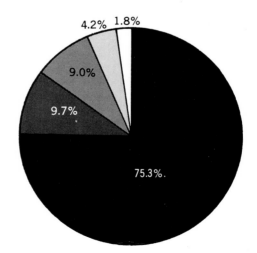

*NEA Research Bulletin 44:69, Oct., 1966.*

Full-time teaching staff, reporting public junior colleges, 1965-1966.

appear that physical education programs would become more purposive, and provide initial preparation for those students desiring to make physical education a career, offer two years of basic instruction in physical education activities, meet the needs of the atypical student, provide college credit for courses taken, develop a broad intramural and intercollegiate program, engage in research activities, and help college students in the development of lifetime skills and understanding and appreciation of the importance of physical activity throughout life for their physical, mental, and social betterment.

The two-year college is an institution that is progressing with great rapidity in our country. This is the institutional level where probably the greatest expansion will take place in our educational system during the next decade. California and New York are two of many states that have instituted extensive systems of junior and community colleges. These colleges are being developed so that students may live at home or will not have to travel very far, and still continue their education beyond high school. For some students these colleges may provide terminal formal education, and for others they may provide the first two years of a four-year college course. These schools recognize the value of regular physical education classes, as well as a broad athletic program for their students.

### The four-year college and university program

The college and university physical education program is designed for providing opportunities for physical conditioning, developing skills in recreational and leisure-time activities, and participating in intramural and intercollegiate athletic competition. In the basic instructional or service physical education programs, college students usually participate for two years in various team sports, dual and individual activities, rhythmical activities, and recreational sports, for the purpose of maintaining good physical condition. At the same time there are many other beneficial results, such as the alleviation of tensions. Probably the most beneficial result from participation is the development of physical skills, making it possible for students to continue physical activity after leaving college. Most college programs offer some freedom in the choice of activities so that the student may further develop his skill in a sport in which he has particular interest. The intramural and intercollegiate sports program also plays an important part in college and university physical education programs, as well as in two-year colleges. Intramural athletics offer an opportunity for all students, regardless of degree of skill, to participate. Leagues are usually formed according to some method of homogeneous grouping and in such a manner as to add flavor and interest to the competition. In many colleges, fraternities, sororities, and other organizations enter teams. This usually adds additional vigor and interest to the rivalry. Participants in intercollegiate sports are for the more skilled players in various sports such as basketball, football, baseball, track, swimming, soccer, and tennis. Teams in these various sports vie with teams from other schools. The National Collegiate Athletic Association and the National Association for Intercollegiate Athletics are set up to govern, regulate, and establish standards for this competition. In many colleges field and play days take the place of intercollegiate athletic competition for the girls.

In addition to the teaching of service courses for college students, there is also a need for teachers of physical education in the many teacher-education institutions throughout the country. As the demand for more physical education personnel grows, there will be an equal demand for teachers to train this personnel. Personnel who work in teacher-training institutions teach such courses as anatomy, physiology, methods and materials, tests and measurements, remedial physical education, principles of physical education, and organization and administration of the physical education program. They also teach various skill courses in the activities and provide other necessary experiences such as camping and outdoor education.

## Special schools

In addition to the nation's public and private schools that serve many of the nation's children and youth, there are also special schools in which other pupils are enrolled. These include trade and vocational schools; schools for atypical persons such as the blind, retarded and crippled; and schools for men and women who are primarily interested in adult education.

### Trade and vocational schools

Many schools exist to prepare for careers in certain trades, crafts, and other vocations. The privately operated schools of commerce, technical institutes, and schools for dental assistants are a mere sampling of the types of schools one sees constantly advertised in newspapers, magazines, subways, or buses. Most of these schools offer some type of physical education program for their students. Such a program is usually similar to those discussed under secondary education and exist in the junior and senior high schools of the nation.

### Schools for atypical individuals

Opportunities exist for teaching individuals who have special physical afflictions such as blindness, deafness, hearing difficulties, who are crippled, or others who find they can obtain greater benefits by pursuing an education with individuals who have similar handicaps. In recent years, particularly with the emphasis on providing education for all persons in our society, such schools have multiplied. As a result, there have been directors of special education appointed in state departments of education, and colleges and universities have introduced courses for the professional preparation of teachers specializing in the education of exceptional children. School, college, and university programs where the handicapped are taught, have been established. Foundations and agencies, such as the American Foundation for the Blind, Inc., have been established. In addition to teachers and counselors being needed to work with handicapped children, they are also needed to work with handicapped adults.

Wherever possible, the disabled are taught in regular school and college classes along with the able-bodied. Nevertheless, in many instances where the affliction warrants, education has proved to be more satisfactory in special schools and colleges especially adapted for such purposes.

### Schools for adults

Adult education is thriving throughout the country. Programs are being established in most communities that provide experiences for men and women who desire to enrich their lives. These experiences cover the gamut of educational activities including English, music, Spanish, art, and typewriting. They also provide opportunities to develop physical fitness, skill in some sport or dance, or other area of competency associated with physical education.

## SERVICE ORGANIZATIONS

There are many service organizations such as the YMCA, American Red Cross, settlement houses, and the armed forces that provide employment for physical educators.

**Young Men's Christian Association,
Young Women's Christian Association,
Young Men's Hebrew Association,
and Young Women's Hebrew
Association**

The YMCA, YWCA, YMHA, YWHA, and similar service organizations serve many groups of people. They serve the people of various communities where they have been established, both the young and adult population. Religious training was the main purpose in forming many of these organizations. However, activities directed at the physical are an important part of their programs. Classes in various physical activities; ath-

**Table 3-1.** *YMCA physical activity schedule*

| Activities | Mon. | Tues. | Wed. | Thurs. | Fri. | Sat. |
|---|---|---|---|---|---|---|
| Basketball | 4:15–5:30<br>6:00–7:30 | 4:15–8:00 | 4:15–5:30<br>6:00–8:00 | 4:15–8:00 | 4:15–5:30<br>6:00–7:30 | 3:30–9:00 |
| Boxing (furnish own speed bag) | 10:00–10:00 | 10:00–10:00 | 10:00–10:00 | 10:00–10:00 | 10:00–10:00 | 9:00–9:00 |
| Boys' swimming class | | | | | | 9:00–1:00 |
| Calisthenics | 12:15–12:45<br>5:30–6:00 | 12:15–12:45<br>6:00–6:30 | 12:15–12:45<br>5:30–6:00 | 12:15–12:45<br>6:00–6:30 | 12:15–12:45<br>5:30–6:00 | |
| Father & son swim | | | | | 7:00–10:00 | 1:00–9:00 |
| Fencing | 8:00–10:00 | | | | 8:00–10:00 | |
| Gymnastics | | 8:00–10:00 | | 8:00–10:00 | | |
| Handball (reservation required) | 10:00–10:00 | 10:00–10:00 | 10:00–10:00 | 10:00–10:00 | 10:00–10:00 | 9:00–9:00 |
| Lifesaving (as scheduled) | | 8:00–10:00 | | 8:00–10:00 | | |
| Swimming—beginners (1st Mon. each month) | 7:00–7:45 | | 7:00–7:45 | | | |
| Swimming—intermediate & advanced (1st Mon. each month) | 7:45–8:30 | | 7:45–8:30 | | | |
| Scuba (as scheduled) | | | Pool<br>8:00–10:00 | Class room<br>8:00–10:00 | | |
| Special programs— gym. | | | 8:00–10:00 | | | |
| Squash (reservations required) | 10:00–10:00 | 10:00–10:00 | 10:00–10:00 | 10:00–10:00 | 10:00–10:00 | 9:00–9:00 |
| Track | 9:00–10:00 | 9:00–10:00 | 9:00–10:00 | 9:00–10:00 | 9:00–10:00 | 9:00–9:00 |
| Volleyball | 12:45–2:00<br>6:00–8:00 | | Advanced<br>12:45–2:00<br>6:00–8:00 | | 12:45–2:00<br>6:00–8:00 | |
| Weightlifting & body building | 9:00–10:00 | 9:00–10:00 | 9:00–10:00 | 9:00–10:00 | 9:00–10:00 | 9:00–9:00 |
| Wrestling | 8:00–10:00 | | | | 8:00–10:00 | |

letic leagues and contests for industries, churches, young people's groups, and boys' and girls' groups; and camping programs are a few of the activities organized and administered by these voluntary agencies. The cost of financing such organizations is usually met through membership dues, community chest drives, and contributions of private individuals.

These organizations are designed to improve our society physically, morally, mentally, and spiritually, through their programs of physical activity. An example of the extent to which these organizations render services in this country and throughout the world can be seen in the Young Men's Christian Association. There are more than 1,850 YMCA's in the United States and 117 in Canada. The YMCA operates in 83 countries of the world. There are approximately 10,000 YMCA's in the world. There are approximately five million members in the U. S. Young Men's Christian Association, and approximately twelve million members around the world.

Usually these agencies have physical directors directing the physical activities who have received specialized training in their field. Many organizations have complete staffs of trained physical education personnel who aid in the organization and administration of the programs.

A typical physical activity schedule of a YMCA is shown in Table 3-1.

## American Red Cross

The American Red Cross in its various program offerings provides a setting for physical education activities, especially along institutional lines. These activities are mainly concerned with some phase of aquatics, water safety, first aid, and hospital recreation. Through this organization many qualified persons in physical education help to demonstrate proper techniques and procedures in these activities to interested persons throughout the coun-

try and help to provide for the needs of individuals who have been hospitalized.

## Settlement and neighborhood houses

Settlement and neighborhood houses are largely confined to cities. In many communities they are also known as community centers or community houses. They are usually organized and administered by a religious or social welfare group in the foreign or low-income sections of cities. Their aim is to establish a higher standard of living by improving the spiritual, mental, and cultural welfare of the people. They work with all types of people regardless of age, sex, and national or racial origin. However, they give special attention to children. They offer varied programs of activities, which include arts and crafts, athletics, games, singing, dancing, photography, music, dramatics, and discussion forums. Physical education activities play an important role in many of these centers where they have gymnasiums, playgrounds, summer camps, swimming pools, and game rooms. Physical directors and staff occupy prominent positions in many of these social enterprises. Physical activity offers many of these people the opportunity for self-expression and helps them gain a better outlook on life in the midst of poverty and poor living conditions.

## Armed Forces and United Service Organizations

The Army, Navy, Marines, Coast Guard, National Guard, and Air Force have extensive physical activity programs that aid in keeping service personnel in good mental and physical condition. Furthermore, the United Service Organizations (USO), an appendage to these various branches of the armed forces, also utilize such programs of activity. The United Service Organizations consist of such agencies as the Young Men's Chris-

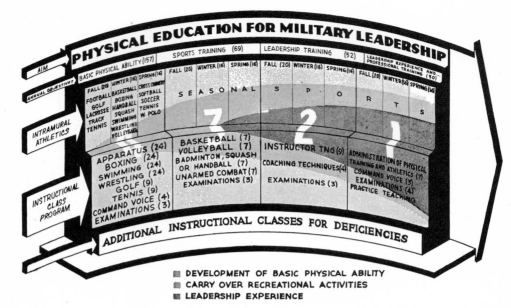

PHYSICAL EDUCATION FOR MILITARY LEADERSHIP

*Office of Physical Education—*
*United States Corps of Cadets.*

Physical education program at United States Military Academy, West Point, N. Y.

tian Association, Young Women's Christian Association, Travelers' Aid, Salvation Army, Catholic Charities Organization, Jewish Welfare Board, and Camp Shows, Incorporated.

The armed forces utilizes thousands of acres of land, hundreds of gymnasiums and other buildings, hundreds of swimming pools, and thousands of qualified persons in physical education to organize and administer a physical training program. These programs are designed to keep military and naval forces in good physical and mental condition at all times, to develop skills so that officers and men will have the foundational equipment to spend leisure hours in a worthwhile manner, and to help build morale through a broad sports program. The armed forces have long known that a strong America means a healthy and physically fit America.

In a recent year the Army had many team and individual sports in their pro-

**Table 3-2.** *Team sports participation at one Army installation\**

| Sport | No. of teams | No. of competitions |
|---|---|---|
| Football | 241 | 1,501 |
| Baseball | 1,197 | 9,137 |
| Softball | 6,205 | 38,347 |
| Basketball | 3,716 | 95,800 |
| Volleyball | 6,958 | 84,875 |
| 6-Man volleyball | 47 | 672 |
| Touch football | 2,350 | 10,450 |
| Handball | 4 | 25 |
| Soccer | 245 | 3,580 |
| Field hockey | 1 | 31 |
| Water polo | 6 | 15 |

\*Personal communication.

gram. Tables 3-2 and 3-3 give a report on sports participation.

**INDUSTRIAL CONCERNS**

Both labor and management recognize the importance of physical education activities as part of the industrial recrea-

**Table 3-3.** *Sports participation at one Army installation**

| Sport | No. of participants | Sport | No. of participants |
|---|---|---|---|
| Boxing | 244,517 | Skeet | 210,858 |
| Bowling | 17,282,040 (Lines bowled) | Horseshoes | 326,958 |
| Swimming | 489,036 | Gymnastics | 89,603 |
| Tennis | 172,982 | Roller skating | 44,840 |
| Badminton | 243,589 | Judo | 19,380 |
| Track | 85,594 | Archery | 12,440 |
| Golf | 602,902 | Wrestling | 41,987 |
| Equestrian | 4,200 | Curling | 120 |
| Basketball | 20,168 | Trampoline | 8,355 |
| Fishing | 143,833 | Shuffleboard | 260 |
| Handball | 183,622 | Skiing | 11,580 |
| Weight lifting | 269,463 | Soccer | 16,030 |
| Volleyball | 12,544 | Boating | 1,623 |
| Table tennis | 1,690,014 | Hunting | 400 |
| Squash | 15,239 | Surfing | 117,280 |
| Fencing | 1,830 | | |

*Personal communication.

tional program which pays mental and physical dividends to all participants. It further results in better health, more efficiency, greater production, and more happiness for employer and employee. Recreational programs in which physical activities play an important part have been organized in industrial plants and in various commercial agencies, such as insurance companies, banks, and department stores. These programs are financed in various ways: by the company, by the employees, or jointly by management and labor. Skating rinks, dance halls, swimming pools, gymnasiums, bowling alleys, and outdoor areas are some of the facilities provided; activities include bowling, tennis, horseshoes, volleyball, basketball, softball, golf, fishing, outings, table tennis, and baseball. Some companies have developed playgrounds in those sections of a community where their employees live, whereas others have leased large buildings where sports can be held and camps where men and women employees, as well as children of employees, have an opportunity to relax and enjoy the out-of-doors.

A typical company recreation program frequently offers more than one-half of its activities in athletic or sports activities. The popularity of these activities among the workers is usually the factor that creates this situation. These activities are offered on an individual participation basis; in family groups; in the form of intramural-type leagues, interdepartmental teams and leagues, varsity teams, club groups; and on a class instruction basis.

Also many different types of physical fitness programs are being developed in the nation's industries. These include fitness programs for workers, and recently there has been much emphasis aimed at fitness for executives. For example, Stromberg Carlson in Rochester, New York has developed a health service area, steam room, private exercise room, shower and locker rooms for their chief executives. Industry is increasingly recognizing that they have considerable money invested in their key men (one company pointed out that when a young executive died from a heart attack it cost them $250,000 to replace him). Physical fitness programs are aimed at helping these executives and other members of the staffs of industry to maintain their health and well-being.

## YOUTH ORGANIZATIONS

There are many clubs and organizations for boys and girls that provide a setting for many physical education activities. Some of the organizations that fall in this group are the Boy Scouts of America, Boys Brigades of America, Girl Scouts, Camp Fire Girls, Big Brother and Big Sister Federation, Incorporated, the American Junior Red Cross, American Youth Foundation, 4-H Clubs, Boys' Clubs of America, Boy Rangers of America, Hi-Y, Junior Hi-Y, Y-Teens, Red Shield Clubs, Future Farmers of America, and Pioneer Youth of America. Some of these organizations are international as well as national in scope. The extent of their membership is very great. For example, the Boys' Clubs of America has 715 Clubs in forty-six states with over 750,000 boys as members. The Girl Scouts of the United States of America has 469

Girl Scout Councils; 152,000 Girl Scout troops; 626,000 adult members; and approximately 3,000,000 girl members. In addition, girl scouting in the United States is affiliated with the World Association of Girl Guides and Girl Scouts. This association links together more than 5,500,000 members in over sixty-five countries around the world. The Boy Scouts of America have approximately 4,300,000 registered Scouts and 1,550,000 volunteer leaders for a total of nearly 6,000,000 members.

The American Youth Hostels, Inc., is an agency which provides overnight housing facilities for individuals who are anxious to travel, see, and study conditions in various parts of the United States and other countries. The mode of transportation in most cases is either hiking or bicycling. Every year many groups of young people, under trained leaders, set out for some distant point. The educational benefits derived from such an experience have proved very valuable. Per-

*The Boys' Club of Wichita Falls,*
*Texas Southwest Boys' Club.*

sonnel are needed to provide the necessary leadership, and physical educators are qualified, by reason of their training, to play an important part in this movement.

The purpose of these organizations is to serve youth in a manner that will prepare them for adulthood and make them better citizens. They are interested in developing in each boy and girl such characteristics as self-reliance, courage, and patriotism. They encourage the development of skills for the worthy use of leisure time. They promote projects that result in better health, better mental hygiene, stronger character, and a sounder physical condition. For example, the four "H's" of the 4-H Club stand for "Head, Heart, Hand, and Health" development.

Physical education activities play a major part in the program of activities for these various clubs and organizations. Out-of-door activities on the playground and in the camp are as important as indoor activities in the gymnasium and in the swimming pool. Sports and other physical education activities strongly appeal to boys and girls, and as long as this interest exists, physical activity will be an essential phase of the total program.

## RECREATIONAL AREAS

Most communities have playgrounds. In small towns the playground functions during the summer months; in larger towns they function in the spring, summer, and fall; and in many large cities they are

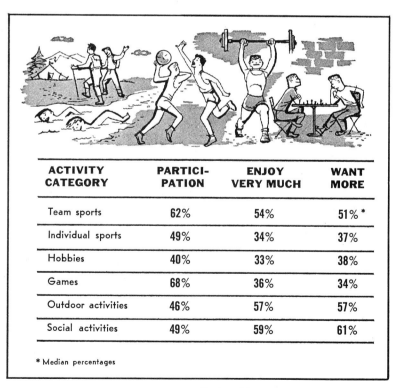

| ACTIVITY CATEGORY | PARTICI- PATION | ENJOY VERY MUCH | WANT MORE |
|---|---|---|---|
| Team sports | 62% | 54% | 51% * |
| Individual sports | 49% | 34% | 37% |
| Hobbies | 40% | 33% | 38% |
| Games | 68% | 36% | 34% |
| Outdoor activities | 46% | 57% | 57% |
| Social activities | 49% | 59% | 61% |

\* Median percentages

*Needs and interests of adolescent Boys' Clubs members—a national survey of members aged 14 to 18, New York, 1960, Boys' Clubs of America.*

Preferences of Boys' Clubs of America participants for various activities in the program, showing popularity of physical education activities.

organized and administered on a year-round basis. Playgrounds are established mainly for children and young people, although adults frequently participate in many of the activities offered. The playground is a place where children may develop skills, enjoy themselves in wholesome physical activity, develop healthy bodies, and develop good citizenship traits under competent leadership. The type of facilities and equipment varies from playground to playground, depending upon the amount of money available for such a purpose and the value placed on such an enterprise by the community concerned. On well-equipped playgrounds, facilities and equipment may be found for all types of games, athletics, dancing, swimming, self-testing activities, and arts and crafts. The number of staff members varies with the size of the playground. Both men and women may be found supervising and directing playgrounds and the special activities within a single playground.

In addition to playgrounds, communities and apartment dwellings are including recreation areas where swimming pools, paddle tennis courts, and other activity areas exist. This is particularly true where new housing developments are coming into being and the developers are making it a practice to include facilities for physical activities for the occupants.

Also many parks and green spaces have been developed and they utilize the services of physical educators. These may be located in a community, city, county, park, or other place where recreational facilities have been created for the use of the populace.

## ATHLETIC CLUBS AND OTHER SPORT ORGANIZATIONS

Because of the increased popularity of sports and physical activity in the United States during the late 1800's and early 1900's, many athletic clubs were organized. The membership at that time was

*Lakeside Tot Lot, Oakland Recreation Department, Oakland, Calif.*

Playgrounds should be well equipped with swings, slides, jungle bars, and play equipment for grade school boys and girls.

usually composed of young adults who wanted a place where they might engage in some form of wholesome physical activity. The idea has gradually grown, until today we find numerous athletic clubs and other sports organizations mushrooming all over the nation. The membership in these organizations is great. Some clubs cater to the wealthy, whereas others serve persons in various income brackets. At first these athletic clubs offered many sports, but today many clubs also cater to individuals who are interested mainly in one sport or, at the most, a very few. Thus can be found such organizations as archery clubs, fencing clubs, golf clubs, tennis clubs, fishing clubs, rod and gun clubs, bowling clubs, yachting clubs, and polo clubs. Also many country clubs stress social life as well as such sports as golf, tennis, and swimming. Many of these clubs are staffed with professionals who are experts in some particular sport as well as other individuals trained in various physical education activities.

In addition to the organizations that have been mentioned, there are Turnvereins and Sokol organizations that are designed to provide a place for physical activities primarily of a gymnastic variety, and also a place for social activities. (See Chapter 12 for more information on Turnvereins.)

## PROFESSIONAL AND COMMERCIAL AREAS

The area of professional sports and other physical education activities offers a setting for many individuals who are highly skilled. Professional football, basketball, baseball, hockey, golf, soccer, and tennis are a few of these areas, and in

*NBC photo.*

Professional golf.

addition, there are other physical education activities that have professional possibilities, such as gymnastic acts on the trampoline, aquatics, and dancing.

In the commercial area can be found dance studios, roller rinks, golf courses, swimming pools, bowling alleys, sports equipment stores, resort areas, and many places of amusement that utilize physical education activities as a means of entertainment. As a rule, the public wants to be entertained, and physical educators have capitalized on this desire.

## CAMPS

Camping has grown in popularity until today there are numerous camps located in nearly every section of the country. There are over 6,000 camps throughout the nation. These are operated by cities, counties, and states; by such social agencies as churches, schools, and settlements; by such youth-serving agencies as YMCA, YWCA, YMHA, YWHA, Boy Scouts, Girl Scouts, Camp Fire Girls, 4-H Clubs, and Boys' Clubs Federations; by employer and labor organizations; and by private individuals and corporations. Some camps are operated for profit, whereas others work on a nonprofit basis. Some are open only during the summer months, others during the spring, summer, and fall, and others all year round. Some are for children, others for adults, and still others for adults and children. Some are day camps, whereas others operate on a seasonal basis. Some are for just one sex, and others operate on a co-recreational basis. In recent years, tennis, football, basketball, baseball and other activity camps have been opened to provide a place for the young person interested in developing further skill in a particular sports activity.

Regardless of the type of camp, all

*State of Michigan.*

School campers have a firsthand experience in timber management.

utilize physical education activities as one of the main features in their program. They stress outdoor living and utilize such activities as sailing, swimming, canoeing, all types of athletics, horseback riding, archery, and dancing.

## GOVERNMENTAL AND WELFARE AGENCIES

Village, county, city, state and national governmental units have provided settings for physical education activities as well as privately supported welfare agencies. Some of these settings are orphanages, homes for the aged, wildlife preserves, and Job Corps and Head Start centers. The last two programs should receive special attention because of their place in modern times.

### Job Corps

As part of the Economic Opportunity Act of 1964 the Job Corps program was established. The Job Corps is a voluntary program that takes place usually in camps, training centers, or other places where programs of education, vocational training, or conservation work for young people can be provided. Many of the underprivileged young men who participate in the Job Corps program are school dropouts, job applicants, or those who failed tests for the Armed Forces.

Each 100-youth camp that is developed by the Job Corps has a staff of approximately twenty-one persons composed of such personnel as teachers, counselors, work leaders, and cooks. The sites for Job Corps centers are located throughout the United States on federal land, such as national parks or national forests.

The training that Job Corps trainees follow is designed to give them an opportunity to assume responsibility and prepare them for useful work. It provides intensive education in basic skills such as reading, writing, and arithmetic, and work experience. It also provides special skill training in such areas as fire control, road maintenance, horticulture, and fencing construction.

As part of camp living there are recreational activities provided, including opportunities to participate in many hobbies and sports designed to teach the value of playing according to the rules of the game. The objective of the program is to see that each person participates. Spectators are not wanted. Physical fitness and sports programs are organized by barracks groups.

Each camp is staffed with a director, and for every one hundred young men there is an educational and counseling staff of four persons. Three of the four-staff members are basic education teachers and one person is a health and recreation teacher, for which a physical educator would qualify. Staff members undergo a training course to prepare them for their work.

### Head Start

The objective of Head Start, another phase of the government's antipoverty program and administered by the U. S. Office of Economic Opportunity, is to take children from disadvantaged neighborhoods and provide eight weeks of preschool experience, plus physical care during the summer, prior to their entering either kindergarten or first grade. In other words, it is preschool education for deprived children.

In its first summer of operation in 1965, Project Head Start enrolled some 560,000 children in 13,400 child development centers in 2,400 communities. It was so successful that it has been continued on a permanent basis with programs running throughout the year as well as in the summer. The government appropriates up to 90% of the cost.

Any community is permitted to initiate its own Head Start program. However, it must comply with such requirements as that of seeing that classes are small and that they are taught by a professional teacher assisted by two other adults. The program is nonstructured and consists of many activities such as painting, reading, listening to music, modeling, playing with all sorts of toys, and engaging in various games.

Each child receives a medical and dental examination, something that many of them have never experienced. Medical and dental problems are referred to the public health department in the local community.

The Head Start program has been successful in showing that pupils have a significant gain in verbal intelligence equivalent to a rise of 8 to 10 points in IQ scores, better social relations as evidenced by the ability to engage in group play, and improved self-confidence.

Thousands of parents are serving as volunteers in the program, including both men and women. Many physical educators who are parents volunteer to make toys and instruct pupils in games. There are many opportunities in this setting to serve youngsters and make sure that they get off on the right foot toward a meaningful, physically healthy, educated existence. Physical educators should recognize the opportunities that are present for them to render this special service.

## CHURCHES

Protestant, Catholic, Jewish, and other religious leaders recognize that the religious life of man is closely tied in with his physical, mental, and social life. They are beginning to see that all are essential to living a "good" life. Furthermore, the old Puritan idea that play is sinful and something that should not be associated with the church is rapidly becoming a thing of the past. The church is concerned with how it can help people to spend their leisure hours in a more profitable manner and how it can further promote fellow-

ship and social and physical well-being among its members.

Many churches are providing leadership and facilities so that physical education activities may become a vital part of their programs. Frequently gymnasiums, bowling alleys, tennis courts, and various items of apparatus are part of a church's physical plant. Churches are organizing programs of physical activity around various age groups. They are finding that it aids considerably in helping to attract youth to the church.

The Catholic Youth Organization is an example of a program that is church sponsored and that carries on a vigorous and interesting sports program. This organization serves not only boys and girls under high school age but also youth not attending school.

## HOSPITALS

The utilization of physical education activities in hospitals is rather new. Federal hospitals utilize various physical education activities to some extent, as do the Veterans Administration Hospitals. In federal hospitals the American Red Cross is largely responsible for such a program, whereas the Veterans Administration has its own specialized staff which is located in central and regional offices and in each hospital. The entire program of physical activity in these hospitals is under the close supervision of the medical staff. The activities that are offered vary according to the condition of the patient and the facilities available. It is individual work to a great degree, and the activity must be adapted to the needs of the patient. A person suffering from a cardiac ailment might need restricted exercise, whereas, according to many doctors, a neuropsychiatric patient would need to engage in active sports to alleviate his mental condition. Therefore it can be seen that sports and other types of physical activity are a form of therapy for individuals who are

*Brentwood Neuropsychiatric Hospital, Los Angeles, Calif.*

Scene of one corner of outdoor gymnasium.

hospitalized, and as such are becoming recognized as a part of the total hospital program.

## PENAL INSTITUTIONS

The method of treating criminals, delinquents, and individuals who have displayed antisocial conduct has changed greatly during recent years. Formerly it was thought that the inmate of a penal institution should be regimented, disciplined, and forced to pay for his crime or misdoing by suffering the rigid routine of prison life. It was believed that he should not enjoy his existence, nor should he be allowed to participate in any activities from which he might receive some satisfaction. Today, however, prison and reform-school authorities realize that the inmate may be rehabilitated. Through a planned program of reeducation, the criminal or delinquent may learn to develop social responsibility to the extent that when he is freed he may become a useful and responsible citizen.

In any program of rehabilitation and reeducation, sports can play and are playing a valuable and important part. They aid in contributing to the physical and mental health of the participants and also aid in demonstrating the need for cooperation, fair play, and other desirable traits.

There are over a million people in the United States in institutions for the delinquent, defective, and dependent. With such a large group of the population in these institutions, physical education activities have much to offer in helping to rehabilitate individuals so they may serve society in constructive action rather than inhibit society's progress through antisocial conduct. The inmates in such institutions as reformatories, prisons, workhouses, penitentiaries, jails, prison farms, and detention homes should have the benefits of what a physical education program under qualified leadership has to offer.

## OTHER COUNTRIES*

On September 21, 1961 the Peace Corps Act was passed by the United States Congress. Today there are thousands of Peace

---

*Information for many of the settings in this international section has been taken from the publication: U.S. Department of Health, Education and Welfare, Office of Education, Washington, D. C., 1964, Teaching opportunities. See also chapters on International Aspects of Physical Education and Employment Opportunities, for further information on teaching abroad.

Corps volunteers serving in foreign assignments. Many physical educators are a part of the Peace Corps, and the American Association for Health, Physical Education, and Recreation is working closely with this organization in administering programs in foreign countries.

The Peace Corps is not the only agency that provides a setting for physical education activities in foreign countries. The American Specialist Program, Fulbright scholarships, International Association for Physical Education and Sports for Girls and Women, the International Council on Health, Physical Education, and Recreation, United Nations Educational, Scientific and Cultural Organization, and other organizations are also active.

### Peace Corps

Since there is so much interest in the Peace Corps and since many openings exist, a further discussion of this agency is

*John and Bini Moss from Black Star.*

A Peace Corps volunteer who teaches in Ghana is on the way to a football match with some of his students.

*Peace Corps Pictures.*

A Peace Corps volunteer teaching the Thailand National Girls' Track Team.

*Courtesy Phil Hardberger, Peace Corps.*

A Peace Corps volunteer in Caracas, Venezuela, in his job as recreational director at one of the YMCA playgrounds.

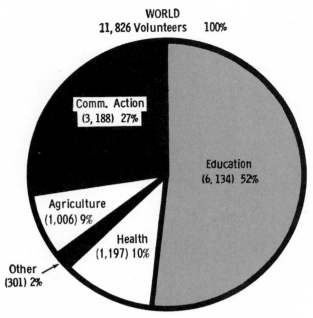

WORLD
11, 826 Volunteers   100%

Comm. Action
(3, 188) 27%

Education
(6, 134) 52%

Agriculture
(1,006) 9%

Health
(1,197) 10%

Other
(301) 2%

*Saturday Review, April 23, 1966.*

Activity categories of Peace Corps volunteers. More than half of them teach, half of these for the first time.

in order. Peace Corps volunteers must be at least 18 years of age, but there is no upper age limit. Members of the Peace Corps receive a living allowance which covers food, clothing, housing, and medical care. In addition, they accumulate $75 a month, which amounts to $1,800 after two years of service. Applicants may obtain Peace Corps questionnaires from the American Association for Health, Physical Education, and Recreation, post offices, or from the Peace Corps, Washington, D. C.

A few foreign countries and areas where health and physical education and recreation specialists have been or are being used are the Ivory Coast, Tunisia, Ceylon, Iran, Thailand, Columbia, and Indonesia. According to the American Association for Health, Physical Education, and Recreation, the criteria used in respect to physical education and athletic programs include obtaining volunteers who are graduates from accredited institutions with a

physical education major, a physical education minor with a recommendation from the college, athletes who have graduated from college and are recommended by the physical education department, and individuals trained in physical education or outstanding athletes strongly recommended by professional people in the field.

**Mutual Educational and Cultural Exchange Act (The Fulbright-Hays Act)**

Under the terms of this act qualified American teachers can teach on an exchange basis in sixteen countries or take a "one-way" teaching assignment in approximately fifty countries where exchange programs have not been developed.

Teaching opportunities are available under the Fulbright-Hays Act to teach in institutions of higher learning in many foreign countries. Grants are made on a one-year basis.

## United States Agency for International Development (AID)

The AID program exists in such areas of the world as Asia, Africa, Far East, Near East, Greece, and Turkey. Most positions are at the teacher training level with two years considered to be the minimum length of assignment.

## United Nations Educational, Scientific, and Cultural Organization (UNESCO)

Approximately six hundred UNESCO field positions exist where educational advisers are used to assist host governments and give lectures in colleges and universities.

## Schools for dependents of military personnel overseas

The Department of Defense operates schools for children of military and civilian personnel who are stationed overseas. The program exists in nearly thirty countries throughout the world. Most of the enrolled children are at the elementary level. Such countries as France, Newfoundland, Iceland, Italy, Morocco, Spain, Sicily, West Indies, Taiwan, Japan, Philippines, and Midway Island provide the settings for these educational programs.

## Schools in outlying areas

Such places as the Panama Canal Zone, Territory of Guam, American Samoa, Trust Territory of the Pacific Islands, and the Virgin Islands offer teaching opportunities in elementary and secondary schools and in colleges.

## Binational centers

Private organizations have established binational centers in many countries in order to bring about better understanding between the United States and these countries. Binational centers are presently located in the Near East, Europe, and the Far East. Classes are offered at all educational levels.

## Schools in the Middle East, Far East, Africa, and Europe sponsored through the International Schools Service

A wide range of educational services are offered through this independent, non-profit organization concerned with international programs of technical aid, diplomacy and industrial efficiency.

## Schools in Latin American republics through the Inter-American Schools Service

American-sponsored administrative and teaching positions exist in Latin America through the Inter-American Schools Service.

## Church-sponsored schools

Protestant, Catholic, and Jewish-sponsored schools and colleges in many countries of the world offer teaching opportunities for those who are interested.

## Schools operated by American firms overseas

Some American business and industrial concerns operate elementary and secondary schools in several countries of the world for the children of American employees, where teaching opportunities exist.

• • •

In this chapter the several areas in which physical educators may utilize their talents have been pointed out. Any student who has a sincere interest in physical education, possesses a degree of skill in the various physical activities, develops qualities that make for good leadership, and has the initiative and drive to get ahead will never have to worry about finding a place for his talents in one of these settings. The responsibility rests with the student. If he or she is interested in becoming an active member of this profession, now is the time to start developing some of the essential qualities that make for success.

Physical education in New Zealand.

## QUESTIONS AND EXERCISES

1. List the various settings in which physical education activities are conducted. Which one do you feel is best adapted to your abilities, needs, and interests? Why?
2. To what extent do the nation's schools offer a prospective employment setting for the physical educator?
3. What are the responsibilities of physical education personnel at the elementary, junior high, senior high, and college levels?
4. How do the physical education programs differ at the various school levels?
5. Describe the physical education program in a Young Men's Christian Association or a Young Women's Christian Association with which you are familiar.
6. Make a survey of your home town to determine the various settings where physical education is being used or could be utilized effectively.
7. What are the objectives of settlement and neighborhood houses? How do physical education activities help in the achievement of these objectives?
8. What is the American Youth Hostels, Inc.?

How does it help to satisfy the needs of American youth?
9. List as many boys' and girls' organizations as possible that utilize physical education activities.
10. Compare the attitude of the early church with the attitude of the church today in respect to physical activity.
11. To what extent are the playgrounds of your community helping to make your town a better place in which to live?
12. What is the importance of physical education to both labor and management?
13. What part do the following play as settings for physical education activities: athletic clubs and other sports organizations, hospitals, camps, penal institutions, professional and commercial areas, and the American Red Cross?
14. In light of the present national emergency, how can physical education contribute to the welfare of the armed forces?

## SELECTED REFERENCES

American Council on Education, College teaching as a career, Washington, D. C., 1965, Publications Division, American Council on Education.

Bucher, Charles A.: Administration of school health and physical education programs, St. Louis, 1967, The C. V. Mosby Co.

Bucher, Charles A.: Health and physical education in other lands, Journal of Health, Physical Education, and Recreation **33**:14, Dec., 1962.

Bucher, Charles A., Koening, Constance, and Barnhard, Milton: Methods and materials for secondary school physical education, St. Louis, 1965, The C. V. Mosby Co.

Bucher, Charles A., and Reade, Evelyn M.: Physical education in the modern elementary school, New York, 1964, The Macmillan Co.

Changing directions in American education, Saturday Review, p. 37, Jan. 14, 1967. (A series of articles presented by Saturday Review with the Committee for Economic Development.)

Ciszek, Raymond A.: A new dimension in international relations for the profession, Journal of Health, Physical Education, and Recreation **33**:17, Dec., 1962.

Hechinger, Fred M.: Head start to where, Saturday Review, p. 58, Dec. 18, 1965.

LaBelle, Tom: The Peace Corps in Columbia, Journal of Health, Physical Education, and Recreation **37**:57, Nov.–Dec., 1966.

Morris, Van Cleve, and others: Becoming an educator, Boston, 1963, Houghton Mifflin Co.

Neilson, N. P., and Bronson, Alice Oakes: Problems in physical education, Englewood Cliffs, N. J., 1965, Prentice-Hall, Inc., Problem Three.

Rosewarren, Leonard: The YMCA physical directorship, Journal of Physical Education **63**:70, Jan.–Feb., 1966.

Ross, Irwin: Head start is a banner project, The PTA Magazine **60**:20, March, 1966.

Shane, Harold G.: How do they rate you, professor? NEA Journal **54**:18, Nov., 1965.

Shriver, Sargent: Five years with the Peace Corps, Saturday Review, p. 14, April, 1966.

Trump, J. Lloyd: An image of a future secondary school health, physical education, and recreation program, Journal of Health, Physical Education, and Recreation **32**:15, Jan., 1961.

U.S. Department of Health, Education, and Welfare, Office of Education, Teaching opportunities, Washington, D. C., 1964 edition.

U.S. Department of Health, Education, and Welfare, Office of Education, Digest of Educational Statistics, Washington, D. C., 1965 edition.

Watkins, Angeline: Physical education activity requirement for women in selected colleges and universities in the south, Journal of Health, Physical Education, and Recreation **37**:71, Jan., 1966.

Wireman, Billy O.: A new concept of the service program, Journal of Health, Physical Education, and Recreation **35**:33, April, 1964.

Wolfbein, Seymour L., and Goldstein, Harold: Our world of work, Chicago, 1961, Science Research Associations, Inc.

# Chapter 4

# Projecting physical education into the future

A new group of professionals called The Futurists has emerged in American society. These specialists look into the future and forecast new developments. With the advances of technology such a profession is regarded as essential to today's existence, as well as being necessary for survival in the future under the different conditions that will exist.

The Futurists predict that in light of the atom's potential energy and the computer's intellect, man will be much better able to control his environment, his thought processes, and the way he evolves.

In this chapter the author attempts to play the role of a futurist in education and in physical education. There are no manuals or textbooks for such forecasting. The basic tool is extrapolation from yesterday and today.

In order to adequately predict the changes that will take place in education and physical education, we must first look at the type of world scientists predict the future holds for each of us.

The General Motors Futurama exhibit at the recent New York World's Fair portrayed a journey into the future based upon the scientific advances that are taking place in our society. The Futurama

provided a trip to the moon where the viewer could see manned "lunar crawlers" and commuter spaceships. Then, you saw life under the ice and an all-weather port in the Antarctic. Here, the ocean floor was tapped for oil, minerals were taken from under the ice, and vacationers relaxed at a beautiful resort.

Next, you visited what was formerly the jungle, but now the wild beasts had been pacified. Laser light cut down towering trees and was followed by road builders that constructed wide transportation lanes which served as superhighways for cars and trucks.

The desert was the next destination where new irrigation techniques produced crops which were harvested by machines.

The last stop was the city of the future with its midtown airports, superskyscrapers, moving sidewalks, and underground conveyor belts for freight.

The Futurama painted a picture of the future in vivid and exciting proportions based on sound, scientific, and logical reasoning.

## SPACE-AGE FORECASTS

What might be a typical day for a man living in the year 2000? Mr. Thompson

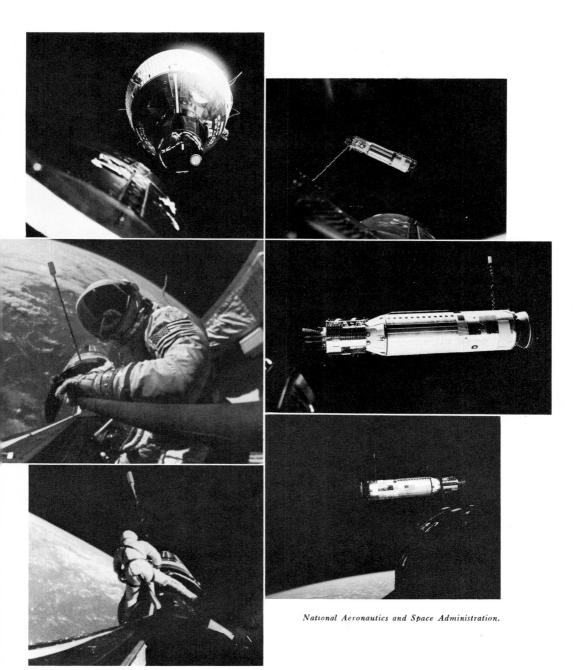

Life in space.

lives in a solar-heated house in smog-free, dome-covered Aerocity on the northwest coast of the United States. Four days a week he arises at 7 A.M. and pulls the kids out of bed to do their physical education homework before the television screen. Breakfast follows and then the children are off to school on the shuttle-copter. Shortly thereafter Mr. Thompson goes out to his three-car garage, jumps into a driverless, plastic jet Special, presses a button, and in five minutes the car stops at the station. Boarding a monorail, he spends the next forty minutes traveling the seventy miles to his office. The morning is filled with appointments and conferences, but two minutes are set aside to tune up his body with an Isotizer. For lunch he swallows a pill containing all the essential nutrients. At 2 P.M. he bids his wife goodbye on the televiewer and boards a rocket cruiser for a dinner engagement in Europe. Arriving in Paris, he throws away his shirt, socks, underwear, and suit and puts on a new disposable outfit. The day's business is finally completed, and he heads for home arriving there at 11 P.M. The space age offers a new and exciting way of life. And it has implications for physical education. Here are some of the conditions that will exist in A.D. 2000.

Three hundred and fifty million people will inhabit the United States as contrasted with today's 200 million. Three out of four persons will reside in cities—elongated strips of land dotted with thousands of homes and other buildings. The cliff dwellers will include many of the younger set, since one out of every five persons in the country will be between fifteen and twenty-four years of age. College will be a reality for four out of five high school graduates, most of whom will later go into the ranks of the professional and white-collar workers. The added years of education will pay off handsomely; for one half of the college grad-

uates are destined to earn minimum salaries of $5,000 to $12,000 a year. And this is not all. Coupled with increased income will be fewer hours of work per week—thirty-two hours on the average.

High income and more leisure will change the lives of most people. Some persons will continue to drink space cocktails, operate their fifty-inch wall television screens, and read about life on the moon. But many will forsake the lazy life for more physically active pursuits. The total population will spend $10 billion a year on sporting goods alone, to play all types of games, many of which will be imported from abroad by some of the four million American who go overseas annually.

By 1970 it is estimated that $58 billion a year will be spent on travel. Photography will become a $2.5 billion industry, with two million cameras sold a year; more than three and a half billion pictures will be taken annually. There will be 8,000 regulation golf courses to accommodate seven million golfers, and $460 million a year will be spent on golf equipment. Eight million tennis players will spend $20 million a year on equipment, and 28 million hunters and fifty million anglers will spend about $5.7 billion a year on equipment, licenses, and trips. Six million persons will ski, spending $1 billion a year on equipment. Seventy-five million Americans will engage in water sports; fifteen million persons will enjoy outboard boats and motors; ten million persons will become water skiers; and twenty-five million persons will learn skin diving.

In the future, homes will be equipped electronically with thermoelectric refrigerators, electroluminescent lights, ultrasonic washing machines, controls on windows to close them when storms develop, coin-fed dry-cleaning machines, picture phones, self-cleaning kitchen floors, microwave ovens, and garbage disposal units built into dishwashers. Clothes and bed sheets will be made of disposable material, eliminating the need for laundry. There will not be locks on doors since special computer arrangements will react to a person's voice, and in this way the door will open on command.

The future will find science developing pills to control the mind. There is much research going on to discover how man's brain works and to discover drugs to influence its operation. It appears probable that the day will come when pills can be purchased to help you to think better, improve your ability to concentrate, and help the memory processes. Much research is being done in connection with the production of a key chemical ribonucleic acid, or RNA, and its influence on the brain cells. There is some evidence to show that this chemical influences learning, and therefore science is trying to find a chemical compound that could be introduced into the brain to increase the production of RNA and thus influence learning.

The future will find that the health of man can be vitally improved for the better. Life expectancy will be increased due to a better understanding of medical science. Interchangeable human parts will help to insure longer life. Other conditions and new techniques that are predicted for the years ahead are: cameras and miniature broadcasting systems that can be swallowed to take pictures inside the stomach and give a listening doctor vital information; transistorized gadgets to stimulate damaged muscles; pocket radars to help the blind to see and the deaf to hear; and drug control of personality.

## EDUCATION AND PHYSICAL EDUCATION AND THE SPACE AGE

As educators and physical educators, we are interested in what life will be like in the years ahead, the great advances that will take place, the impact our technology and inventive genius will have upon our day-to-day routines, and the influence of medical science upon our health and length of life. But we are especially interested in the future of education and physical education.

## A LOOK BACK

As physical educators look back, they can see the great progress that has been made in the last half-century, but this will be small in comparison to the progress that can be made in the next fifty years. Some of the changes that have taken place over the last few decades are:

1. The transformation from the one-room schoolhouse to a building complex that includes spacious gymnasiums, costing millions of dollars.
2. The curricular change from the 3R's to the inclusion of a whole proliferation of offerings.
3. Colleges attended by only a few students to where one out of every two high school graduates now attend.
4. College physical educators merely members of the staff without academic rank to where members of the profession now hold professorial status and also distinguish themselves on faculty councils and university committees.
5. The AAHPER, once an organization with only a few hundred members, serves more than 50,000 members today.
6. The program of physical education, once regarded as a frill and an appendage on the school program, has become an important part of the general education offering.
7. Physical education, a term that very few people had heard some years ago, has had wide exposure through the pronouncements of American presidents.
8. The relationship of physical education to academic achievement, once thought to be negligible, is being increasingly supported through research findings.
9. Physical education's influence, once limited to regional and national boundaries, now crosses all the borders of various countries of the world.

Physical educators can be proud of the

changes that have taken place over the years. But they cannot rest on their laurels. They must move ahead. Regardless of how exciting, sensational, and revolutionary the changes have been in the past half-century, they will be viewed as mediocre in the next half-century. The technological explosion, mechanical knowledge, and inventive genius of our leaders in all walks of life will produce an era in history that would sound like a fairy tale today. Furthermore, in the future more than ever before, the nation will rely heavily upon education for the solution to major social and political problems including poverty, delinquency, leisure, unemployment, and world peace.

## GENERAL EDUCATION IN THE FUTURE

A factor that impresses the person who investigates the future of education in America is to discover the great number of students who will be pursuing their education. Within the next ten years alone, there will be an increase of 6 million students in our elementary and secondary schools and an increase of 3.7 million students in our colleges and universities. There will be twice as many persons getting master's and doctor's degrees.

The increase in the number of students will cost more. Within the next ten years the cost of education will increase by 47% in the elementary and secondary schools and 89% in colleges and universities. The explosion in terms of numbers and costs will continue to grow each decade in the future.

Elementary and secondary schools will continue to attract students to their doors regardless of level of intelligence, emotional stability, desire for education, and socioeconomic levels. However, as the years pass, the gap will grow wider in the type of education offered to the student who has the intellectual ability to profit most from a rapid academic pace, compared to the student who is lower on the intellectual scale and must therefore pursue a slower academic pace. This trend will be encouraged on the one hand, by the growing demand for people in America who have intellectual ability to work with complex ideas, and on the other hand, with a decline in the opportunities for well-paying, high-status jobs for those with mediocre education, or little or no education. The gap will also grow wider as grade lines become blurred through the introduction of nongraded schools where talented students will be permitted to move forward rapidly. A great expansion in vocational schools will also support the trend.

The nongraded schools will characterize the majority type of schools by the year 2000. Children will therefore move at an academic pace during their elementary and secondary school years, in accordance with their ability and degree of motivation. Placement in classes will not be done according to age, but instead by intellectual and scholastic ability. After basic education has been completed, a choice will be made by the student whether to follow a vocational or a college preparatory program.

At the college and university level the students served will fall sharply into two classes. On the one hand, will be the most promising students with outstanding mental capabilities, who will go to the university where they will have the best teachers, the finest of facilities, and many opportunities to learn. The teachers will arrange their time and attention to mold and inspire the intellectually gifted and creative students so that they may develop their talents to the utmost.

At the other end of the ability scale will be the average or subpar student, who does not possess exceptional intellectual promise. This boy or girl will be exposed to a greater depersonalized education, which due to the shortage of outstanding teachers will be influenced greatly by teaching machines, films, television, and other products brought by the era of automation. These students who are lower on the academic scale, will go to the two-year colleges and state-college systems where standards will be lower than those in the universities. There will be more than 1,000 two-year colleges by the year 2000 that will fulfill the educational needs of the large number of students who need this type of education.

Students will go to schools and colleges on a twelve-month basis. A greater number of offerings and more students will dictate this change. There will be staggered vacations for both students and their teachers. The year-round school idea will not only ease the teacher's work load, but it will also help to relieve the overcrowded conditions that exist for all recreational facilities in the light of the growing population, and the increased interest and the additional time available for recreation.

At the college level, there will be a decentralization of administration and social control, through a division of the student body into "houses" or "colleges." Each of these units will be self-sustaining with its own cafeterias, dormitories, classrooms, educational facilities, gymnasiums, and recreational facilities. Physical education staff members will be assigned to these "colleges" or "houses" to direct and teach their programs.

Another organizational trend at the college level will be the proliferation of satellite universities and junior colleges to provide for increased enrollments that will surge to the campuses of institutions of higher learning in the years ahead.

## TEACHING

The status of teaching as a profession will be upgraded slowly in the years ahead as education becomes a more important consideration in our society. Elementary and secondary school teachers, at least for the next decade, will continue to be recruited from backgrounds that stress lower–middle-class values, and conventional means of obtaining economic security. Teacher-training institutions will be slow to change because of the delaying tactics of the educational establishment.

### Teachers more militant

Teachers will become more militant. Labor unions will infiltrate into the schools and colleges on a wide scale. The National Education Association and the American Association of University Professors will revise their thinking in regard to certain bargaining techniques in order to appeal to the more militant teachers and professors. The unions, utilizing strikes and other labor union techniques, however, will be effective and, consequently, in our materialistic society will receive considerable endorsement by those they serve.

### Video tape

The teacher of the future will not have to repeat himself since taped classroom discussions will be kept on file to facilitate make-up work for students who have missed class for some reason, or have failed to get material that has already been presented. Video tapes will also assist the teacher in critically evaluating his own presentation, and in this way teaching will become more of an art.

The student who is a fast learner will have much source material and equipment readily made available to him and have many opportunities for independent research.

### Computerized typewriters

While the teacher is working with individual pupils, other children can be gaining knowledge on their own as they watch television monitors, listen to tape recordings, or work with computerized typewriters. Talking typewriters will be common where children, upon pushing certain keys, will get specific responses. For example, if a child punched out the letters C-A-T the computer typewriter responds by actually saying the word "cat" and also showing a picture of a cat on a television monitor.

### Salaries

Salaries for teachers and professors will continue to increase sharply in the years ahead, particularly for those persons who become master teachers and instructors and research scholars. The single-salary schedule will eventually give way to a merit plan that pays salaries to outstanding teachers and professors on a scale comparable to the business and industrial executive class. The great number of the nation's teachers who are compelled to take other jobs, thereby making education one of a secondary nature, will eventually diminish.

### Released time

Teachers in schools will increasingly be given more released time from teaching duties to pursue research studies and conduct experiments in their local research and development centers. Sabbatical leaves will be common to all schools and colleges. The teaching load of college professors will continue to decline as research and service activities make up a greater proportion of their loads.

### Automated techniques

Automation, new techniques, and frontier-type ideas will be continually introduced into education. The fear of newness and change that is characteristic of many teachers will gradually be overcome as they realize that of all people they must be in favor of the best learning for the most children with the least time and effort. Every tool and shortcut will be utilized. For this reason, teaching machines, programmed instruction, language

labs, educational television, movie projectors and tape recorders, opaque projectors, four-speaker sound systems, and an extensive electronics system will become part and parcel of education.

### THE COMPUTER AND EDUCATION

Electronic information retrieval will make it possible to store in computers the contents of books and other information that can be instantly obtainable.

Computer centers will be established on a regional basis throughout the United States, each of which will link many colleges and research institutions together in a high-speed computer network. Small institutions, as well as large ones, will benefit from these high-level computer services that will enable simultaneous computer use by many persons. The heart of each center will be large, high-speed computers capable of doing more than one million information manipulations a second. Through the utilization of typewriter-to-computer connections, involving regular telephone lines at many remote stations, the colleges will have round-the-clock access to this stored information.

Eventually, there will be extensive computer hookups to homes to help adults or children in solving advanced mathematics problems or obtaining valuable research information on health or other matters. By 1990, Professor Kemeny of Dartmouth College predicts, computer terminals will be as commonplace, and as important a part of the American home, as television or telephones are today. Professor Kemeny goes on to predict that each household will be connected to a central computer that can be used by thousands of people at the same time through the medium of teletype consoles connected through an ordinary telephone line. If a person wants some information he will dial the computer as he would use a telephone today. In addition to getting valuable knowledge about academic studies the computer will prove useful to housewives in preparing balanced menus, placing orders for groceries, or doing their banking. For the education-minded housewife it will also provide an opportunity to work for an advanced degree at a university without leaving her living room. Children will also use the computer to do their homework for school.

It has been suggested that the computer may even be used in coaching. By feeding the computer information about football, for example, such as certain plays, the role that each player is assigned to play, the capabilities of the opponent, and as much other information as possible, the computer could then help to plan game strategy and also furnish valuable material for postgame critiques. It has been predicted that a coach on the bench might even feed into the computer the down and yards to go, time left in the game, the score, the playing con-

ditions, the physical condition of each player, wind velocity, and other factors, and find the best plays that will work against the opponents.

Another feature of the automated era of the future will make it possible for persons to engage in many dual sports by themselves. Computer mechanical arms will be developed so that a person can play such dual games as tennis or badminton, for example, between himself and a robot.

Furthermore, the accuracy of the official will be enhanced in such sports as baseball, for example, where an umpire with a photographic electronic eye will accurately record whether it is a strike or ball, fair or foul.

## THE TEACHERS OF PHYSICAL EDUCATION

The teacher of physical education in the future will have a specialized role to play.

*Division of Birdair Structures, Inc., Buffalo, N. Y.*

Airshelters. The city of the future.

All teachers will not perform the same duties. For the elementary and secondary school levels, two types of teachers will be trained. First, there will be the teacher who is primarily interested in teaching physical skills. This teacher will be a specialist in this area and utilize an analytic method, breaking down the various skills into their most minute subdivisions, and then teaching from a kinesiological approach so that the student learns the basic scientific principles underlying good movement.

The other type of physical education teacher will be an expert in research techniques, and will understand thoroughly the scientific basis underlying physical activity as it relates to human development. Furthermore, through his knowledge of teaching techniques he will be able to apply this information to program development, as well as communicate this knowledge to the student in an interesting, clear, and accurate manner.

These two types of teachers of physical education will make up one part of a team that handles the program in the gymnasium, playground, and swimming pool, as well as in the classroom. Other members of the team will include clerical help, student-teachers and consultants from the disciplines of biology, psychology, and sociology.

At the college and university level, both types of teachers are also present in the basic instruction, and in the professional preparing programs. As in the case of the precollege level, many members of the faculty will have released time to do research. Teachers and professors in some cases, will have joint appointments in the biology, psychology, or sociology departments.

## THE PHYSICAL EDUCATION PROGRAM

The physical education program for students in our schools and colleges will experience many changes in the years to come. The increased number of students will mean the extensive utilization of computers and measurement instruments to accurately group students into teaching units, according to abilities, traits, skills, physical fitness, and previous experiences in physical education. A vast system of record keeping will be kept for each student from the time he is in kindergarten until he graduates from college.

These records will insure a program better organized and related to each individual's needs and a more progressive program through the grades and college. These records will follow the pupil everywhere he goes in school or college, and contain such information as physical fitness ratings, skills mastered, and knowledge accumulated. At the college level these records will have particular value in determining those students who will pursue the voluntary program in physical education, and those who will have to take the required program because they have entered college with below-standard development in physical skills, knowledge, or some other aspect of fitness. Physical education will not be required of every student—only those who fall below acceptable university standards.

The program of physical education will be aimed at developing physically educated students, with a trend away from teacher-induced learnings toward student motivated learnings. The conceptualized approach will be utilized as a result of the identification of the most important concepts to be transmitted to the student. These concepts will define the domain of physical education and the most important contributions the field makes to human beings. They will be developed in a sequential, developmental, progressive pattern from kindergarten through college, with the elimination of the overlapping, the repetition, and the trial-and-error methods of teaching that characterize some physical education programs of to-day.

Textbooks will be used in physical education classes, and homework assigned as in other subject-matter fields. The aim will be to get at the *why* of the activity as well as the activity itself, with physical education meeting in the classroom as well as in the gymnasium. Although physical education will remain activity-oriented, the goal will be to physically educate students so that they understand and identify closely with the importance of physical activity in their lives and its relationship to their physical, psychological, and sociological development. Such a goal, it has been determined, cannot be effectively accomplished without imparting a body of knowledge in the classroom that is closely related to the activity they engage in on the playground. Scientific knowledge that has been researched by our scholars will be articulately communicated to the students during the classroom sessions. Specialists in physical education will be in charge of programs starting with the fourth grade and continuing through college. At the primary grade level, the classroom teacher will work very closely with the specialist in the conduct of the physical education program.

The movement emphasis will permeate the program throughout the school and college life of the student, showing him how to use his body most efficiently under all conditions. Physical movement will be analyzed in relation to the basic motion factors of weight, space, time, and flow. Many activities will be provided that give rise to the exploration and analysis of free and spontaneous movements of the whole body. Students will learn how a movement feels and become aware of the relationships of the different parts of their body. Furthermore, through broad training opportunities they will enrich their movement possibilities and learn to think in terms of movement.

There will be many other program developments in physical education to provide for the mentally retarded, the orthopedically handicapped, the blind, and all types of atypical human conditions. Specialized programs and teachers trained for working with the handicapped will find prominent places in programs of physical education at both pre-college and college levels.

The "club" movement will grow as a means of providing students and persons with special activity interests and opportunities to engage in their favorite activities. There will be all sorts of clubs including bicycling, surfing, skydiving, hiking, and skish. Faculty, school, and college sponsorship will give support to this development. The only criterion for membership will be interest in the activity. The only eligibility rule will be that the participant be a bona fide student.

Research will grow and result in the frontiers of knowledge being pushed back and new discoveries made in the relation of physical activity to mental, physical, and social development.

Effective public relations programs will continue to be emphasized so that parents and the public in general may more fully appreciate the importance and significance of physical education.

Elementary-school physical education will be the focus of much professional effort, in order that a firm and strong foundation may be laid for future physical education experiences of students.

The simple pleasures will continue to attract most participants: swimming, bicycling, fishing, hunting, camping, ice skating, hiking, walking, and sledding. But due to increased income, more activities usually associated with people in upper income brackets will be popular: boating, horseback riding, tennis, skiing, squash, sailing, water skiing, and golfing. Furthermore, school programs will place more emphasis on the activities that can

Supersonic transport of the future.

be used throughout a lifetime. The controversial sport of boxing will not be permitted in school and college programs, and outside of the educational setting will be scored as in fencing, with blows to certain parts of the body each counting a set number of points and the head outlawed as a target.

The speed and increased frequency of travel will find many sports played on an international basis. Teams will be scheduled in Europe, South America, and Asia. There will be international sports leagues at the college level; Yale and Oxford may be battling it out for the rugby title and Reed and Nihon for the tennis championship. High schools will have television meets with their counterparts in other lands—Shaker Heights High School in Cleveland may schedule King George V High School in Hong Kong for archery.

Games that are popular in other countries will find a warm reception in the United States. The game of Sipa, in which a rattan ball is kicked skillfully with the foot or hit with the head or shoulders, will be imported from the Philippines and Malaya. Japanese tennis, with three players on each side, will find wide acceptance as a means of making this sport available to more people. American boys will take a lesson from their counterparts in Asia and play field hockey on the high school and college level.

Precollege athletics will be drastically reformed over the years with sanity becoming the byword and with athletics contributing to, rather than detracting from, a sound education.

Through the untiring efforts and dedication of many educators a great change will come about in the control of educational sports. These devoted and informed men and women have proved they are the leaders in educational sports and the persons who determine the standards and policies to be followed. And they have rigorously and aggressively interpreted the difference between educational sport and professional sport to the American public. As a result, there is a clear distinction between the two. Educational sport will be interested solely in the participant and what it can do to make him a better man or woman, mentally, physically, emotionally, and socially. It recognizes that sport is not an end in itself, but instead, is a means to an end—the end being the development of a better educated individual. Educators will so organize sports that players will be permitted to spend more time on their studies, and pressures will be removed for championship teams. Under this system such features as the following will be instituted:

1. Athletic programs are organized on a developmental pattern.
2. Athletic sports seasons and number of games played are restricted in length— most school administrators feel that ten weeks is a sufficient length of time for any one sports season.
3. Athletic practices are limited to not more than 1½ hours per day.
4. Major sports have been made the minor sports and minor sports the major sports —the lifetime sports get special consideration.
5. Gate receipts are eliminated with the cost being paid out of the general fund, the same as for English, mathematics, history, and other parts of the educational program.
6. Sport contests are conducted only on school premises—the public arena with its gamblers, foul language, and rabid spectators is a thing of the past.
7. Coaches are appointed on the basis of their educational qualifications, not won-lost records. A knowledge of the participant physically, mentally, emotionally, and socially, is one of the most important qualifications.
8. Athletics are an integral part of the total physical education program. The director of physical education has been assigned all the duties in regard to the athletic program.
9. All games are played on weekday afternoons prior to days when school will not be in session—night games are out.

At the college and university level, athletics will experience many changes. A major study of college athletics will take place similar to the Carnegie study of the 1920's. This study will expose many of the questionable practices being followed in our colleges and universities at the present time. New guide lines will be established for the future which will spell out in detail such things as: (1) the role of athletic associations to academic institutions, (2) the relationship of professional to amateur athletics, (3) the responsibility of college administrations to keep sports within a proper educational frame of reference, and (4) the role of the coach as a member of a university staff and faculty.

Intramural programs and coeducational recreational programs will increase. A further development will be the increase in the number of special club programs in many sports, including club football in many universities where there is a disinclination to be exposed to the pressures connected with "big time" sports. Grants-in-aid for athletes will change to where all monies are deposited in a central university fund regardless of talent, whether in athletics, science, or debating, or some other talent, the student will be given financial help based on need, and willingness to pay part of his own way through loans and campus work.

## ATHLETIC RECORDS

Records will fall as new training techniques are developed, more physiological research is produced, and new medical knowledge becomes known. Pills will increase energy output. Isometrics and other strength and power builders will be developed more scientifically. Practice periods will be shortened as teaching machines help football and other players to learn their plays more thoroughly. Coaches will follow more scientific procedures taught to them in college profes-

sional preparatory programs specializing in such areas as psychology, sociometrics, and physiology.

The champions who break the amateur records will be teen-agers more often than not. Better training procedures, diet, and earlier maturation will produce a younger crop of record breakers. The scoreboard by the year A.D. 2000 will read as follows:

| | |
|---|---|
| High jump | 8 ft., 2 in. |
| Pole vault | 25 ft. |
| Broad jump | 30 ft. |
| 100-meter dash | 9 sec. |
| 1-mile run | 3 min., 30 sec. |
| Shot put | 75 ft. |
| 1-mile swim | 14 min. |
| 100-meter freestyle swim | 49.6 sec. |
| 100-meter breast stroke | 1 min. |

## PARTICIPANTS AND SPECTATORS

There will be more participants and more leagues, tournaments, and other attractive features of athletic programs. A larger, younger population will tax facilities to the hilt and consume billions of dollars worth of sports equipment. Girls will be as active as boys; a new hair spray will enable girls to play vigorously, take a shower, and still keep every hair in place. Even the older population will get into the act, with flourishing Golden Age clubs directing them in active as well as passive activities.

The spectator problem will continue to be a bane on society. The automated existence, with moving sidewalks, dustless homes, snow-melting driveways, controlled grass growth, instant cooking and baking, and electric eyes to open doors and windows in houses and offices, will take its toll. Significant medical research showing the long and productive life to be associated with physical activity will go unheeded by a large number of people.

## EDUCATION FOR LEISURE

Education and physical education will be vitally interested and concerned with leisure and its implications for the future. Forecasts predict that the average 38-hour work week we enjoy today will drop to 36 by 1976, and to 32 by the year 2000. In fact, there is a good possibility, according to one estimate, that only 10% of the population will be working, and the rest have to be paid to be idle. According to John Fischer, a futurist, by 1984 a man's life will be so influenced by leisure that the first twenty-five years will be spent getting an education, the second twenty-five years working, and the final twenty-five years enjoying the fruits of his labor. In fact, some futurists gloomily expect that the increased amount of leisure will result in a society run by a small elected elite who will preside over a multitude who have not developed their minds and who are kept happy through drugs and circuses.

The need to teach for the creative and productive use of leisure will be readily apparent. As one answer, Margaret Mead, the famous anthropologist, has suggested a new kind of vacation center where expert tutors would be provided vacationers who want to learn new languages, marine biology, food chemistry, mechanics, writing, or other pursuits.

A leisurely life in the future will not be an entire bed of roses. Problems will continually confront Americans, many of which are created by the new technology and increased populations in the strip cities. For example, the amount of open space available per person will tend to decrease at a faster rate than the population increases. The green spaces will be devoured by concrete and mortar, thus placing greater demands on city, county, state, and national parks. Reservations will need to be made many months and years in advance to visit a place like the Yellowstone National Park. Cities will need to ration recreation, particularly in such an activity as golf. In the Los Angeles area at the present time, for ex-

ample, it takes about four new 18-hole golf courses a year just to accommodate the growing number of golfers.

The increased amount of leisure time in the future with the shorter work week will present many mental health and other problems. People will find it difficult to know what to do. Many will become bored. Sports will offer one source of help. Education will be a major activity for all ages, since people will seek education as a way to use leisure and escape boredom.

## FACILITIES

Increased population, rising school enrollments, city life, limited space, and skyrocketing labor and material costs will alter sports facilities. Outdoor swimming pools will be used year round, with plastic bubbles covering them when the snow comes. Playgrounds and athletic fields will also be used continuously and, in addition, will have convertible features; baseball fields and football gridirons will become hockey areas and basketball courts within an hour's time. Neighborhood playing fields on the roofs of apartment houses and civic buildings will serve inhabitants of housing developments in congested areas. Golf courses will be laid out in skyscrapers, three or four holes on each floor.

New ideas and new materials will be used in all construction. Artificial turf will make indoor facilities similar to the out-of-doors. New methods of supporting roof structures will be evidenced everywhere. This will produce large areas where activities can be engaged in free from poles, columns, and other obstructions. The "floating roof" will become common in all amphitheaters. The size of rooms and play areas will be flexible with increasing use of electrically powered equipment to change partitions, fold bleachers, and remove apparatus from play areas.

Weather will not prove a deterrent to the holding of athletic contests. Seasonal activities will operate the year around, if desired. Huge arenas with roofs that roll back and form an outdoor amphitheater, or when closed, protect against rain, wind or snow, will exist in every section of the country.

Nighttime will not prove a handicap to participation, since golf courses, tennis courts, and playfields will be illuminated so as to give daylight effect and serve the greater number of people who desire to participate.

Gymnasiums will become larger, more adaptable, more all-purpose, and more mechanical. Teachers will operate a control board, and at the push of the right buttons, the necessary equipment for each class will, in the span of a few seconds, either come out of the wall, lower from the ceiling, or come up out of special floor compartments. There will be plastic gym flooring, requiring little maintenance, guaranteed not to warp, and with all the necessary marking and lines impregnated and wear-proof. There will be wall and ceiling panels sensitive to electrical impulse, instead of light bulbs.

Audiovisual centers will be readily available for individual student study on various sport skills, or other aspects of physical education. Centers will contain TV, movies, tapes, and teaching machines. Materials such as rules, strategies, facts of anatomy, and first aid will be programmed, so more time will be free for skill development.

At the college level, athletic and recreation facilities, such as tennis and handball courts, and swimming facilities will be strategically located throughout the entire campus, using the open green space around dormitories and other campus structures. Furthermore, in order to cut costs, there will be interinstitutional cooperation among colleges and universities that are geographically close to one

another. Colleges will share gymnasiums, libraries, cafeterias, and other facilities.

Manufacturers will continue to discover new ways to improve equipment. New and better materials for shoes and clothing will make them lighter and provide for easier movement. Uniforms for physical education classes will be made of throw-away material and will be disposed of after wearing. It will be cheaper to do this than laundering them even once.

• • •

These startling developments mean that there must be much planning and building for the years ahead. Physical educators must not be complacent. Instead, they must exercise vision and imagination in progressing toward this new way of life. If they exercise prescience, they will have much to look forward to, and their programs will reach new heights of service and hope for humanity.

A Space Age Conference attended by students, professors and teachers of the public schools, held at the University of California, Los Angeles, California, drew implications for the space age for physical education. Some of the main points discussed at this conference were as follows: *

1. *Tidal wave of people* will mean larger classes and less space for activity programs.
2. *Technology and automation* will mean more emphasis on carry-over skills and programs for parents and adults. Television and moving pictures will be more widely utilized.
3. *Atomic power* will necessitate educational programs to help in handling stress. More emphasis will be placed on rest and relaxation and teaching self-survival.
4. *Economic, political, and scientific competition among nations* will put more stress upon facts, skills, and appreciations

---

*Cassidy, Rosalind, and Brown, Camille: Journal of Health, Physical Education, and Recreation 29:16, Sept., 1958.

that undergird movement in living and understanding self.

5. *Sociopsychosomatic unity* will mean new integration of physical education subject matter involving the disciplines from which its validity stems.

6. *Space travel* will place emphasis on research focused on movement in different space dimensions, together with new and more economical ways and means of achieving and maintaining fitness.

## A TEN-POINT PROGRAM FOR THE FUTURE OF PHYSICAL EDUCATION*

Keeping up with the times and serving present-day needs of people is as basic to education as to government and politics. Those educational programs that fail to keep abreast of such important developments as the knowledge explosion, technological advances, and new theories of learning, will fail and be relegated to a second-rate position in the nation's schools and colleges, just as readily as a nation's leader will be ousted from his position of responsibility.

Education is on the move. Curriculum reform, new facilities, experimental programs, research projects, and innumerable innovations, characterize today's institutions of learning. The nongraded school, flexible scheduling, conceptualized teaching, independent study, and programmed instruction are only a few features of the *New* education. Discovering the best way to help people learn is not a static but instead a dynamic, constantly changing entity, involving sixty million persons in the nation's classrooms, nearly three million teachers, and annual expenditures of more than $49 billion. Leading business corporations, recognizing the emphasis America is placing on education, are investing in microfilms, texts and reading material, copying machines, language laboratories, and learning systems. The fed-

eral government is providing financial aid—more than 60% of the antipoverty program of the Economic Opportunity Act is directly allocated to education.

All the disciplines and subject-matter fields of modern education must keep abreast of new developments in order to meet the needs of their constituency. In today's educational world, to remain impervious to change and become stagnant as a profession is to invite disaster and oblivion.

Physical education must also expect to change. Although change for change itself is never justified, the new developments that are occurring and have already altered the programs of other subject-matter areas, also have implications for physical education. Consequently, we need to study our present programs and practices and determine if we are meeting the needs of our students and keeping up with the times.

Although there is a risk in trying to forecast and write prescriptions for the future, and in discussing such recommendations very briefly, the author would like to set forth what he personally considers to be some needed changes in physical education. It is hoped that members of the profession will receive them in the spirit in which they are presented, for the purpose of discussion and consideration. As we consider these and other suggestions it will be possible to develop a dynamic program of action.

The following ten-point program is proposed for the physical education of the future:

1. *Strengthen our leadership.* Today's scholarly high school senior is as vigorously recruited by business, government, and education, as the star football player is by the National or American Football League. A college or university gains academic prestige in proportion to the number of National Merit Scholarship winners it can attract to its campus and

*Adapted from a speech given by the author at the AAHPER Convention in Chicago, March, 1966.

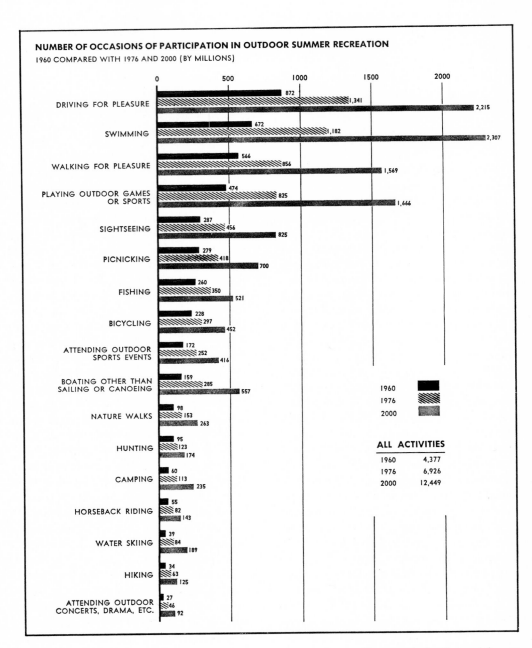

NUMBER OF OCCASIONS OF PARTICIPATION IN OUTDOOR SUMMER RECREATION

1960 COMPARED WITH 1976 AND 2000 (BY MILLIONS)

| | 1960 |
| | 1976 |
| | 2000 |

DRIVING FOR PLEASURE — 872 / 1,341 / 2,215

SWIMMING — 672 / 1,182 / 2,307

WALKING FOR PLEASURE — 566 / 856 / 1,569

PLAYING OUTDOOR GAMES OR SPORTS — 474 / 825 / 1,666

SIGHTSEEING — 287 / 456 / 825

PICNICKING — 279 / 418 / 700

FISHING — 260 / 350 / 521

BICYCLING — 228 / 297 / 452

ATTENDING OUTDOOR SPORTS EVENTS — 172 / 252 / 416

BOATING OTHER THAN SAILING OR CANOEING — 159 / 285 / 557

NATURE WALKS — 98 / 153 / 263

HUNTING — 95 / 123 / 174

CAMPING — 60 / 113 / 235

HORSEBACK RIDING — 55 / 82 / 143

WATER SKIING — 39 / 84 / 189

HIKING — 34 / 63 / 125

ATTENDING OUTDOOR CONCERTS, DRAMA, ETC. — 27 / 46 / 92

**ALL ACTIVITIES**

| | |
|---|---|
| 1960 | 4,377 |
| 1976 | 6,926 |
| 2000 | 12,449 |

*Report to the President and Congress by the Outdoor Recreation Resources Review Commission: Outdoor recreation in America, Washington, D. C., Jan., 1962.*

The simple pleasures will continue to attract most participants.

business, and the professions thrive as they interest learned men and women in their fields of endeavor.

This is the age of the scholar. Therefore, physical education must attract scholarly students to its ranks. Physical education cannot move ahead without dynamic, erudite leadership. If we subscribe to the premise that physical education is intellectually oriented (a requirement for professional status), requiring lengthy training and preparation in such areas as foundational sciences, skills, methods, and measurement, we must be sure that each practitioner who enters the ranks is qualified and equipped mentally, as well as in other ways, to perform the required service.

The profession of physical education should be so attractive that the high school student clearly recognizes it is a privilege to belong and that he needs strong qualifications, rather than discovering there is an "open-door" policy that admits any boy or girl who has the inclination to enter.

Although no arbitrary cut-off point is recommended on college entrance examination board tests (or similar instruments), most of our students in the future, it seems, should fall in the upper levels on both verbal and mathematical components of the test, be in the upper quarter of their high school graduating classes, possess personal characteristics that indicate they have promise for our field of endeavor, and have their application backed by strong recommendations.

The student who is interested in the physiological, psychological, and sociological aspects of physical activity and human development, has potential in the area of science, and possesses a yearning to do research, should be recruited as vigorously as a student who is strong in motor skills.

Another characteristic of a profession is that it must have the machinery and ability to police and control itself. Therefore, there must be some effective means to insure that professional preparing institutions select and train, and administrators employ, students who have met the high standards essential to quality leadership.

2. *Conduct a national inventory of our human resources.* This is an age in which many specialized human skills and talents are needed to successfully investigate, teach, and interpret the many-faceted aspects of modern-day physical education.

The profession of physical education needs to know the nature and extent of its human resources—those members who have special skills, abilities, and talents—at all educational levels and in all types of agencies. Our human resources need to be assessed in an objective, analytical manner. We need to know who has ability to do different types of research, who are the experts in fund raising and public relations, personally know government officials and legislators, have skill in group dynamics and public speaking, and have knowledge about movement analysis and adapted physical education.

After physical education's human resources are inventoried, the information should be carefully analyzed and organized in a meaningful manner. Then, this information should be stored in computers so that when special talents or skills are needed anywhere in the nation or world, they can be mobilized within a very short period of time and put to good professional use.

Each physical education professional is an expert in something, but we do not have this information readily available. Such an inventory will not only provide valuable information, but will also insure a greater feeling of belonging for each of our members. How many times has a dedicated but not well-known professional and talented person said to himself or herself: "I wish I could help." But because of failure to know about this special talent and lack of proper communication, the profession has been the loser.

3. *Develop and enforce a professional code of ethics.* To be rightfully labeled as a profession in today's world means that a field of endeavor has members who adhere to desirable codes of behavior. Such a code for physical education would embody relationships with students, colleagues, employers, and the public in general. It would also point out the primary obligations of the physical educator and stress his role of service and public trust.

As a profession we have developed codes of ethics, but they have not always been known or used to guide the behavior of our colleagues. Therefore, in addition to establishing such a code of ethics the necessary machinery would be developed to see that it is adequately publicized. Furthermore, where there is an infraction of the code, the case would be reviewed before a professional board, council, or committee. Here, the facts and circumstances would be heard and proper action taken. Although the implementation of this recommendation involves many problems, strong professional action would eventually serve to enhance desirable codes of behavior among all members.

4. *Create a center for reflective and advanced thinking.* To move ahead in the future the profession needs to exploit the wisdom and experience of the past.

The personal relationship of the author with the late Jay B. Nash is one of his most cherished memories. He studied under Dr. Nash, assisted him in his classes, shared his confidence, and was a colleague of his for many years. He knew him particularly well for his ability to do reflective and creative thinking in physical education until the time he passed away.

Dr. Nash retired from New York University in 1953. Until the time of his death he was an energetic, dynamic individual. On the morning he died he was working on a speech to be given to the Boys Clubs that afternoon.

It often occurred to the author that our national association should have tapped Dr. Nash's experience and wisdom much more than it did during the period that followed his retirement from New York University. Dr. Nash had much to offer that would have helped his profession to grow and prosper.

There are many Dr. Nash's in this country and many more to come. We still have an Ainsworth, Cassidy, Langton, Rogers, Scott, Staley, and Steinhaus, to name a few. Let's utilize their invaluable ideas, suggestions, and criticisms to help us grow in the years ahead. Let's profit from their many years of experience.

*A center for reflective and advanced thinking in physical education* should be established where these great leaders would periodically congregate, exchange views, mull over problems facing the profession, impart their wisdom, and give those of us who are still on the action front the benefit of their thinking. Our profession will be much better for having created such an institution.

5. *Develop a New physical education.* Education has a *New* math, a *New* English, and a *New* physics. We should also have a *New* physical education. The first step in achieving this goal might be a major curriculum study to identify, through scientific means, the basic concepts of physical education, and then assign responsibilities for each grade and education level—K through College—for fulfilling and teaching these concepts. The final blueprint would be a sequential and progressive developmental pattern for teaching skills, knowledges, appreciations, and other aspects of our professional programs. The *New* physical education would give direction to all physical educators as to *what skills* are to be taught, and

*when; what knowledges* are to be imparted, and *when; what fitness standards* are to be achieved, and *when;* and, *what social outcomes* are to be expected, and *when.* The progression to be followed, the sequential development to be adhered to, and the desirable standards to be met would be clearly delineated. The sum total of all experiences would result in graduating from our schools and colleges *physically educated* students.

6. *Expound only supported claims regarding the worth of physical education.* "Exercise will prevent disease," "Sports are a 'cure-all' for juvenile delinquency," and "Physical fitness will improve a student's I.Q." are examples of claims that have been made by some physical educators in the past. They are unsupported and have misled the public and contributed to loss of respect among our academic colleagues. One reason for making such false claims may be that the facts have not been known or that they have not been adequately interpreted to the profession.

The physical education of the future should expound only claims that are substantiated by sound research findings. To help in implementing this recommendation, conducting more significant research, financing needed studies, and disseminating research findings to practitioners in the field, *A National Institute* should be established where research studies would be encouraged and records on all studies would be stored. Research findings would be filed away in computers on a regional basis throughout the United States, and thus enable members of our profession, by a mere push of a button, to mobilize all the significant research on any particular subject with which he or she is concerned. For example, if a teacher in Nebraska wants the latest information on how to teach skish, a teacher in California desires to know about the role of exercise in weight control, or a doctoral student in Florida seeks the studies that have been conducted on the relation of motor skills to scholastic achievement, it would be possible to obtain answers within a few hours' time.

As the frontiers of knowledge are pushed back in regard to the worth of physical education and as the facts are made more readily available to our membership, the problem of expounding unsupported claims will diminish.

7. *Take strong professional stands on controversial issues where we provide the expertise.* The American Medical Association did not take a back seat in regard to Compulsory National Health Insurance, and similarly, the AAHPER, if it wishes to be an outstanding force for the profession in the future, should speak out loud and clear on matters where it is knowledgeable and is an authoritative source of information.

As a profession we should be recognized as being the experts in certain areas of sport, physical fitness, skill teaching, the relation of physical activity to human growth and development, and other areas directly related to our training and experience. Ironically, the advice of the professional boxer, ballplayer, physical culturist, or faddist, is sometimes sought before the public looks to us for help. We are still smarting from the time President Eisenhower invited several professional athletes to the White House to help him in deciding how to eliminate the physical softness of the youth of America. This situation was later corrected, thanks to some of our leaders.

One reason for this dilemma may be that we have not spoken out authoritatively and unilaterally as a profession on some of the major issues of the day. We have not agressively called attention to the fact that *we are the experts in these areas.* Too often we may have either remained silent or taken a middle-of-the-road position. Perhaps we may have been afraid of hurting someone else's feeling. Or we felt greater security by tying ourselves to the apron strings of some other educational or athletic organization. In such cases, the profession, educators, and the public in general did not benefit from a sound analysis of the problem by our profession and our leaders.

The profession needs to be heard on the major issues of the day, where we provide the expertise. After an examination of all the facts, a discussion of each of the alternatives, and a careful weighing of the evidence, we as a profession should take strong positions on such matters as coaching ethics, weight-reducing gimmicks, who should teach elementary school physical education, the place of physical fitness in a well-rounded school physical education program, poorly qualified physical educators being assigned to teach health education courses, qualifications and training for coaches, swimming pools as a facility in a school, credit for physical education, small-fry sports competition, athletic standards, and other controversial issues of the day.

After the profession has arrived at a sound position, we should then use all types of communication media to gain the headlines so that we will be heard clearly in the offices of school and college administrators as well as in the homes of America. We are the experts in physical education and all that the term implies. We have a national association of 50,000 members. We can speak with authority and be heard.

Educators and the public in general look to us for leadership and direction on many of the controversial issues of the day where our training and experience make us the authorities. They should not be found wanting. If we are the experts in these areas, let us provide the leadership that goes with such a label.

8. *Develop a comprehensive public relations program.* The area of public re-

lations needs considerable attention in the years ahead. There are many misunderstandings about physical education that need to be corrected. We need the help and support of general educators and the public in general. This goal cannot be achieved, however, unless they know what we are doing and the service we render to society. It is our responsibility to provide the service but we also should get credit for it—the reason for a program of public relations.

A basic program of public relations might include five parts:

(1) Create a bureau of public relations in the national office of the AAHPER that would be manned by a specialist trained in Public Relations. This bureau might have such responsibilities as giving counsel on publications; developing films; arranging meetings; and preparing newspaper, radio, and television releases; writing articles for magazines; and developing a roster of lecturers to interpret the contributions of physical education from coast to coast.

(2) Arrange for periodic regional meetings to be held where physical educators and school and college administrators would be in attendance. The purpose of these meetings would be to provide effective two-way communication between these two groups in order to promote a better understanding of physical education and the educational service it renders.

(3) Assign representatives of the Association to work full time on state and national legislation. These representatives would plan a vigorous and aggressive program to support legislation that would improve physical education programs throughout the nation.

(4) Assign a representative to the staff of AAHPER who is knowledgeable and possesses skill in the art of writing proposals for government, foundation, and other grants of monies (it takes a high degree of skill). This person would more than pay for his salary in a short period of time.

(5) Develop a coordinated plan for more cooperative working arrangements between college and university personnel and elementary and secondary school people. The plan would be designed to insure throughout the school and college life of the student, a better exchange of ideas, implementation of research

findings, in-service education for teachers, identification of problems, and better progression in the development of skills and subject matter, and a more meaningful implementation of other parts of the program.

9. *Place more emphasis upon the basic instruction or service physical education program at both high school and college levels.* The basic instruction program for all students represents the "gold mine" of physical education now and in the future. This is where the majority of students are exposed to physical education, the sub-par students (poorly skilled, physically soft, poor body mechanics, etc.) can get attention, the future leaders of America participate, and life-long impressions are formed by young people as to the worth of our program.

Service programs deserve our best full-time teachers, facilities, hours for scheduling activities, and budget priorities. We should objectively determine each student's physical status and plan a program that fits his needs. Individual counseling should play an important role.

After participating in the basic instruction program students should know that we firmly believe that the service program has top priority and does not rate second to the professional preparing courses, variety athletics, intramurals, or other aspects of our total program. It ranks first.

10. *Advocate a program of educational athletics.* Sports represent one of the most popular aspects of the American culture. Since they are conducted in all types of settings and for many reasons that have little or no relation to education, there needs to be a clear definition of the type of program we endorse for our schools and colleges.

A program of educational athletics is needed that clearly distinguishes between athletics that are offered in schools and colleges and those offered in community leagues, agencies, and clubs outside the educational institution. The educational athletic program should follow a sequential, developmental pattern using sound human growth and developmental principles as guidelines. Furthermore, the program should clearly demonstrate that schools and colleges are concerned with students who are pursuing their education rather than with spectators who find in athletics a means of entertainment.

The platform that has been described for the future of physical education may be thought of by some members of the profession as being too ambitious an undertaking. To those members the author would like to say that it is the essence of leadership that our reach must exceed our grasp. As Carl Schurz, an immigrant to this country pointed out long ago: "Ideals are like the stars. You will not succeed in touching them with your hands. But like the seafaring man on the desert of waters, you choose them as your guides, and following them you will reach your destiny."

## OTHER CONSIDERATIONS FOR PHYSICAL EDUCATION IN THE SPACE AGE

Throughout the world man appears to be living a more and more inactive life. He rides instead of walks, sits instead of stands, and watches instead of participates. What are the results of this inaction? Is inactivity detrimental to mental and physical health? Books, periodicals, and newspapers proclaim that atomic power will soon perform most of the work now done by man. How will man spend the increased leisure he will derive from the application of atomic energy to industry? Juvenile delinquency is at an all-time high. What is the relationship between juvenile delinquents and youth who engage in sports? Tension diseases are believed by many to be our number one killer. How can physical education help to alleviate the tension experienced in modern-day living? These are a few of the questions that arise when a person attempts to analyze the contributions of physical education to modern-day living. Physical education can be of great service in our society in promoting healthful living. It seems that individuals who engage regularly in adapted physical activity lead a more vigorous, a more interesting, and, to a great extent, a healthier existence than individuals who are content to follow sedentary pursuits. More specifically, the contributions of physical education in modern-day living will be discussed as follows:

1. Physical education—an instrument for contributing to a peaceful and prosperous world
2. Physical education and balanced living
3. Physical education and the automation era
4. Physical education and a nation of onlookers
5. Physical education and juvenile delinquency

6. Physical education and modern-day tensions

### Physical education—instrument for contributing to a peaceful and prosperous world

Education of and through the physical is needed in the space age just as enlightened thinking and sound reasoning are essential. In addition to the contribution physical education can make to America as a bulwark of strength for the greatest democracy on earth, a contribution can also be made to other countries and people throughout the world. A prosperous, healthful existence in every part of the globe will not be achieved solely through academic pursuits—as important as they are. Instead, it will be achieved as the total individual is educated. As a former United States Ambassador to the Dominican Republic stated, "Germany under the Kaiser and under Hitler made a fetish of the teach-

*Far Eastern University, Manila, Philippines.*

Far Eastern University folk dance group presents Sagayan, a Muslim dance from Mindanao, Philippines.

ing of science and math. Yet, Germany was responsible for two world wars. Under Hitler, the Nazis used mathematics and science for human destruction and cruel butchery. Now, under communism, the same fetish for science and mathematics is still being used to destroy, to undermine human dignity and morality, and to complete the destruction of freedom and religion."

He went on to say that such subjects as science and mathematics are very important in our schools, but so are physical education, foreign language, and other offerings. There is a need to educate people as much in how to live and learn together, for example, as in how to design a land-to-land missile or a fifty-megaton bomb. People must be educated to develop their total selves, physically, spiritually, mentally, emotionally, and socially, so they can contribute as much as possible to humanity.

Physical educators are now helping to promote peace and a prosperous world, but their talents and services will be needed even more in the days and years ahead. One of the greatest demands for Peace Corps personnel is physical educators who can go to Asia, Africa, and other continents to utilize their skills in helping the natives to develop better physical education programs for their countries.

The Olympic games bring together participants from more than seventy nations for athletic competition, enabling peoples of the world through the medium of sports and games to get to know each other a little better.

In my travels around the world I have found that a physical educator has a common bond with foreigners. The interest in physical activities exists wherever he goes.

Peace and prosperity are not going to be determined by bombs, rockets, and great military machines. Permanent peace and prosperity will become a reality only as people understand and respect each other, just as athletes do in the Olympic stadium. Furthermore, men, women, boys, and girls in all countries must be given an opportunity to be healthy, happy individuals capable of living vigorous, interesting lives. Physical educators can make a valuable contribution to these goals.

## Physical education and balanced living

There is a very great need for physical education as a part of balanced living. An individual will obtain the greatest value and happiness from life as he learns to spend each day in the most desirable manner. This means providing time for work and study, eating a nutritious diet, obtaining proper sleep and rest, engaging in recreation, and doing some self-evaluation. One other essential is providing time for engaging in some form of physical activity. This is important to meet the needs of his total well-being. It is needed to keep the organic systems of his body in proper condition, to provide release from the strain of work and study, and as a way of making himself more vigorous and productive, whether it be on the job, at home, or in service to the community.

Physical education is not something that you engage in once in a while. Instead, its true value comes into play as it is utilized as a medium to promote the best type of existence. When a former President of the United States was criticized for playing golf, a minister in New York City proclaimed from the pulpit that instead of being criticized he should be commended for knowing how to live a balanced life. Only as human beings learn to provide for the essentials of well-rounded living will they realize the greatest values that life has to offer.

Physical educators have the responsibility to so interpret their profession to the public that it will be seen not as an end in itself but, instead, as a means to a happier and more productive life. This is one of the greatest contributions that physical education can make to the space age.

## Physical education and the computer age

Dr. Robert Milliken, a Nobel prize winner in science, has said, "The age of invention brought the age of discovery; the age of discovery brought the age of power; the age of power has brought the age of leisure with its many unsolved problems."

In this twentieth-century computer world it seems that Americans are becoming more and more "sitdownish." People dream of times when laborsaving devices will give them more leisure hours. The nation's technology is directed toward this end, but the public in many instances does not spend its increased leisure in a constructive manner.

The Industrial Revolution brought the machine, which has given man many leisure hours. More free time will be available with the utilization of atomic energy. A newspaper editorial stated that the thirty-hour working week is a probability in the future, barring too great an armaments race with the Communist world. This means that man will have more and more leisure. If this country is to be strong, society has the responsibility of seeing that man spends his leisure time in a manner that will be conducive to his well-being.

How can physical education help? All individuals in our society should become familiar with the long list of physical activities that are incorporated in this profession. They should experience the joy that comes from rolling a ball down the alley and getting a strike, serving a tennis "ace," or landing a six-pound trout. They should experience the feeling of exhilaration and well-being that comes after a good workout and a shower. They should experience the mental uplift that results from getting their minds occupied by constructive physical activity instead of destructive worrying about such things as their job, social life, and world affairs. They should experience the satisfying sleep that comes at night after physical activity.

It is a convenience and a pleasure to use one's automobile to visit friends who live six miles away, but what about using it to go to work six blocks away? A refreshing, stimulating walk to and from work offers the opportunity to get a modified form of exercise which is more beneficial than riding in a car. The benefits of the industrial age should not be allowed to rob man of the benefits that were enjoyed before the machine.

Television, a leisure-time activity, is encouraging more and more inaction. It has become an accepted piece of equipment in every bar, hotel, and home where economic means make it possible. Adults and children alike are spending their free time watching the various plays, sports, and other programs on the screen. It can readily be seen that instead of becoming participants in activities that pay dividends in mental, physical, and social well-being too many people are content to sit at the ringside of television. This can be a worthwhile pastime if followed with discretion, but when it occupies every leisure moment, it is not a good substitute for activities of a more vigorous and educational nature.

It is not difficult to see the trend in men's lives with atomic development. Forecasts may be made for more luxurious ways of travel, more efficient laborsaving devices, and a thousand and one gadgets that will free man from arduous duties and give them more free time. The day of air travel that exceeds the speed of sound, the day of 150 miles to a gallon of gasoline, the electric automobile, and the day of vast conveyor systems that will carry people from point to point is at hand. One man has said, "Man can half control his doom." The future of this country in the atomic era will depend to a great extent on how these added leisure hours are spent. In ancient Rome, ill-spent leisure was a contributing cause to the fall of a great civilization. Physical and mental decay resulted because this ancient people became victims of in-activity and suffered from indulgence. Is America going to follow the way of ancient Rome? Physical education cannot in itself prevent American civilization from taking this road, but it can be a contributing factor toward the better use of leisure time and the leading of a more vigorous and healthy life on the part of everyone.

## Physical education and a nation of onlookers

Overplaying the part of a spectator is one of the curses of modern-day civilization. As a result of too much "spectating," individuals are failing to incorporate in their lives activities that will pay them many dividends in physical, mental, and emotional health. A spectator is one who looks on, a beholder, an individual who fails to participate. The term "specta-toritis" was used by one physical educator as a title for a book which points out the evils and cures for this malady.

It may be recalled that when the meaning of the term *education* was considered, it was pointed out that education is a "doing" phenomenon—one learns by doing. Being a beholder at a baseball game, the opera, a play, or at the races may be a "doing" experience and may have worthwhile educational implications. However, at the same time it must be recognized that the benefits from many worthwhile activities can be gained only by being a participant. Many physical, moral, mental, social, and emotional dividends are

realized only when the individual actually experiences the joy of participation. In fact, too much looking-on can contribute to physical and moral decay, as in the case of the Romans. In respect to physical activity, looking-on is not a substitute for actual participation.

What evidence is there that America is a nation of onlookers? Sixty thousand fans can be found in a Rose Bowl, Sugar Bowl, Cotton Bowl, Salad Bowl, Tangerine Bowl, 'Gator Bowl, Orange Bowl, or Rubber Bowl and twenty-two players on the gridiron. Seventy thousand spectators at a ball park watch eighteen men on the diamond. Forty thousand fans look at eight horses running. Eighteen thousand devotees of basketball sit in the stands and ten players participate on the floor. Ten to forty thousand people wildly cheer two pugilists trying to beat each other into unconsciousness. More than 500 million man-hours a day are spent in looking at television or listening to radio programs, the selector dial being adjusted mostly to family serials, comedians, and thrillers. Approximately 3,000 man-years are spent each day in motion picture theaters in the United States.

John Locke, the famous English philosopher, once stated that a sound mind in a sound body is a short but full description of a happy state in this world. These words have meaning for living in the twentieth century. If one is going to be mentally and physically fit to carry on routine daily tasks at school, at home, or at work it is imperative that he have enough stamina, strength, and skill to accomplish these duties without undue fatigue and still leave a margin of safety for any emergencies that may arise.

These characteristics are developed through physical activity. They cannot be developed by watching action from the stands, reading about it in a book, or seeing it on the screen. They are developed only through actual participation.

America does not have to be a nation of onlookers. Ample facilities are provided by schools, settlement houses, athletic clubs, camps, recreation departments, and the like from coast to coast. In addition to these, there is the great out-of-doors, the setting for all sorts of activities. Specialized leadership is waiting to guide, instruct, and help interested individuals.

Probably one of the main reasons individuals do not engage in these various activities more than they do is that they are not aware of the values inherent therein. Perhaps physical educators have assumed too much. The entire population must be educated to the benefits that may be derived from participation and the detrimental effects of being just onlookers.

### Physical education and juvenile delinquency

J. Edgar Hoover of the Federal Bureau of Investigation made a statement a few years ago, which still has implications today, to the effect that if the current trend in juvenile delinquency continues crimes within the next three decades will total approximately 8 million automobile thefts, 16 million burglaries, 2 million robberies,

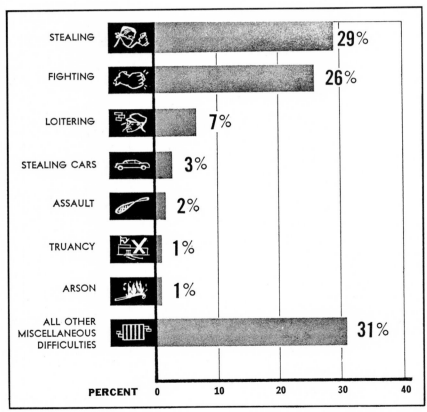

*Needs and interests*
*of adolescent Boys' Clubs members—a national*
*survey of members aged 14 to 18,*
*New York, 1960, Boys' Clubs of America.*

Thirty-three percent of members of Boys' Clubs are in trouble with the police, 66% have not been in trouble, and 1% not ascertained.

3 million aggravated assaults, and 200,000 murders.

Nearly one-third of the individuals arrested each year for robbery, arson, receiving stolen property, burglary, larceny, counterfeiting, auto theft, forgery, fraud, and embezzlement are under 21 years of age. Delinquency among young people is skyrocketing at four times the rate of national population growth. Every year about 100,000 youngsters are jailed in penal institutions. Three out of one hundred youngsters between the ages of 10 and 17 years are judged delinquent each year. About one out of every nine persons between these ages has a delinquency record.

Mr. Hoover reports that crime is increasing and that we spend more than four times as much money on the criminals in the United States as we do on all forms of public and private education. Furthermore, he states that of all the arrest records received daily, more than one-fifth are concerned with persons who are under 21 years of age. He states that, whereas youth at one time stole bicycles, they now steal automobiles and hold up banks and other business establishments.

Juvenile delinquency is a complex social problem that has its roots in the home and in parental neglect. Under such conditions what can physical education do to alleviate this pressing problem? It seems that some of the main reasons youth turns to crime are for want of something to do, for want of excitement and adventure, for want of "belonging" to a gang, for want of an outlet for their energy, and a desire for activity. Youth wants action, youth wants excitement, and youth wants to "belong." If facilities, leadership, and equipment were available for the pursuit of sports and other physical activities, many boys and girls would, under proper guidance, choose this medium of spending their leisure hours. However, lacking the opportunity to get their activity, their ex-

citement, and their "belonging" in wholesome physical activity, they will readily turn to crime as a means of fulfilling these natural human desires. A boy or girl loves to display his or her skill in tennis, basketball, badminton, swimming, bowling, horseshoes, or some other physical activity. Therefore it is the responsibility of society to see that the opportunities are available for the teaching of these essential skills to youth. When boys or girls have skill in an activity, they want to participate in that activity, and they will spend at least a portion of their time in this participation. Physical education activities abound in action, interest, and excitement for youth. Furthermore, within various activity circles, youth, through physical skill, will experience a feeling of "belonging." They will also experience accomplishment, and consequently life will become more purposeful. *Criminals are made, not born,* is an important truth, and a society that fails to provide for the utilization of physical education activities for its youth would appear to be ignoring a medium through which certain factors contributing to juvenile delinquency may be combated. J. Edgar Hoover has pointed out that if "youngsters leave their homes for entertainment, the least the community can do is to provide them with wholesome outlets for their abundant physical energy."

## Physical education and modern-day tensions

Man is finding it very difficult to adjust his nervous system and his emotions to the fast pace he lives in modern-day America. He finds it difficult to free himself from hate, worry, and fear. He finds it difficult to adjust himself to the bright lights, the screeching noises, the jostling crowds, and the rushing madness of urban and city life. He finds it difficult to refrain from engaging in a highly competitive race for a higher salary and better

Physical activity—a wholesome outlet for abundant physical energy.

position than his fellow worker. He finds it difficult to relax and enjoy living.

A well-known physical educator once raised this question: "Can man live healthfully in this world that he has created?"* He then went on to point out that man has been catapulted many, many years ahead to live in an era marked by great technological advancement, whereas his emotions and nervous system are still largely those of primitive times. Man's main pursuits in primitive times were concerned with providing shelter for his family, seeking food for them, and protecting them against a hostile environment. He did not have to worry about providing for his retirement in old age, catching an 8:05 train each morning, and watching the stock exchange ticker. He spent many hours in the out-of-doors and this, together with other characteristics

*Nash, Jay B.: Physical education: interpretations and objectives, New York, 1948, A. S. Barnes & Co.

of his mode of living, provided him with a strong muscular and nervous system.

Today, however, man is a victim of his mode of life. He cannot stand the mad pace, and as a result, it is literally "killing him off." Hal Boyle, in his syndicated Associated Press column several years ago, raised the question as to why some people commit suicide. He answered his own question by pointing out that it was probably due to unbearable tension. He went on further to state that tension is probably greater in peace than it is in war and that danger excites, but tension destroys.

If a person compares the killers of mankind in 1900 with the killers of mankind today, he can find further proof that tension is destroying mankind. He will discover that, in the order listed, the leading killers of mankind in 1900 were pneumonia and influenza; tuberculosis; diarrhea, enteritis, and intestinal ulcers; heart diseases; cerebral hemorrhage; and nephritis. Today, however, the order has changed to some extent. Diseases of the heart now lead the list, with such maladies as cancer, intracranial lesions of vascular origin, nephritis, and pneumonia following along on the list. It is interesting to note that pneumonia has dropped from first to fifth place and that heart disease has jumped from fourth to first. It can be seen from these listings that infectious diseases are being brought under control by the medical profession. However, diseases that are concerned with the heart, blood vessels, and kidneys have rushed to the front, and it is difficult to bring them under control. Some experts believe that these deaths are partly due to the tensions of modern-day living and the fact that man is finding it difficult to stand the pace of his existence. Howard Whitman wrote an interesting article which is completely documented as evidence of this fact. He pointed out that heart disease has increased in proportion to the increase in the tempo of American life. He stated that heart disease takes 700,000 lives a year—more than all of the next five leading killers combined. He showed how cases of coronary thrombosis fluctuated with the action of the stock market, how many top executives in business were paid large salaries but killed themselves in an attempt to break production records, how heart rates increased through emotional tension, and how coronary disease was twice as prevalent among people doing sedentary work as among those who were active in their jobs. He stated that to live a healthy life a man must not lead a highly competitive existence and be a money slave but that, instead, he must enjoy life with his family and neighbors and learn to play and enjoy day-to-day living.

Dr. Hans Selye in his book *The Stress of Life* shows the need for sports, hobbies, and other activities in breaking the tension of modern-day living.

Physical education activities may con-tribute considerably in relieving the tension of modern-day living. When an individual is attempting to break par at golf or when he is attempting to serve a tennis "ace," he forgets all about the conference with the boss the next day, about the final exam in English, or about getting a higher salary and a better job than his next-door neighbor. The tension that has gripped his body all day is finally relieved through his interest and enthusiasm for this wholesome activity.

Play and exercise should not be put away with one's commencement gown and mortarboard when high school or college is finished—they are not solely the possession of youth. Regardless of sex and regardless of age, they should be part of one's routine throughout life. They will supply many mental, physical, and social dividends that will contribute in great measure to a rich and full life.

## QUESTIONS AND EXERCISES

1. What implications does educational television have for the future of physical education?
2. How will the use of textbooks help to better physically educate the youth of the future? What kinds of material should these textbooks contain?
3. Write an essay of approximately 250 words describing the contributions of physical education to modern-day living.
4. Make a list of contributions that physical education can make to enriched living. Rank the various items according to their relative importance.
5. Describe the needs for physical education before and after the Industrial Revolution.
6. What are ten inventions that have tended to make man inactive?
7. What has been the effect of television on the public at large?
8. What evidence is available in your home town to show that America is rapidly becoming a nation of onlookers?
9. What are the advantages and the disadvantages of being a spectator?
10. Describe the role of the spectator in ancient Rome. How is he similar to the spectator here in the United States?

11. What is meant by the term *adapted physical activity?*
12. What are some of the reasons why many individuals feel that exercise is harmful?
13. What is the relationship between physical education and juvenile delinquency?
14. What are some of the needs of youth? How can physical education meet some of these needs?
15. Interpret the statement "Criminals are made, not born."
16. What are some of the causes of modern-day tensions? How can physical education help to alleviate them?
17. What are the implications that can be drawn from analyzing a list of the leading killers of mankind in 1900 and those to-day?
18. In approximately 250 words discuss the statement "Play and exercise are not solely the possession of youth."

## SELECTED REFERENCES

American Association for Health, Physical Education, and Recreation: The growing years —adolescence, Washington, D. C., 1962, The Association.

Bardsley, F. G., and Eck, T. W.: Closed circuit instructional television, Journal of Health, Physical Education, and Recreation 36:32, May, 1965.

Blake, O. William: Innovations in preparing the elementary school physical education teacher, Journal of Health, Physical Education, and Recreation 36:60, May, 1965.

Brightbill, Charles K.: Man and leisure, Englewood Cliffs, N. J., 1961, Prentice-Hall, Inc.

Bucher, Charles A.: Must there always be a winner? Your Life, May-June, 1955.

Bucher, Charles A., issue editor: Helping adolescents meet their problems (Theme), Education, Dec., 1955.

Bucher, Charles A.: Fitness and health (editorial), Educational Leadership 20:356. March, 1963.

Hoover, John Edgar: Secularism—a breeder of crime, Washington, D. C., Nov. 19, 1947. U. S. Department of Justice, Federal Bureau of Investigation, U. S. Government Printing Office.

Layman, Emma McCloy: Mental health through physical education and recreation, Minneapolis, 1955, Burgess Publishing Co.

Nash, Jay B.: Spectatoritis, New York, 1938, A. S. Barnes & Co.

Nash, Jay B.: Philosophy of recreation and leisure, St. Louis, 1953, The C. V. Mosby Co.

Report to the President and Congress by the Outdoor Recreation Resources Review Commission: Outdoor recreation in America, Washington, D. C., 1962, U. S. Government Printing Office.

Selye, Hans: The stress of life, New York, 1956, McGraw-Hill Book Co.

Trekell, Marianna: Speaking to the future, Journal of Health, Physical Education, and Recreation 37:29, Feb., 1966.

U. S. Department of Justice, Federal Bureau of Investigation: Uniform crime report for the United States, Washington, D. C., annual publication, U. S. Government Printing Office.

Van Dalen, D. B.: Dynamics of change in physical education, Journal of Health, Physical Education, and Recreation 36:39–41, Nov.–Dec., 1965.

Wallace, Ralph: Pyrotechnics by Mayor Morrison, Reader's Digest, June, 1948.

Whitman, Howard: Richest man in the cemetery, Colliers, July 30, 1949.

Winnet, Nochem S.: The real delinquents—parents or society? New York Times (Magazine Section), Feb. 16, 1947.

The competitor

*Works of R. Tait McKenzie.*
Courtesy Joseph Brown, School of Architecture,
Princeton University.

**PART TWO**

# Philosophy of physical education as part of general education

# Chapter 5

# Philosophy of education

> *I would have his outward manners, and his social behaviors and the carriage of his person formed at the same time with his mind. It is not a mind, it is not a body that we are training; it is a man, and he ought not be divided into two parts.*
>
> —Montaigne
>
> *It is a lamentable mistake, to imagine that bodily activity hinders the working of the mind, as if these two kinds of activity might not advance hand in hand, and as if the one were not intended to act as a guide to the other.*
>
> —Rousseau
>
> *The union of mind and body has to be acknowledged as being for us primary and ultimate. All voluntary movements, all sensations and passions rest on the union, neither mind by itself nor body by itself can suffice to account for their occurrence. The movements as being willed, are foreign to the body, the sensations and passions are foreign to mind as well as body.*
>
> —Descartes

The news of the Russians rocketing into space made education as well as defense front-page news in America. The public schools became, and still are, the center of a raging controversy as to what type of training our boys and girls should have. The "Reds" provided a launching pad for such scientists and writers as Rick-over, Bestor, Keats, Teller, and countless others to ignite their own missiles.

These eminent citizens have fired away at such subjects as home economics, music, and physical education, saying they are "frills" and "duds" that we can ill afford during the space age. They have bombarded progressive and life-adjustment education as unwarranted, unwanted, and needless educational piffle placed in the schools by the educationists to further their own dynasty.

Our educational system has been compared with Russia's, pointing out that Communist youth go to school six days a week, ten months a year, start English at 12 years of age, take five years of math, physics, and chemistry before they are 16, and jump into calculus by their seventeenth birthday.

On the other hand, our critics lament that only one out of three of our high school students takes chemistry, one out of four physics, and one out of eight trigonometry or solid geometry. The nation's students, according to them, cannot think, add, subtract, or read but may excel at fly casting, cooking, and square dancing.

Admiral Rickover, the father of the atomic submarine, looks askance at our educational system and says it must be

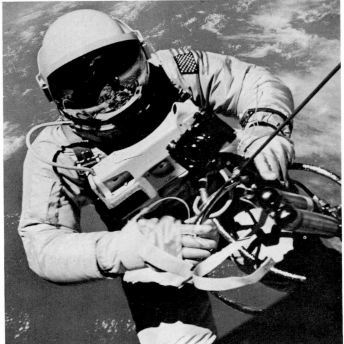

*National Aeronautics and Space Administration.*

The space age catapulted education into the headlines.

completely overhauled. His vitriolic words are orbiting throughout the United States: "Schools are a place for work and not for a course in social adjustment or alligator wrestling . . . if we are going to enter into a race with the Russians, for God's sake let it be in educational and not military fields."

---

*Yet some relaxation is to be allowed by all . . . there is nothing that can bear perpetual labor. . . . Boys, accordingly, when reinvigorated and refreshed, bring more sprightliness to their learning. . . . Nor will play in boys displease me; it is a sign of vivacity. . . .*

—Quintilian

*. . . what a disgrace it is for a man to grow old without ever seeing the beauty of which his body is capable.*

—Xenophon

*That form of exercise is best which not only exercises the body but also is a source of joy to the participant. . . . Therefore that form of exercise is recommended which contributes to the health of the body and to the harmonious functioning of the parts and to the strength of the soul.*

—Galen

*To learn to think we must therefore exercise our limbs, our senses, and our body organs which are tools of the intellect; and to get the best use out of these tools the body which supplies us with them must be strong and healthy.*

—Rousseau

---

Dr. Robert Hutchins, President of the Fund for the Republic, says that survival in the nuclear age means that each citizen must be educated to the limit of his capacity. By education, he points out: "I don't mean trained, amused, exercised, accommodated or adjusted. . . . I mean that his intellectual power must be developed." He stresses that "those subjects, those activities, and those people that make no contribution to the development of intellectual power" should be removed from education.

Have these attacks been successful? A Gallup poll showed that out of more than 20,000 high schools in the United States over half have either made curricular changes and raised requirements or are planning to do so. Of more than 1,100 high school principals sampled, 61% thought too much attention was paid to athletics in high school. Others point to the "frills," such as music and physical education. As one Kansas principal commented: We give students too much music, physical education, and so forth, and not enough of the "three R's."

Never in the history of mankind has education been under attack as much as it is at present. These criticisms make it imperative that educators reexamine their role in society. An understanding of philosophy is imperative to meet the challenges of the day.

Philosophical thought represents the highest level of thinking. As such, it is a discipline that all educators should understand. This chapter has been written to present some considerations in the building of an educational philosophy. It defines philosophy and discusses its component parts. Then it presents some of the more popular philosophies that have prevailed down through the years and that exist today. Next it considers the philosophy of the "good life" as a suggested goal for educational programs. Finally, a discussion is presented concerning philosophical implications for education in a twentieth-century world in order to achieve the "good life."

## WHAT IS PHILOSOPHY?

Philosophy is a field of inquiry that attempts to help man evaluate, in a satisfying and meaningful manner, his relationship to the universe. Philosophy seeks to help man evaluate himself and his world by giving him a basis on which to deal with the problems of life and death, good and evil, freedom and restraint, and beauty and ugliness.

Aristotle says that philosophy is the grouping of the knowledge of the universals. A dictionary definition reports that it is the love of wisdom, the science that investigates the facts and principles of reality and of human nature and conduct. Copleston* writes: "Philosophy . . . is rooted in the desire to understand the world, in the desire to find an intelligible pattern in events and to answer problems which occur to the mind in connection with the world." In defining the word "philosophy" Webster† says, "Love of wisdom means the desire to search for the real facts and values in life and in the universe, and to evaluate and interpret these with an unbiased and unprejudiced mind." As can be seen from these definitions, philosophy offers an explanation of life and the principles that guide human lives.

In order to comprehend more clearly the meaning of philosophy, one should briefly examine the major components of which philosophy is composed.

1. *Metaphysics* is associated with the principles of being. This component attempts to answer a series of related questions: "What is the meaning of existence?" "What is real?" "How are man's actions governed?" "How and why did the universe evolve?" "What is the nature of God?" Will Durant, a contemporary philosopher, says that metaphysics investigates the reality of everything that is concerned with man and his universe.

2. *Epistemology* deals with methods of obtaining knowledge, and the kinds of knowledge that can be gained. It is a comprehensive study of knowledge that

attempts to define the sources, authority, principles, limitations, and validity of knowledge. Epistemology seeks to answer the question "What is true?"

3. *Axiology* helps to determine to what uses truth is to be put. It asks "How do we determine what has value, and on what criteria do we base this judgment?"

4. *Ethics* is a more individualized and personalized subdivision of axiology. It helps to define moral character and serves as a basis for an individual code of conduct. Ethics attempts to answer the question "What is the highest standard each person should strive to attain?"

5. *Logic* seeks to provide us with a sound and intelligent method of living. Logic describes the steps that should be taken in thinking, and puts ideas into an orderly, structured sequence that leads to accurate thinking. It helps to set up standards by which the accuracy of ideas may be measured. Logic does not deal with the accuracy of facts, but rather with the orderly connection of one fact or idea with another. It asks the question "What method of reasoning will lead to the truth?"

6. *Aesthetics* is the study of, and determination of criteria for, beauty in nature and the arts, including dance, drama, sculpture, painting, music, and writing. Aesthetics, which is a less scientific branch of axiology, is concerned not only with art, but with the artist and the appreciation of what he has created. In an attempt to determine the close relationship of art to nature, aesthetics asks the question "What is beauty?"

The components known as metaphysics, epistemology, axiology, ethics, logic, and aesthetics represent aspects of philosophy. In developing a philosophy for any particular field, one would turn for information to each of these areas. These components would be applied in formulating a philosophy for any particular field within the educational endeavor, such as in

---

*Copleston, Frederick, S. J.: Contemporary philosophy, Westminster, Md., 1966, The Newman Press.

†Webster, Randolph W.: Philosophy of physical education, Dubuque, Iowa, 1965, Wm. C. Brown Co.

health, physical education, or recreation. Philosophy yields a comprehensive understanding of reality, which, when applied to education or any other field of interest, gives direction and method that would very likely be lacking otherwise.

## PHILOSOPHY AND LEVELS OF DISCUSSION

Broudy* lists four levels of discussion that are applicable to a progressive step-by-step exploration of educational problems. These levels of discussion help to clarify more clearly the implications of philosophy for the physical educator.

1. *Emotional or uncritical level.* At this level a person discusses the pro or con of an issue mainly in terms of his or her own limited experience. The arguments presented are not based on reflective thinking but, instead, on impulse and impression of emotional feeling. There is general agreement that this level of discussion is the most unreliable. Few differences of opinion can be settled by using the emotional level of thought and action.

2. *Factual or informational level.* This level of discussion involves the gathering of factual evidence to support one's arguments. By mobilizing statistics and other types of factual evidence tangible support is often given to a particular argument. However, this level of discussion can be unreliable and misleading since it depends on the facts used: whether or not they are valid and applicable, how significant they are, and other conditions that exist in the particular situation in question. However, the mobilizing of facts in a discussion can frequently result in the solution of a problem and the satisfactory finalizing of a discussion on an argumentative topic.

3. *Explanatory or theoretical level.* Facts offer solid support, but they are

---

*Broudy, Harry S.: Building a philosophy of education, New York, 1954, Prentice-Hall, Inc., pp. 20–24.

most effective as they are associated with theories that make them dynamic and applicable. Broudy illustrates this by citing the value of making facts important by utilizing psychoanalytical theories stemming from Freud in attempting to prove one method of instruction better than another. At this level of discussion the introduction of a reliable scientific explanation giving force to facts provides strong evidence for rational men.

4. *Philosophical level.* The highest level of discussion involves asking questions relative to *what is really true, valuable, right, or real?* The application of such values is universal, eternal, and for all men. This is the ultimate to which any discussion can go. This level of discussion finds the greatest use when problems fail to yield a clear solution and when facts and science are limited and inconclusive. (There are many such problems in education and in physical education which merit a philosophical discussion.)

Physical educators should strive to develop their educational philosophies in a rational manner which is logical and systematic and which represents the best interests of all men. This means scientific facts must be assembled and workable theories applied, which support the worth of physical education as an important and necessary service to humanity.

## SOME GENERAL PHILOSOPHIES

Five philosophies have prevailed down through the years and have influenced educational thinking. They are referred to as idealism, realism, pragmatism, naturalism, and existentialism.

### Idealism

The philosophy of idealism has come down to us through the ages as a heritage from the earliest Greek philosophers and thinkers. The key concepts of idealism are as follows:

1. *A man's mind is the focus of his be-*

*ing.* The idealist believes that the mind of man is more real than anything else that exists. Anything that is real is essentially a product of the mind, and is equated by thoughts and ideas. Thus, the things a man experiences are the only things that have reality for him.

2. *In the scheme of the universe, man is more important than nature.* Because to the idealist, the mind and spirit are the keys to life, the physical world plays a subordinate role to man. Man interprets nature in terms of his mind, his spirit, and his being. Physical objects are a result of man's creativity.

3. *Values exist independently of man, and are permanent.* Man is capable of exercising free will. Through the use of this power, man recognizes the existence in the world of good and evil, beauty and ugliness, freedom and restraint, and interprets them in relation to himself. The idealist acknowledges that man may interpret values incorrectly, but says that these values are permanent and do not change in the light of varying interpretations.

4. *Reasoning and intuition help man to arrive at the truth.* Man's mind is considered to be the basic, creative force that helps him learn more about his world. But the idealist also believes that scientific methods of investigation and research are valuable aids in seeking the truth.

The Greek philosopher Plato is often referred to as the father of idealism. He believed that ideas had an enduring quality, and that physical objects were ideas expressed in a less-than-perfect fashion. Plato said that there were, in fact, two classes of ideas: those that exist in the mind of men, and those that exist outside of man's mind. Aristotle expanded on Plato's philosophy, and was responsible for the earliest origins of the scientific method. Aristotle stressed arriving at the truth through reasoning and observation.

René Descartes is one of the most famous of the idealist philosophers. His often cited quotation "I think, therefore I am" is the essential element in the philosophy of the idealist. Both Baruch Spinoza and Gottfried W. Leibniz expressed the view that something enduring and unchanging exists beyond man's universe. While Spinoza referred to this phenomenon as a "substance," Leibniz termed it a "God." George Berkeley, Immanuel Kant, and George Hegel all espoused the belief that the mind of man is the key to all things. Some of the more modern idealists, whose views encompassed many of the same elements as the men who preceded them were Louis Agassiz, Henry Barnard, Carl Follen, Francis Lieber, Henry Wadsworth Longfellow, and Horace Mann.

The idealist views education as a process that originates within the self. He considers the pupil to be a creative being who is guided by the teacher. The pupil formulates ideas, and thus learns, in the environment set by the teacher. The pupil arrives at the truth through a continual process of ideation. The learning environment of the idealistic teacher would include the formulation of ideas through the project method of teaching, the lecture method, and/or the question and answer method. The idealist does not consider teaching methods to be rigid patterns, but keeps them flexible so that they may be geared to the learner.

The idealistic teacher would expect his students to form their own conclusions from many possible answers to a problem. Rather than dictating answers, the teacher guides his students through a thought process that will lead to the truth.

The curriculum under an idealist philosophy would stress those activities, areas of study, and experiences that would help the pupil to build an ideal intellectual, spiritual, and moral character. Art, literature, and history in their classic forms would form the foundation of the curriculum in an idealistic school.

The truly idealistic teacher of physical education believes that this field is more than "physical" education, and seeks a term that more explicitly describes what he is attempting to do. Since idealism places the emphasis on moral and spiritual values, it demands that physical education strive to help the individual reach the full potential of his personality through the teacher, activities, and the methods employed.

Idealism implies that physical education must be ideal-centered. Those activities must be offered that aid the student to develop honesty, courage, leadership, sportsmanship, creativity, and fair play. The effect of the activity on the student is more important than any single phase of the activity itself. Thus, the idealist would accept vigorous exercise for the self-discipline and effort required. He would reject it if its sole aim was building physical fitness or improving posture. The idealist would encourage student-created gymnastic and dance routines. He would reject a football or basketball game that was teacher- or coach-dominated.

Idealism says that the firm and rather paternalistic guidance of the teacher is more important to carry out this philosophy than are the equipment and facilities available. Idealism emphasizes a well-organized, well-guided program that contributes to the full mental and physical development of the individual.

### Realism

Realism asserted itself as a distinct and separate philosophy during the late nineteenth and early twentieth centuries. For many centuries preceding that time, realism was greatly overshadowed by idealism. The roots of realism date back as far as the origins of idealism, and it was, in fact,

*National Aeronautics and Space Administration.*

The physical world is a real world.

a philosophical revolt against idealism. The growth of scientific methods and the philosophy of modern realism emerged at about the same time. Realism has many subdivisions, and its adherents do not always agree on particular interpretations, but the key concepts of realism may be defined in general terms.

1. *The physical world is a real world.* The realist accepts the physical world, or world of nature, as it is. He does not contend that the world is man-made, but says that it is made up of matter. The physical world is in no way dependent on man's mind. The realist says that man comes to an understanding of his physical world through his senses and through experience.

2. *All of the physical events that occur in the universe are the result of the Laws of Nature.* The realist contends that forces within the universe, which are physical laws, control man's physical world. This belief has given rise to the physical sciences. The realist says that man's environment is a result of cause and effect, and that good, morality, and beauty conform to the Laws of Nature. Those things that do not conform to the Laws of Nature are bad, immoral, and ugly. Man perceives the physical world through observation.

3. *The truth may be best determined through the Scientific Method.* The realist does not hope for, or anticipate full control or complete comprehension of everything in the physical world. He does expect to modify and understand it as best as he can through the tools of science. The realist feels that science and philosophy form the best method of arriving at the truth.

4. *The mind and the body have a close and harmonious relationship.* The realists have two views on the origin of human behavior. One school of thought says that man's behavior may be a result of natural laws. A second opinion is that all of man's behavior may be a result of learning. Both sides agree, however, that the mind and the body are inseparable, and that neither takes precedence over the other.

5. *Religion and philosophy can co-exist.* The realist can hold religious beliefs without compromising either religion or his philosophy. He may be a staunch atheist or even a pantheist, or hold beliefs anywhere between the two extremes. The philosophy of realism does not insist on any one position as being the correct one. The individual realist is free to coordinate his religious beliefs with his philosophical viewpoint.

Philosophers often lend their thinking to the shaping of more than one philosophy. Thus, many of the men who helped to define idealism also adhered to elements of realistic thinking. The early realists were men who ascribed much to a belief in the powers of a supreme being, or God. Aristotle said that truth and reality were one and the same, and that man's powers of reasoning made him unique. Because of this viewpoint, Aristotle is often referred to as the father of realism. St. Thomas Aquinas and René Descartes both said that matter was real, and created by a God. Descartes' writing is believed to be the basis for the field of mathematical physics. Comenius, Spinoza, Kant, John Locke, and William James all helped to put forth clarifications of this philosophy.

To the realist, education is a process of learning how to acquire knowledge, acquiring knowledge, and putting that knowledge to practical use. The realist believes that education is basic to life, and that all education should have a useful purpose. Education is viewed as an important aid in adjustment to the world, in understanding it, and in controlling it.

The realistic teacher would guide students through a process of inductive reasoning, eventually leading to a unified concept of the physical world. The teacher would employ objective methods of teaching, testing, and evaluation. Although mastery of fundamental facts would be accomplished through drill and memorization, the mastery of a body of knowledge would be implemented by experimentation, demonstration, observation, and through extensive use of audiovisual aids. The teacher would present as fact only those facts that have been proved by objective means.

The curriculum under a realist philosophy would stress mathematics and the sciences. The progress of the pupil would be evaluated by objective, standardized tests. Realism has often been credited with being a major influence on the development and use of standardized tests.

The realist views physical education as a valuable part of the school curriculum. It is considered to be a unit of study that prepares the student to adjust to the world. Activities in themselves are viewed as a means of learning to adjust, and the emphasis is placed on the outcome of the activity in terms of adjustment.

The realist says that the building of a sound and healthy body is one of the major objectives of physical education. This is to be accomplished through a scientifically formulated curriculum that is logical and follows a definite sequence. The teaching emphasis is placed on fundamentals of games and activities, with each skill broken down into its component parts.

The realist would use drills extensively, and break all units of work down into orderly progressions. He would favor a period of physical education for each student each day, so that they could become healthier and more physically fit. He would employ demonstrations, and make use of many self-testing activities. He would emphasize the use of textbooks, and would grade his students objectively.

Besides developing a sound body, the realist physical educator would also stress sportsmanship, good moral behavior, and a scientific knowledge of the body.

**Pragmatism**

Pragmatism emphasizes experience as a key to life. Rather than being concerned with reality, this philosophy is concerned with knowledge. Because of this view, pragmatism was, in its early stages, often called "Experimentalism." The term "pragmatism" was not coined until the late 1800's, and in its modern concept, this philosophy is considered to be an American one.

1. *The experience of man causes changes in the concept of reality.* The pragmatist believes in change. He does not hold that ideas, values, or realities are inflexible. He contends, instead, that the experiences of man cause ideas, values, and realities to be dynamic. The pragmatist says that experience is the only possible way to seek the truth, and that that which is not experienced cannot be known or proved.

2. *Success is the only criterion of the value and truth of a theory.* Knowledge and experience help man to discover what is true. But truth is considered to be flexible, and today's truth may be tomorrow's falsehood. The pragmatist strongly believes in the scientific method of problem solving. He considers it the best way to gain knowledge. Knowledge itself is thought to be only a stepping-stone on the path to further knowledge and experimentation. The pragmatist believes that a workable theory is a true theory, and that the unworkable theory has been proved false.

3. *Man is an integral part of a larger society, and his actions reflect on that society.* The pragmatist contends that man and society must live harmoniously, and that the actions of one directly affect the other. He believes in democracy, that is, the needs of a group must always incorporate the needs of each individual

in the group. To the pragmatist, values are an individual matter, and what is right or wrong depends on the judgment of the individual, his environment, and the circumstances. However, the result of any action by any individual is to be measured in terms of its worth to society as a whole.

Heraclitus was an early Greek exponent of pragmatism. He stated the still-held belief that the world and its values and ideas are in a constant state of flux. Quintilian said that learning was a product of experience. Francis Bacon, an Englishman, put forth the theory that society and science must work together in order to achieve knowledge, and that one could not function effectively without the other. The first outstanding American pragmatist was Charles S. Peirce. He wrote that the practicality of a truth was the only criterion on which that truth could be measured. William James said that a theory was good if it worked, and wrong if it was not practical. The most famous of the American pragmatists was John Dewey. At times, pragmatism is referred to as "Deweyism," because of the influence of Dewey's thinking on the philosophy. Dewey brought forth the theory that everything we know is subject to change, and can in no way be considered static. Dewey viewed life as a continuing, never-ending experiment. He felt that learning how to think was one of the most important goals in life. Dewey's philosophy is the most profound influence on the field of education.

The pragmatic approach to general education today follows the outline set down by Dewey. Experience is viewed as the key to all learning, and the application of intelligence to new experiences the thing that makes the educational process effective. Problem solving is considered to be the best way to gain experience.

The pragmatic teacher serves as an inspiration, guide, and leader. To the teacher, the child is the most important thing in the school, and he is seen as a whole being, rather than an intellect without a body. The needs, interests, and prior experiences of the child, and the individual differences between children, guide the teacher toward best helping each child to learn how to think and adjust to society.

The curriculum as well as the classroom is child-centered. Meeting the needs of each individual is more important than the subjects that are taught. This way of thinking has given rise to core courses and vastly expanded and experimental curricula, such as is found in the ungraded school.

The pragmatic approach to physical education is one of integrating the child and society. Any activity that has a social value is acceptable. The more formal and rigid systems of drills, exercises, and calisthenics do not have a place or value in the pragmatic curriculum.

The physical education program is seen as an important part of the total school curriculum. Adjustment, growth, success, and knowledge are desired outcomes of the lifelike competition of sports and games.

The more varied the physical education curriculum is, the happier the pragmatist is, because more experience will accrue. Creative activities, such as dance, and experiences in camping and outdoor living are highly valued. Through these, the student not only learns by doing, but gains a measure of self-control and discipline, and learns to cooperate with others. The pragmatic curriculum in physical education, like that of general education, is determined by the needs and interests and experiences of the learner. Rather than conducting formal classes in marching, the physical educator guides his students through activities in which they have shown an interest, adapting the activity to the child rather than the reverse.

## Naturalism

Naturalism, pragmatism, and realism share many key concepts, although naturalism as a philosophy is the oldest one known to the Western world. Naturalism is often referred to as a materialistic philosophy, since it says that those things which actually and physically exist are the only things that have value.

1. *Any reality that exists exists only within the physical realm of nature.* To the naturalist, the physical world is the key to life. It contains all we see, observe, and think about, including the beauty or ugliness of a tree and the complexities of nuclear physics. The physical world is viewed as being in a constant state of growth and change, but it is considered to be a predictable and reliable force. Since the physical world is the key to life, the naturalist does not accept the existence of a God or any other supreme being. The philosophy of naturalism says that scientific methods are the best ways to gain knowledge about the world of nature.

2. *Nature is the source of value.* Because nature is omnipotent, anything that is of value exists only within nature, and is predicated by nature. No values can exist separately from nature in any form. Like pragmatism, a thing is of value if it is workable.

3. *The individual is more important than society.* Naturalism does agree, however, that democracy comes from a group process, but contends that each individual is more important than the group as a whole. Society reaps the benefits of the interaction of man and nature. Conversely, it is the individual who advances nature.

The men who first defined the philosophy of naturalism were in strong agreement that all things are derived from nature, including learning. This view was especially put forth by Democritus, Leucippus, Epicurus, and Comenius. In the eighteenth century, Rousseau, Basedow, and Pestalozzi set the foundations for the naturalistic process in education. Rousseau is more of a prime source for these educational objectives, but Basedow put them into actual use. Herbert Spencer further defined education under naturalism, and is mainly responsible for modern educational thought among the naturalists.

Naturalism is not a complete educational philosophy in itself; its aims and objectives serve as influences on the educational philosophies of realism and pragmatism. The naturalist deeply believes in the child-centered school. He sees the child as undergoing growth continually, and education as a vital part of the growth process. He says that education must be geared to the individual growth rate of each child, and to his needs and interests.

Naturalism advocates the education of both mind and body, with neither taking precedence. It is the job of the teacher to learn how each child learns, and to guide him through the educational process. Rather than resorting to drills and memorizing, the teacher should encourage the child to take an active part in his own educational growth. The teacher, through example and demonstration, guides the child through an investigatory procedure that helps him to draw his own conclusions.

The influence of naturalism on physical education, as in general education, is felt more through other philosophies. Naturalism advocates paying careful attention to the known facts of child growth and development. The child is to be considered as a single unit rather than a part of a larger, homogeneous group. The needs, interests, and activities of the child must be considered in the light of helping him to reach his full mental and physical potential.

The naturalist believes in keeping the

child as active as possible both mentally and physically. Through physical activity, the naturalist wants the child to learn to become a contributing member of a group, to develop high moral standards, to be able to express himself in an acceptable manner, and to become an individual who has reached his full potential.

The naturalist feels that a wide variety of activities must be offered to the child. He approves of all physical activity, including team and individual sports, vigorous exercise, and outdoor education. He firmly states that new activities should be introduced only when the child is ready for them, and has a need for and interest in that activity. The naturalist does not approve of intense competition between groups. He does say that the child must compete against himself to better his performance and to improve in light of what he himself has done in past performances.

### Existentialism

The chief concern of this philosophy is the individuality of man. The existentialist fears that man is being forced to conform to society, and is thus forfeiting his individuality. Existentialism received its impetus immediately after World War II. It is entirely a modern philosophy in that it did not arise from any of the ancient philosophies. Existentialism as a way of philosophical thought had its earliest beginnings in the mid-nineteenth century:

1. *Man's existence is the only true reality.* A man is what he causes himself to become, and no more and no less. He has the ultimate responsibility for his past, present, and future. He has the choice of accepting those things that exist outside his own experience, but if he does accept them, he forfeits a part of himself. The existentialist does not contend that God does or does not exist, but only that each man must decide the answer to this question himself in the light of an objective analysis of his own being.

2. *Each man must determine his own system of values.* Any value that a man has not fully decided upon for himself cannot be a real value for him. Any value that is dictated is a meaningless value. To accept a value that is not self-determined leads away from individuality. A man can respect himself only if his ideals and values are of his own choosing, and once decided upon, he is willing to accept the responsibility for them.

3. *The individual is more important than society.* The existentialist believes that society as a whole is indifferent to the individuals that compose it. The individual can make his mark and keep contact with reality only if he continually searches for his own place as an individual. Once a man subjugates his values, personality, and ideals to those of society, he ceases to function as a man.

Soren Kirkegaard, a nineteenth-century theologian and philosopher, is considered to be the father of existentialistic thought. He was seeking the meaning of each man's individuality and Christianity. Most of the modern existentialist philosophers are still alive, but many of their views are divergent and do not necessarily follow the guides set down by Kirkegaard, although they all place the major emphasis on the individual and his behavior. Jean-Paul Sartre is the outstanding atheistic existentialist. He denies that man will make any progress, and sees the ultimate failure of both man and society. Karl Jaspers, Paul Tillich, and Reinhold Niebuhr are theistic existentialists, and have offered viewpoints that have been far more optimistic than Sartre's. They have said that man, to reach the ultimate reality, must participate in life rather than be a mere spectator. Martin Heidegger has remained fairly clear of the atheist–theist controversy, and instead has written that man cannot stop searching for the meaning in life, no matter what he may find that meaning to be.

General education is viewed by the existentialist as an individual rather than a group process. The individual student, and his learning process, must be the prime consideration. The purpose of the school is to set an environment that allows the student to learn what he is interested in learning at the time that he is interested in learning it. Education to the existentialist is an adventure in the discovery of the self. The school supplies the environment, the tools, and the opportunity for this discovery. The teacher serves as a stimulus. He encourages the student to discover his own truths by prodding his moral and intellectual curiosity. The student rather than the teacher selects the subject matter and the learning method. The student bases these decisions on his view of himself in the present, and projected into the future. The existentialist would evaluate the individual's progress in terms of his successes. He would not use group tests, standardized tests, or norms. The curriculum would offer many courses in the arts, humanities, and social sciences.

Although existentialism holds many implications for physical education, it presents a confusing picture when exposed to the problem of implementation. Given absolute freedom of choice and decision making, it is conceivable that among a class of thirty students, up to thirty different activities might be selected for pursuit during a single class period. However, where a wide variety of individual and dual activities are offered, the existentialist aim can be carried out at least in part. Dance and gymnastics especially seem to fit into the existentialist curriculum.

The existentialist-oriented physical education program would help the student to make himself not only physically fit, but morally fit as well. Although compe-

tition is acceptable, the effect of competition on the individual is more important than winning or losing. The existentialist looks for a balanced and varied program that satisfies all individual needs and interests, including competition. Within the activities selected, the student is expected to evaluate himself and, on this judgment, make a selection of the skills and activities he will pursue. It is the job of the teacher to provide the activities, and to create an atmosphere in which the student learns to take the responsibility for himself, but only after he has shown that he has the maturity to have earned this privilege. The teacher acts in the role of counselor and guide, explaining the possibilities and the latitudes, and giving enough direction so that the student does not founder.

## PHILOSOPHIES OF GENERAL EDUCATION

Five general philosophies have been discussed. These have left their mark on educational thinking and practice. There are some philosophies concerned specifically with general education which also should be considered. These represent some of the current thinking among educators as to how learning should be guided in our schools. As will be seen, some reflect traces of the general philosophies already discussed.

### Instrumentalism

The first of the philosophies of general education to be discussed is labeled instrumentalism. Instrumentalism, identified by some thinkers as progressivism and experimentalism, comes mainly from pragmatism. Instrumentalists believe that education of the child should involve natural growth and provide physical, mental, moral, social, and spiritual experiences adapted to the age, health, interests, and abilities of each pupil. As explained by Harold Taylor, former president of Sarah

Lawrence College, this philosophy looks at general education in this way.

In education, the instrumentalist holds that in order to reach the mind of the pupil the teacher must pay attention to the quality of the pupil's total experience, his desires, interests, and needs, and must take account of the social influences which produce certain attitudes of mind in the individual pupil. In other words, once the mind is conceived to be a part of nature which interacts with every other part, the development of intelligence in the human being becomes a matter of the total experience through which the human being goes. It is up to the educator to arrange things so that the pupil's experience with ideas and values is one which engages his deep attention and concern. . . . The instrumentalist insists that education must be built, not upon the materials of knowledge per se, but upon the capacities and needs of the individual student or of groups of individual students. Those materials of knowledge which are useful, important, or aesthetically exciting are then brought to the curriculum, not as a priori decisions as to what all human beings should learn, but as materials and experiences through which these human beings at this stage in their development are able to learn, to think, to enjoy, to perceive, and to know.*

## Neo-humanism

Neo-humanism or humanism has parts of several general philosophies embodied in its makeup. In the sense that it means that the answers to life and education are found within the realm of the human or natural, as opposed to supernatural experience, it can be linked to naturalism and some forms of realism. Then, too, one can discern elements of pragmatism within its explanation as the neo-humanists purport to strive for change in the light of what is considered at the moment to be something better. There is also an element of the idealistic philosophy in its emphasis upon the cultural heritage and in its search for the absolutes of Good and Beautiful.

*Association for Higher Education of the National Education Association: College and University Bulletin No. 7, Nov. 1, 1954.

Robert C. Pooley of the University of Wisconsin interprets the neo-humanism philosophy.

Humanism as an educational philosophy means the transmission from generation to generation of what man has learned and discovered in his business of surviving, of adapting himself to his surroundings, and in striving to change these surroundings in light of what at the moment he considers better. . . . The humanist finds no goals other than what lie within the cultural heritage itself. These are relative rather than positive. Education for the humanist, then, is transmission of experience together with certain eternal questions: What is True? What is Good? What is Beautiful? And, on the contrary, what is False, Evil, Ugly? No system or scheme supplies all the answers. Man will always seek them. The cultural past supplies both the raw material toward the answers and the long history of striving; of answers partially satisfactory for a longer time. The quest continues, and this quest is the rationale of humanism.*

## Rationalism

Rationalism is identified in a sense with all five general philosophies, although probably drawing its main avenue of thought from the idealists and the realists. Rationalism stresses that the purpose of the educative process is to develop the mind—to develop the rational powers of the learner. All of the general philosophies would subscribe to the importance of developing the mind. The differences would arise in the method to be used in achieving this objective. The rationalist theory has been outlined in part by Charles Wegener of Long Beach State College in California:

(1) the primary responsibility of the educational institution engaged in general education is the intellectual development of the student;
(2) the primary aim of this intellectual training is the development of a capacity for intelligent judgment in the student—a "criti-

*Association for Higher Education of the National Education Association: College and University Bulletin No. 7, Nov. 1, 1954.

cal" capacity appropriate to the generally or liberally educated man or woman;

(3) this critical capacity is to be "general" in the sense of being developed by a curriculum the core of which provides a systematic and comprehensive range of experience of materials in the humanities, the social sciences, and the natural sciences employed for the purpose of reflective analysis.*

There is lack of uniform thinking as to what philosophy should guide American education. This disagreement sometimes causes the public to comment that the educator does not know where he is going. Looking at it in another way, however, it probably is a healthy sign. Conflicting philosophies mean discussions, examinations, and perusals of what is being done. This makes it possible for all to promote and encourage that type of education which will best meet the needs of the individual and of society.

## PHILOSOPHY OF THE "GOOD LIFE"— AN EDUCATIONAL GOAL

In order to build a workable philosophy of education it is important to know something more than the nature of certain philosophies that influence educational thinking. Educators must have a clear concept of the person they want to produce—the end product of their efforts. It is important therefore, to define that type of life which reflects the most satisfying and worthwhile type of existence. This is the type of life on which educational aims, methods, facilities, staff, and other essentials should be focused. For purposes of discussion this may be called the "good life."

Philosophers have used the term "good life" to indicate the happiest and most successful type of existence. For example, Bertrand Russell in his book *Education and the Good Life,* lists vitality, sensitive-

---

*Association for Higher Education of the National Education Association: College and University Bulletin No. 7, Nov. 1, 1954.

ness, courage, intelligence, and love as his characteristics of the "good life." Others have said it is characterized by pleasure. These thinkers differ, however, as to the meaning of the word "pleasure." John Stuart Mill and Epicurus were two such philosophers. Still others have varied in saying the "good life" is the simple life, or the one characterized by vast possessions and great power, or the one devoted to worthy causes and religious fervor. Broudy, in his book *Building a Philosophy of Education,* points out that, although philosophers have not agreed entirely in their thinking, most have said that the "good life" consists of the following characteristics. First, it is a life that is pleasurable with excessive pain eliminated, and in which disease, poverty, and hardship are kept to a minimum. Second, the "good life" emphasizes love, emotional security, and understanding. There is freedom from fears, anxiety, frustration, despair, and loneliness. Third, the "good life" means that the individual accomplishes, achieves, renders a service, is respected, and is allowed to exercise his potentialities. There is respect for the dignity and worth of the human being. Finally, the "good life" is interesting and exciting. If the interest and excitement are permanent and of the highest type, they are tied in closely with other people and future events. They are not solely self-centered and concerned with what is going on at present.

Any analysis or definition of the "good life" must include the viewpoints of both the individual and society. Both play an important part in determining the true ingredients. Alger Hiss, for example, may have thought he was living a good life during his "Communist" years; however, most of society felt otherwise.

In order to understand more completely the components of a "good life" it is important to discuss each aspect more fully.

Educators must have a clear concept of the person they want to produce. Washington Irving Elementary School, Waverly Public Schools, Waverly, Iowa.

### A pleasurable life

A pleasurable existence is the first characteristic of the "good life." A definition of pleasure, however, is the subject of much discussion. Certainly if a person is to enjoy life it must be a pleasant experience. A person should be happy and satisfied. The philosophers say that the greatest pleasure and happiness come from doing good and helping others. As Emerson said, "He who does a good deed is instantly ennobled." Pleasures which are temporary, sensuous, and degrading are not the kind that contribute to the "good life." True pleasure is gained through a life characterized by high ideals. Aristotle thought happiness was achieved by leading a virtuous life. John Stuart Mill felt that the things that brought happiness to the greatest number were the ingredients that characterized this essential in the "good life." A pleasurable life also is one that is free from excessive pain and in which hardships and poverty have not been present in excessive amounts.

Education can help individuals achieve the "good life." It can help establish a philosophy of life that guides toward desired goals. It can provide the fundamental skills, knowledges, and understandings that will enable one to provide sustenance, shelter, and the essentials for maintaining life without needless pain. It can provide the ability to appreciate and enjoy the things of beauty in nature and art. It can help avoid unnecessary hardship and pain. Diseases caused by ignorance and physical suffering caused by carelessness can be eliminated through proper health knowledge and health care.

Also, much pain and suffering can be eliminated by developing a strong, healthy body.

### Emotional security

A "good life" is characterized by emotional security. Inner peace is a necessity. Love and a feeling of belonging are very important. Good mental health is a must. No one wants to live a life of frustration, despair, and loneliness.

Education can help to establish a sound standard of values, develop skills for a worthy use of leisure time, instill good human relations, and develop an appreciation for service to others. It can demonstrate the importance of loving and being loved; it can clarify the place of the family, church, and school in a well-ordered community. It can stress through precept and example the importance of sound moral and spiritual values. It can provide experiences that develop emotional security.

### Worth and achievement

A sense of worth and achievement is an aspect of the "good life." However, it must exist not only in the individual's eyes but also in the eyes of society. A person must feel that he is recognized, is needed, and is contributing something to the group. He must feel that he has accomplished important things such as achieving prominent position or title. He must be satisfied in his own heart that he is getting ahead in the world and is developing the talents with which he has been endowed. Society, also, must feel this way about his accomplishments.

Education can help direct a person's life toward worthwhile goals, provide training for a job, develop skills to achieve, enable a person to utilize his abilities to the fullest, help him to develop physically, and give him knowledge and habits that will contribute to good

health. In this case health is a means to an end and not an end in itself. It is a means of achieving greater things for mankind.

### An interesting life

The last aspect of the "good life" is that it must be interesting. A person cannot be bored. A person who enjoys a "good life" looks forward to each day for new and exciting things. His future concerns not only himself but also others. He has a stake in future happenings and is looking into the future and to the part he will be playing in these events. His interest in life exists because of worthwhile goals for which he is striving. Accomplishing these goals helps not only him but also others.

Through a study of history and literature, those persons who have lived interesting and rewarding lives become known. Education can help to direct an individual to seek goals that are worthwhile, satisfying, and interesting. It can equip each one with skills, knowledge, and understanding that represent the basic equipment and foundation for living an interesting life.

• • •

The four characteristics of the "good life" have been discussed. These according to the great thinkers of history, represent those goals toward which all people should strive, and, as a result, they are also the goals that education should endeavor to develop.

### PHILOSOPHICAL IMPLICATIONS FOR EDUCATION IN TWENTIETH-CENTURY WORLD

*Education is preparation for the "good life."* The goal is to help people develop their potentialities and guide them in such a way that they can live a healthy, satisfying, and useful life. It is the business

*Hutchinson High School,
Hutchinson, Minn.*

Sports and physical activities contribute to an interesting life.

of education to impart the knowledge, skills, understandings, techniques, culture, and any other necessities that prepare a person to live a type of life that will be satisfying not only from this standpoint but also from the viewpoint of society.

The schools have the potentialities for playing an important role in helping all people to live a meaningful and purposeful life. It would seem, however, they have failed to render the contribution of which they are capable. They have failed to noticeably change the behavior of individuals for the better.

The power of education is tremendous. H. G. Wells has pointed to the fact that society is involved in a race between chaos and education. In a sense, education has much more power than that which resides in the atom. Yet, the atomic energy program since World War II has momentous implications for mankind. On the other hand, education has lagged far behind. It has failed to act in accordance with its power. It has failed to eliminate the threat of war. Juvenile delinquency is at its highest rate in history. Mental health is the most serious problem of all the diseases. The moral and spiritual fiber of the nation is weak. Many people spend their leisure in destructive rather than constructive ways. Such conditions as these indicate the need for a reexamination of our educational system. These factors are associated with living a life. Education is preparation for living and as such should play a leading role in solving these problems.

Education must be concerned with developing an understanding of the following:

1. A person's cultural heritage and the ability to evaluate it
2. The world of nature and the ability to adapt to it
3. The contemporary social scene and the values and skills necessary for effective participation
4. The role of communication and skill in communicating
5. The nature of self and others and growth

in capacity for continuing self-development and for relating to others

6. The role of aesthetic forms in human living and the capacity for self-expression through them.

The twentieth-century world needs an education which can accomplish these things.

## MODERN PHILOSOPHY OF EDUCATION

John Dewey's philosophy of education has resulted in much scientific research into the nature of learning, the makeup of the child, teaching methodology, and the complexity of culture. This has placed education on a much sounder footing than ever before. To link the best educational theory and practice of today with a chaos and confusion in the schools reflects a total misunderstanding of what Dewey advocated. Some of the critics need to read a little more of this great philosopher's works before they make such damaging accusations.

Education in this country is geared to the needs of the individual—not like Russia's, where it is geared to the state and what it needs. We have continually asserted we do not believe in a "crash" program of education in order to catch up with Russia.

The purposes of education in American life are focused on all children and youth to provide them with the opportunities to become all they are capable of becoming. This is part and parcel of our heritage as the greatest example of democratic living on this earth. We in education are commissioned to prepare the young for life. To accomplish this job our duties include such things as teaching the basic skills of learning, science, mathematics, and the arts and passing along the cultural heritage. It also means offering young people the opportunity to develop their physical,

---

### Comparison of school programs guided by traditional and modern educational philosophies

| Modern | Traditional |
|---|---|
| Child-centered | Teacher-centered |
| Permissive classroom atmosphere | Rigid classroom atmosphere |
| Based on pupil's interests and needs and relating to needs of society | Based on fact, knowledge, and subject matter, irrespective of societal changes or needs |
| Teacher a guide—plans along with child | Teacher a taskmaster |
| Focus on total development of child—physical, emotional, and social complement and supplement the mental | Focus on intellectual development |
| Self-directed study; opportunities for creative expression, socialization, problem-solving, and experimentation | Formal drills, memorization, lectures, questions-answers, and examinations |
| Close school-community relationship and parental cooperation | School isolated from home and community |
| Self-discipline | Discipline by external authority |
| Broad curriculum | Limited curriculum |
| Healthful school environment | Austere environment |
| Geared to individual student | Geared to mass of students |
| Classroom a laboratory for testing new ideas | Classroom impervious to change |

**Amount of Emphasis**

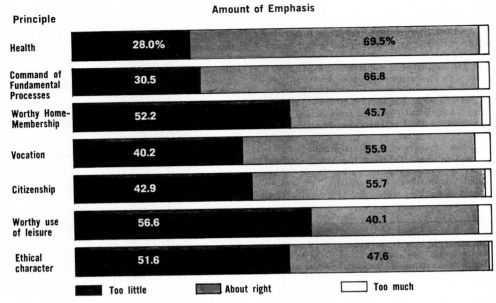

| Principle | | |
| --- | --- | --- |
| Health | 28.0% | 69.5% |
| Command of Fundamental Processes | 30.5 | 66.8 |
| Worthy Home-Membership | 52.2 | 45.7 |
| Vocation | 40.2 | 55.9 |
| Citizenship | 42.9 | 55.7 |
| Worthy use of leisure | 56.6 | 40.1 |
| Ethical character | 51.6 | 47.6 |

■ Too little    ▨ About right    □ Too much

*Teacher-Opinion Poll, A new look at the seven cardinal principles of education,*
*NEA Journal 56:54, Jan., 1967.*

A national survey of teachers to determine where they thought the emphasis is placed in modern-day education.

intellectual, and social selves and providing them with opportunities for self-discipline and self-direction.

What is peculiar to our education is that in keeping with the democratic spirit we provide for the needs of each individual in our society. For example, we offer a variety of courses to help each boy and girl capitalize on his own particular abilities and interests. This nation has been an example to the world in showing that each individual has worth. Therefore we in education are as much concerned with the boy who has an intelligence quotient of 80 as the girl with the I.Q. of 140 and are as interested in the youngster who wants to be an automobile mechanic as the young person who wants to be a scientist.

The United States opens its doors to a far greater proportion of children and educates them for a longer period of time than any other nation. This is in keeping

with the American way of providing opportunities for all, and for this reason it is unfair to compare the performance of *all* of our children with that of the intellectual elite who go to the selective European schools—a favorite reference for the critics. The average academic performance in America will of course be lower. If one takes the top 10 to 20% of our youth, however, and makes a comparison with the youth in Europe, the results will be much more favorable.

In leaving the latchkey out for all youth it has been necessary to provide vocational education in our schools. And certainly there can be little disagreement that this has made a great contribution to America, whose industrial output is second to no other nation's. America does not believe in the "class" system. Those who earn their living by the sweat of their brows are as important to our society as those who achieve their livelihood through

Hutchinson High School,
Hutchinson, Minn.

Educational programs should develop well-integrated persons, wherein the mental, emotional, social, and physical are in proper balance.

more academic pursuits. We are not interested only in "eggheads" and "longhairs."

We have continually increased the offering in the public schools with all types of courses, from typewriting to science, from homemaking to French. The inclusion of many of the vocational courses, incidentally, has been requested by public groups rather than by the educationists.

The schools are trying to educate the "whole" child. To listen to some of our critics you would think that children are composed of minds that are separate from their bodies. Certainly, we would agree we want to develop the intellect and the ability to reason and think clearly. And John Dewey's philosophy does not advocate doing without thinking or a life adjustment devoid of learning. However, there are other considerations.

A man is as strong as his weakest link. We are interested in developing well-integrated persons wherein the mental, emotional, social, and physical are in

proper balance and complement each other in the total makeup of the human being. In this way man will be most productive and provide the type of leadership and followership America desperately needs in the space age.

Our better schools have done a masterful job. They are a paragon for the world to follow. They have shown that modern education is based on valid research and does not slight intellectual training. More of their students are taking foreign languages, science, and mathematics today than ever before. Their programs for the gifted are in operation. Discipline comes from within their students, not through some external force applied by the teachers. Their instructors are not steeped in methodology at the expense of subject-matter content. Their students who go on to college perform just as well as or better than those who come from private schools.

In some communities educational standards are not as high as we would like. Why? Because education reflects what the public wants and has the ability to pay for and what the enrollment will allow! Many cannot have a full program in foreign language, mathematics, and science because they have only a dribbling of students. Conant's report bears this out: "Unless a graduating class contains at least one hundred students, classes in advanced subjects and separate sections within all classes become impossible except with extravagantly high costs."* The public controls the schools, forms the policies, and determines the standards. They do not reflect what the educationists want, as the critics assert.

The challenge facing American education is to bring all the schools up to the standards of the better ones—not to destroy the curriculum, the teachers, the methodology, and everything else we have developed and accomplished over the course of the last 200 years.

Education is not as black as the critics have painted it. Of course there is room for improvement—and progress *is* being made, constantly. But we have made great strides since colonial days when the youngster sat in the corner with the dunce hat, kids hated to go to the cold, drab school building, there was just a handful of courses, and only a select few students went on to college. Today, every child has the opportunity to equip himself for the role he is destined to play in life. And the education our children get rests upon a sound scientific basis, developed by such men as John Dewey, who devoted a full lifetime to thinking about such problems—not upon short-term, superficial studies based on the conquest of space.

### QUESTIONS AND EXERCISES

1. Why is there a need for philosophical thinking in regard to educational problems today?

---

*Conant, James Bryant: The American high school today, New York, 1959, McGraw-Hill Book Co.

2. Define philosophy. Describe its component parts.
3. Describe each of the following philosophies: (a) naturalism, (b) idealism, (c) realism, (d) pragmatism, (e) instrumentalism, (f) neo-humanism, (g) rationalism, and (h) existentialism.
4. Discuss your concept of the "good life." What implications does the good life have for the professional fields of health, physical education, and recreation?
5. List as many philosophical implications as you can for education in a twentieth-century world.
6. Write an essay of approximately 200 words on the title "My Philosophy of Education."

### SELECTED REFERENCES

Adler, Felix: An ethical philosophy of life, New York, 1918, D. Appleton & Co.

Albert, Ethel, Denise, Theodore, and Peterfreund, Herbert: Great traditions in ethics, New York, 1953, American Book Co.

Arrowhead, Charles Flinn, and Eley, Frederick: Development of modern education, New York, 1940, Prentice-Hall, Inc.

Berry, Elmer: The philosophy of athletics, New York, 1927, A. S. Barnes & Co.

Brameld, Theodore: Philosophies of education in cultural perspective, New York, 1955, The Dryden Press.

Broudy, Harry S.: Building a philosophy of education, New York, 1954, Prentice-Hall, Inc.

Brubacher, John S.: Eclectic philosophy of education, New York, 1951, Prentice-Hall, Inc.

Butler, Donald J.: Four philosophies and their practice in education and religion, New York, 1951, Harper & Bros.

Conant, James Bryant: The American high school today, New York, 1959, McGraw-Hill Book Co.

Cowell, Charles C., and France, Wellman L.: Philosophy and principles of physical education, Englewood Cliffs, N. J., 1963, Prentice-Hall, Inc.

Davis, Elwood Craig: The philosophic process in physical education, Philadelphia, 1961, Lea & Febiger.

Davis, Elwood Craig: Philosophies fashion physical education, Dubuque, Iowa, 1963, Wm. C. Brown Co.

Demiashkevich, Michael: An introduction to the philosophy of education, New York, 1935, American Book Co.

Durant, Will: The story of philosophy, New York, 1953, Simon & Schuster.

Frankel, Charles: A review for the teacher—philosophy, National Education Association Journal 51:50, Dec., 1962.

Friedrich, John A., and McBride, Frank A.: What is your physical education philosophy? The Physical Educator 20:3, Oct., 1963.

Gulick, Luther Halsey: A philosophy of play, New York, Charles Scribner's Sons.

Horne, Herman Harrell: The philosophy of education, New York, 1908, The Macmillan Co.

Horne, Herman Harrell: The democratic philosophy of education, New York, 1938, The Macmillan Co.

McCloy, Charles Harold: Philosophical bases for physical education, New York, 1940, F. S. Crofts & Co.

Morris, Van Cleve: Physical education and the philosophy of education, Journal of Health, Physical Education, and Recreation 27:21, March, 1956.

Perry, Ralph Barton: Philosophy of the recent past, New York, 1925, Longmans, Green & Co.

Perry, Ralph Barton: Present philosophical tendencies, New York, 1926, Charles Scribner's Sons.

Redden, J. D., and Ryan, F. A.: A Catholic philosophy of education, Milwaukee, 1942, The Bruce Publishing Co.

Runes, Dogobert D.: Dictionary of philosophy, New York, 1942, Philosophical Library.

Russell, Bertrand: Education and the good life, New York, 1926, Liveright Publishing Corp.

Russell, Bertrand: Philosophy, New York, 1927, W. W. Norton Co.

Slusher, Howard S.: Existentialism and physical education, The Physical Educator 20:4, Dec., 1963.

Van Dalen, D. B.: Philosophical profiles for physical educators, The Physical Educator 21:3, Oct., 1964.

Webster, Randolph W.: Philosophy of physical education, Dubuque, Iowa, 1965, Wm. C. Brown Co.

Ziegler, Earle F.: Philosophical foundations for physical, health, and recreation education, Englewood Cliffs, N. J., 1964, Prentice-Hall, Inc.

# Chapter 6

# Objectives of physical education

A field of endeavor is characterized by the purposes or objectives for which it exists. These objectives help the members of a specialized group to know where they are going, what they are striving for, and what they hope to accomplish. Physical education has clearly stated the objectives toward which it is working. The student preparing for a career in physical education or a leader working in the field should understand the objectives and be guided by them.

## WHAT DO WE MEAN BY THE TERM "OBJECTIVES"?

The word "aim" usually defines a general purpose or direction. It is a goal that is more remote, more encompassing, and less concrete. If the author were to state an aim for physical education he would use the definition of physical education on page 21. Educators sometimes organize objectives into remote, intermediate, and general, and immediate and specific objectives. These usually reflect the purposes that will hopefully be realized in the distant future, near future, and immediate future.

In this chapter the term "objectives" is used in a general sense to include aims, purposes, and outcomes that are derived from participating in the physical education program. In other words, participation in physical activities under skilled leadership should result in certain constructive outcomes for the participant. These outcomes are the objectives of physical education.

Children, youth, and adults are involved with *movement*—getting their bodies into action. Movement is the medium through which physical education achieves its objectives. Boys and girls and men and women during various stages of life engage in running, jumping, hanging, walking, climbing, skipping, throwing, and leaping. Their bodies are activated in rhythms, games, stunts, exercises, and sports. Movement offers human beings an avenue for fun, recreation, physical fitness, sociability, release of expression, communication, exploration, and healthful growth. Movement is a medium for educating people in regard to their physical, mental, emotional, and social development.

There is worth in using the body as a vehicle to learn about one's self and others, games and activities, and cultures and countries. Movement is basic to physical education as it takes place in our schools and colleges, recreation centers, hospitals, camps, and youth and adult programs.

Essentially, when discussing the objectives toward which physical educators strive, the profession is concerned with

*George Peabody College,
Nashville, Tenn.*

Movement is a medium for educating people in regard to their physical, mental, emotional, and social development.

*Seattle Public Schools,
Seattle, Wash.*

Boys' wrestling class.

physical movement and the potentials this movement has as an educational medium. Movement is essential to human welfare and an important part of the education of people. This chapter is concerned with the objectives that can be achieved through movement.

## WHY DO WE NEED OBJECTIVES IN PHYSICAL EDUCATION?

Physical educators must have clearly stated objectives. Some of the reasons for objectives are as follows:

1. *Objectives will help physical educators to understand better what they are trying to achieve.* There is purpose in physical education. This purpose must be clearly imprinted upon the teacher's mind when he is instructing students in physical skills, and the leader's thinking when he is instructing an activity class in a YMCA. If the objectives are clearly understood this will have an impact on what activities are taught and how they are taught. The objectives will serve as guide-lines for the physical educator in steering a course that is meaningful, worthwhile, and in the interest of human beings.

2. *Objectives will help physical educators to understand better the worth of their field in education.* Physical educators are concerned with *physical education,* not *physical training* or *physical culture.* Physical education objectives must therefore be compatible with general education objectives. The objectives of physical education that are identified and delineated represent goals that are compatible with and essential to the total educational effort in our society.

3. *Objectives will help physical educators to make more meaningful decisions when issues and problems arise.* Physical educators will face problems daily as they carry out their responsibilities and administer their various programs. Parents, civic clubs, booster clubs, general administrators, professional sports promoters, big league players, and others who do not understand the objectives of physical edu-

*Shaker Heights High School,*
*Cleveland, Ohio.*

There is purpose in physical education.

cation may try to influence programs in the direction they feel important. An understanding of the objectives of physical education will help leaders in the field to make wise decisions when such pressures and issues arise.

4. *Objectives will help physical educators to interpret better their field of endeavor to general educators and lay persons.* Physical education is often misunderstood. One reason for this misunderstanding is that professional objectives are not known. Therefore, if physical educators know the objectives of their field and are imbued with their worth, they will be better able to correct the misunderstandings that exist and interpret their programs accurately.

## WHAT ARE THE OBJECTIVES OF PHYSICAL EDUCATION?

The objectives of physical education have been stated many times by current and past leaders in the field. It is interesting to look first at what was conceived as the objectives of physical education in the past.

### Historical analysis of the objectives of physical education

The physical education of primitive man was informal and unstructured, with the main purpose being survival. Early man needed physical strength and prowess to fight his enemies, build shelters, obtain food, and resist some of the forces of nature.

The Greeks probably represented the first people to give some structure to physical education. Some of the thinking about physical education during this time was reflected in the writings of Plato, the Greek philosopher. Plato stressed that there were other objectives to physical education than organic development when he pointed out the relation of mental development to physical development. "They are not intended, one to train body, the

other mind, except incidentally, but to insure a proper harmony between energy and initiative on the one hand and reason on the other, by tuning each to the right pitch. And so we may venture to assert that anyone who can produce the best blend of the physical and intellectual sides of education and apply them to the training of character, is producing harmony in a far more important sense than any musician."

Much of Plato's thinking has influenced philosophers and physical educators down through history to accept the premise that close mind–body relationships do exist. Although this thinking did not have much impact on the early settlers in Colonial America because of the doctrine of Puritanism, the concept of the *unity of man* became increasingly recognized.

The early history of America saw systems of gymnastics, philosophies, and objectives imported from Europe. The programs to a great extent were formal in nature and gave precedence to the development *of* the physical rather than outcomes that could be accomplished *through* the physical.

At the turn of the century, however, we saw a "New Physical Education" developing, which resulted in a broadening of objectives and a recognition of the contributions that physical education could make to the "whole" individual. For example, in the 1880's, Dudley A. Sargent, the Director of Physical Education of the Hemenway Gymnasium at Harvard University, cited such objectives in his program as hygienic, educative, recreative, and remedial. During this same period, Thomas D. Wood, of Stanford University and later of Columbia University, another leading physical educator of the time, stressed that physical education should contribute to the complete education of the individual. Clark Hetherington, a colleague of Dr. Wood's and one of the greatest thinkers ever produced by the field of physical education, also stressed along with Dr. Wood that physical education was concerned with mental, moral, and social contributions to the student. Jesse Feiring Williams of Columbia, also during the early 1900's, stressed the need for a physical education program that was concerned with education *through* the physical as well as an education *of* the physical.

The thinking of these early leaders constitutes the objectives of the "New Physical Education" which are largely embraced by physical educators today.

### The foundations from which today's objectives of physical education are derived

In a strict sense of the term, physical education is not a discipline in itself but derives its objectives and scientific foundations from the disciplines of philosophy, biology, psychology, and sociology. Each of these areas is treated in detail in this text. The scientific foundations derived from the discipline of philosophy are discussed in Chapter 5. The scientific foundations derived from the discipline of biology are discussed in Chapters 15 and 16. The scientific foundations derived from the discipline of psychology are discussed in Chapter 17. The scientific foundations derived from the discipline of sociology are discussed in Chapter 18. As these chapters are studied, it will be possible for the reader to understand better the scientific foundations underlying his field of endeavor and the supporting evidence that underlies the objective's worth in general education.

### OBJECTIVES OF LEADERS OF PHYSICAL EDUCATION*

The objectives of physical education in the United States have been stated in

*See references at the end of this chapter for publications of leaders of physical education and their objectives.

professional literature by many leaders in this field (see Table 6-1). These objectives are the goals toward which this profession is striving in a twentieth-century world. Space permits the listing of the objectives of only a few of the leaders of physical education.

### American Association for Health, Physical Education, and Recreation

The publication entitled *This Is Physical Education* incorporates a statement prepared by professional leaders of the physical education division of the AAHPER. This publication lists five major educational purposes for physical education:

1. To help children move in a skillful and effective manner in all the selected activities in which they engage in the physical education program, and also in those situations which they will experience during their lifetime.
2. To develop an understanding and appreciation of movement in children and youth so that their lives will become more meaningful, purposive, and productive.
3. To develop an understanding and appreciation of certain scientific principles concerned with movement that relate to such factors as time, space, force, and mass–energy relationships.
4. To develop through the medium of games and sports better interpersonal relationships.
5. To develop the various organic systems of the body so they will respond in a healthful way to the increased demands placed upon them.

### Bookwalter*

Bookwalter has outlined the purposes of physical education in an interesting manner as shown in the accompanying chart. As outlined in the hierarchical arrangement, Bookwalter lists at the philosophical level the ultimate aim of phys-

*Bookwalter, Karl W.: Physical education in the secondary schools, Washington, D. C., 1964, The Center for Applied Research in Education, Inc.

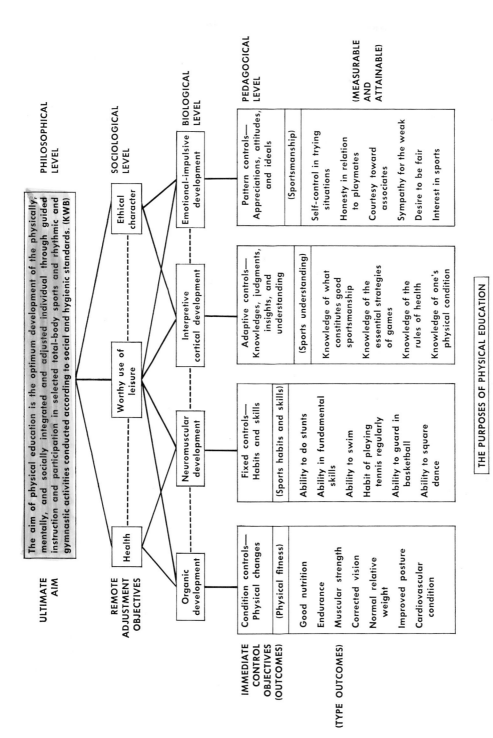

THE PURPOSES OF PHYSICAL EDUCATION

*From Bookwalter, Karl W.: Physical education in the secondary schools,
Washington, D. C., 1964, The Center for Applied Research in Education, Inc.*

ical education. At the sociological level, he lists remote adjustment objectives of health, worthy use of leisure, and ethical character. Evolving from these three objectives is the biological level and the intermediate objectives of development, namely, organic development, neuromuscular development, interpretative cortical development, and emotional–impulsive development. Finally, to give meaning and understanding to these objectives, Bookwalter lists certain controls at the next or pedagogical level. The immediate control objectives (outcomes) at the pedagogical level listed by Bookwalter are: condition controls–physical changes (physical fitness), fixed controls–habits and skills (sports habits and skills), adaptive controls–knowledge, judgments, insights, and understanding (sports understanding), and pattern controls–appreciation, attitudes and ideals (sportsmanship). The total chart indicates that the process of education is founded on the belief that specific outcomes will occur, and will lead to the attainment of the remote objectives and ultimate aim.

### Clarke

Clarke lists three objectives of physical education: physical fitness, social efficiency, and culture.

Clarke's objective of physical fitness refers to that state in which an individual has developed great endurance and is able to perform on a basis equivalent to his own potentiality. The quality of being physically fit is essential to leading a happy, vigorous, and abundant life.

Clarke's objective of social efficiency is concerned with a person's proper adaptation to group living. Through physical education activities, which are conducted under qualified leadership, an individual develops such traits as cooperation, respect for the rights of others, loyalty, sportsmanship, followership, responsibility to the group, initiative, resourcefulness,

and self-confidence—all of which help him to have a more harmonious association with others and help to make him a good citizen.

Clarke's third objective of culture aims at developing a fuller understanding and appreciation of one's own local environment as well as the environment that is world wide in scope. Through a study of and the participation in various physical education activities, such as dance, games, and sports, a person more fully understands the history of other countries and the aesthetic values associated with these activities. Furthermore, the objective of culture is concerned with providing individuals with an understanding and an appreciation of certain activities in the physical education program, which will guarantee the wise use of leisure hours.

Clarke has also recorded a proposed list of physical education objectives for girls. These include the objectives of physical fitness, personal appearance and beauty, human relationships, recreational skills, and appreciations.

### Cowell and Schwehn

Cowell and Schwehn classify the general and specific objectives of physical education into five groups: organic power, the ability to maintain adaptive effort; neuromuscular development; personal–social attitudes and adjustment; interpretive and intellectual development; and emotional responsiveness.

Cowell and Schwehn discuss the organic development objective in terms of building strength and endurance, and being able to resist fatigue. Their definition of neuromuscular development means developing general motor ability, rhythm of movement and grace, and specific skills in games and sports. It also includes reaction time. In respect to personal–social attitudes and adjustments, the authors mean the development of a feeling of be-

**Table 6-1.** *Frequency of physical education objectives as listed by leaders in the field\**

| Authority | Organic development | Interpretive development | Neuromuscular development | Personal-social adjustment |
|---|---|---|---|---|
| AAHPER | X | | X | X |
| Bookwalter | X | X | | X |
| Brace | X | X | X | X |
| Brownell-Hagman | X | X | X | X |
| Bucher | X | X | X | X |
| Clarke | X | | | X |
| Cowell-Hazelton | X | X | X | X |
| Daniels | X | | X | X |
| Davis-Lawther | | X | X | |
| Duncan-Johnson | X | X | X | X |
| Evans-Gans | X | X | X | X |
| Hughes-French | X | X | X | X |
| Irwin | X | X | X | X |
| Knapp-Hagman | X | X | X | X |
| Kozman and others | X | X | X | X |
| LaPorte | | X | X | X |
| Larson-Hill | X | X | X | X |
| LaSalle | X | X | X | X |
| Mathews | X | | | X |
| McCloy | X | X | X | X |
| Miller-Whitcomb | X | X | | X |
| Nash-Hetherington | X | X | X | X |
| Neilson-Van Hagen | X | X | X | X |
| Nixon-Cozens | X | | X | X |
| Oberteuffer | X | X | X | X |
| O'Keefe-Aldrich | X | X | X | X |
| Salt and others | X | X | X | X |
| Seaton and others | X | X | X | X |
| Sharman | X | X | X | |
| Staley | X | | | X |
| Vannier-Fait | X | X | X | X |
| Voltmer-Esslinger | X | X | X | X |
| Williams | X | | X | X |

\*Data from Adams, Miller K.: Principles for determining high school grading procedures in physical education for boys, Doctoral thesis, New York University, 1959.

longing, social poise, and the acquisition of such traits as self-confidence and self-initiative. Interpretive and intellectual development refers to the ability to think, solve problems, decision making, and arriving at logical conclusions. Finally, the fifth objective of emotional responsiveness refers to the ability to enjoy and realize satisfaction from the many challenges offered in mastering physical skills and engaging in competitive sports experiences.

**Hetherington**

Hetherington lists five classifications of objectives: the immediate objectives, the remote objectives, the objectives in development, the objectives in social standards, and the objectives in the control of health conditions.

Under the immediate objectives, Hetherington discusses the necessity of adult leadership in giving organization to the play life of children. He points out that with effective adult leadership the children's interest is increased, progress is much more rapid, the satisfaction derived from play is greater, there is more democratic organization, and play life is much more efficient.

Under the remote objectives, Hetherington stresses the role of physical education in developing abilities that make it easier for children to adapt themselves to adult group living. In the various physical education activities, growth needs are met which lay a foundation for effective group living.

In the third classification, objectives are divided into the development of instinct mechanisms, the development of intellectual mechanisms, the development of neuromuscular mechanisms, and the development of the organic mechanisms.

The development of instinct mechanisms has implications for the development of character traits. As a result of participation in physical education activities, certain inherent instinct tendencies and emotions are expressed. The way a person reacts to participation in these activities depends upon the satisfactions or annoyances that result. Furthermore, whether or not character traits such as initiative, honesty, cooperation, self-subordination to the leader, and loyalty to the group are developed will depend upon the quality of the leadership that is provided.

The development of the intellectual mechanisms takes place through participation in a planned physical education program. Through activity, motor coordinations are learned, and thus the intellectual mechanism is brought into play, strategic judgments are made in the various game situations, and, finally, a greater insight into human nature is gained through the various social experiences that take place in play activities.

The development of neuromuscular mechanisms and nervous power, as another objective in development, empha-

sizes the fact that the nervous system is developed only as the muscular system is developed. Nervous connections are strengthened when muscles are exercised. Furthermore, nervous development occurs over a long period of time and after much repetition. You learn to consistently hit a golf ball straight down the fairway only after doing it hundreds of times. This nervous development must take place during the growth years. It is not developed as easily and effectively when maturity has been reached. The skill and strength gained by youth in physical activity will help to guarantee physical efficiency in the adult.

Finally, the development of organic power is, with the exception of heredity, brought about through physical activity. Organic power means vitality, vigor, capacity to assimilate food, stamina, and resistance to fatigue. The development of the circulatory, respiratory, digestive, heat regulatory, and other organic systems depends upon vigorous activity, and this development, together with sleep and proper nutrition, determines physical condition. To fulfill this objective, elementary school children should have from four to five hours and secondary school children from two to three hours of vigorous physical activity each day.

Social standards is Hetherington's fourth classification of objectives. By social standards, he refers to the criteria used in the guiding and in the judging of activities that result in adjustment to society. Children are not concerned with adult standards, and they utilize standards only as established through leadership. Physical education is concerned with objectives in respect to various social standards, including those concerned with items such as posture on the one hand and those concerned with morals, manners, and health on the other.

Hetherington's fifth classification of objectives is concerned with the control of health conditions. This refers to the steps taken to make the school a healthful place to live by eliminating all handicapping influences and encouraging and promoting healthful school practices.

## LaSalle

LaSalle lists five classifications of objectives: organic aspects of development, neuromuscular aspects of development, emotional aspects of development, social aspects of development, and the intellectual aspects of development.

The objectives of organic aspects of development, as listed by LaSalle, are related to the development of endurance, the end product of organic development. Through vigorous activity, the trained individual results. The trained individual has a heart that nourishes the cells better than that of the untrained individual, carries away waste products more effectively, and serves the individual better in his day-to-day living.

The objectives of neuromuscular development refer to such physical characteristics as sufficient strength to perform daily tasks proficiently; body control to allow for quick, graceful, and efficient movement of the body; recreation skills in games, dance, and other activities to the extent that they may be utilized as tools in the wholesome use of leisure time; relaxation with its accompanying release from muscular tension; and flexibility which will allow an individual's body joints to move through their normal range.

The objective of emotional aspects of development referred to by LaSalle are incorporated under three specific objectives. First, the objective of release from tensions may be realized through participation in physical education activities under qualified leadership. Second, the objective of adequacy, with the implications for one's faith in his own success, may be brought about through successful

experience in physical activities. Third, the objective of happiness may be found in physical education activities if the right guidance has been given and adequate skill developed. All three of these specific objectives in emotional development, if achieved, will result in an integrating process that makes for better adjustment on the part of the individual.

The objectives of social aspects of development, as mentioned by LaSalle, mean several things to the teacher of physical education. These objectives mean attempting to develop the "we" feeling of group consciousness; determining the objectives of the group in the light of what is best for all the members; working together in a spirit of cooperation in an attempt to achieve these purposes; developing a feeling of "belonging" in each member of the group; developing an attitude of friendship and respect for each individual; living by the Golden Rule; sharing one's responsibility as a member of the group; and encouraging self-direction by each member of the group in a manner that will result in success for all members of the group as well as himself.

The objectives of intellectual aspects of development revolve around the concept that we think with the body as well as the mind. Decisions are frequently made that affect our various actions. The degree to which we make the right decisions will depend a great deal on the degree to which our bodies and minds have been conditioned.

## Nash

Nash lists four objectives of physical education: organic development, neuromuscular development, interpretive development, and emotional development. By organic development Nash means the end results of the training process that achieves physical power for the individual. This physical power is developed through big-muscle activity after freeing the body from physical defects and strains that are a drain on the human mechanism. The building of this physical power assures the individual of the ability to produce peak performance in activities requiring endurance, skill, speed, agility, and strength.

By neuromuscular development Nash means cortical control over the motor mechanism of the human body, the ability to cut down on waste motion so that actions are performed gracefully with little energy expended, and a longer period of rest between heartbeats or a longer glide in relation to the stroke of the heart. Such

development implies a training period which begins early in youth and the opportunity to practice continually skills which are worthwhile and useful.

By interpretive development Nash means the training that helps an individual make judgments and interpret situations correctly. It implies that a person thinks through his previous experiences. The more experiences an individual has had and the better their quality, the better able he will be to interpret new experiences.

By emotional development Nash means the drives within the human being that

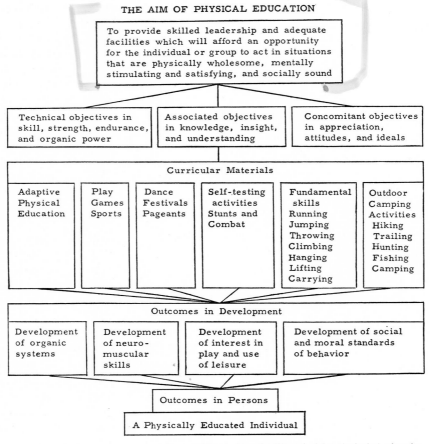

THE AIM OF PHYSICAL EDUCATION

To provide skilled leadership and adequate facilities which will afford an opportunity for the individual or group to act in situations that are physically wholesome, mentally stimulating and satisfying, and socially sound

| Technical objectives in skill, strength, endurance, and organic power | Associated objectives in knowledge, insight, and understanding | Concomitant objectives in appreciation, attitudes, and ideals |
|---|---|---|

Curricular Materials

| Adaptive Physical Education | Play Games Sports | Dance Festivals Pageants | Self-testing activities Stunts and Combat | Fundamental skills Running Jumping Throwing Climbing Hanging Lifting Carrying | Outdoor Camping Activities Hiking Trailing Hunting Fishing Camping |
|---|---|---|---|---|---|

Outcomes in Development

| Development of organic systems | Development of neuro-muscular skills | Development of interest in play and use of leisure | Development of social and moral standards of behavior |
|---|---|---|---|

Outcomes in Persons

A Physically Educated Individual

*From Williams, Jesse F.: The principles of physical education, Philadelphia, 1964, W. B. Saunders Co.*

The aim of physical education.

result in action. The drives of desires, ideals, interests, and hungers impel individuals to act either in constructive or in destructive ways. If proper emotional development has taken place and has been brought under control, it can be directed toward great social advances rather than into antisocial behavior. Within physical education activities there are many inherent values that will grow and bear fruit under proper guidance. A child must have confidence, must experience success, and must have a feeling of "belonging" if he is to direct his emotions to the advantage of group living.

## Oberteuffer and Ulrich

Oberteuffer and Ulrich list several immediate and long-range objectives or outcomes toward which physical educators should direct their efforts. The first group of these outcomes includes those that are immediate, easily recognized, and may be gained by the individual through participation. They are skill in an activity, organic values, and fun and amusement. The second group consists of those outcomes that, although frequently seen, are more difficult to achieve. These are psychological characteristics and social controls. The third and last group is composed of those outcomes that have outstanding value but are very difficult to produce. However, their achievement is possible, and any physical education program designed to make the greatest contribution to the individual and to society will reach these goals. They are a deeper understanding of human nature and human relations, an understanding of the democratic way of life, and practice in reflective thinking.

## Williams

Williams first sets forth a broad aim of physical education as one that would provide qualified leadership, adequate facilities, and experiences having physical, mental, and social implications. Then he goes on to list general concrete objectives of physical education. These include preventive and corrective objectives of individual gymnastics as concerned with the adjustment of the various body parts to each other; objectives in games and sports that will guarantee further participation in these activities; objectives of dance, involving the development of the whole individual; objectives in hiking, camping, fishing, and hunting, concerned with military and social preparedness; objectives in self-testing, stunt, and combat activities, including the development of confidence, courage, and the ability to control the body effectively; objectives in fundamental skills such as walking, running, jumping, leaping, throwing, hanging, climbing, lifting, and carrying, which are important for their utilitarian value in day-to-day living; and the objectives in equipment and staff, based upon the needs of children and the social needs of society, making imperative an adequate school plant and well-qualified teachers.

## Wood and Cassidy

Wood and Cassidy list two general objectives and certain specific objectives. The first general objective is the harmonious development during childhood of such qualities of the individual as interests, capacities, and abilities through the medium of natural physical education activities. The second general objective, which evolves naturally from the first, is the harmonious development of those interests, ideals, and habits that will make for a happy, healthful, and useful adult life.

The specific objectives listed by Wood and Cassidy help in the achievement of the general objectives. Such specific biological objectives are listed as muscular growth, organic vigor, nervous vitality, good health habits, correction of defects, good health service, and supervision of mental hygiene. Specific social and ethical objectives are listed that have to do with the development of the individual along social and ethical lines with a view to good citizenship. Specific intellectual objectives are listed that have to do with the development of intelligent leadership.

## OBJECTIVES IN TERMS OF SCIENTIFIC PRINCIPLES

Principles that give support and a scientific foundation to objectives have been set forth by Adams based on his research into the writings of many of the outstanding leaders in the field.*

1. *Education involves the whole organism.* Oneness of mind and body or the unity of man is a recognized basic tenet of education.

2. *Physical education is a phase of general education.* The objectives toward which physical education is striving are compatible and contribute to the objectives of general education.

3. *Physical education activity is conducive to growth and development.* The optimum development of the organic systems of the human body is dependent upon physical activity.

4. *Physical education contributes to the constructive use of leisure time.* Many skills and activities learned in physical education have implications for free hours during all of a person's life.

5. *Physical education provides for leadership training.* There is great potential and opportunity within physical education to involve students in the planning and operation of the program.

6. *Physical education provides opportunity for expression and creativity.* There are many opportunities in physical edu-

*Adams, Miller K.: Principles for determining high school grading procedures in physical education for boys, Doctoral thesis, New York University, 1959.

cation to utilize the body as a means of expressing one's feelings and creating new patterns of movement and ideas.

7. *Physical education provides for cultural development.* Sports and physical activities play an important role in the cultures of all peoples. These activities are a positive source of both esthetic appreciations and artistic production for the participant.

8. *Physical education provides for training emotions—sportsmanship.* The give and take of games and sports offers opportunities for both emotional release and the training of the emotions.

9. *Physical education provides for personality and character development.* Group effort, loyalty to the team, and strong ties, are much in evidence on play and sports fields. As such, they provide a valuable contribution to the development of character and personality. The daily adjustments to teammates and opponents become a laboratory in personal social adjustment.

10. *Physical education provides for organic development—physical fitness.* Exercise and knowledge about one's body and its requirements contribute immeasurably to physical fitness.

11. *Physical education develops neuromuscular skills.* Skills in a variety of sports and activities present many opportunities for instructing pupils in this phase of their development.

12. *Physical education develops habits of health and safety.* The teacher of physical education instructs the pupils in habits of health and safety, and games and contests are played under conditions conducive to learning safety and health practices.

13. *Physical education provides for mental development.* The learning of game rules, techniques and strategies, as well as the judgments necessary to good play in competitive games, requires interpretive development. Other avenues for

mental development are inculcating understanding in regard to one's body and how it functions, the history of sports, the place of athletic activities in the cultures of the world, and other knowledge that is closely allied to physical education.

14. *Physical education contributes to democratic processes.* The physical education class is conducted in a manner that provides pupils with the opportunity to participate in planning and carrying out class activities.

15. *Physical education has biological, psychological, and sociological foundations.* Physical education has its bases in the sciences of biology, psychology, and sociology. The program is planned by teachers and administrators who draw upon these sciences for realistic and effective programs.

16. *Physical education is based on human needs.* Movement is recognized as an important human need. The need for physical activity is essential to life itself. Modern living with its sedentary aspects presents a challenge to physical education.

17. *Play is an instinctive drive that has educational potential.* The dynamic quality of play can be utilized to instill in participants proper forms of conduct and behavior.

## FULLER DISCUSSION OF OBJECTIVES OF PHYSICAL EDUCATION

A study of the objectives as stated by leaders in physical education reveals a great deal of similarity. This is as it should be in that the physical education profession should be united and directing itself toward common goals. Only through a uniformity of purpose will it be possible for the thousands of professional leaders in this field to be continually conscious of what they are trying to accomplish when they meet their class, organize a game, supervise a program of activities, and

evaluate their work. In unity there is strength.

The aim of all education is to enable one to live an enriched and abundant life. This is the ultimate goal on which all who are concerned with education have trained their sights. The objectives of physical education are more definite and specific than this aim, and through these objectives the ultimate goal is brought nearer to realization.

A study of the child reveals four general directions or phases in which growth and development take place: physical development, motor development, mental development, and social development. Each of these phases contributes to the well-rounded individual who will become a worthy member of society. Physical education can play a very important part in contributing to each of these phases of child growth and development. The objectives listed by present-day leaders of physical education in the majority of cases may be incorporated under these groupings. Therefore I have used these four phases as objectives for the field. It is believed that physical education will justify its existence in the educational process if it can accomplish the objectives that are set forth under these four headings.

Any discussion of objectives must be interpreted in light of the phenomenon that the individual needs to be *well-integrated*, possessing optimum development in each phase of his total development.

The AAHPER publication *This Is Physical Education* points out the importance of movement experiences in transforming the child into a fully integrated person. Thinking, learning, and body behavior are all tied closely together, and function as a whole. What is very important to understand is that many ideas are translated into perceivable forms by body movement and the better a person understands movement the better he will perform. Children are concerned with concepts, symbols, and skills of movement, and physical education can render a valuable contribution in a subject "in which children learn to move as they move to learn."

### Physical development objective*

The objective of physical development deals with the program of activities that builds physical power in an individual through the development of the various organic systems of the body. It results in the ability to sustain adaptive effort, the ability to recover, and the ability to resist fatigue. The value of this objective is based on the fact that an individual will be more active, have better performance, and be healthier if the organic systems of the body are adequately developed and functioning properly.

Muscular activity plays a major role in the development of the organic systems of the body. The term *organic* refers to the digestive, circulatory, excretory, heat regulatory, respiratory, and other systems of the human body. These systems are stimulated and trained through such activities as hanging, climbing, running, throwing, leaping, carrying, and jumping. Health is also related to muscular activity; therefore activities that bring into play all of the fundamental "big muscle" groups in the body should be engaged in regularly. Furthermore, the activity should be of a vigorous nature so that the various organic systems are sufficiently stimulated.

Through vigorous muscular activity several beneficial results take place. The trained heart provides better nourishment to the entire body. The trained heart beats slower than the untrained heart and pumps more blood per stroke with the result that more food is delivered to the cells and there is better removal of waste products. During exercise the trained heart's speed increases less and has a

longer rest period between beats, and after exercise it returns to normal much more rapidly. The end result of this state is that the trained individual is able to perform work for a longer period of time, with less expenditure of energy, and much more efficiently than the untrained individual. This trained condition is necessary to a vigorous and abundant life. From the time an individual rises in the morning until the time he goes to bed at night, he is continually in need of vitality, strength, endurance, and stamina to perform routine tasks; he must be prepared for emergencies; and he must lead a vigorous life. Therefore, physical education should aid in the development of the trained individual so that he will be better able to perform his routine tasks and live a healthful and happy existence.

Hein and Ryan* did an extensive research study collecting and analyzing clinical observations and scientific findings on the contributions of physical activity to physical health. They feel the following conclusions can be justified as a result of their work:

1. Regular exercise can assist in the prevention of obesity with the result that the shortened life span and degenerative conditions caused by such a condition can be influenced.
2. Regular physical activity throughout life appears to inhibit coronary heart disease.
3. Regular physical activity assists in delaying the aging process and probably favorably influences longevity.
4. Regular physical activity contributes to a body condition that enables the individual to better meet emergencies and thus, in turn, enhance health and avoid disability.

### Motor development objective

The motor development objective is concerned with making physical move-

---

*See also Chapters 15 and 16.

*Hein, Fred V., and Ryan, Allan J.: Research Quarterly, AAHPER **31**:263, May, 1960.

Physical development as an objective of physical education.

ment useful and with as little expenditure of energy as possible, and being proficient, graceful, and aesthetic in this movement. This has implications for one's work, play, and anything else that requires physical movement. The name *motor* is derived from the relationship to a nerve or nerve fiber that connects the central nervous system or a ganglion with a muscle. As a consequence of the impulse it transmits, movement results. The impulse it delivers is known as the motor impulse.

Effective motor movement is dependent upon a harmonious working together of the muscular and nervous systems. It results in greater distance between fatigue and peak performance; it is found in activities that involve such things as running, hanging, jumping, dodging, leaping, kicking, bending, twisting, carrying, and throwing; and it will enable a person

to perform his daily work much more efficiently and without reaching the point of being "worn out" so quickly.

In physical education activities the function of efficient body movement or neuromuscular skill, as it is often called, is to provide the individual with the ability to perform with a degree of perfection. This will result in his enjoyment of participation. Most individuals enjoy doing those particular things in which they have acquired some degree of mastery or skill. For example, if a child has mastered the ability to throw a ball consistently at a designated spot and has developed batting and fielding power, he will like to play baseball or soft ball. If he can kick and throw a ball with some degree of accuracy, he will like soccer or football. If an adult can consistently serve tennis "aces," he will like tennis; if he can con-

Boys' physical education golf instruction.

sistently drive a ball 250 yards straight down the fairway, he will like golf; and if he can consistently throw ringers, he will like horseshoes. A person enjoys doing those things in which he excels. Few individuals enjoy participating in activities in which they have little skill. Therefore, it is the objective of physical education to develop in each individual as many skills as possible so that his interests will be wide and varied. This will not only result in more enjoyment for the participant, but at the same time it will allow for a better adjustment to the group situation.

Other values of skill are that it cuts down on expenditure of energy, contributes to confidence, brings recognition, enhances physical and mental health, makes participation safer, and contributes to the aesthetic.

Physical skills are not developed in one lesson. It takes years to acquire coordina-

tions, and the most important period for development is during the formative years of a child's growth. The building of coordinations starts in childhood, when an individual attempts to synchronize his muscular and nervous systems for such things as creeping, walking, running, and jumping. A study of kinesiology shows that many muscles of the body are used in the most simple of coordinated movements. Therefore, in order to obtain efficient motor movement or skill in many activities, it is necessary that an individual's training start early in life and continue into adulthood. Furthermore, a child does not object to the continual trial-and-error process of achieving success in the performance of physical acts. He does not object to being observed as an awkward, uncoordinated beginner during the learning period. However, most adults are self-conscious when going through a period of learning a physical skill. They do not like to perform if they cannot perform in a creditable manner. The skills they do not acquire in their youth are many times never acquired. Therefore, the physical education profession should try to see that this skill learning takes place at a time when a person is young and willing and is laying the foundation for his adult years.

The motor objective also has important implications for the health and recreational phases of the program. The skills that children acquire will determine to a great extent how their leisure time will be spent. A person enjoys participating in those activities in which he excels. Therefore, if a child excels in swimming, much of his leisure time is going to be spent in a pool, lake, or other body of water. If he excels in tennis, he will be found on the courts on Saturdays, Sundays, and after dinner at night. There is a correlation between juvenile delinquency and lack of constructive leisure-time activity. If a parent would have a child spend some of his leisure moments in a physically wholesome way, he should see that the child gains skill in some physical education activity.

While considering the value to an individual of having in his possession fundamental skills which will afford him much satisfaction and happiness throughout life, it is important to consider the balance that should exist in any physical education program between team sports and dual and individual sports. Team sports such as football, basketball, and baseball perform a great service in providing an opportunity for students to develop physical power and enjoy exhilarating competition. However, in many school programs of physical education they dominate the curriculum at the expense of various individual and dual sports, such as tennis, swimming, badminton, handball, and golf. In such cases the student is being deprived of the opportunity for developing skills in

activities that he can play until the time he dies. It has been estimated that only one out of every one thousand students who play football, for example, ever play the game again after they leave school. On the other hand, if they have the skill, many students will swim, play tennis, badminton, handball, or golf. Comparatively few students engage in many team sports after formal schooling ends. Team sports such as football, basketball, and baseball have much to offer and if possible should be included in every physical education program. However, it would seem wise to have an adequate program of individual and dual sports also. Only through a well-balanced program will it be possible to develop the well-rounded individual.

Ever since man first learned to coordinate his muscular and nervous systems for physical action there has been popular interest in acts of human skill. David casting the deadly stone accurately with his slingshot, William Tell splitting the apple on his son's head with his bow and arrow, Pheidippides racing to announce the Greek victory at Marathon, and Ben Hur driving his chariot at breakneck speed down the stretch to victory— all are a part of the world's literature that inspire young and old alike.

Physical skill plays an important role in the culture of all peoples. It packs stadiums, crowds palestras, and usurps television screens. It emblazons the names of champions on printed programs, newspaper scareheads, and advertising billboards. It captivates men's thoughts, holds them spellbound, and receives their plaudits.

Physical educators should be proud to be the teachers and the nurturers of skill. They help to shape men's lives, build a strong people, and further international peace. Their services are sought by schools, colleges, boy's clubs, Girl Scouts, hospitals, Peace Corps, churches, country clubs, and other organizations. Yes, theirs is an important business in this world.

The role physical educators play in the skill education of boys and girls is one of their most important responsibilities. Here they have an opportunity to apply their art in a manner that will influence a young person's life for the better. Just as the sculptor takes clay and with his hands molds a lifelike image of a person, so physical educators, through expert skill instruction, mold human bodies that possess aesthetically beautiful qualities. To show young people how to hit a backhand shot effectively, execute a flying camel spin, and send the arrow accurately into the gold circle are contributions to human betterment well worth the time, efforts, and energies of physical educators.

Physical skill has values for many persons. The spectator thrills to the chase, struggle, competition, and challenge. The sportswriter prospers as his copy spells out the exciting action. The keeper of the coffers smiles as the coins tinkle into the treasury. Mothers and fathers brag as they bask in the glory of their children's achievements. And coaches are imbued with a sense of pride as their charges gain fame. *But* great as these values may be for the people who vicariously profit from human skill, *none can compare to the worth it has for the participant.*

Physical educators can and should be proud of the contribution they make to humanity. It is within their power to give boys and girls physical skills and thus help them to lead healthier, happier, and more worthwhile and productive lives. The world is a better place in which to live as a result of their work, because *physical skill has worth.*

### Mental development objective

The mental development objective deals with the accumulation of a body of knowledge and the ability to think and to interpret this knowledge.

Physical education has a subject matter concerned with movement. There is a body of knowledge that comes from the sciences, humanities, and other sources that interprets the nature of human movement, and the impact of movement upon the growth and development of the individual, and upon his culture. Scientific principles regarding movement, including those that relate to such factors as time, space, and flow, should be considered. This subject matter should be part of the education of each person who comes in contact with a physical education program.

Physical activities must be learned; hence there is a need for thinking on the part of the intellectual mechanism, with a resulting acquisition of knowledge. The coordinations involved in various movements must be mastered and adapted to the environment in which the individual lives, whether it be in walking, running, or wielding a tennis racquet. In all these movements the child must think and coordinate his muscular and nervous systems. Furthermore, this type of knowledge is acquired through trial and error, and then as a result of this experience there is a changed meaning in the situation. Coordinations are learned, with the result that an act that once was difficult and awkward to perform becomes easy to execute.

The individual should not only learn coordinations but should also acquire a knowledge of such things as rules, techniques, and strategies involved in physical activities. Basketball can be used as an example. In this sport a person should know such things as the rules, the strategy in offense and defense, the various types of passes, the difference between screening and blocking, and, finally, the values that are derived from playing this sport. Techniques that are learned through experience result in knowledge that should also be acquired. For example, a ball travels faster and more accurately if one steps with a pass, and time is saved when the pass is made from the same position in which it is received. Furthermore, a knowledge of followership, leadership, courage, self-reliance, assistance to others, safety, and adaptation to group patterns is very important.

Knowledge concerning health should play an important part in the program. All individuals should know about their bodies, the importance of sanitation, factors in disease prevention, importance of exercise, need for a well-balanced diet, values of good health attitudes and habits, and the community and school agencies that provide health services. Through the accumulation of a knowledge of these facts, activities will take on a new meaning and health practices will be associated with definite purposes. This will help each individual live a healthier and more purposeful life.

A store of knowledge will give each individual the proper background for interpreting new situations that confront him from day to day. Unless there is knowledge to draw from, he will become helpless when called upon to make important decisions. As a result of participation in physical education activities, an individual will be better able to make discriminatory judgments, by which knowledge of values is mentally arrived at. This means that he has greater power for arriving at a wise decision and that he can better discern right from wrong and the logical from the illogical. Through his experience in various games and sports he will develop a sense of values, an alertness, the ability to diagnose a tense situation, the ability to make a decision quickly under highly emo-

*Seattle Public Schools,*
*Seattle, Wash.*

In physical education a person gains an insight into human nature.

tionalized conditions, and the ability to interpret human actions.

In physical education activities a person also gains insight into human nature. Physical education, as expressed in the various forms of activity, consists of social experiences that enable a participant to learn about human nature. For all children, this is one of the main sources of such knowledge. Here they discover the individual's responsibility to the group, the need for followership and leadership, the need to experience success, and the feeling of "belonging." Here they learn how human beings react to satisfactions and annoyances. Such knowledge contributes to social efficiency and good human relations.

### Social development objective

The social development objective is concerned with helping an individual in making personal adjustments, group adjustments, and adjustments as a member of society. Activities in the physical education program offer one of the best opportunities for making these adjustments, provided there is proper leadership.

Each individual has certain basic social needs that must be met. These include a feeling of belonging, recognition, self-respect, and love. When these needs are met, the individual becomes well adjusted socially. When they are not met, antisocial characteristics develop. For example, the aggressive bully may be seeking recognition, and the member of the gang may be seeking a feeling of belonging. The "needs" theory has tremendous implications for the manner in which we conduct our physical education programs. The desire to win, for example, should be subordinated to meeting the needs of the participants. This may mean that the fellow who is out in right field should be brought in to pitch a couple of innings or that the girl who has a great loyalty to the team but little skill should be

allowed to become a member of the squad.

Social action is a result of certain hereditary and derivative tendencies. There are interests, hungers, desires, ideals, attitudes, and emotional drives that are responsible for everything we do. A child wants to play because of his drive for physical activity. A man will steal food because of the hunger drive. Americans are opposed to totalitarian governments because of the desire for personal freedom. The response to all these desires, drives, hungers, and the like may be either social or antisocial in nature. They are social or antisocial, depending on whether the experience is pleasing or displeasing. The value of physical education reveals itself when we realize that play activities are one of the oldest and most fundamental drives in human nature. Therefore, by providing the child with a satisfying experience in activities in which he has a natural desire

If children are happy, they will make the necessary adjustments.

to engage, the opportunity is presented to develop desirable social traits. The key is qualified leadership.

All human beings should experience success. This factor can be realized through play. Through successful experience in play activities, a child develops self-confidence and finds happiness in his achievements. Physical education can provide for this successful experience by offering a variety of activities and developing the necessary skills for success in these activities.

If children are happy, they will make the necessary adjustments. An individual who is happy is much more likely to make the right adjustment than the individual who is morbid, sullen, and in an unhappy state of mind. Happiness reflects friendliness, cheerfulness, and a spirit of cooperation, all of which help a person to be contented and to conform to the necessary standards that have been established.

Therefore, physical education should instill happiness by guiding children into the activities in which this quality will be realized.

In the democratic society in which we live it is necessary to have all individuals develop a sense of group consciousness and cooperative living. This should be one of the most important objectives of the program. Whether or not a child will grow up to be a good citizen and contribute to the welfare of all will depend to a great extent upon the training he receives during his youth. Therefore, in various play activities, the following factors should be stressed: aid for the less skilled and weaker players, respect for the rights of others, subordination of one's desires to the will of the group, and realization of cooperative living as an essential to the success of society. The individual should be made to feel that he belongs to the group and has the responsibility of directing his ac-

*New York University Camp.*

Good human relations in a camp setting.

tions in its behalf. The rules of sportsmanship should be developed and practiced in all activities that are offered in the program. Such things as courtesy, sympathy, truthfulness, fairness, honesty, respect for authority, and abiding by the rules will help a great deal in the promotion of social efficiency. The necessity of good leadership and followership should also be stressed as important to the interests of society.

The needs and desires that form the basis for people's actions can be controlled through proper training. This training can result in effective citizenship, which is the basis of sound democratic living. This effective citizenship is not something that can be developed through the setting up of artificial stimuli. It is something that is achieved only through activities in which individuals engage in their normal day-to-day routine. Since play activities have such a great attraction for youth and since it is possible to develop desirable social traits under proper guidance, physical education should realize its responsibility and do its part in contributing to good citizenship, the basis of our democratic society. In this chaotic world with its cold wars, hot wars, hydrogen bombs, racial strife, imperialistic

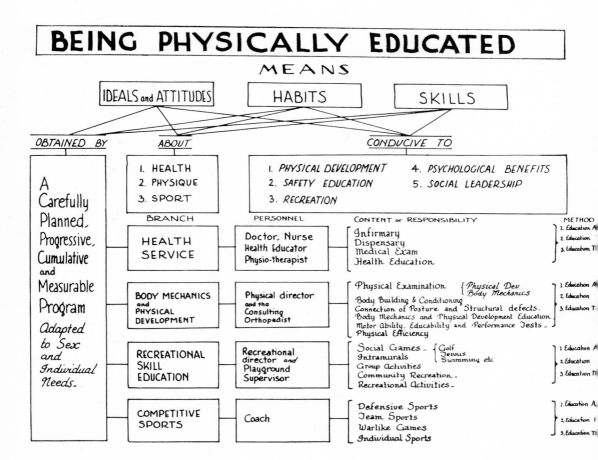

*Courtesy Thomas K. Cureton, Jr., Professor of Physical Educa.*
*University of Illinois, Champaign.*

Chart interpretation of what it means to be physically educated.

aims, human ambitions, and class struggles, human relations are more and more important to personal, group, and world peace. Only through a better understanding of one's fellowman will it be possible to build a peaceful and a democratic world.

## IS THERE A PRIORITY FOR OBJECTIVES OF PHYSICAL EDUCATION?

Leaders of physical education are beginning to ask such questions as: Is one objective of physical education more important than the others? Where should the emphasis in physical education programs be placed? Physical educators can not do everything—what comes first? Does physical education have a master purpose? Is there a hierarchy of objectives?

Historically, we have seen where physical education in its early days was primarily concerned with organic development. However, at the turn of the century with the introduction of the New Physical Education, other objectives more closely identified with general education, such as social development, were included. Today, there are varying viewpoints in regard to the question of priority of objectives.

A survey of selected leaders in the field of physical education, asking for their views as to a priority of objectives, resulted in some interesting information. Most professionals contacted felt that organic development and neuromuscular development are the objectives that should get highest priority. They listed such reasons as: they are most uniquely tied in with physical education, are essential for fitness throughout life, provide the impetus for the program, and represent the objectives that can more readily be achieved. After organic development and neuromuscular development, the leaders surveyed indicated that the most widely accepted objective in terms of importance is mental or interpretive development.

The reasons listed for the importance of this objective included the fact that it is important to develop a favorable attitude toward physical education if any objective is to be achieved at all. Also included was the fact that education is primarily involved with developing a thinking, rational human being in respect to all matters, whether it be concerned with his physical development or other aspects of living. Social development ranked lowest in the survey. Reasons given to support this place on the priority listing were that all areas of education are interested in the social objective and that it was not the unique responsibility of one field, such as physical education. Therefore, the other objectives should receive a higher priority rating.

The survey of national leaders in physical education brought out another important consideration. Many professional leaders stressed the point that, with the national curriculum reform movement taking place today and with increased emphasis on educational priorities, physical educators should rethink their positions in regard to their place in the educational system. They should reexamine how they can contribute their greatest effort and make their greatest contribution in today's changing world.

Perhaps it will help the reader to clarify his own priority system by answering the following questions.

1. *Does the nature of education give us a clue to a priority arrangement of physical education objectives?* According to many educational leaders today, the business of education is concerned primarily with the development of the intellect, the power of good reasoning, and the application of logic. The "life adjustment" type of education is being sidetracked and more and more emphasis is being given to the development of mental skills, the aquisition of knowledge, and cognitive development. Does this mean that physi-

cal education, since it is a part of education and since we use the term physical education, should also give more emphasis in this direction? The emphasis in this direction would not be for the purpose of being labeled *academic,* but instead to help human beings to become more fully aware of the values of physical activity in their physical, social, and mental development.

2. *Does history give us a clue?* A historical analysis of objectives of physical education indicates that in addition to organic development and the teaching of physical skills it is also important to consider the interpretive-mental and social development objectives. History seems to have recorded that physical educators should not limit themselves to merely muscular grace but should also be concerned with these objectives, which can be accomplished through the physical. The emphasis upon human relations, for example, the fact that this nation is a democracy, and the belief that the individual has worth, should permeate programs of physical education.

3. *Do the outcomes we more readily achieve give us a clue?* Physical educators proudly demonstrate through measurement and evaluation instruments the amount of strength and other qualities of physical fitness they develop in their students. The headlines of newspapers and other communication media proclaim the success that is theirs in developing skills. However, data are not readily available to show the degree to which physical educators develop mental skills and such qualities as sportsmanship, respect for opponents, and courage. It is not difficult for physical education to show its accomplishments in the physical and skill objectives, but the evidence is not as readily available for the other objectives. Part of the reason for this lies in the lack of objective instruments for measurement purposes, such as being able to measure qualities of sportsmanship. However, at the same time it may also mean the lack of interest on the part of many physical educators to gear their programs in these directions, their failure to recognize the importance of these objectives, the difficulties encountered in trying to achieve these goals, or a feeling that such responsibilities should be accomplished by the academic subjects or the home.

4. *Do the nature and needs of society and the individual give us a clue?* Will the study of society's social problems, including poverty, juvenile delinquency, crime, and health, give us a clue as to what we should be concerned with in physical education? If so, does this mean that objectives become more important in some segments of our society than in others? Also, what about the needs of the individual? What represents the needs of human beings for the "good life"? Are they physical, mental, neuromuscular, social? What needs are the most important for physical education to consider? What needs should be met by the home, church, and school? Which ones should be met by academic subjects—by physical education—by agencies outside the school? If a boy or girl is subpar physically, does this mean that the organic development objective should get priority? If he or she is a delinquent, should the social objective get priority? What does it mean?

5. *Does the desire for professional status give us a clue?* Chapter 1, Physical Education as an Emerging Profession, listed the criteria for a profession and then raised questions as to whether physical education meets these criteria. Does a review of Chapter 1 indicate a priority of objectives for physical education? What are the implications for physical education objectives of such professional criteria as intellectual orientation, service, code of ethics, and training?

6. *Does the term "physical education" give us a clue?* If physical education is concerned with education of and through the physical does this indicate a priority?

All the objectives of physical education are implied in the term as defined. We are concerned with the *physical* and also with *education*. This means that all objectives should be involved. But does it give us a priority rating?

*7. Does the "fitness" movement give us a clue?* As a result of the concern of the government for the physical fitness of the nation's children and youth, and as a result of the establishment of the President's Council for Physical Fitness, with its wide exposure through communication media, there has been much emphasis upon physical fitness—one objective of physical education. In some institutions of learning and other agencies, priority has been given to the organic development or the physical fitness objective. Has this been good or harmful?

Should all objectives get equal emphasis? Is this the answer? How do physical educators resolve this important problem? Professional associations should give considerable time and effort to resolving this answer. Leadership must be given because many practitioners are seeking the answer.

Regardless of what the outcome is, in the last analysis the individual physical educator will be the person to make the decision. What he emphasizes within his own program from day to day will be the answer. This will depend upon his philosophy, his understanding of the worth of physical education, and what physical education can and should be trying to contribute to human beings and to society. This text is designed to help the reader think profoundly about such questions and help him in arriving at an intelligent answer.

## SHOULD PHYSICAL EDUCATION STATE ITS OBJECTIVES IN THE FORM OF CONCEPTS?

Jerome Bruner, in his book *The Process of Education,* discusses the structure of subject matter and states, "the more fundamental or basic the idea learned, the greater will be its breadth of applicability." A concept is an idea and is derived from the Latin word meaning "to conceive." Webster defines a concept as "a mental image of a thing formed by generalizations from particulars." In other words, it means abstracting and generalizing. Concepts are derived from facts and are expressed in the form that is understandable. They evolve gradually. Concept formation results as the individual is exposed to material little by little. He then associates the concept with past experiences and perceives it as a familiar object.

According to Bruner, any educational discipline includes basic concepts, principles, generalizations, and insights. The curriculum should have a structure that contains subdivisions of knowledge pertinent to the field of specialization. The problem is then one of developing a structure that embraces the basic concepts, around which basic principles, theories, and knowledge can be organized and discussed in meaningful terms. The real purpose of education is to teach concepts. If a student knows a concept it will free him from remembering many isolated facts.

Physical education should consider the use of established concepts as a means of structuring its field so that physical education can be taught to students in a much more meaningful manner. The basic concepts of physical education are to be found within the stated objectives of the field.

The goal of education is to help boys and girls to become mature adults, possess ability to make wise decisions, and be capable of intelligent self-direction. The school experiences the student has in first through twelfth grades should prepare him for these responsibilities.

Physical education, as a part of education, should provide each boy and girl with carefully planned experiences that result in knowledge about the value of physical activity, essential motor skills, strength, stamina and other essential physical characteristics, and the social qualities that make for effective citizenship.

Over the years, physical educators in many of our schools have attempted to achieve these goals in a dedicated and conscientious manner. However, most physical educators will agree there is still much room for improvement. Those persons who advocate change cite educational systems where there is lack of progression, sequential treatment of subject matter, and an orderly developmental pattern for teaching motor skills. Furthermore, they say, physical education curricula vary from school to school and state to state without any degree of uniformity. As a result of these conditions, they lament, students are not becoming as physically educated as they could be, and also, physical education is not gaining the respectability in the educational process it justly deserves.

Each subject matter field has objectives toward which it teaches and that represent the worth of the field for the students. Physical education has traditionally advocated the four objectives of organic development, neuromuscular development, mental development, and social development. These goals have proved valuable as targets toward which both the teacher and student strive. At the same time, they are rather general in nature and do not provide the best basis for the most effective structural organization of physical education.

The student should be aware of the general objectives of physical education; in addition, as a result of his school experiences, he should be sensitive to, understand, and know the framework that constitutes the field of physical education. He should be aware of the unity, the wholeness, and the interrelatedness of the many activities in which he engages from kindergarten through grade twelve. He

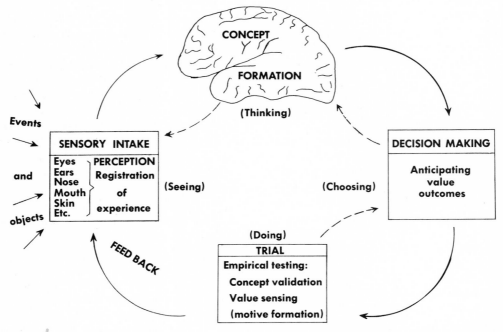

From Woodruff, Asahael D.: *Cognitive models of learning and teaching.* In Siegel, L. (editor): *Contemporary theories of instruction,* San Francisco, Chandler Publishing Co., Chap 4, in press.

Cognitive cycle in behavior and learning.

should even think at times as a physical educator might think, particularly from the standpoint of recognizing the importance and value of such course experiences to human beings. He should understand what constitutes the master plan of education and the structure of physical education as it fits into this master plan.

In creating this structure of physical education we might draw an analogy between our field and the construction of a house. Just as there are key pillars and beams which give the house form and support, so are there key unifying elements within physical education which give it a strong foundational framework and hold it together as a valuable educational experience for every boy and girl. These key elements would be identified and would tie together the various parts of the discipline into a meaningful and cohesive learning package. These elements would be the *concepts* of physical education, and as such, would represent the basic structure of physical education in the school program. They would be the key ideas, principles, skills, values or attitudes that represent points upon which we as physical educators should focus the child's efforts throughout his school life. They would be part of both the teacher's and the student's thinking and would range from very simple ideas to high-level abstractions. They would start with simple, elementary, fundamental experiences and in a sequential, progressive, and developmental pattern gain depth and comprehensiveness over the years as schooling progresses and the student matures. These concepts would thus define the domain of physical education.

Concepts in physical education would not be memorized by the students. Rather, they would be ideas, analytic generalizations that would emerge and be understood by the student as a result of his school experiences in physical education. They would also provide him with a reservoir of information, skills, and understandings that would help him to meet new problems and situations.

The concepts, of course, would need to be carefully selected according to acceptable criteria and be scientifically sound. Furthermore, after the concepts have been identified, there would be need for extensive testing of their validity by many experts, including teachers in the field and specialists in curriculum development.

To implement the concepts within the physical education structure, there would be a need to delineate the identified concepts into meaningful units and topics that would be progressive in nature, and reinforce the concepts that had been identified. The subdivisions of concepts in the structure would represent basic elements needed to develop a meaningful course of study and bring about desirable behavior. Furthermore, they would emanate and flow from the key concepts, and would help to give greater meaning and understanding to them. As the conceptual unifying threads were developed at each ascending grade and educational level, the student would be provided with new challenges, where the information, skills, and understanding he has acquired could be applied. The result would be that finally the student would reach a point where he could arrive on his own at valid answers and make wise decisions in the area of physical education.

As a result of the conceptual approach, students would have a greater mastery of the field of physical education, increased understanding and power in dealing with problems related to their physical self that are new and unfamiliar, and be better motivated to want to become physically educated in the true sense of the term. The approach would provide a stable system of knowledge and provide guideposts for thinking intelligently about physical education.

The conceptual approach would have particular value to physical education because of the great breadth of skills, knowledge, values, etc., that make up this field of endeavor. It would provide a logical and systematic means for identifying among the many elements those that give form and structure to the type of physical education program professionals want taught in schools. The identified concepts would have permanence, and as the explosion of knowledge takes place in the years ahead through the efforts of our scholarly researchers, this new information can become part of the structure, wherever applicable. Finally, the conceptual approach would be readily adaptable to individual differences that exist among students, as well as be sufficiently flexible to provide for the many geographic types of facilities, and other factors that differentiate one community or school from another.

Some physical educators might say that the subject matter, skills, etc., of physical education are the same under the conceptual approach as under the traditional approach. It may be that the facts will be the same in some cases but the approach will be different. For example, in the "new" mathematics, as developed by one professional group in grade nine, there is still concentration upon algebra, but the complete emphasis is not on the solving of algebraic equations; instead it is on the behavior of numbers, a verbalization of concepts.

Under the traditional approach, the organization of courses involved topics and activities, but without sufficient regard to the relationship of the topic and activity to what had gone on previously for the student and what lies ahead. This new method would still discuss topics and conduct activities, but topics and activities would be related to key concepts which the topic and activity are designed to elaborate upon, contribute more understanding, and make the area of learning more meaningful in the life of the student.

Health educators have developed a conceptual approach for health education.* They have identified three key concepts, ten conceptual statements, and thirty-one substantive elements, that form the structure and framework for health education. Such a framework will upgrade the teaching of health and give order, form, uniformity, and meaning to the teaching of health in our schools.

A conceptual framework for social studies has been developed for the State of Wisconsin Public Schools.† The state finds it difficult to keep up with the demand for this publication which lists a framework of concepts for the social studies including: History, Anthropology, Sociology, Political Science, Economics, and Geography. In many other subject matter areas, a conceptual approach has also been developed.

Physical education needs a national curriculum study, with careful consideration being given to the conceptual approach. At a time when the curriculum reform movement is sweeping the nation and when there already is a "new" mathematics, a "new" physics, a "new" English, and a "new" social studies, physical education can no longer be apathetic about what it teaches and how it teaches. The 85,000 public elementary schools and 25,000 public secondary schools, as well as the private institutions, need a "new" physical education. The conceptual approach is one that should be very carefully weighed for this *new physical education.*

---

*Health education: a conceptual approach, School Health Education Study, Washington, D. C., 1965.

†The State Department of Public Instruction in Madison, A conceptual framework for the social studies in Wisconsin schools, Madison, Wisconsin, 1964.

## Preamble*

1. Physical education activities should be progressively administered from simple to complex levels throughout the period of the secondary school.
2. Appropriate records on all students should be maintained.
3. Appropriate provisions should be made for the handicapped and low-fitness students.
4. Comprehensive and effective intramural and interschool programs supplement the instructional program.
5. Participation in musical organizations, driver education, or military training should not be permitted to serve as a substitute for instruction in physical education since the specific objectives and the means of attaining the objectives of each differ widely.

## The Physically Educated Boy and Girl

**Attitudes**

1. Interest in health and being healthy
2. Desire to participate in physical education activities and enjoy play with group
3. Desire to become physically educated

**Knowledge and appreciations**

1. Understanding and appreciation of his or her body and a feeling of responsibility for personal maintenance
2. Basic understanding of physical movement and relaxation
3. Knowledge of interrelationship of physical, mental, emotional and social aspects of the human being
4. An understanding of the rules, strategies, techniques, and history of games, sports, and other physical activities important in our culture
5. An understanding of the importance of exercise to health
6. An insight into individual capacities and limitations in regard to physical activity
7. An understanding of the signs and symptoms of fitness and unfitness

**Skills**

1. The body in proper balance while standing, sitting, and walking
2. Ability to relax
3. Proper rhythmic response to music including basic skills in square, folk, social and modern dance
4. Application of fundamental skills such as running, jumping, skipping, and throwing to actual game situations
5. Swim one-quarter mile and be secure in deep water
6. Skill and proficiency in a minimum of one different team sport each season of the year
7. Skill and proficiency in a minimum of one different individual sport each year
8. An annual experience during the secondary school period in self-testing activities such as apparatus, tumbling, track and field, marching, calisthenics, etc.

**Social attributes**

1. Secure in social situations, i.e., acts with confidence, is courteous, etc.
2. Respects his opponent
3. Respects and cooperates with authority
4. Plays within the letter as well as the spirit of the rules
5. Uses acceptable language in all situations
6. Maintains self-control at all times

*National Conference on Fitness for Secondary School Youth, Washington, D. C., Dec., 1958 (mimeographed).

## PHYSICALLY EDUCATED BOYS AND GIRLS: AN IMPORTANT PROFESSIONAL OBJECTIVE

When a boy or girl becomes mathematically educated, we know that he or she has taken fundamental courses in arithmetic, algebra, geometry, trigonometry, and calculus. When he or she becomes science-educated, we know that experiences have been provided in general science, biology, physics, chemistry, and the other sciences.

What does it mean to be *physically educated?* An important challenge facing the profession of physical education is to establish standards in regard to skills, knowledge, attitudes, and social attributes for the various educational levels, the mastery of which will result in a student being physically educated. When this job has been accomplished, we as a profession will have taken a forward step in establishing ourselves as a more important part of the educational program.

In one of the subcommittees of the National Conference for Fitness of Secondary School Youth on which I served, the material on page 179 was prepared as an attempt on the part of this committee to formulate some standards for the physically educated boy and girl. It represents an effort to establish standards for the profession of physical education.

Dr. Thomas Cureton of the University of Illinois has illustrated what he believes is meant by being physically educated. His chart is reproduced on page 172 to show one person's thinking of what it means to be *physically educated.*

Wireman* lists the qualities he feels constitute a physically educated person. They are presented here in adapted form.

1. *The physically educated person understands the history of physical educa-*tion. No person can become physically educated unless he understands and has historical perspective concerning the events that have affected the historical growth of man's feelings about physical education and what is possible in the years to come.

2. *The physically educated person is proficient in leisure-time skill and utilizes this skill for relaxation and recreation.* Some skill is necessary for enjoyment of the physical activity. Furthermore, leisure hours are utilized to some degree in putting the skill to use.

3. *The physically educated person is cognizant of the relationship of exercise, diet, and weight control.* An understanding of what constitutes a desirable weight control program and the role of exercise and diet in such a program is desirable.

4. *The physically educated person is knowledgeable about the role of sports in the nation's culture.* Sports play a significant role in the American culture and therefore it is important to be informed as to the influence of sport on culture. Also, within reasonable limits, a person should be an intelligent spectator as well as a skilled participant.

5. *The physically educated person has a body capable of meeting the demands of day-to-day living.* It is important to have an understanding of such factors as physical fitness, the ingredients that make it up, and how it is maintained.

6. *The physically educated person understands the concept of total health.* An understanding and appreciation of what constitutes total fitness including the mental, physical, and psychological aspects and the interrelationship of each, is important.

### QUESTIONS AND EXERCISES

1. State and discuss the objectives of physical education as listed by AAHPER, Bookwalter, Clarke, Cowell and Schwehn, Hetherington, LaSalle, Nash, Oberteuffer and Ulrich, Williams, and Wood and Cassidy.

---

*Wireman, Billy O.: What are the underlying values in physical education? The Physical Educator 22:53, May, 1965.

2. Why are objectives essential to any profession?

3. Discuss the physical development objective and tell to what degree it is being fulfilled in the physical education program of the public schools with which you are familiar.

4. What are the implications of the motor development objective for any well-organized physical education program?

5. Discuss how physical education can help in developing the mental resources of the individual.

6. What is the human relations objective and what implications does it have for modern-day physical education?

7. How do the objectives of present-day physical education compare with the objectives of physical education in ancient Greece?

8. To what degree do you feel the objectives, as stated in this chapter, are being achieved by present-day physical education programs in the United States?

9. Justify physical education in this twentieth-century world in the light of the objectives of the profession.

10. How do the objectives of physical education, as outlined in this chapter, meet the needs of the consumer?

11. What do you feel should be the priority arrangement for objectives of physical education?

## SELECTED REFERENCES

American Association for Health, Physical Education, and Recreation, This is physical education, Washington, D. C., 1965, The Association.

Bloom, Benjamin S., editor: Taxonomy of educational objectives, Handbook I: Cognitive domain, New York, 1956, David McKay Co., Inc.

Bookwalter, Karl W.: Physical education in the secondary schools, Library of Education Series, Washington, D. C., 1964, The Center for Applied Research in Education, Inc.

Brown, Camille, and Cassidy, Rosalind: Theory in physical education, Philadelphia, 1963, Lea & Febiger.

Bucher, Charles A.: Objectives of physical education, health education and recreation, Connecticut Teacher Education Quarterly 5:73, Winter, 1948.

Bucher, Charles A., editor: Methods and materials in physical education and recreation, St. Louis, 1954, The C. V. Mosby Co.

Bucher, Charles A.: Administration of school health and physical education programs, St. Louis, 1967, The C. V. Mosby Co.

Bucher, Charles A., Koenig, Constance, and Barnhard, Milton: Methods and materials for secondary school physical education, St. Louis, 1965, The C. V. Mosby Co.

Bucher, Charles A., Olsen, Einar A., and Willgoose, Carl E.: The foundations of health, New York, 1967, Appleton-Century-Crofts.

Bucher, Charles A., and Reade, Evelyn M.: Physical education and health in the elementary school, New York, 1964, The Macmillan Co.

Clarke, H. Harrison: The application of measurement to health and physical education, New York, 1967, Prentice-Hall, Inc.

Cowell, Charles C., and Schwehn, Hilda M.: Modern principles and methods in secondary school physical education, Boston, 1964, Allyn & Bacon, Inc.

Davis, E. C.: The philosophic process in physical education, Philadelphia, 1961, Lea & Febiger.

Halsey, Elizabeth: Inquiry and invention in physical education, Philadelphia, 1964, Lea & Febiger.

Hetherington, Clark W.: School program in physical education, New York, 1922, World Book Co.

Krathwohl, David R., and others: Taxonomy of educational objectives, Handbook II: Affective domain, New York, 1956, David McKay Co., Inc.

LaSalle, Dorothy: Guidance of children through physical education, New York, 1957, A. S. Barnes & Co.

Nash, Jay B.: Physical education: interpretations and objectives, New York, 1948, A. S. Barnes & Co., chaps. 6-12.

Neilson, N. P., and Bronson, Alice Oakes: Problems in physical education, Englewood Cliffs, N. J., 1965, Prentice-Hall, Inc.

Oberteuffer, Delbert, and Ulrich, Celeste: Physical education, New York, 1962, Harper & Row.

Shepard, Natalie M.: Foundations and principles of physical education, New York, 1960, The Ronald Press Co.

Steinhaus, Arthur H.: Fitness beyond muscle, Speech before American College of Sports Medicine, Dallas, Texas, March 18, 1965. Mimeographed.

The contributions of physical activity to human well-being, Research Quarterly, AAHPER 31: May, 1960.

Weiss, Raymond A.: Is physical fitness our most important objective? Journal of Health, Physical Education, and Recreation 35:17, Feb., 1964.

Weston, Arthur: The making of American physical education, New York, 1962, Appleton-Century-Crofts.

Williams, Jesse F.: The principles of physical education, Philadelphia, 1964, W. B. Saunders Co.

Wireman, Billy O.: What are the underlying values in phsyical education? The Physical Educator 22:53, May, 1965.

Wood, Thomas Denison, and Cassidy, Rosalind Frances: The new physical education, New York, 1931, The Macmillan Co.

Chapter 7

# Physical education's dynamic role in general education—pursuit of excellence

Education contributes to the development, advancement, and perpetuation of the nation's culture. Schools, colleges, and universities are clearly the most powerful and effective institutions our society has for the achievement of intellectual skill, knowledge, understanding, and appreciation necessary to make wise decisions, good judgments, and logical analysis of problems. Directly or indirectly, these educational institutions are the chief agents of society's progress, whether it is progress concerned with knowledge, arts, technology, social conscience, or other areas essential to a nation's growth. Schools and colleges should be concerned with the well-being of the individual student in his preparation for a productive and happy life in which his potentialities as an individual are enlarged and fulfilled and where his freedom will be real. Schools and colleges must also be concerned with the society and culture of which they are a part. This means concern for such areas as social equality, industrial and commercial power, economic integrity, political wisdom, and military strength. It also means concerns for the values by which the people live and by which their judgments are made and their purposes defined.

Physical education, as a phase of the total educational process, helps in realizing these purposes. It is one link in a chain of many influences that helps to realize the country's ideals and contributes to the proper functioning of American society. It is continually striving for excellence so that it can become an increasingly dynamic force in general education.

## EDUCATION AND FREEDOM

The educational system in a democratic society must be concerned with the freedom it enjoys. As such it must indoctrinate the concept of freedom and the essentials necessary for its preservation and enhancement in every child, youth, and adult. Each area of education—curricular or extracurricular—and each teacher and administrator must assume responsibility in this critical obligation. Physical education must do everything within its power to contribute to the freedom which has enabled it to realize the professional heights that have been achieved in this society. For this reason, and to this purpose, a section on Education and Freedom has been incorporated into this text—it has vital implications for each student who reads these pages.

Freedom is an unusual term and educators should spell out its meaning in an articulate manner. Each young person should know what it means and how it is protected and preserved for himself and for future generations.

1. *All young persons should know that freedom is not an end but a means to an end.* Freedom is the catalyst that releases their energies. It is the key that unlocks

*Seattle Public Schools,*
*Seattle, Wash.*

Education should help young people to see themselves as contributors and builders of democratic ideals.

doors to opportunities and makes it possible for them to become all they are capable of becoming. It is an instrument for their self-realization—mentally, physically, socially, and spiritually. It is their avenue for achieving excellence. Without this freedom they would be like the boy in East Berlin who is brainwashed with communist thinking and must crash through "The Wall" in order to breathe free air.

2. *All young persons should clearly understand that freedom is never a "fait accompli."* Freedom was not won with the surrender of Cornwallis at Yorktown. It was not a permanent possession of the United States with the signing of the Declaration of Independence by Benjamin Franklin and his colleagues in Philadelphia. Woodrow Wilson stated that freedom cannot be laid away in a document— "Democratic institutions," he stressed, "are never done, they are like the living tissue, always a-making." Young people must clearly see that freedom is never complete as a result of a successful political campaign, the election of a famous man to public office, or the winning of a war. Americans must never lower their guard, be complacent, or drop their vigilance. Freedom is an elusive thing and can vanish into the air like a soap bubble when those persons who share its benefits fail to put forth daily efforts to guarantee its preservation. The Czechoslovakians, Poles, and Hungarians will attest to this fact.

3. *All young persons should know their freedom is best preserved as they develop intellectual, physical, and other powers and use them constructively to further their democratic ideals.* The word democracy comes from the Greek *demokratia* (*demos* = people + *kratein* = rule). Education, therefore, is essential because an enlightened society is necessary for the proper conduct of affairs in a democracy. Thomas Jefferson once wrote, "The most effective way of preventing (tyranny) is

to illuminate as far as practicable the minds of people (everywhere)." Each person in a democracy must be capable of intelligent self-direction and contribute his mental efforts, physical strength, social awareness, and spiritual values to the society of which he is a part, so that it may be dynamic and strong.

Unfortunately, young people are often confused as to the best way to preserve their freedom when they hear public-spirited leaders voice their feelings: the militarist says the answer is to build a bigger bomb, the scientist proclaims we must be the first country to have a man on the moon, and the businessman shouts that the secret is to keep the gold supply in Fort Knox.

Not long ago a military leader in an off-the-cuff remark suggested that we unleash a massive atomic war against the Reds. "Let's obliterate them from the face of the globe," he caustically advised. "Let's give them some of their own medicine. Let's use our most devastating ICBM's, most deadly germs, and longest ranged atomic submarines. Let's strike at them from the air, sea, and land. Let's leave their lands parched and barren and their people destitute. This is the way," he cried, "to make the world safe for democracy and to preserve our freedom."

Young people should know that in the long run, whether or not our freedom is preserved for them and future generations will not be determined by bombs but by wisdom; not being the first on the moon but being the first to help in the elimination of poverty and suffering wherever it exists in the world; not seeking some magic political formula but seeking the truth; and not possessing great wealth but possessing knowledge and dynamic ideas. Young people must not be deceived into thinking that freedom can be won through military power and dollars rather than through sound thinking and wise decisions. Freedom lies in their minds, guided by truths which each of them has the opportunity to possess.

Education should help young people to see themselves as contributors and builders of democratic ideals. It should help them to be worthy examples to the world that they are free to make choices on their own, formulate their own standard of values, and fulfill their destinies, and then it should guide them in the use of their freedom so that they act wisely, direct their lives meaningfully, search for the truth, achieve excellence within their abilities, and continually seek opportunities for self-realization and self-fulfillment.

If education will help our young people to so prepare themselves it will fire the world with enthusiasm for the American way of life. It will show those people struggling for freedom in the far corners of the earth that our way of life, "American Style," is worth waiting for, fighting for, sacrificing for, and dying for. The cry will reverberate throughout the world that the future lies with democracy and freedom and not with those nations that proclaim freedom through their mouthings, but in actual practice make a mockery of the ideal. We know what freedom is because our every thought and action expresses it clearly.

## EDUCATION AND SCHOOLS AND COLLEGES

Education is not confined to the limits of the schools and colleges. It is much broader than this. Education is present in all the experiences an individual may go through in the home, church, clubhouse, and alley, as well as the school. However, schools and colleges represent settings where the highest organized form of education takes place in the United States. The schools and colleges exist for the purpose of indoctrinating the youth in the spirit of democratic living and to improve on the existing social order wherever pos-

sible. The schools and colleges represent places where young people spend a great portion of their time between the ages of 4 or 5 years and up to 16 or 20 years. The schools and colleges represent a locale where an attempt is made to mold children into law-abiding citizens who contribute to the welfare of society. The schools and colleges represent a setting where growth and development take place during formative years. As such, the schools and colleges receive the main consideration in a discussion of the role of physical education in the educative process. Physical education has much to contribute during these school and college years when an individual can develop his body into a strong and beautiful machine or allow it to become weak and flabby, when an individual can learn the secret of skillful movement and coordinated action or remain awkward and lack a sense of rhythm, when an individual can develop his intellectual mechanism or allow it to become rusty, and when an individual can learn to live as a contributing member of society or be an antisocial being.

## RESPONSIBILITY FOR EDUCATION

The responsibility for education falls to each of the states in the nation. The Tenth Amendment to the Constitution of the United States reads: "The powers not delegated to the United States by the Constitution, nor prohibited by it to the States, are reserved to the States respectively, or to the people." Education comes within the interpretation of this Amendment. The states, however, do not retain complete autonomy over the educational system. Instead, in most cases they delegate the educational responsibility to a local unit of organization within their boundaries, such as the school district, village, or city. The states, however, do contribute in many ways toward helping the local communities discharge this responsibility. In many instances they give financial aid and guidance as well as supply instructional assistance and other services. The federal government also contributes in many ways toward the betterment of the educational system of the country. Although the states guard the rights endowed by the Tenth Amendment with jealous fervor, the national government has, nevertheless, contributed help in building schools, providing land, furthering health services, and in many other ways. It appears that federal aid to education on a much larger scale will become a part and parcel of our culture before too many years have passed.

## NATURE OF EDUCATION

The word *education* to many people implies knowledge or the filling of the mind with facts. This belief, very popular during the Middle Ages, is still prevalent in some quarters. To a large degree, it is a carry-over from the scholasticism of the medieval period. Some school and college administrators and teachers still feel that the essential responsibility of the school and college is to open the minds of youth, jam them full of facts, close them, and send them out into the world where they will be ready to solve any and all problems with which they will be confronted. Fortunately, not all educators agree with

*Richwoods Community High School, Peoria Heights, Ill.*

The training that takes place in the swimming pool has educational implications.

the scholastics. The Educational Policies Commission points out that the function of education cannot be confined to facts but includes also ethics, training of the body and spirit, and experiences to develop a better social order. Knowledge in itself is not sufficient in the achievement of excellence.

Ethics play a part in education. In physical education, for example, it would not be wise to develop strength in an individual if this strength were to be directed toward the destruction of civilization, and it would not be sound to develop skill if it were to be used in the oppression of the weak. The question must be raised as to whether education is being directed toward what is good for society. There must be discrimination between what is good and what is evil.

The training that takes place in the gymnasium, auditorium, swimming pool, laboratory, and shop also has educational implications. Many times the experiences in these settings are much more valuable for day-to-day living than what comes out of books.

Finally, education aims at developing a better social order. Experiences that stress such things as the dignity of the individual, freedom of expression, mutual respect, and tolerance make for a better society. America represents democratic living; therefore education must assume the responsibility of furthering this way of life. This means that the experiences provided by the schools should stress human liberty, freedom of thought, the worth of the individual, human equality, group discussion, honesty, respect, and appreciation of ability. The right to work, the common good, provision for the individual to develop according to his own desires, equality of opportunity, and respect for minorities should also prevail. The statement is often made that education is the key to a peaceful world. The challenge is present. Will education succeed before the holocaust of global war is visited upon the world?

## MODERN PHILOSOPHY OF PHYSICAL EDUCATION

The author's philosophy of education is based on the premise that education is designed to help man achieve excellence and that physical education as a part of general education plays a vital part in this job.

### Physical development

No one can look at the world today with its rush, tensions, competitive living, and physical demands and say that the physical body can be ignored. It must be recognized that human beings are a mass of protoplasm and have an organic base that requires activity as a form of nourishment. This is true of every human being, from the cradle to the grave. All people need strength, endurance, and the other components of physical fitness. *Such qualities are essential for excellence.*

And this physical activity is especially important for children. Play is their work. They are laying a foundation for future years. They have an inner drive that must be expressed. It cannot be suppressed. Nature has not taken any chances. She has actually placed a hand on the backs of children and pushed them into activity in order to make sure they are exposed to this ingredient so essential to their optimum growth and development. As long as youngsters possess this limitless capacity for activity, drive for action, and desire for play, it is possible to have *education through movement!* Educators should help children to do better those things they are going to do naturally.

### Skills

The push-button era through which the nation is passing has created a need to develop many skills that can be utilized

*Toledo Public Schools,*
*Toledo, Ohio.*

The physical body cannot be ignored in today's world.

to great advantage during leisure hours. This is one way in which free time can be used profitably. As one educator has said, "education also consists of knowing what to do when you have nothing to do." Skills have many other values, but this is one that is particularly valuable in the space age. The educated person recognizes that he must sharpen not only his mental but also his physical skills because of the way they can contribute to his total development and to excellence.

## Mental development

If physical educators limit themselves to the physical they will never achieve the excellence of which they are capable. They will never scale the heights and fulfill their destiny. They must also contribute to the mental.

There are many ways that physical educators can contribute to mental development. They must always remember that the mental and the physical are closely interrelated. The purpose of the body is not just to carry around the mind. The development of physical fitness will contribute to more effective use of the mind. Modern psychology stresses this important phenomenon.

Physical educators also have a body of knowledge that is important for students. Knowledge about human bodies, disease, the role of exercise, and the importance of physical fitness, together with information about rules, regulations, and strategies in regard to many physical activities and their history and place in the cultures of other peoples, is important.

Members of the profession of physical education can also intellectualize its activities more and add intellectual respectability to what goes on in the gymnasium and the playground. Physical activities should not be performed in a vacuum. Physical educators should continually encourage their students to ask the question "Why?" Why is it important

Recreation Department,
City of Oakland, Calif.

Modern dancers in outdoor concert.

to play this activity? Why should an hour a day be devoted to physical education? Why is exercise important? Why is it important to play according to the rules? Physical educators should also make it possible for their students to do more thinking—make choices, plan strategies, and call plays—and not usurp this responsibility themselves. *The more thinking that takes place on the part of the student the more educational the activity becomes.* The members of the profession must stretch minds as well as muscles and be concerned with inspiration as well as perspiration. In this way they will achieve excellence.

## Social development

The social aspects of physical education are also an important consideration for excellence. Skills are not performed without something happening to the person—to his or her personality and behavior.

Physical educators should find as many ways as possible to influence human behavior for the good.

The rules of the game are the rules of the democratic way of life. One sees democracy in action. One appreciates an individual on the basis of his ability, his performance. His economic status, background, race, or other discriminatory characteristics do not play a role. How he performs is the sole criterion of success.

> *I give no thought to my neighbor's birth*
> *Or the way he makes his prayer*
> *I grant him a free man's room on earth*
> *If his game is only square.*
>
> —Badger Clark, Jr.

## "Plus factor"

There is another factor that should not be overlooked. This is the "plus factor." This is something above and beyond the call of duty—going the second mile, something we will have to stretch a little to

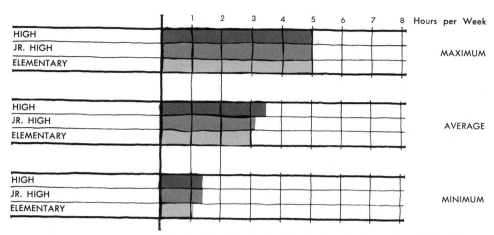

*From Partial shelter for physical education: A study of the feasibility of the use of limited shelters for physical education, College Station, Texas, 1961, Texas Engineering Experiment Station, Texas A & M University.*

Time spent by students in the physical education program.

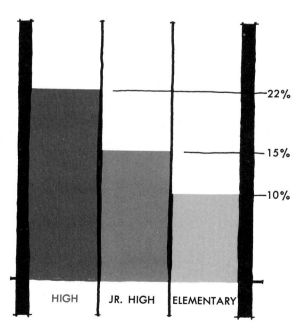

*From Partial shelter for physical education: A study of the feasibility of the use of limited shelters for physical education, College Station, Texas, 1961, Texas Engineering Experiment Station, Texas A & M University.*

Building space devoted to physical activities.

accomplish. But, as Browning says, "Ah! but a man's reach should exceed his grasp or what's a heaven for?"

Physical educators cannot be content once they have developed the physical body, laid down the skills in the nervous system, and developed the amenities of social behavior. There is still something else, and this represents one of the greatest challenges to the field in which so many young people have a drive to engage. Boys and girls look to members of the profession for guidance and want to emulate them. The weight of such responsibility lies heavily upon their shoulders.

Physical educators have to make sure that all this strength, skill, and knowledge are used toward desirable ends. Hitler and Stalin used theirs to hurt people. On the other hand, Samson's strength found its highest value when he used it to deliver Israel from pagan tyranny. David's skill with the sling and Jonathan's use of the bow and arrow also served to help promote the finer things in life.

Members of the physical education profession must be concerned with ethics, making value judgments, and promoting the finer things in life. If they achieve these things their profession will grow and prosper because it has been built upon strong foundations—it will be used in the interest of helping human beings to live a more abundant life and to achieve excellence in their endeavors.

*One ship drives east and another drives west,*
*With the selfsame winds that blow.*
*'Tis the set of the sails and not the gales*
*That determines the way they go.*
                              —Ella Wheeler Wilcox

## GROWTH OF PHYSICAL EDUCATION IN SCHOOLS AND COLLEGES

Until recently in the history of the United States, physical education has not been recognized as an important part of the educational process. Many factors were responsible for this social lag. Two

such factors are the attitude toward play, as exemplified by the Puritans who thought of it as being the work of the devil, and the belief in the early schools in America that play was a frill and something that should not be included in a curriculum with the three R's. The belief in scholasticism with its stress on book knowledge, the lack of adequately trained teachers, and the belief that money should be spent on aspects of the school plant other than gymnasiums and swimming pools were also cogent factors in retarding the progress of physical education. More recently in our history, however, there has been a rapid advancement of physical education as a result of such events as the introduction of the Swedish and German systems of gymnastics into the United States, the industrialization of the country, the increased number of children going to school, the recognition of the importance of training the "whole" child, the mushrooming of teacher-training institutions, and the growth of athletics in colleges, with the secondary schools aping the higher educational institutions. These factors have resulted in an increased number of physical education buildings being added to school plants, legislation being passed providing for physical education in the schools, training of teachers of physical education, and an upgrading of the requirements of such teachers.

Physical education has taken its place alongside the other major subjects in the school curriculum. It has a major contribution to make in the growth and development of all youth. By reason of this fact, physical education personnel should hold positions of high respect and prestige on school faculties and in community life.

## CONTRIBUTIONS OF PHYSICAL EDUCATION TO GENERAL EDUCATION

A fuller description of the role of physical education in the educational process is needed at this point. For purposes of organization such a discussion may be grouped under four headings which have been adapted from the Educational Policies Commission's list of objectives toward which education is striving.* These objectives are designed to help man achieve excellence as an intellectual being, as a social being, as an economic being, and as a civic being.

### Objective—to help man achieve excellence as an intellectual being

The objectives of intellectual self-realization are aimed at developing the individual so that he realizes his potentialities. This development means much more than the accumulation of knowledge. It means that the individual in the process

———
*See Chapter 17.

of constant interaction with his environment has achieved his rightful place, that a proper relationship has been established, and that he recognizes and associates with what is best in his culture. It means that education is interested not only in shaping the individual for his future role as a member of society but is interested also in his development and growth as he progresses toward adult life. Physical education should contribute to the objectives of intellectual self-realization in the following ways:

1. *Physical education should contribute to academic achievement.* Research findings indicate that physical education programs can contribute to academic achievement by providing daily movement experiences and instruction in selected basic motor activities, consistent with the de-

*Detroit Public Schools, Detroit, Mich.*

Physical education has a major contribution to make to the growth and development of all youth.

velopmental level of the students; by promoting physical fitness; by providing knowledge and modifying behavior in regard to good health practices; and by aiding in the process of social and emotional development which leads to a more positive self-concept. For further explanation of the evidence to support the relationship between physical education and academic achievement, see Chapter 17 on "Psychological Foundations of Physical Education."

2. *Physical education should contribute to an inquiring mind.* An inquiring mind is essential to the educated person. Only through curiosity is it possible to probe into the makeup of one's environment.

The motor mechanism of the child enables him to explore, to cruise, and to see his environment. It stimulates his curiosity. He wants to see what is on the other side of the fence, how hot the stove is, what happens when he pulls the light cord, what is in the box with the cover, how people react to certain situations, and the like. Motor activity helps develop the inquiring mind and aids in the solving of problems that at times thwart the individual. In fact, Newell C. Kephart, Executive Director of the Achievement Center for Children, at Purdue University, points out that motor activity is related to higher thought processes. He also indicates that a child's behavior cannot function better than the motor abilities upon which it is based.

As a person grows older, physical education activities open up new fields of curiosity. The student seeks to discover the answers to such questions as why a vigorous workout and a shower are exhilarating and why exercise improves his appetite, circulation, respiration, stamina, and endurance; why Jim can lift his own weight in the air and Dick cannot; why Henry can wield a tennis racquet with great skill; and why Sally can swim so gracefully. A new and interesting phase of living is

opened to the individual through activity. His inquiring mind is active, and he seeks the answers to his health and physical problems.

3. *Physical education should contribute to the ability to speak, read, and write effectively.* Physical education, through the various activities that it sponsors, can indirectly help an individual to speak, read, and write with more effectiveness and clarity.

Through the development of a healthy and physically fit body one may possibly have better poise to command the attention of one's listeners. Francois Delsarte, a French teacher of voice and dramatics, pointed this out when he developed a special system of physical exercises which were aimed at more effective dramatics and singing. This system spread to America where it was received with a great deal of interest. Many teachers of oratorical public speaking were in accord with Delsarte's methods, combined them with their own ideas, and developed a system of exercises that contributed to health, poise, grace, and beauty of face and figure.

The ability to read efficiently is important to an individual's development. It has been pointed out that there are three types of illiterates. First, there are those who cannot read; second, those who have mastered the mechanics of reading but do not use this acquired art; and, third, those who read material of insignificant value. Physical education can contribute to discrimination in reading by pointing out scientific materials that are available in regard to the maintenance and promotion of one's health and physical fitness. It can discount the literature of health and physical culture "faddists," quacks, quick-cure artists, and medicine men who are exploiting the public. It can refer students to sources of information where scientific information may be obtained. It can develop in the student a critical attitude toward quick health cures and other misleading advertising that is chronicled daily in newspapers and magazines and broadcast over radio and television. Through this medium of discriminatory reading, physical education can contribute to self-realization.

Physical education should aid an individual to write effectively. The ability to express one's views in a clear, concise manner is a medium that contributes immensely to the solving of problems. In the presentation of physical education reports on activities, in health lessons, and in the writing of examinations, there should be a constant alertness on the part of the physical education teacher to see that acceptable standards of written work are adhered to. This work should not be the sole prerogative of the English profession. Instead, it is the duty of all educators to utilize every "teachable moment" in the improvement of the writing ability of their students.

4. *Physical education should contribute to knowledge of exercise, health, and disease.* The educated person has an understanding of the facts that are pertinent to exercise, health, and disease. To a great degree, a person's success is dependent upon his health. His state of health and physical fitness will determine to a great extent whether or not he succeeds in realizing his potentialities. An individual cannot expect to be a top executive in the business world if he is sick and stays away from work two or three days a week. He cannot expect to achieve stardom in professional athletics without a physically strong and healthy body. He cannot aspire to a high-salaried position in radio, engineering, the ministry, education, advertising, law, medicine, or dentistry unless his body can stand the rigors of long hours of study and work. He cannot expect to achieve happiness in living unless he is in good health. Therefore a knowledge of exercise, health, and disease is a contributing factor to self-realization so

that health obstacles, handicaps, and strains may be guarded against.

Physical education contributes to this knowledge by instructing the individual as to the importance of nutrition, physical activity, rest, and sleep; by informing him of the preventive and control measures that exist to guard against disease; by providing opportunities for vigorous out-of-doors activity; by motivating the formation of wholesome health attitudes and habits; by following up the correction of defects; by stressing safety factors for the prevention of accidents; and by establishing various health services. Through the experiences and knowledge provided by a physical education program, the objectives of self-realization are brought much closer to attainment.

5. *Physical education should contribute to family and community health.* The educated person protects his own health, his dependent's health, and the health of the individuals within the community where he resides. The educated person has a knowledge of health and disease and applies these facts to himself, to his family, and to his community. He sees that his body is cared for in the manner prescribed by the authorities on health and disease and has periodic health examinations. He obtains adequate amounts of exercise, rest, and sleep; eats the right kind of food; engages in activity conducive to mental as well as physical health; and sees that others also have the same opportunities to maintain and improve their health in accordance with his standards. He realizes that health is a product that increases in proportion as it is shared with other individuals, and he knows that health is everybody's business.

Physical education provides a program of activity to improve the physical and mental health of the individual, his family, and the entire community. In the schools a planned program of physical activity is offered as an essential to the optimum body functioning of young people during this developmental period of their lives. It enables them to experience many pleasurable emotions and to develop organic power that is essential to a healthy, happy, and interesting existence. The groundwork for adult years is laid during this formative period. Recreational programs provide facilities and opportunities for the adult to continue, after leaving school, physical activity adapted to his needs. They offer adults the opportunity to lose themselves in wholesome activity and thus be relieved of some of the tension experienced in modern-day living. Such a program is essential to the health of all.

6. *Physical education should contribute to skill as a participant and spectator in sports.* Recognizing that the body and mind represent a unity in man, the educated person recognizes the value of physical activity. Sports and physical education activities are an important part of our culture. Furthermore, the stress of modern-day living, with its quest for material possessions, its machine-type labor, its sedentary pursuits, and its competitive nature, has implications for all who would enjoy some of the simple, natural, and wholesome forms of activity. Modern-day man has been bitten by a bug which has destroyed to some extent his sense of values in regard to entertainment. Many persons no longer wish to find entertainment through their own resources but, instead, desire to have professionals satisfy these needs. Too frequently they turn to night clubs, horse races, or games of chance for amusement. The educated person selects the manner in which he will spend his leisure time with discretion and with regard for enriched living.

Participating in a game of softball, tennis, or badminton or going for a swim not only provides an interesting and happy experience during leisure hours but at the same time contributes to mental and physical health. The development of physi-

cal skills in all persons rather than in just a few select individuals is an objective that is educationally sound and should be encouraged more and more by educators. The so-called recreational sports should receive greater emphasis so that activities may be better adapted to the older segment of the population. Swimming, golf, tennis, camping, and similar activities should occupy a prominent place in all physical education programs.

Physical education not only develops skill in the participant but at the same time develops an interest and knowledge of other activities which at times may be engaged in by individuals from the standpoint of a spectator. Although it seems the benefits from participation would outweigh the benefits of being a spectator in regard to physical activity, nevertheless, many leisure hours may be spent in a wholesome manner observing a ball game or some other sports activity. The wise person, however, discovers the proper balance between the amount of time he will utilize as a participant and as a spectator. The balance is destroyed if a person fails to realize that being a spectator cannot result in the same values for an individual as being a participant. Physical education can help by supplying a knowledge of various sports so that the role of the spectator may be more meaningful and interesting.

7. *Physical education should contribute to resources for utilizing leisure hours in mental pursuits.* The educated person has mental resources for the utilization of leisure hours. Recreation is not confined to sports and exercise. Instead, there is a whole gamut of activities that are more inactive in their nature but offer entertainment and relaxation after working hours for a great many people. Such activities as reading, photography, music, and painting may be included in this group. Physical education contributes here by providing the material for interesting

stories of great athletes, such as Babe Ruth, Jackie Robinson, Glenn Cunningham, Ben Hogan, and Lew Alcindor. These individuals, through the stories that have been written about them, allow others to live vicariously their struggles in attaining fame and fortune amidst obstacles that seemed almost insurmountable. Physical education offers photography and painting enthusiasts subjects for their pictures. Everyone has seen works of art that were inspired through some sports event. Physical education also offers many hobbies. A sport such as fishing motivates a hobby such as tieing flies. Many other examples could be listed.

8. *Physical education should contribute to an appreciation of beauty.* The educated person has developed an appreciation of the beautiful. From the time of early childhood the foundation of an appreciation of beautiful things can be developed. Architecture, landscapes, paintings, music, furnishings, trees, rivers, and animals should ring a note of beauty in the mind of the growing child and in the adult.

Physical education has much to offer in the way of beauty. The human body is a thing of beauty if it has been properly developed. The Greeks stressed the "body beautiful" and performed their exercises and athletic events in the nude so as to display the fine contours of their bodies. Nothing is more beautiful than a human body that is perfectly proportioned and developed. Physical activity is one of the keys to a beautiful body. Also, there is a beauty of movement which is developed through physical activity. When a person picks up an object from the floor, it can be done with great skill and grace, or it

*Detroit Public Schools, Detroit, Mich.*

Physical education is one of the keys to a beautiful body.

can be done crudely and awkwardly. When a football pass is caught, a basketball goal made, a high jump executed, a two and one-half somersault dive performed, or a difficult dance displayed, there can be included in the performance of these acts rhythm, grace, poise, and ease of movement which is beauty in action. Anyone who has seen Jim Ryun run, Jack Nicklaus drive a golf ball, Mickey Mantle field a fly in deep center, Rod Laver stroke a tennis ball, Wilt Chamberlain hook a shot through the net, or Roger Maris hit a home run knows what beauty of performance means. Such beauty comes only with practice and perfection.

9. *Physical education should contribute to directing one's life toward worthwhile goals.* The educated person conscientiously attempts to guide his life in the proper direction. Upon the shoulders of each individual rests the responsibility of determining how he will live, what religion he will choose, the moral code he will accept, the standard of values he will follow, and the code of ethics he will believe in. This is characteristic of the democratic way of life. In a democracy man can in reality "half control his doom."

Man must develop his own philosophy of life. The way he treats his fellowmen, the manner in which he assumes responsibility, the objectives he sets to attain on earth, and the type of government he believes in will all be affected by this philosophy. Through the philosophy that he has established, man forms his own destiny.

Physical education can help in the formulation of an individual's philosophy of life. Through the medium of physical education activities, guidance can be given as to what is right and proper, goals that are worth competing for, intrinsic and extrinsic values, autocratic and democratic procedures, and standards of conduct. Children and youth are great imitators, and the beliefs, actions, and conduct of the coach and the teacher are many times reflected in the beliefs, actions, and conduct of the student. In education, leadership is the key that unlocks the door to self-realization for many of our youth.

## Objective—to help man achieve excellence as a social being

Human relationships may be defined as the relationship that exists between individuals. Good human relations may be summed up in the Golden Rule: "Do unto others as you would have others do unto you." Good human relations imply that people live together, work together, and play together harmoniously. Each individual appreciates the other person's viewpoint and attempts to understand his actions. Good human relations are found in families where brother and sister, mother and father, father and son, and mother and daughter live cooperatively and happily together. They are found among friends who are willing to help each other in time of need, among classmates who share responsibilities, among neighbors who thrill to the accomplishments of others, and among workers who help solve each other's problems. Poor human relations also exist. These occur when a business competitor seeks an unfair advantage, when a football player drives a cleated shoe into an opponent's face, when a boy shows disrespect for his parents, and when a fellow worker condemns a colleague.

The question of human relations is one of the most pressing problems of this day and age. Good human relations is the key to a happy and successful life and a peaceful world. Therefore it is important that education play its role to the fullest extent in accomplishing the objectives of human relationships.

Physical education can make a worthwhile contribution in this area of human relations. This can be done through placing human relations first; enabling each individual to enjoy a rich social experience through play; helping individuals play cooperatively with others; teaching courtesy, fair play, and good sportsmanship; and contributing to home and family living.

1. *The physical education program aimed at excellence places human relations first.* The human being is the most valuable and the most important consideration in this life. Nothing is more important than human life. One human life is worth more than a handful of diamonds or any other abundance of material possessions that could be accumulated. It rates at the top of all the values in the world. Therefore human welfare should receive careful consideration in all walks of life. When a new law is passed by Congress, there should be due consideration for its effect on human welfare; when a machine is invented, we should take into consideration if it will affect human beings beneficially or adversely; and when an accusation is made, the effect on human welfare should be considered. The more human welfare is considered, the happier are all.

The ideal physical education program places human welfare first on its list. When an activity is planned, it takes into consideration the needs and welfare of the participants; when a rule or regulation is made, the player's welfare is considered; when a student is reprimanded, his welfare and that of others are considered. The desire or convenience of the teacher is not the first consideration. The physical education program takes into consideration the weak and the less skilled and makes sure adequate arrangements have been made for such individuals. It is a student-centered program with the attention focused on the individuals for whom the program exists. Throughout the entire procedure there is prevalent among students, teachers, and administrators the thought that the human aspects are the most important consideration. Through

the media of precept and example, consideration of others is the keynote of the program. When the student plays, he considers the welfare of others; and when the teacher plans, he considers the welfare of all. By placing human relations first, a spirit of good will, fellowship, and joyous cooperation exists.

2. *The physical education program aimed at excellence enables each individual to enjoy a rich social experience through play.* Play experiences offer an opportunity for a rich social experience. This experience can help greatly in rounding out a child's or youth's personality, in helping him to adapt to the group situation, in developing proper standards of conduct, in creating a feeling of "belonging," and in developing a sound code of ethics.

Children and youths need the social experience that can be gained through association with other persons in a play atmosphere. Many children and youths live in cities, in slum areas, and in communities where delinquency runs rampant, where their parents do not know the next door neighbor, and where the environment is not conducive to a rich social experience. In such neighborhoods the school is one place where children and youths have an opportunity to mingle, and physical education offers a place where they have opportunity to play together. The potentialities are limitless in planning social experiences through "tag" and "it" games, rhythms, games of low organization, and the more highly organized games. Here the child or youth learns behavior traits that are characteristic of a democratic society. Because of his drive for play, he will be more willing to abide by the rules, accept responsibility, contribute to the welfare of the group, and respect the rights of others.

3. *The physical education program aimed at excellence helps individuals to play cooperatively with others.* The physi-

cal education program should stress co-operation as the basis for achieving the goals an individual or group desires. Each member of the group must work as though he were a part of a machine. The machine must run smoothly, and this is possible only if every part does its share of the work. Pulling together and working together bring results that never are obtained if everyone goes his separate way. Former President Truman in a speech delivered at Madison, Wisconsin stressed the effectiveness of cooperation in our day-to-day living, citing such examples as farm cooperatives, cooperative stores, and the bringing of electricity to rural areas through cooperative means. He then went on to stress that world peace is possible only through cooperation among the nations of the world and that the problems confronting the nations of the world today will be solved only through working together.

A physical education program that would teach individuals to play cooperatively should stress leadership and followership traits. The success of any venture depends on good leadership and good workers or followers. Everyone cannot be a captain on a basketball, relay, or soccer team. Everyone does not have leadership ability. Those who are good leaders should also be good followers. A leader in one activity might possibly make a better fol-

*Oak Park and River Forest High School,*
*Oak Park, Ill.*

The excellent physical education program helps individuals to play cooperatively with others.

lower in another activity. These are a few of the points that should be brought out. The important thing to stress is that both leaders and followers are needed for the accomplishment of any enterprise. All contribute to the undertaking. All deserve commendation for work well done. All should reap the rewards.

A physical education program that would teach individuals to play cooperatively should stress cooperation as the first consideration, rather than competition. Competition is good, but it seems that cooperation is the first concern of education. Students in our schools compete for grades, to make the honor roll, to receive a bid to certain societies, to be a member of the squad, and to be an officer of their class. This may be good if conducted according to proper procedures, but in many of our schools it breeds discontent, cheating, and cliques and results in personality maladjustments. The person who takes home the honors, accumulates the prizes, and makes the headlines is too often the hero in the eyes of the public, whereas the diligent, hard-working, quiet individual who cooperates to his utmost for the success of a group enterprise receives nothing for his efforts. The success of the democratic way of life depends on cooperation among members of society and not on the exploits of a few who seek honor, prestige, and glory. The "all for one and one for all" motto will accomplish much more than the "all for me" motto. In adult life people follow many of the objectives that were formulated in their youth. If competition rather than cooperation receives the main consideration in school, it will aggravate the competitive "survival of the fittest" existence that is so characteristic of modern-day living. Cooperation is the secret of successful living.

4. *The physical education program aimed at excellence teaches courtesy, fair play, and good sportsmanship.* The ame-

nities of social behavior are a part of the repertoire of every educated person. They have developed as part of our culture just as the playing of baseball, eating "hot dogs," and democratic living have. Some individuals in our societies are referred to as "ladies" and "gentlemen," whereas others are called "hussies" and "rowdies." Many times such courtesies as saying "please" or "thank you," tipping one's hat, offering a lady your arm, and acting in a polite, quiet manner have made the difference in these labels being attached to certain individuals.

Courtesy and politeness are characteristic of good family training just as fair play and sportsmanship are characteristic of good training in physical education activities. On the one hand, it reflects the character of the parent or guardian and, on the other, the teacher or coach. When a player kicks his opponent in the groin, trips him up, or does not play according to the rules, he reflects the spirit of his leader. Some coaches and teachers will use any means to win a game or achieve a goal. Others feel that winning is not the prime objective. Instead, their main objective is to provide an experience that will help the members of a group realize values that will help them live an enriched life.

Courtesy, fair play, and sportsmanship contribute to good human relations. The player who is a gentleman on the field is usually a gentleman off the field as well. Such an individual makes friends easily, builds good will, and inspires trust among those with whom he comes in contact. Others know that he believes in playing according to the rules, that he will not take unfair advantage, that he assumes responsibility, and that he is considerate of others. These characteristics should be developed in every child who visits a physical education class or tries out for any athletic team.

5. *The physical education program*

*aimed at excellence contributes to family and home living.* Physical education has a contribution to make to family and home living. The makeup of a child depends to a great extent on the type of family and home environment he lives in. Many times such an environment determines whether an individual is kind or mean, quiet or boisterous, or polite or rude. In view of the imprint of the home and family upon the child, the school has the educational responsibility to improve and nurture the child, to interpret society to him in its correct light, and to strengthen family ties. Physical education can assume part of this responsibility.

The coach and the physical education teacher are many times the ones in whom a child puts his trust and confidence and whom he desires to emulate. The nature of physical education work and its appeal to youth probably are the causal factors of such practice. Consequently, physical education personnel should utilize their advantageous position to become better acquainted with the youth and his home and family life. Many times divorce and separation have affected children's lives. A change from rural to urban life with the difficulties of adjustment might be an experience through which a child is passing. There may be a lack of "belonging" or a protected existence, which causes anxiety and worry. By having a knowledge of the whole problem, the teacher or coach will be able to help in the adjustment process and in making for better home and family living. This could be done through proper counseling and guidance, helping youth to experience success in play activities, talks with parents, and home visitations.

The increased complications of family living, because of such factors as the prevalence of divorce, the desire for careers on the part of women, the turmoil of urban existence, and juvenile delinquency, place more and more responsibility upon education to help children make proper life adjustments. Physical educators, because of their program in which children have a natural desire to engage and because children look to them for guidance and help, can contribute considerably in these adjustments.

### Objective—to help man achieve excellence as an economic being

A third objective of education deals with the production and consumption of goods and services. Education has the opportunity of informing the young in respect to both the vocational aspects of living and the consumer aspects. Both are important and are necessary for a happy and successful life. Most people select and follow various vocations in the matter of earning a living, placing them in the role of a producer. At the same time they buy goods and services, which places them in the role of a consumer. Schools and colleges should train youth to be both good producers and good consumers. Physical education can aid in more efficient production of goods and services and also can aid in the establishment of certain standards that will guide the public in the wise consumption of certain goods.

1. *Physical education should contribute to good workmanship.* Excellence in workmanship is tied in with intellectual, physical, social, and emotional qualities. The total individual must be developed if good workmanship is to be achieved. A man will be as strong as his weakest link. Work is an essential for all individuals. Through work one contributes goods and services to the wider community of which he is a part. Everyone, by reason of his ability, skill, and knowledge, can contribute to the needs of a great population. The man who screws a bolt on an assembly line at an automobile plant, the woman who types a letter, the boy who washes a car, and the girl who sweeps the living room all contribute goods or ser-

vices. It is characteristic of the democratic way of life for everyone to contribute according to his capacity and ability. Only through work is democratic living achieved.

Work is something that should be enjoyed and something from which one should receive satisfaction. Frequently remarks are heard relative to the fact that work is degrading, a thing that should be avoided, and a curse upon life. This feeling should not exist. Workers who have been unemployed and without work for long periods of time deteriorate physically and mentally. They lack a challenge, something to occupy their minds, and some way in which they may contribute to group living. They are dejected, depressed, fatigued, and feel that life is not worth living.

Children and youths should have opportunities for work. As part of their educational training children and youths should be assigned tasks around the house and around the school or college. In physical education, children could help in developing playfields, taking care of equipment, and instructing those with less skill. Through regular duties, a young person can discover that he is contributing to the welfare of the group and is providing goods or services that will help others to live a little more comfortably, happily, and successfully. A young person also takes pride in achievement. He feels a sense of satisfaction in accomplishment. Such an educational experience has implications for successful living in a democracy.

2. *Physical education should contribute to vocational placement.* The happiness and success of an individual is dependent to a great extent upon his selecting the right position or field of work. There are thousands of positions to which one may turn for work. The individual is anxious to select the one that is best suited to his personal ability, skills, and makeup. This process of selection can prove very disheartening without some type of professional guidance. Schools should assume part of the responsibility of seeing that students are guided into those positions where they will be the happiest and where they will be able to serve society best. Physical educators should be constantly alert for individuals who can become desired members of their profession.

The physical educator in the secondary school is in a most advantageous position to guide youth either into or away from the physical education profession. Many students turn to him for vocational guidance who are not suited for this profession. Others, because of their skills, good human relations, scholastic achievements, personality, and health, are wanted in this expanding profession. The undesirable candidates can be guided into work where their qualifications are needed, and to the desirable candidates can be explained the advantages of being in physical education work. The physical educator should be a virtual talent scout on the lookout for good material. The physical educator performs a service for the students by guiding them into a profession where they will be happy in their work, and he also performs a service for the profession of physical education and ultimately for the public at large that receives the benefits of the services of properly guided individuals. Such students should be taken into the confidence of the physical educator and opportunities provided for continuous development of their interest in physical education. Opportunities for working in various phases of the physical education program could be provided, deficiency in skills could be made up, and desirable personality traits emphasized.

3. *Physical education should contribute to successful work.* The success of any job depends to a great degree upon the health and physical fitness of the worker. If one

is in the best of health and is physically fit, it is expressed in many ways. His human relations are such that he greets his colleagues with a cheery "good morning," his personality reflects enthusiasm and an abundance of energy, his capacity for work is great, he is not absent from work because of illness, his poise and leadership qualities are enhanced, and he reflects a satisfaction in his work that instills confidence in his employers.

The benefits of participation in various forms of physical education activities have proved of financial value. Thisted, in studying various groups of graduates of the University of Iowa, found that individuals who had participated in varsity basketball and football earned higher income than nonathletes in similar groups. This study is not sufficient to provide conclusive evidence in this respect. However, it seems that experience in physical education activities should contribute to physical health, mental health, human relations, and other social assets which could not help but contribute to better work.

4. *Physical education should encourage professional growth.* A person's training is not complete when he graduates from college or trade school, finishes a training course, or works in a particular vocation for a certain number of years. There is always some additional knowledge or skill that can be further developed which will make the work a little more productive. One individual has stated that the more a person learns the more he realizes how little he knows. Conversely, many individuals with little knowledge about a particular subject sometimes give the impression that they know everything there is to learn about the field. There is so much to know in this world that it is a physical and mental impossibility to do anything but scratch the surface. In order to compromise in this situation, we specialize; but even as we specialize there are multitudinous skills and items to master.

Therefore if a person wishes to make a success of his chosen vocation, it is necessary to continually learn new things. It is necessary to keep abreast of current developments in the field and to be constantly vigilant so that services and goods to the public may be improved.

The profession of physical education should continually provide for in-service training. Such items as new skills should be mastered. The implications of new ideas pertinent to child growth and development should be considered in the light of physical activity. Standards should be established in regard to the types of programs that should be administered at various school and college levels. New coaching techniques should be discussed, and an attempt should be made to solve the problems that arise from the tension of modern-day living. Physical education is a growing profession, and new facts in the areas of biology, psychology, and sociology are continually evolving which have implications for this profession. Only if physical educators are constantly studying new developments will they serve human welfare in the most favorable light.

The physical educator realizes the social value of his work and impresses this fact upon students desiring to enter the profession. The physical educator realizes that the profession of which he is a member helps to build a better society through such things as building a healthier and more physically fit population, providing for enjoyable and profitable use of leisure hours, providing for the optimum growth and development of children, and contributing to the democratic way of life. The physical educator realizes that he is helping through his work to build a better society in which to live.

5. *Physical education should contribute to the wise consumption of goods and services.* The educated person buys his goods and services with wisdom. He is well informed as to the worth and utility

of various goods and services. He utilizes standards for guiding his expenditures, and he follows appropriate procedures to safeguard his interests.

Physical education can help to inform children and adults as to the relative values of goods and services that influence their health and physical fitness. The field of health is an area in which goods and services of doubtful value find a ready public market. If a person selects many of the more popular magazines and reads the advertisements with care, it would seem that he would need to eat certain types of cereal to be an outstanding athlete, drink certain whiskeys to be a man of distinction, take certain pills for proper elimination, smoke certain cigarettes to keep the throat healthy, visit certain salons and slenderizing parlors to have a well-developed body, use special types of toothpaste to keep teeth shiny, and use specially prepared tonics to keep hair from falling out. Literature that offers advice on health matters occupies prominent places on newsstands, drugstore counters, and various shops throughout the country. Advice is also seen and heard through billboards, posters, press, radio, and films. Much of the material is specially prepared and disseminated as a money-making scheme to exploit the public. Human welfare has no consideration in much of the advice that is being given.

Physical educators have the opportunity by nature of their position and background in health matters to help the student and the adult to take a critical view of such literature and pronouncements. Physical educators should instill in all persons the necessity for disregarding every remedy or cure until it has been successfully proved worthwhile through research and experimentation. The need for consulting the family physician should be impressed on all persons. The practice of self-medication should be discouraged. Many times harm rather than help results

if such practice is followed. The individual should be a shrewd and intelligent buyer when it concerns his health and physical well-being. He has only one body, and this has to go with him throughout life. The physical educator should also be careful not to trespass on medical domain in giving advice. He should never attempt to diagnose or treat. These are the physician's prerogatives.

## Objective—to help man achieve excellence as a civic being

Civic responsibility falls upon each member of a democracy. Only as each individual assumes his civic responsibility and contributes to group welfare will democratic ties be strengthened. Education can do much in teaching the wide disparities that exist among men and the action that is necessary to correct these conditions.

1. *Physical education should contribute to humanitarianism.* Youth should be well informed as to the needs of mankind everywhere. A humanitarian view of the conditions of mankind should become a part of every student. There should be established in each individual the desire to contribute to human welfare, and this desire should not be passive but should be translated into action.

Physical education can, within reason, emotionalize democratic play experiences to the point where youth sees the importance and the value of cooperative living and contributing to the welfare of all. Here is an ideal setting for developing humanitarian values. Children and youth from all walks of life, all creeds, colors, and races are brought together for a social experience. Interest and a natural drive for activity provide a laboratory for actual practice in developing these values.

2. *Physical education should contribute to tolerance of other people's views.* It is the prerogative of every person to think out solutions to various problems,

form his own opinions, and attempt to bring others around to his point of view. At the same time, he should realize that it is everyone else's prerogative to do the same thing. Frequently one sees friendships and personal relations destroyed because one person is diametrically opposed to another person's views. When there appears to be no opportunity to bring the other person around to his way of thinking, there is a breaking of friendly relations, and each goes his separate way. This would be a strange world if each individual felt and thought the same way. Differences, to a great extent, forecast a more careful study and approach to the solution of a problem. Consequently, the action that is finally taken should be more in the interests of the majority welfare.

Physical educators can help in developing tolerance of other people's opinions in the various activities they conduct. Stu-

dents can be trained to participate intelligently in the discussion of common problems that develop in a game situation. All can be encouraged to contribute their thinking. Thoughts and ideas are respected by all, and the final settlement of the problem can be made by group opinion. When the time occurs for the election of captains for the basketball team, there usually is a difference of opinion; when Johnny, Jim, Dick, and Harry all want to pitch in the softball game, there is a difference of opinion; when Mary, Ruth, and Nancy feel the umpire has made a bad call and Dorothy, Diana, and Lee think it is a good call, there is a difference of opinion; and when there are twenty-five in a class and there are twenty-two positions on teams to be filled, there is a difference of opinion as to who should play. All of these situations present opportunities for the physical educator to allow the democratic process of respecting

*State of Michigan.*

Education for conservation of natural resources.

the opinions of others to operate. Physical educators should be alert to take advantage of such "teachable moments."

3. *Physical education should contribute to conservation of natural resources.* Part of the great wealth that is America's is represented in terms of wildlife, fish, forests, water, soil, and scenic beauty. These resources of the nation contribute to the living standard, appreciation of beauty, recreation, and pride that characterize this country. Every resident should feel it his personal responsibility to maintain and improve these resources whenever possible.

Physical educators should be especially concerned with preserving such national resources as wildlife, fish, water, and forests. These represent the media through which many enjoyable moments are spent by sportsmen, campers, and seekers of recreation and relaxation. If these resources are destroyed or allowed to deteriorate, many of the nation's chief sources of beauty and happiness will have been lost. Therefore, physical educators should inform the youth and the public of the value of such resources to the health and physical fitness of the country. It is important to impress upon all persons the value of knowing the right method and procedure of making a camp fire, the laws concerned with the taking of wildlife and fish, the importance of preventing forest fires, the contribution of forests in preventing floods and soil erosion, and the harmful results of recklessly destroying the nation's resources. Through an educational program which points out that natural resources are directly related to the welfare of each resident of this country much good can be done in conserving this form of the nation's wealth.

4. *Physical education should contribute to conformance with the law.* In a democracy laws are made by the people and for their benefit. Therefore, these laws should be adhered to by everyone.

Obedience is essential to a well-ordered society. Laws should be obeyed even though a person is not in agreement with them. Such statutes are on the books because the people directly or through their representatives voted for them. They are designed to protect the people's interest and welfare. If a person feels that they are not in accordance with public welfare, then every attempt, through democratic means, should be made to erase them. The solution to the problem is not to break laws. They should either be followed or be discarded through legislative action.

The prevalence of crime in this country is evidence of the fact that many people in the nation do not live within the law. The growing crime rate represents a grave concern for the democratic way of life. People should realize that laws are for their benefit and that any failure to live up to the law infringes upon the rights of others. When a law is passed stating that a person should not drive more than fifty miles per hour, it is to protect not only the driver but other people who may be driving or walking along the road. When a law is passed making it unlawful to break into a store and take someone else's property, it is protecting the right of the property owner. A democracy differs from a totalitarian type of government in this respect. In a democracy the laws are made for the benefit of everyone, whereas in a totalitarian state they are frequently made for the welfare of only a few. Everyone should appreciate this fact and stay within the laws that have been created for his benefit.

Schools and colleges can do much toward developing law-abiding citizens. There are certain rules and regulations that are established in school and college for the protection and benefit of all. The library should be kept quiet so that students may study. No one should swim alone because of the danger involved, and all should attend classes regularly, since this is deemed necessary in order to get the right kind of education. These rules and regulations are similar to the laws outside of school and college. They are for the protection and welfare of all concerned. Adherence to them should be taken as a necessary, desirable, and democratic procedure. Wherever possible, the students should formulate their own rules. This is in keeping with democratic administration.

Physical education can contribute to developing a law-abiding attitude in youth. The rules of safety that have been established for the playground, gymnasium, and other places where physical education activities are held should be made clear to each student. Furthermore, the purpose behind such rules should be explained.

Physical educators can set a good example for students by being law-abiding citizens. They should abide by the rules and laws that have been established. They should teach through example as well as precept. Organizations, leagues, and athletic conferences have rules governing them. The National Collegiate Athletic Association sets up certain eligibility rules for intercollegiate participation. When these rules are broken by certain members it is not in keeping with the democratic way of life. The National Collegiate Athletic Association is a representative athletic body. Each member has a vote. When a rule is passed by the majority, it should be accepted by all and strictly adhered to. If some are in disagreement, they can work for its repeal, but in the meantime the letter and spirit of the rule should be kept. This is setting the right example for that great mass of youth and adults who attend or follow the field of sport. Representatives of every athletic league and conference should draw up rules and regulations to govern competition in accordance with the general welfare of the participants, the educational

institutions concerned, and society in general. Through such a procedure, athletics may be conducted in a much more meaningful and purposeful manner.

5. *Physical education should contribute to civic responsibility.* It is the responsibility of every citizen to have a clear understanding of his civic duties and to see that they are carried out in an intelligent manner. The principal duties that involve action on the part of the citizen are voting intelligently, developing an appreciation of the various governmental services, and knowing the law.

Every citizen should cast his vote in an intelligent manner. In order to vote intelligently a citizen must know the issues involved and the arguments, pro and con. He should make a thorough study of the whole problem in the light of what it means for the general welfare. This means that a citizen should know about local, state, national, and international affairs. He should be well informed. He should not be influenced by all the propaganda that is cast in his direction. He should think through the issues in a calm, intelligent manner. The physical educator, when faced with important decisions, should follow a similar plan in determining what course he will follow. Many times the decision that is arrived at will not be popular with one's colleagues. However, a person must have a skin that is tough rather than sensitive to the interests of those who are often more concerned with their own welfare than with the welfare of the participants or of the students. This seems especially true of many coaches who have public, alumni, and student pressure on them to produce winning teams.

6. *Physical education should contribute to democratic living.* The educated citizen believes in the democratic way of life and his every action is symbolic of his loyalty to its ideals. He is aware of the freedom of worship, speech, and assembly;

of the worth of the individual; of equality for all; and of the right to be a part of and to participate in government. At the same time, he realizes that in order to participate in these benefits he must contribute to the group, must work for the happiness of all, and must live up to the ideals that are characteristic of democratic living.

Despite all the advantages and opportunities that are offered for democratic living in America, there are many shadows that fall across its path. America is being challenged as to whether this shining star of democracy will continue to shine as a hope and a goal for all civilizations to attain or whether it will dim and fade with time. Such factors as unbridled science, failure of government to meet the needs of human welfare, lack of interest in religion and moral codes, racial inequality, and settlement of controversial issues by force help to darken the road to democracy. There must be a change toward the principles and way of life that are truly democratic. All individuals, organizations, and professions must contribute in this movement. Education, by reason of its close association with youth who are at a formative period in life when the values of democratic living can become a part of them, should carry its share of responsibility. Physical education, with its activities in which children have the natural desire to engage, can help to provide one of the most natural laboratories for the right social experiences. America is being challenged. It has the tools with which to create a truly democratic society. The future will tell whether it has succeeded.

## QUESTIONS AND EXERCISES

1. In approximately 300 words discuss the role of physical education in the educational process.
2. Comment on the statement "All education takes place within the walls of the public schools."

3. What level of government has responsibility for public education? Comment on the advisability of leaving this responsibility at this level.
4. In what ways does the federal government contribute to education?
5. To what extent is education concerned only with knowledge?
6. Describe the growth of physical education in the public schools.
7. What are the objectives of education as outlined by the Educational Policies Commission?
8. Discuss the objective of self-realization. How does physical education contribute to its achievement?
9. Discuss the objective of human relationship? How does physical education contribute to its achievement?
10. Discuss the objective of economic efficiency. How does physical education contribute to its achievement?
11. Discuss the objective of civic responsibility. How does physical education contribute to its achievement?
12. To what extent is the physical education profession, through the programs that exist today, contributing to the objectives as set forth by the Educational Policies Commission?
13. In the light of the discussion in this chapter, why should the public feel that physical education is an essential to the educational program in the schools? What type of public relations program should be instituted by the physical education profession to bring such facts to the attention of those individuals who are not cognizant of the values of a well-organized physical education program?

## SELECTED REFERENCES

Brameld, Theodore: Philosophies of education in cultural perspective, New York, 1955, The Dryden Press.
Bucher, Charles A.: Administration of school health and physical education programs, St. Louis, 1967, The C. V. Mosby Co.
Bucher, Charles A.: Health, physical education, and academic achievement, NEA Journal 54:38, May, 1965.
Bucher, Charles A., Koenig, Constance, and Barnhard, Milton: Methods and materials for secondary school physical education, St. Louis, 1965, The C. V. Mosby Co.
Bucher, Charles A., Olsen, Einar A., and Willgoose, Carl E.: The foundations of health,

New York, 1967, Appleton-Century-Crofts.

Educational Policies Commission, National Education Association and American Association of School Administrators, Washington, D. C.:

An essay on quality in public education, 1959.

The unique function of education in American democracy, 1937.

The purpose of education in American democracy, 1938.

Education and the defense of American democracy, 1940.

Education of free men in American democracy, 1941.

Education for all American youth, 1944.

Policies for education in American democracy, 1946.

Education for all American children, 1948.

Fraleigh, Warren P.: Should physical education be required? The Physical Educator **22:** 25, March, 1965.

Gardner, John W.: Excellence, New York, 1961, Harper & Bros.

Havinghurst, R. J., and Neugarten, B. L.: Society and education, Boston, 1957, Allyn and Bacon, Inc.

Mayer, Martin: The schools, New York, 1961, Harper & Bros.

McCloy, Charles H.: Philosophical bases for physical education, New York, 1940, F. S. Crofts & Co.

Oberteuffer, D.: Some contributions of physical education to an educated life, Journal of Health and Physical Education **16:**3, Jan., 1945.

Radler, D. H., and Kephart, Newell C.: Success through play, New York, 1960, Harper & Row.

Rickover, H. G.: Education and freedom, New York, 1959, E. P. Dutton Co., Inc.

Thisted, M. V.: College alumni evaluate intercollegiate athletics, Research Quarterly, AAHPER **5:**77, May, 1934.

Whitehead, Alfred North: The aims of education, New York, 1929, The Macmillan Co.

The sprinter

*Works of Robert Tait McKenzie, Courtesy Joseph Brown, School of Architecture, Princeton University.*

PART THREE

# Relationship of physical education to health, recreation, camping, and outdoor education

# Introduction

## INTRODUCTION

The next three chapters are devoted to areas of endeavor with which physical educators are frequently associated. Health, Recreation, Camping, and Outdoor Education are specialties that have grown rapidly during the last decade. With this growth many questions have been raised as to their relationship with physical education. "Should they be associated with physical education?" "Should each of them go it alone?" "Are health, physical education, and recreation closely related?" "Should each of these fields of endeavor be a part of the same professional organization?" "How should these specialties be administered—separately or collectively?"

The student of physical education needs to know the relationship of physical education to health, recreation, camping, and outdoor education. He needs to understand how the various fields evolved, and the "pros" and "cons" of furthering a close relationship among the special areas or encouraging the separateness of each.

The next three chapters outline each of these fields of endeavor so that the reader may have a better understanding of the nature and scope of each and the relation of physical education to each. First, however, this introduction identifies several statements of fact about the relationship that exists among physical education, health, recreation, camping, and outdoor education.

1. *History indicates that physical education is the parent.* Physical education is as old as primitive man. Historically, physical education has reached many heights, including the great emphasis placed upon this area during the early Greek civilization. It also found considerable emphasis later on in history among the Scandinavian countries and Germany. Various gymnastic systems from these countries were introduced into America. In 1885, physical education's largest professional organization was established under the title of the American Association for the Advancement of Physical Education. In 1903, the name was changed to the American Physical Education Association. The areas of recreation, camping, outdoor education, and health education as organized fields of endeavor came into being later in history. The birth of recreation is frequently marked with the construction of the sand gardens in Boston. Health, in its early history, was concerned as much with facilities as with the health of the child. Early health instruction took place primarily at the college level. In the later nineteenth century a majority of the colleges had courses in hygiene. The association of camping and outdoor education with schools and colleges is the most recent entrant into educational circles.

Common interests and goals prompted the Department of School Health of the

National Education Association in 1937 to join the national association to form the American Association of Health and Physical Education. In 1938, recreation was also added to the title of the national association. Camping and outdoor education have never been included in the title of the national organization, but sections have been established within the association.

Each of the special fields of health, physical education, recreation, camping, and outdoor education has grown considerably since it joined together professionally with the allied special areas. The purpose of the national association is to bring about a closer relationship among the various members, upgrade the standards of each area, stimulate an interest in and understanding of the work being accomplished, distribute informative materials, and take other necessary actions to make for a greater contribution to our society by each of the special areas.

2. *Health, physical education, recreation, camping, and outdoor education are viewed today as distinct and separate fields of endeavor.* Today, each of these professional fields of specialization has its own distinct program, teachers and leaders who have special training, and its own subject matter and underlying philosophy. The emphasis upon specialization has helped to clarify the uniqueness of each area. It is difficult for a person to be trained in more than one of these fields. Each field has become a specialty that requires many years of preparation in order to acquire the knowledge and skills that are peculiar to the area.

3. *Professional organizations frequently incorporate all areas.* Such organizations as the American Association for Health, Physical Education and Recreation; the Society of State Directors of Health, Physical Education and Recreation; and the Canadian Association for Health, Physical Education and Recreation are ex-

amples of organizations that incorporate all of these subject areas. In addition, other organizations such as the American Academy of Physical Education, Delta Psi Kappa, and Phi Epsilon Kappa include members in these areas and are involved in activities peculiar to each of the fields.

4. *Administrative units in colleges and universities and in schools frequently incorporate all areas.* Institutions of higher learning engaged in the preparation of leaders for these special fields and some agency programs have administrative units that carry such titles as: School or College of Health, Physical Education and Recreation; Division of Health, Physical Education and Recreation; and Departments of Health, Physical Education and Recreation. Many of these administrative units also include camping and outdoor education. Similarly, many school districts incorporate these areas into their administrative structure. The New York State Department of Education has established a certification program for the Director of Health, Physical Education, and Recreation.

5. *Publications and course offerings in colleges and universities frequently incorporate all these areas.* A check of professional libraries, magazines, articles, and courses that are offered in colleges and universities will result in the realization that all areas are frequently referred to in the same publication or course.

6. *Physical education is related to health.* Physical education is designed to further the health of those who participate in its programs. Opportunities abound for the development of physical, mental, emotional, and social health in human beings. Physical education helps in the correction of remediable physical defects, alleviates tension, develops vitality, and offers a chance for emotional expression. The physical educator needs to be familiar with sound health practices and

should have experiences in the field of health. He will be a better physical educator if he has some preparation in health. Physical educators are involved with such things as injuries, medical examinations, physical fitness, and facility management, all of which have implications for the health of the participant.

Health education recognizes that physical activity contributes to health and sees games and sports as a means of making contributions to mental as well as other aspects of health.

Desirable health practices are objectives of both the fields of health education and physical education.

7. *Physical education is related to recreation, camping, and outdoor education.* Physical education develops many skills in such activities as dancing and sports which can be utilized in recreation, camping, and outdoor education settings. Physical education develops wholesome attitudes that emphasize the need and motivation for constructive recreational, camping, and outdoor education pursuits. Physical education facilities are frequently a part of recreation and camping programs. The basic instructional physical education program helps to develop proper attitudes for recreation. One of the strongest reasons for physical education programs to exist is the teaching of recreational skills.

8. *Health, recreation, camping, and outdoor education are related.* A widely accepted belief by professionals is that wholesome play and recreation are important to the total health of the individual. Practitioners of health, recreation, camping, and outdoor education are interested in the well-being of the people they serve. They are interested in relieving fatigue and tensions and in rehabilitating the sick, injured, and infirm. They are interested in helping people to live a healthy, vigorous, happy, and productive life.

9. *A rationale exists for a close relationship among health, physical education, recreation, camping, and outdoor education.* Leaders in all the special fields have pointed out why they feel the fields are related and why they should work together to achieve their objectives. All fields have some objectives that are similar. A strong unity among the fields can add strength to each area's place in education and society, and its success in achieving educational goals. A strong professional association combining all areas can help in furthering each separate area and the unique contributions each makes to the good of mankind. Personnel who are knowledgeable in two or three areas can help in furthering administrative efficiency and in contributing to the growth and prestige of these areas. Duplication of efforts can be avoided and less expense incurred as a result of a close coordination of all areas.

10. *A rationale exists for separating the areas of health, physical education, recreation, camping, and outdoor education.* Leaders in each of the special areas have also indicated reasons why the fields should be separated. Each has its own subject matter and trained specialists. An area like recreation is primarily voluntary in nature, whereas health and physical education are more formal in nature and primarily serve a captive audience. Recreation is more directly related to park executives, municipal recreation, and social agency personnel than it is to educators in the schools. Physical education is primarily concerned with such physical activities as games and sports, whereas recreation is concerned with the whole gamut of activities in which people engage, including drama, music, and arts and crafts. Health education is concerned with instruction in scientific health matters. The science and skills associated with health are different from those associated with physical education. Health educa-

tion is as much related to medicine and public health as it is to physical education. Camping and outdoor education are not related to physical education in some school, college, and agency programs.

11. *The relationship of health, physical education, recreation, camping, and outdoor education needs considerable study.* The very nature of the problem and the complexities involved defy a ready answer. Perhaps it would help to point out what Wegener* sets forth as functions of education:

The functions of education are: (1) to contribute to the systematic development of each individual toward his full potentialities in the intelligent pursuit of the good life, (2) to coordinate the progressive and conservative functions of an enduring society, (3) to serve the individual and society, and (4) to give man systematic assistance in the development of his whole self, intellectually, morally, spiritually, socially, economically, polit-

_____

*Wegener, Frank C.: The organic philosophy of education, Dubuque, Iowa, 1957, Wm. C. Brown Co.

ically, *physically,* domestically, aesthetically, and *recreationally.*

Health, physical education, recreation, camping, and outdoor education can contribute to the systematic development of man. Each of these fields has a unique and important contribution to make. Each of these fields is related in many ways to the other. The question to be decided is how each can make its contribution most effectively. In making the decision, personal considerations, petty annoyances, and selfish motives must be cast aside. The answer must rest with what is best for mankind and an enduring democratic society. In addition to considering the relationships of the special areas under discussion, it would also be wise to explore relationships with other disciplines, such as history, social work, medicine, social science, philosophy, and psychology. All professional disciplines might be viewed as potential members of a team. Such exploration may result in an arrangement where our special programs can make even greater contributions to the attainment of broad educational objectives and the development of man.

# Chapter 8

# School health program

The health program in the schools is a phase of the educational process that attempts to build in the student a sound foundation of scientific health knowledge, health attitudes, and health habits.

Health science, a comparatively new subject in the school program, derives its foundations from the biological, behavioral, and health sciences. It is an academic field and subject. It helps human beings to apply scientific health discoveries to their daily lives. It is best conducted in institutions of learning by professionally trained health educators.

The earliest forms of health programs in the schools were evidenced in the latter part of the nineteenth century and were concerned primarily with the temperance movement. A large amount of time was devoted to discussing the ill effects of alcohol on the human body. A state program of health instruction was introduced in Ohio in 1872 as a result of pressure on the part of the Women's Christian Temperance Union. Early instruction in health, other than that of temperance, emphasized a knowledge of the structure and function of the human body.

During the early part of the twentieth century a movement started that emphasized the formation of healthful attitudes and habits. Instead of stressing the names of the various anatomical parts of the human body or the harmful effects of alcohol, the emphasis was along the lines of better living.

On June 28, 1937, the Department of School Health and Physical Education of the National Education Association and the American Physical Education Association were combined to form the American Association for Health and Physical Education. This was in keeping with the rise of health to a place of importance in the educational system.

The results of the medical examinations, which were reported to Selective Service officials during World War II and which pointed out the incidence of dental caries, postural abnormalities, and other defects, gave impetus to an increased emphasis on health in our schools. These statistics also did much to stimulate thinking toward the better preparation of health teachers. Teacher-training institutions were called upon to make provision in their programs for such preparation.

Today, health programs in schools and colleges are gaining increasing stature as educators recognize the importance of instilling in young and old alike a body of health knowledge based on scientific fact, wholesome health attitudes, and desirable health practices. Health education is not unique to the United States. It is included in many educative programs throughout the world. For example, the chart on page 218 shows the organization of health education in the schools of Russia.

## WHY HEALTH EDUCATION?

There is a renewed interest in the area of school health because of the many problems that affect the health of young people. The increased incidence of smoking, self-medication, alcohol consumption, drug use, accidents, venereal disease, sexual experimentation, and physical inactivity are only a few of the many problems of concern to parents and communities throughout the country. It is felt that schools and colleges have a responsibility to do something to alleviate these problems. School and college health programs are being looked to for help. In order to have a health-oriented citizenry, it is essential that health education be offered during the formative school and college-age years.

Today, there is increased recognition that health education can play a very important role in eliminating many of the problems that adversely affect young people, as well as adults. It can provide the individual with scientific facts to make an informed decision. It can help to make individuals aware of their responsibility for their own health and also that of others.

Public health officials, medical doctors, dentists, and other representatives of professional services are taking more interest in health. More research in the health area is providing new and better directions to help schools and colleges in changing the health behavior of young people.

The future of America depends to a large degree upon what is done to improve the health of the students in the nation's schools and colleges. Although parents must help, institutions of learning must assume some responsibility for health education.

The School Health Education Study shows that health is not being taught properly in many schools at the present time. In some educational systems the curriculum is not planned, the teacher is not qualified, classes are too large and meet on a hit or miss basis, and the information imparted is not scientifically accurate.*

## PROGRESS IN SCHOOL HEALTH

School health programs have made great progress over the years. Five ways in which they have improved are as follows:

1. *Health education has changed from a hygiene class to one that is dynamically involved in the total health of the child.* Whereas the old-type programs were concerned with anatomy and physiology, today's health education programs include topics involving the basic needs and interests of students. Teaching methods and textbooks have been changed to meet the challenge by presenting health material in an interesting, attractive, challenging, and thought-provoking manner, designed to develop desirable health attitudes and practices in students.

2. *There is greater emphasis on safety and mental health.* The health problems of school children have changed in the last few decades. Communicable diseases are being brought under control, but in their place accidents have evolved as one of the important causes of death among school children. Also, emotional disturbances are widespread, making imperative the need for health instruction and health services aimed at furthering good mental health.

3. *Professional organizations contribute leadership.* Such organizations as the

*See page 219 for a more detailed description of the School Health Education Study.

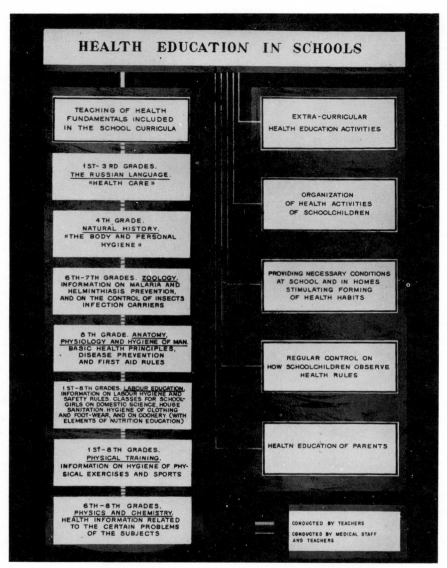

HEALTH EDUCATION IN SCHOOLS

| TEACHING OF HEALTH FUNDAMENTALS INCLUDED IN THE SCHOOL CURRICULA | EXTRA-CURRICULAR HEALTH EDUCATION ACTIVITIES |

1 ST- 3 RD GRADES. THE RUSSIAN LANGUAGE. «HEALTH CARE»

ORGANIZATION OF HEALTH ACTIVITIES OF SCHOOLCHILDREN

4 TH GRADE. NATURAL HISTORY. «THE BODY AND PERSONAL HYGIENE »

6 TH-7 TH GRADES. ZOOLOGY. INFORMATION ON MALARIA AND HELMINTHIASIS PREVENTION, AND ON THE CONTROL OF INSECTS INFECTION CARRIERS

PROVIDING NECESSARY CONDITIONS AT SCHOOL AND IN HOMES STIMULATING FORMING OF HEALTH HABITS

8 TH GRADE. ANATOMY, PHYSIOLOGY AND HYGIENE OF MAN. BASIC HEALTH PRINCIPLES, DISEASE PREVENTION AND FIRST AID RULES

1 ST-8 TH GRADES. LABOUR EDUCATION. INFORMATION ON LABOUR HYGIENE AND SAFETY RULES. CLASSES FOR SCHOOL-GIRLS ON DOMESTIC SCIENCE, HOUSE SANITATION, HYGIENE OF CLOTHING AND FOOT-WEAR, AND ON COOKERY (WITH ELEMENTS OF NUTRITION EDUCATION)

REGULAR CONTROL ON HOW SCHOOLCHILDREN OBSERVE HEALTH RULES

1 ST-8 TH GRADES. PHYSICAL TRAINING. INFORMATION ON HYGIENE OF PHYSICAL EXERCISES AND SPORTS

HEALTH EDUCATION OF PARENTS

6 TH-8 TH GRADES. PHYSICS AND CHEMISTRY. HEALTH INFORMATION RELATED TO THE CERTAIN PROBLEMS OF THE SUBJECTS

CONDUCTED BY TEACHERS
CONDUCTED BY MEDICAL STAFF AND TEACHERS

Hoyman, Howard S.: *Journal of School Health* 33:57, Feb., 1963.

Health education in the schools of Russia.

American Association for Health, Physical Education, and Recreation, American School Health Association, National Education Association, and the American Medical Association have sponsored in-service programs, workshops, and research, and provided other forms of help and leadership for school health programs in the United States.

4. *Teacher preparation has been upgraded.* Numerous professional conferences have been held that have tended to raise the standards of preparation for classroom teachers, health educators, phys-

ical educators, and other personnel associated with school health programs.

5. *Books have been published that have resulted in a broader understanding of health education in the schools.* Such publications as *Health Education, Healthful School Living,* and *School Health Services,* sponsored by the Joint Committee on Health Problems of the National Education Association and the American Medical Association, as well as those publications authored or sponsored by many leaders and organizations in the field of health, have served to assist in communicating articulately the important place that health plays in modern educational programs.

## SCHOOL HEALTH EDUCATION STUDY

A significant study in the area of health education is the School Health Education Study. The Study conducted a nationwide status study of health education in the public schools, including the testing of students at all grade levels. It produced information on the kind of instruction students receive, what health misconceptions they have, who does the teaching, the content areas that are emphasized, how the subject is organized and scheduled, and many other factors of importance to educators and to all persons interested in the health of children and youth.

The Study was initiated in September, 1961, and involved such procedures as a survey of 135 public school systems, the health practices of approximately six million students in more than one thousand elementary schools, and 359 secondary schools. It also included the development of experimental curriculum materials and an experimental curriculum demonstration project in four school system tryout centers: Alhambra, California; Evanston, Illinois; Great Neck–Garden City, New York; and Tacoma, Washington. The results have been very favorable and work

is proceeding so that the results of this study may be available to all schools throughout the nation.

The Study has had the services of an interdisciplinary advisory committee of individuals, with representatives from national health-education-related organizations serving as ex-officio members of the committee. Dr. Elena M. Sliepcevich has served as Director of the School Health Education Study since its beginning.

The concept approach to teaching various subject matter fields of specialization has won much acclaim in educational circles in recent years. It is felt that the decisions that people make and their behavior patterns are determined largely by their concepts. Concepts that evolve can have an impact on cognitive (knowledge, intellectual abilities, and skills) and affective (values, attitudes, and appreciations) domains. Recognizing the value of the concept approach, the School Health Education Study developed, on an experimental basis, an outline, *A Conceptual Approach to Health Education.*

The concept approach outlined by the School Health Education Study recognizes the three closely interwoven dimensions of health: mental, physical, and social. Furthermore, it stresses the triad of health education—the unity of man in respect to his physical, mental, and social aspects; the knowledges, attitudes, and practices, as factors important to influencing health behavior; and the focus of health education upon the individual, family, and community. All of these components of the triad are interdependent and constantly interacting.

The Study identified three key concepts, ten conceptual statements, and thirty-one substantive elements that represent the conceptual framework for health.

Another important health education study is the one conducted by the Curriculum Commission of the American As-

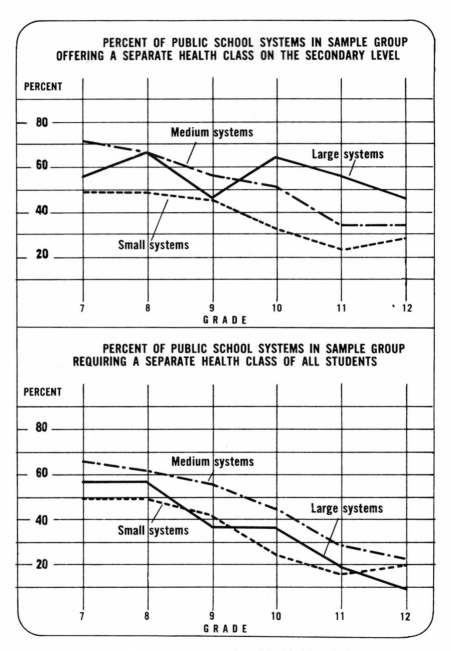

PERCENT OF PUBLIC SCHOOL SYSTEMS IN SAMPLE GROUP
OFFERING A SEPARATE HEALTH CLASS ON THE SECONDARY LEVEL

PERCENT OF PUBLIC SCHOOL SYSTEMS IN SAMPLE GROUP
REQUIRING A SEPARATE HEALTH CLASS OF ALL STUDENTS

*From School health study: Summary report of a
nationwide study of health instruction in the public
schools, 1961 to 1963, Washington, D. C., 1964,
School Health Education Study.*

HEALTH
CONCEPTS
guides for
health
instruction

Concepts and supporting data
pertaining to major health
problems facing youth today

American Association for Health,
Physical Education, and Recreation

*AAHPER Health Education Division:*
*Health concepts—guides for health instruction,*
*Washington, D. C., 1967, The Association.*

sociation for Health, Physical Education, and Recreation.*

This study includes the identification of key concepts and supporting data pertaining to some of the major health problems of today and those that will exist in the next decade. This material will be helpful as a reference for teachers, curriculum committees, and other persons interested in some of the main health problems facing young people today. It covers

---

*American Association for Health, Physical Education, and Recreation: Health concepts—guides for health instruction, Washington, D. C., 1967, The Association.

such important health areas as accident prevention, aging, alcohol, disaster preparedness, disease, economics of health care, environmental conditions, food protection, occupational health, air pollution, radiation, family health, international health, mental health, nutrition, and smoking.

## TERMINOLOGY FOR SCHOOL AND COLLEGE HEALTH PROGRAMS

The following definitions were drawn up by the Committee on Terminology which represented the American Association for Health, Physical Education, and

Recreation, the Society of Public Health Educators, and the American Public Health Association. They are presented here for the reader's information.*

**Dental examination.** The appraisal, performed by a dentist, of the condition of the oral structures to determine the dental health status of the individual.

**Dental inspection.** The limited appraisal, performed by anyone with or without special dental preparation, of the oral structures to determine the presence or absence of obvious defects.

**Health appraisal.** The evaluation of the health status of the individual through the utilization of varied organized and systematic procedures such as medical and dental examinations, laboratory test, health history, teacher observation, etc.

**Health observation.** The estimation of an individual's well-being by noting the nature of his appearance and behavior.

**Medical examination.** The determination, by a physician, of an individual's health status.

**Screening test.** A medically and educationally acceptable procedure for identifying individuals who need to be referred for further study or diagnostic examination.

**Cumulative school health record.** A form used to note pertinent consecutive information about a student's health.

**School health program.** The composite of procedures used in school health services, healthful school living, and health science instruction to promote health among students and school personnel.

**Healthful school living.** The utilization of a safe and wholesome environment, consideration of individual health, organizing the school day, and planning classroom procedures to favorably influence emotional, social, and physical health.

**Health school environment.** The physical, social, and emotional factors of the school setting which affect the health, comfort, and performance of an individual or a group.

**Health science instruction.** The organized teaching procedures directed toward developing understandings, attitudes, and practices relating to health and factors affecting health.

**School health services.** The procedures used

*Report of the Joint Committee on Health Education Terminology, Journal of Health, Physical Education, and Recreation **33**:27, Nov., 1962.

by physicians, dentists, nurses, teachers, etc., designed to appraise, protect, and promote optimum health of students and school personnel. (Activities frequently included in school health services are those used to (1) appraise the health status of students and school personnel; (2) counsel students, teachers, parents, and others for the purpose of helping school-age children get treatment or for arranging education programs in keeping with their abilities; (3) help prevent or control the spread of disease; and (4) provide emergency care for injury or sudden sickness.)

**School health education.** The process of providing or utilizing experiences for favorably influencing understandings, attitudes, and practices relating to individual, family, and community health.

**Safety education.** The process of providing or utilizing experiences for favorably influencing understandings, attitudes, and practices relating to safe living.

**Health counseling.** A method of interpreting to students or their parents the findings of health appraisals and encouraging and assisting them to take such action as needed to realize their fullest potential.

**School health coordination.** A process designed to bring about harmonious working relationship among the various personnel and groups in the school and community that have interest, concern, and responsibility for development and conduct of the school health program.

## RELATIONSHIP OF PHYSICAL EDUCATION TO SCHOOL HEALTH PROGRAM

For many years the relationship of physical education to health has been a confused issue. Among professional persons working in these specialized programs this confusion has abated to some degree since the end of World War II, but among educators and lay people in general there is still considerable misunderstanding. Many school administrators feel that a program of physical activity satisfies the health needs of children. Some persons feel that training in physical education qualifies a person for full-time work in health. Still others feel that health and physical education are allied but not the same and that each requires trained spe-

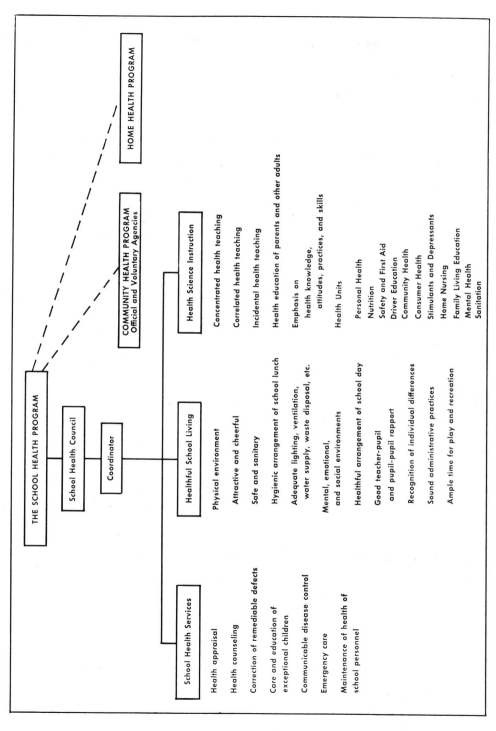

Suggested health education for the schools of the United States.

cialists. The continued emphasis on having qualified teachers of health has resulted in major programs specifically designed to provide the training essential to teaching health being established in professional-preparing institutions.

From the foregoing discussion it can be seen that health and physical education are not synonymous and their activities are different. At the same time, they have common goals and are closely related, and physical education personnel can play an important part in school health programs. Although concentrated or direct health instruction is desirable, health education should take place not only in the classroom but on the athletic field, playground, swimming pool, gymnasium, and in every other room and part of the school plant. The health program utilizes the services of the doctor, nurse, dentist, physical educator, home economics teacher, and other specialized personnel in furthering its program of health instruction, health services, and healthful school living.

Many schools find it impossible to have both a health educator and a physical educator on the staff. In such cases the physical educator who has adequate training in health can do much in the way of organizing and coordinating a working health program. In larger communities where sufficient funds make it possible to have personnel with broader training and experience in the health education area, the physical educator can still play a prominent part in teaching health education classes and helping in various other health activities. In all cases the physical educator, through the program of physical activities, can play a major role in contributing to the health of every child with whom he works.

Physical educators interested in the field of health should, in addition to having a working knowledge of many health areas, know the health aspects of physical activity and the outcomes of sports and activity programs that have implications for the individual's physical, emotional, and social welfare. There is also a need for physical educators to know what constitutes desirable activities, the special problems of physical education relating to girls and women, and the need for a knowledge of such things as first aid, body mechanics, and adapted physical education.

The Third National Conference on Physicians and Schools sponsored by the American Medical Association recommended that coaches should be adequately prepared in "(1) principles of growth and development; (2) health needs of adolescent boys and girls; (3) desirable health practices, particularly those related to the conduct of athletics; (4) principles of first aid and accident prevention; (5) physiology of exercise; (6) conduct of interscholastic athletics so their maximum contribution may be made to the physical, emotional, mental, and social development of youth."*

In discussing the relationship of physical education to school health, it can be seen that each is closely related to the other, but at the same time, each is distinct. Each area has its own specialized subject-matter content, its specialists, and media through which it is striving to better the living standards of human beings. In the larger professional-preparing institutions, each area has its own separate training program. In several states each area has its own certification requirements.

There is, however, a close relationship between health and physical education teachers since, in many cases, they use the same facilities, perform work in each other's area, work on committees together, and have professional books and magazines which cover the literature of both

*Dukelow, Donald A., and Hein, Fred C., editors: Physicians and schools, report of the Third National Conference on Physicians and Schools, Chicago, 1952, American Medical Association, pp. 29-30.

fields. Both are concerned with the total health of the individual. Both recognize the importance of activity in developing and maintaining good personal health. Both are concerned with the physical as well as the social, mental, emotional, and spiritual aspects of health. Both are interested in promoting the total health of the public at large as a means to enriched living, accomplishment of worthy goals, and increased happiness.

In discussing the relationship of health and physical education, one thing should be stressed above all others: there must be cooperation between the two. In working toward their objectives, personnel must be utilized in a way that will be most advantageous in furthering the health and happiness of all with whom they come in contact. Facilities, supplies, and equipment must often be shared. Programs must be planned cooperatively and the objectives kept closely in mind. Both should help one another and follow practices that will provide the most benefits for the greatest number of people.

## HOW MANY PHYSICAL EDUCATORS TEACH HEALTH?

A survey conducted a few years ago by Sliepcevich,* which involved writing to each of the state directors of health, physical education, and recreation in the fifty states and requesting information as to what percentage of the health education offered in the junior and senior high schools was taught by physical educators, provided these interesting statistics:

1. The health education being taught in the schools by physical educators ranges all the way from 10% to "nearly all."
2. More than 90% of the health education is being taught by physical educators in 8 states.
3. 90% of the health education is being taught by physical educators in 9 states.
4. 80 to 85% of the health education is

---

*Sliepcevich, Elena M.: Journal of Health, Physical Education, and Recreation 32:32, Jan., 1961.

taught by physical educators in 5 states.
5. 75% of the health education is being taught by physical educators in 4 states.
6. 50 to 70% of the health education is being taught by physical educators in 16 states.

These statistics showed that in approximately one third of the states 75% or more of the health education was being taught by physical educators, and in twenty-one states 70% or less of the health education was being taught by physical educators. The record shows clearly that at the time this survey was conducted, most of the health education classes in this country were being taught by physical educators.

During the intervening years there seems to have been a trend toward more trained health educators assuming the responsibility for teaching health classes. However, many physical educators still continue to teach health classes in the nation's schools.

## QUALITY OF HEALTH TEACHING

Sliepcevich also lists the results of other surveys that reflected the quality of the health teaching in the secondary schools. In many cases a poor teaching job was being done. Some of the reasons listed for poor health instruction are as follows:

1. Poor preparation
2. Teachers not interested
3. Health education conducted only on rainy days
4. Large classes
5. Repetitious
6. Poor methodology
7. Out-dated textbooks
8. Poor facilities
9. Dull environment

In some instances where a poor job was being done, physical educators were doing the teaching. In such cases the reason for the "poor job" was sometimes because of other interests and pressures, lack of enthusiasm, inadequate preparation, and/or too many duties to perform.

Sliepcevich also listed some guides that needed to be followed if the quality of

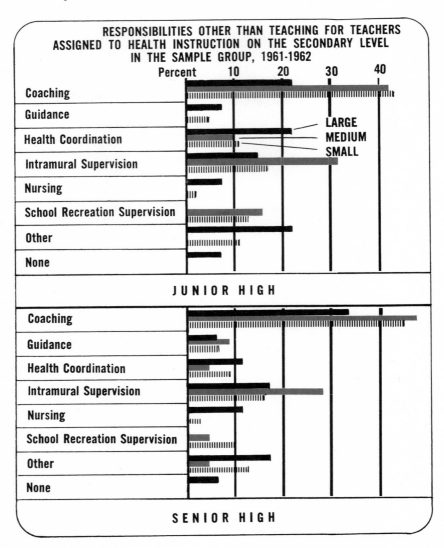

*From School health study: Summary report of a nationwide study of health instruction in the public schools, 1961 to 1963, Washington, D. C., 1964, School Health Education Study.*

health instruction by physical educators is to be improved.

1. Physical educators need training in physical and life sciences, such as anatomy, chemistry, bacteriology, and genetics. There is also a need for training in the behavioral sciences, such as social anthropology and psychology.

2. All physical educators should have the equivalent of at least a minor in health education because it is likely they will be required to teach health.

3. When assigning health teaching to physical educators, school administrators should recognize the great amount of time needed for the preparation and teaching of health. In addition, the variety of teaching methods required, resources available, and need for motivating pupils also require enormous amounts of time and effort on the part of the teacher.

4. Physical educators need to be impressed with the responsibility they have for making a contribution to the improvement of health instruction. This requires adequate pre-service and in-service preparation, which in addition to subject-matter content in health, also requires a familiarity with curriculum development and the basic principles involved in the integrating and correlating of health content with other subjects in the school program.

5. Physical educators who are interested in and have the necessary competencies for good health teaching should strive to become certified in this special field.

Johns* has developed a set of guidelines for effective health teaching based on such things as research data, thinking of experienced teachers, and personal experience. They are presented here in outline and adapted form.

Effective health teaching requires an outstanding teacher because:

**The teacher is the key to good health teaching.** Therefore, the teacher must be well-prepared, interested, emotionally stable, intelligent, and resourceful.

**Effective health teaching requires adequate time comparable to other important academic subjects.** Adequate time is needed in the school program if the desired information is to be communicated and the lives of children and youth are to be affected.

**Effective health teaching means the teacher should view health teaching as a science and an art.** The teacher must keep up to date in regard to the latest information in regard to health, and also teach in a manner that enables the student to identify with the material being taught.

**Effective health teaching means that the resources of both the school and the community are utilized.** Such school resources as health materials, library, and health office must be utilized. In addition, the resources of the community, such as provided by professional, voluntary, and official health agencies, must be mobilized.

**Effective health teaching means careful planning.** The health teacher must plan in a meaningful manner for the teaching experi-

ence, including conferences with such persons as the school nurse and school physician, an analysis of home and community health conditions, and meetings with students.

**Effective health teaching means that the teacher knows his students.** The teacher of health must know the problems and needs of his students, the health knowledge they possess, the health practices they follow, and other vital information about their health status. In addition, the teacher must be acquainted with the instruments and techniques that are utilized to obtain this information.

**Effective health teaching means that the teacher formulates objectives in relation to outcomes desired.** The teacher must know the behavioral changes desired in his students, not just the knowledge to be gained.

**Effective health teaching means that the teacher organizes material and experiences so they are meaningful to the student.** This means that the teacher can so organize the material to be used that key concepts are identified and have meaning and purpose for the students.

**Effective health teaching means that methods, procedures, and techniques are functional.** Motivation is one of the most important considerations in an effective learning situation. As such, methods, procedures, and techniques will play an important role in determining the effectiveness of health teaching.

**Effective health teaching means that the materials are scientifically accurate and up to date.** This means that textbooks must be up to date, current periodicals are used, and criteria established and used for selecting materials that are authoritative.

**Effective health teaching means that evaluation takes place.** The teacher should utilize an evaluation procedure using scientific instruments and techniques to determine the degree to which objectives that have been established are met.

**Effective health teaching also means the provision for a healthful and wholesome environment.** A proper environment takes into consideration proper lighting, heating, and ventilation standards; audiovisual instruction; and other factors that are conducive to learning.

## AREAS OF SCHOOL HEALTH PROGRAM

The school health program is divided into three parts: teaching for health, liv-

---

*Johns, Edward B.: Effective health teaching, The Journal of School Health **34:**123, March, 1964.

Health instruction lecture at Evergreen Park High School, Evergreen Park, Ill.

ing healthfully at school, and services for health improvement.

### Teaching for health*

The school has a major responsibility in the area of health instruction. It should instruct youth in such things as the structure and functioning of their bodies, the causes and methods of preventing certain diseases, the factors that contribute to and maintain good health, and the role of the community in the health program. Such an instructional program, if planned wisely and taught intelligently, will contribute to good health habits and attitudes on the part of the student.

Health instruction should avoid too much stress on the field of disease and medicine. This is pointed out by Dr. Bauer, health authority, in an article entitled "Teach Health, Not Disease." He says that teachers should primarily teach health, how to live correctly, and how to protect one's body against infection,

rather than teaching disease and medicine. Proper health instruction should impress upon each individual his responsibility for his own health and, as a member of a community, for the health of others.

Teaching for health should take place in many ways in the school. There should be provision for concentrated health teaching in courses specifically set up for this purpose. Health teaching should also take place in other subjects in which aspects of health are covered. An example of this would be the subject of nutrition in a home economics course. In addition, such instruction should take place incidentally every time a "teachable moment" occurs. Furthermore, through many school experiences such as the school lunch and the medical examination, opportunities arise for teaching health.

Major health areas covered in teaching for health are as follows:

1. Personal living
2. Nutrition
3. Sanitation

*See also discussion of development of health knowledge, p. 238.

4. Community health
5. Consumer health
6. Mental and emotional health
7. Stimulants and depressants
8. Family life education
9. Safety education
10. First aid
11. Home nursing
12. Driver education

The School Health Education Study indicated current practices in the health topics offered in schools throughout the United States (see accompanying charts). Content areas most frequently covered in health science courses at all grade levels included food and nutrition, exercise and relaxation, accident prevention, cleanli-

ness and grooming, and dental health. From the fourth to twelfth grades, such topics as posture and body mechanics, rest and sleep, vision and hearing, and communicable diseases were introduced. At the seventh grade, boy-girl relationships, smoking, and structure and function of the human body were introduced in a majority of the school districts surveyed. Topics most frequently omitted by school districts include boy-girl relationships, consumer education, health careers, international health activities, sex education, venereal diseases, noncommunicable diseases, and foot care.

The personnel chiefly involved in in-

**Table 8-1.** *Health worries of secondary school students**

| | Per cent indicating worries | | | | | | | | | |
|---|---|---|---|---|---|---|---|---|---|---|
| | Grade level | | | | | | | | | |
| Health worries | 9 | 10 | 11 | 12 | 13 | 14 | Total | G† | B | P |
| Cancer | 50 | 73 | 53 | 47 | 49 | 53 | 54 | 59 | 50 | — |
| What I'll be like in 15 years | 34 | 70 | 43 | 43 | 40 | 30 | 44 | 47 | 40 | — |
| Automobile accidents | 27 | 63 | 43 | 30 | 30 | 33 | 38 | 39 | 37 | — |
| Personal grooming | 30 | 33 | 40 | 37 | 37 | 37 | 35 | 45 | 26 | 0.01 |
| Dental problems | 44 | 47 | 33 | 34 | 7 | 27 | 33 | 36 | 31 | — |
| Lack of exercise | 30 | 33 | 30 | 17 | 38 | 44 | 31 | 39 | 23 | 0.01 |
| Dandruff | 27 | 43 | 43 | 30 | 23 | 20 | 31 | 31 | 31 | — |
| Acne | 14 | 50 | 33 | 37 | 35 | 10 | 30 | 35 | 24 | 0.01 |
| Overweight | 13 | 30 | 30 | 24 | 47 | 33 | 29 | 45 | 13 | 0.01 |
| Lack of sex knowledge | 23 | 47 | 37 | 24 | 17 | 30 | 20 | 27 | 30 | — |
| Leukemia | 14 | 47 | 23 | 34 | 33 | 20 | 28 | 31 | 27 | — |
| Mental illness | 17 | 47 | 17 | 23 | 20 | 40 | 27 | 39 | 15 | 0.01 |
| Childbirth | 40 | 30 | 17 | 20 | 30 | 10 | 25 | 48 | 3 | 0.01 |
| Ability to have children | 40 | 27 | 20 | 20 | 14 | 27 | 25 | 38 | 11 | 0.01 |
| Drowning | 27 | 33 | 17 | 20 | 20 | 20 | 23 | 26 | 20 | — |
| Underweight | 44 | 10 | 13 | 27 | 13 | 20 | 22 | 14 | 29 | 0.01 |
| Unpleasant breath odor | 17 | 53 | 3 | 10 | 37 | 20 | 22 | 20 | 23 | — |
| Blindness | 24 | 37 | 23 | 10 | 20 | 17 | 21 | 21 | 22 | — |
| Vitamin deficiencies | 14 | 7 | 23 | 14 | 20 | 30 | 18 | 18 | 18 | — |
| Being burned | 20 | 33 | 7 | 17 | 7 | 10 | 16 | 21 | 12 | — |
| Frequent headaches | 17 | 24 | 17 | 7 | 23 | 10 | 16 | 17 | 14 | — |
| Body odor | 14 | 30 | 10 | 14 | 10 | 7 | 14 | 16 | 12 | — |
| Losing leg or arm | 14 | 22 | 7 | 7 | 22 | 7 | 13 | 9 | 13 | — |
| Venereal diseases | 14 | 17 | 10 | 7 | 15 | 7 | 11 | 10 | 11 | — |
| Poison by gas | 4 | 7 | 10 | 16 | 4 | 4 | 7 | 8 | 7 | — |

*From Dowell, Linus J.: A study of selected health education implications, The Research Quarterly **37**:29, March, 1966.

†*Symbols read:* G = Girls; B = Boys; P = Level of confidence found by the chi square test of significant differences between boys and girls in health worries.

**Table 8-2.** *Health interests of secondary school students**

| Health interests | Per cent indicating interest by grade level | | | | | | Per cent of interest | | | |
|---|---|---|---|---|---|---|---|---|---|---|
| | 9 | 10 | 11 | 12 | 13 | 14 | Total | G† | B | P |
| Emotions | 57 | 43 | 47 | 67 | 57 | 57 | 54 | 67 | 42 | 0.01 |
| Fitness | 53 | 47 | 73 | 67 | 47 | 33 | 53 | 48 | 59 | 0.01 |
| Drugs | 54 | 33 | 43 | 60 | 43 | 67 | 50 | 59 | 41 | 0.01 |
| Heredity | 27 | 37 | 47 | 46 | 40 | 60 | 47 | 51 | 43 | — |
| Weight control | 40 | 43 | 50 | 37 | 64 | 44 | 46 | 62 | 30 | 0.01 |
| Reproduction | 44 | 33 | 63 | 33 | 53 | 46 | 45 | 49 | 42 | — |
| Posture | 64 | 57 | 53 | 30 | 40 | 30 | 45 | 55 | 35 | 0.01 |
| Diseases (communicable) | 34 | 47 | 53 | 30 | 43 | 43 | 42 | 40 | 44 | — |
| Alcohol | 37 | 33 | 33 | 27 | 37 | 53 | 37 | 30 | 43 | 0.01 |
| Medical care | 33 | 50 | 37 | 33 | 30 | 33 | 36 | 41 | 31 | 0.01 |
| Skin | 27 | 30 | 37 | 37 | 44 | 34 | 35 | 55 | 15 | 0.01 |
| Rest and sleep | 43 | 53 | 23 | 14 | 27 | 37 | 33 | 30 | 36 | — |
| Noncommunicable diseases | 23 | 60 | 40 | 24 | 13 | 33 | 32 | 40 | 24 | 0.01 |
| Eyes | 30 | 37 | 43 | 20 | 24 | 30 | 31 | 40 | 21 | 0.01 |
| Nutritional needs | 27 | 10 | 40 | 10 | 30 | 34 | 24 | 27 | 21 | — |
| Foods | 17 | 13 | 33 | 17 | 33 | 17 | 21 | 21 | 22 | — |
| Immunity | 17 | 13 | 20 | 10 | 10 | 20 | 15 | 15 | 16 | — |
| Water | 14 | 7 | 7 | 17 | 17 | 10 | 13 | 13 | 13 | — |
| Ears | 4 | 20 | 20 | 7 | 13 | 7 | 12 | 9 | 14 | — |
| Ventilation | 7 | 10 | 0 | 7 | 0 | 13 | 6 | 7 | 6 | — |
| Digestion–utilization | 4 | 0 | 10 | 0 | 7 | 7 | 5 | 5 | 5 | — |

*From Dowell, Linus J.: A study of selected health education implications, The Research Quarterly **37**:28, March, 1966.

†*Symbols read:* G = Girls; B = Boys; P = Level of confidence found by the chi square test of significant differences between boys and girls in health interests.

structing and in transmitting health knowledge to students include the health educator, elementary school teacher, physical education teacher, biology teacher, general science teacher, home economics teacher, social studies teacher, school nurse, dental hygienist, school lunch manager, and parents.

The physical educator who is teaching health should do the following:

1. Discover the health needs and interests of pupils
2. Organize meaningful health units in terms of health needs and interests of pupils
3. Know thoroughly the subject matter that is imparted to pupils
4. Possess an understanding of what constitutes a well-rounded school health program and the teacher's part in it
5. Utilize problem solving and other recommended methods in teaching for health

6. Possess an enthusiasm for the teaching of health
7. Take time to prepare thoroughly for classes
8. Make classes interesting and exciting experiences for the students
9. Provide students with opportunities to participate and exercise their initiative
10. Use up-to-date textbooks which have been carefully evaluated as to their worth for classes
11. Provide an attractive setting for classes
12. Tap the many resources in the school and community that are available and that will make health teaching more dynamic
13. Assist students in solving their own health problems

### Living healthfully at school

The second area into which the school health program may be divided is that of healthful school living. This implies that

## HEALTH CONTENT AREAS EMPHASIZED IN GRADES K TO 8 BY 50 PERCENT OR MORE OF THE RESPONDENTS IN SAMPLE GROUP OF PUBLIC SCHOOL SYSTEMS, 1961-1962

| HEALTH CONTENT AREAS | K | 1 | 2 | 3 | 4 | 5 | 6 | 7–8 |
|---|---|---|---|---|---|---|---|---|
| Accident Prevention | ●○• | ●○• | ●○• | ●○• | ●○• | ●○• | ●○• | • |
| Alcohol | | | | | | ○ | | • |
| Boy-Girl Relationships | | | | | | | | • |
| Cleanliness and Grooming | ●○• | ●○• | ●○• | ●○• | ●○• | ●○• | ●○• | • |
| Communicable Diseases | ○ | ●○ | ●○• | ●○• | ●○• | ●○• | ●○• | • |
| Community Health Programs | | | | | ●○ | ●○ | ●○ | |
| Community Helpers | ●○• | ●○• | ●○• | ●○ | ●○ | • | • | |
| Consumer Education | | | | | | | | |
| Dental Health | ●○• | ●○• | ●○• | ●○• | ●○• | ●○• | ●○• | • |
| Drugs and Narcotics | | | | | | | • | • |
| Environmental Hazards | | | | | | ○• | ○• | |
| Exercise and Relaxation | ●○• | ●○• | ●○• | ●○• | ●○• | ●○• | ●○• | • |
| Family Life | ●○ | ○ | ○ | ○ | ○ | ○ | ○ | |
| First Aid | ○ | ○ | ○ | ○ | ○• | ○• | ○• | • |
| Foot Care | | | | | | | | |
| Food and Nutrition | ●○• | ●○• | ●○• | ●○• | ●○• | ●○• | ●○• | • |
| Health Careers | | | | | | | | |
| Health Examination and Appraisals | ●○ | • | • | • | ●○ | ●○ | ●○ | |
| Health Heroes | | | | | • | | | |
| International Health Activities | | | | | | | | |
| Mental Health and Personal Adjustment | | | | | ●○ | ●○ | ●○ | • |
| Non-Communicable Diseases | | | | | | | | |
| Personality Development | ○ | ○ | ○ | ●○ | ●○ | ●○• | ●○• | • |
| Physical Changes During Growth and Development | ○ | | | | | • | ●○• | |
| Posture and Body Mechanics | ●○ | ●○• | ●○• | ●○• | ●○• | ●○• | ●○• | • |
| Rest and Sleep | ○• | ●○• | ●○• | ●○• | ●○• | ●○• | ●○• | • |
| Sex Education | | | | | | | | |
| Skin Care | | | | | • | • | • | • |
| Smoking | | | | | | • | • | • |
| Structure and Function of the Human Body | | | | | ○ | • | • ●○• | • |
| Venereal Disease | | | | | | | | |
| Vision and Hearing | ○ | ●○ | ●○ | ●○• | ●○• | ●○• | ●○• | • |

● LARGE  ○ MEDIUM  • SMALL

*From School health study: Summary report of a nationwide study of health instruction in the public schools, 1961 to 1963, Washington, D. C., 1964, School Health Education Study.*

## HEALTH CONTENT AREAS EMPHASIZED IN GRADES 7 TO 12 BY 50 PERCENT OR MORE OF THE RESPONDENTS IN SAMPLE GROUP OF PUBLIC SCHOOL SYSTEMS, 1961-1962

| HEALTH CONTENT AREAS | GRADE LEVELS | | | | | |
|---|---|---|---|---|---|---|
| | 7 | 8 | 9 | 10 | 11 | 12 |
| Accident Prevention and First Aid | ●○• | ●○• | ●○• | ●○• | ●○• | ●○• |
| Alcohol, Drugs and Narcotics | ○• | ○• | ○• | ●○• | ●○• | ●○• |
| Boy-Girl Relationships | ●○• | ●○• | ●○• | ●○• | ●○• | ●○• |
| Cleanliness and Grooming | ●○• | ●○• | ●○• | ●○• | ●○• | ●○• |
| Communicable Diseases | ●○• | ●○• | ●○• | ●○• | ●○• | ●○• |
| Community Health Programs | • | ●○ | • | • | ●○ | ○• |
| Consumer Education | | • | • | • • | • | • • |
| Dental Health | ●○• | ●○• | ●○• | ●○• | ●○ • | ●○ • |
| Environmental Hazards | • • | • | | • | ○• | ●○• |
| Exercise, Rest and Sleep | ●○• | ●○• | ●○• | ●○• | ●○• | ●○• |
| Health Careers | • | • | | | | • |
| International Health Activities | | | | | | ○ |
| Mental Health and Personal Adjustment | ●○ | ●○ | ●○• | ●○• | ●○• | ●○• |
| Non-Communicable Diseases | ○• | ●○• | ●○• | ●○• | ●○• | ●○• |
| Nutrition | ●○• | ●○• | ●○• | ●○• | ●○• | ●○• |
| Parenthood and Child Care | | | | ○• | ●○• | ○• |
| Physical Changes During Adolescence | ●○• | ●○• | ○• | ●○• | • • | • |
| Posture and Body Mechanics | ●○• | ●○• | ●○• | ●○• | ●○• | ●○• |
| Preparation for Marriage | | | | | ○• | ○• |
| Research Developments in Health and Medical Science | | | | | | |
| Smoking | ●○• | ●○• | ●○• | ●○• | ●○• | ●○• |
| Structure and Function of the Human Body | ●○• | ●○• | ●○• | ●○• | ●○• | • |
| Venereal Disease | | | | ○• | ○• | ○ |
| Vision and Hearing | ●○• | ●○• | ●○• | ●○• | ●○• | ●○• |
| Weight Control | ○ | ○ | ●○• | ●○• | ●○• | ●○• |

● LARGE      ○ MEDIUM      • SMALL

*From School health study: Summary report of a nationwide study of health instruction in the public schools, 1961 to 1963, Washington, D. C., 1964, School Health Education Study.*

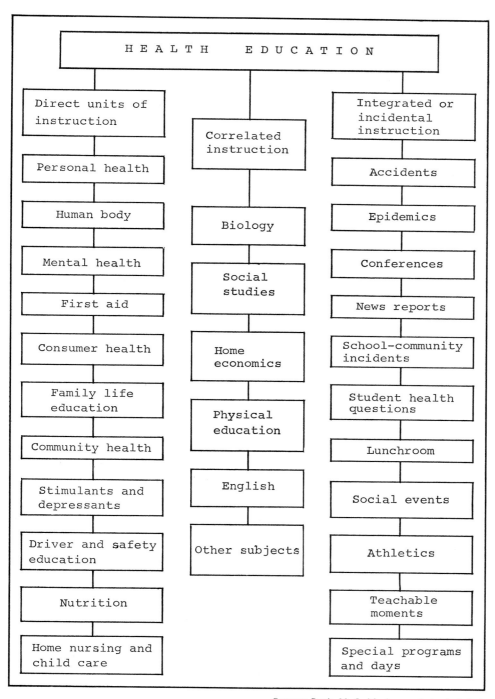

Courtesy Bettie M. Smith, former doctoral student,
New York University, New York, N. Y.

Organization of health education science instruction.

the time children spend in school should be spent in an environment and atmosphere that is conducive to physical, social, mental, and emotional health. The environment will be sanitary and cheerful, the teacher will have a pleasing personality, the school program will be well balanced, and educational methods will be in accordance with good health standards.

A sanitary and cheerful school environment has implications for healthful school living. Such factors as proper lighting, ventilation, facilities, play areas, and proper seating should be taken into consideration. The teacher, administrator, and custodian all play an important part in accomplishing this objective. The teacher must assume responsibility for the classroom. Among other things, she should see that the classroom is at an optimum temperature, is clean, has adequate lighting, and is equipped with seats that fit the childen. The administrator and custodian should see that the school in general meets proper healthful living standards and that the teacher is given help and support in her attempts to accomplish this objective.

The teacher's personality has a strong bearing on the health of the child. The teacher should have a sense of humor, ready smile, sympathetic attitude, and good health. This will help the child to adjust satisfactorily to school living, to enjoy his time in school, to have a successful experience, and to feel that he belongs.

A well-balanced school program is a necessity for healthful school living. There must be adequate time for rest, relaxation, play, and study. Close work with books and writing materials should not be of such length as to cause undue fatigue. Play periods should be of adequate length to enable the child to have sufficient exercise. Lunch periods should be long enough to allow for leisurely eating.

Educational methods should be in accordance with good health practices. Class size should be such as to allow the teacher to give personal attention to each student and at the same time allow for group experiences. The teaching load should not be too demanding of the teacher's time and efforts. Promotion policies should conform to what is in the best interests of the child's health. Home-school relationships should allow for adequately knowing the child's background and permitting parents to be informed as to the child's progress in school. Homework should contribute to the development of the whole child, which takes into consideration his so-called academic needs and also his needs in respect to such essentials as recreation, leisure, and play.

Personnel involved in providing a healthful school environment are the school administrator, classroom teacher, custodian, city health department, sanitarian, school physician, school nurse, health educator, physical educator, school bus driver, and school lunch director.

The physical educator interested in students living healthfully at school should do as follows:

1. Meet with the school physician, nurse, and others in order to determine how best to contribute to a healthful environment
2. Participate in the work of the school health council; if none exists, interpret the need for one
3. Provide experiences for living healthfully at school
4. Help pupils assume an increasing responsibility for a clean and sanitary environment
5. Try in every way possible to obtain good mental health in order to be a living example for the students
6. Set an example for the child in healthful living
7. Motivate the child to be well and happy
8. Help supervise various activities that directly affect health, such as school lunch, rest periods, etc.
9. Be aware of individual differences of pupils

10. Keep emotions under control at all times

11. Provide in every way possible for the safety of pupils so that accidents may be kept to a minimum

12. Check regularly the temperature, ventilation, lighting, water supply, waste disposal, and other physical features to see that they provide for the health of students

## Services for health improvement

Health services are an important part of any school health program. The health services of the school should include health appraisal and counseling, correction of remediable defects, emergency care of sickness and injury, communicable disease control and prevention, and education of the exceptional child.

Health appraisal and counseling are achieved in the schools as a result of medical, dental, and psychological examinations; teachers' observations; screening tests for vision and hearing; and records of growth and height statistics. The best results in these various phases of health appraisal are obtained when medical examinations are given before entering school and each year that the child is in school, when vision and hearing tests are given annually, and when there is continual teacher observation. As a result of the findings of the various examinations and observations, health counseling should take place as conditions warrant, with both pupils and parents.

Although it is usually recognized by authorities in the field of health that it is desirable to have complete medical examinations every year, this is not regarded as being practical by many school administrators. In such cases a *minimum* program would provide for medical examinations before entering school and approximately every third year the child is in school.

Health appraisal and counseling will be of little value unless there is a "follow-through" to see that remedial health defects are corrected. This is an important health service. There should be periodical

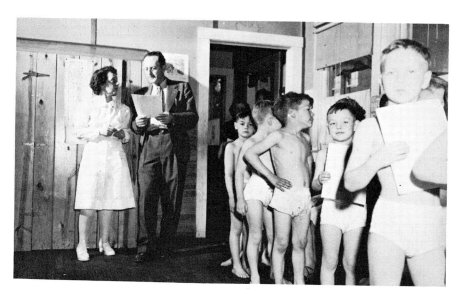

*Lawrence Central High School, Lawrence, Ind.*

A thorough medical examination should be one of the main bases for the selection of physical activities.

checks to see that such things as dental caries are remedied, eyeglasses are provided, and other defects attended to. School health programs can render a valuable service if they follow through to see that the remediable defects they discover are corrected.

Emergency care of sickness and injury is needed for the great number of children that are regularly injured through accidents or become unexpectedly sick while at school. The teacher, as well as the nurse, school physician, and administrator, has responsibilities in this emergency program. Through proper first-aid procedures, safety education, and regard for the health of children, the injured or sick child will be properly and quickly cared for and accidents can be reduced.

Communicable disease prevention and control should be included in school health services. In carrying out this func-

tion, schools should coordinate their program and work with the local department of health. Such measures as isolating the child who is suspected of having a contagious disease, educating the parents to take advantage of immunization and other preventive measures, informing the health department of suspected cases of communicable disease, encouraging sick children and teachers to stay home, and teaching the causes of the development and spread of diseases are a few of the services that may be rendered in this phase of school health.

Another health service that should be included in the school health program is the provision of an adequate educational program for the exceptional child. This includes children who are handicapped by physical or mental disabilities; speech, vision, hearing, and nutritional deficiencies; and those with emotional disorders need-

**Table 8-3.** *Type and professional preparation of persons currently serving as health coordinators** *

| Reporting school's enrollment | Type of coordinator | Major area of preparation | |
|---|---|---|---|
| | | Undergraduate | Graduate |
| 305 | 1 | Phys. ed. | None |
| 475 | 1 | Health & phys. ed. | Health & phys. ed. |
| 590 | 1 | Health & phys. ed. | Education |
| 620 | 2a | Phys. ed. | Phys. ed. |
| 1,053 | 1 | Health | Phys. ed. |
| 1,300 | 2b | Health & phys. ed. | Health & phys. ed. |
| 1,300 | 3 | Health & phys. ed. | None |
| 1,350 | 1 | Health & phys. ed. | None |
| 1,667 | 2c | Health & phys. ed. | Phys. ed. |
| 1,800 | 3 | Health & phys. ed. | None |
| 2,000 | 3 | Biology | Health ed. |
| 2,250 | 2d | Health & phys. ed. | Health & phys. ed. |
| 2,300 | 1 | Health & phys. ed. | Psychology |

1  Serving as chairman of the department of health and physical education.
2a  A full time coordinator of health and physical education for an entire school system.
2b  A coordinator of health and physical education in two junior high and one senior high school.
2c  A full time coordinator of health and physical education in all grades for the school system.
2d  Coordinator of health and physical education for eleven elementary, two junior high, and one senior high school, total enrollment of 10,265 students.
3  Serving as a health coordinator on an individual school basis.

*From Sheets, Norman L.: Wanted: health coordinators, Journal of School Health 34:489, Dec., 1964.

ing special attention. It also refers to the gifted child who needs special attention. Special provisions for these children guarantee a better educational experience, with a greater saving of human resources. For example, sight-saving classes may be held for the children with vision defects, lip reading instruction for some of those with hearing defects, and a restricted program for children with a history of rheumatic heart disease and those convalescing from serious illness.

The personnel involved in the school health services program include school and family physicians, school and public health nurses, school and family dentists and dental hygienists, school dietitian, health educator, physical educator, classroom teacher, school administrator, guidance counselor, psychologist, and parents.

The physical educator interested in health services for students should do as follows:

1. Meet with the school physician and nurse to determine how to contribute most to the health services program
2. Become acquainted with the parents and homes of students
3. See that children needing special care are referred to proper places for help
4. Be versed in first-aid procedures
5. Continually be on the alert for children with deviations from normal behavior and signs of communicable diseases
6. If feasible, be present at health examinations of pupils
7. Follow through in cooperation with the nurse to see that remediable health defects are corrected
8. Prescribe a physical education program to meet the physical needs of each student
9. Utilize their position to provide wise health counseling to both students and parents
10. See that athletes are given a medical examination and provided with other health services as needed.

## KEY PERSONNEL IN SCHOOL AND COLLEGE HEALTH PROGRAMS

The key personnel in school and college health programs are as follows:

**The teacher of health.** The most important ingredient for an effective school health program.

**Health coordinator.** Has the job of developing effective working relationships with school, college, and community health programs and coordinating the total school or college health program with the general education program.

**School administrator.** Can provide leadership that ensures a sound health program, qualified personnel, adequate budget, proper facilities, and the sympathy and support of faculty and parents.

**Physician.** Plays key role in the conduct of medical examinations, correction of remediable defects, and giving support to the total school health program.

**Nurse.** Provides liaison with medical personnel on the one hand and with students, teachers, and parents on the other. She can stimulate support for and give direction to all phases of the school health program.

**Physical educator.** Can contribute much to the school health program. Is in a position to impress upon students the importance of gaining desirable health knowledge, developing desirable health attitudes, and forming desirable health practices. Many teachable moments are present in a physical education program to teach about health opportunities closely related to the health and fitness of students.

**Dentist.** Conducts dental examinations, gives or supervises oral prophylaxis, and advises on curriculum material in dental hygiene.

**Dental hygienist.** Usually assists dentists and does oral prophylaxis. Has the opportunity to relate her work to educational outcomes.

**Custodian.** Helps to ensure healthful school living by providing a sanitary school environment.

**Nutritionist.** Plans student meals and can also be of help with nutritional problems of students and as a consultant on subject matter for health education.

**Guidance counselor.** Concerned with area of health as it relates to student effectiveness and productivity and has the opportunity to impress upon students the role of health in scholastic and vocational success.

## WHAT OUTCOMES SHOULD BE EXPECTED FROM THE SCHOOL HEALTH PROGRAM?

The long-term, over-all outcome to be expected from the school health program is improved health of human beings. This refers to all aspects of health, including physical, mental, emotional, and social. It applies to all individuals, regardless of race, color, economic status, creed, or national origin. The school has the responsibility to do everything within its power to see that all students achieve and maintain optimum health. This applies not only from a legal point of view but also from the standpoint that the educational experience will be much more meaningful if optimum health exists. A child learns more easily and better when in a state of good health.

The commonly mentioned educational outcomes to be expected from the school health program are concerned with the development of health knowledge, desirable health attitudes, desirable health practices, and health skills.

### Development of health knowledge

In order to develop health knowledge, health education must present and interpret scientific health data that will then be used for personal guidance. Such information will help individuals to recognize health problems and to solve them by utilizing information that is valid and helpful. It will also serve as a basis for the formulation of desirable health attitudes. In the complex society that exists today many choices confront the individual in regard to factors that affect his health. For this reason a reliable store of knowledge is essential.

Knowledge of health will vary with different ages. For younger children there should be an attempt to provide experiences that will show the importance of living healthfully. Such settings as the cafeteria, lavatory, and medical examination room offer these opportunities. As the individual grows older, the scientific knowledge for following certain health practices and ways of living can be presented. Some of the areas of health knowledge that should be understood by students and adults include nutrition, the need for rest, sleep, and exercise, protection of the body against changing temperature conditions, contagious disease control, the dangers of self-medication, and community resources for health.

For example, if students are properly health educated, they should understand the germ theory of disease and also have a desire to prevent disease whenever possible through desirable health practices. Boys and girls should understand where to find the health services necessary to cope with various types of health problems. Young people should know the effects of using tobacco, narcotic drugs, alcohol, and other depressants and stimulants. In addition, they should appreciate the fact that health is everybody's business—each person has a responsibility for the health of others in the family, community, nation, and world. There should be a recognition of the part played by nutrition, physical activity, rest, and sleep in physical fitness; the part played by safety in accident prevention; and the importance of good mental health. If such topics are brought to the attention of persons everywhere and if the proper health attitudes and practices are developed, better health will result.

### Development of desirable health attitudes

Health attitudes refer to the health interests of the individual or the motives that impel a person to act in a certain way. Health knowledge will have little worth unless the person is interested and motivated to the point that he wants to apply this knowledge to everyday living. Attitudes, motives, drives, or impulses, if properly established, will result in the person's seeking scientific knowledge and utilizing it as a guide to living. This interest, drive, or motivation must be dynamic to the point where it results in behavior changes.

The school health program must be directed at developing those attitudes that will result in optimum health. Students should have an interest in and be motivated toward possessing a state of buoyant health, feeling "fit as a fiddle," being well rested and well fed, having wholesome thoughts free from anger, jealousy, hate, and worry, being strong, and possessing enough physical power to perform life's routine tasks. They should have the right attitudes toward health knowledge, healthful school living, and health services. If such interests exist within the individual, proper health practices will follow. Health should not be an end in itself except in cases of severe illness. Health is a means to an end, a medium that aids in achieving noble purposes and contributes to enriched living.

Another factor that motivates people to good health is the desire to avoid pain and disturbances that accompany ill health. They do not like toothaches, headaches, or indigestion because of the pain or distraction involved. However, developing health attitudes in a negative manner through fear of pain or other disagreeable conditions does not seem to be a sound approach.

A strong argument for developing proper attitudes or interests center around the goals a person is trying to achieve in life and how optimum health can help to achieve such goals. This is the strongest incentive or interest that can be developed in a person. If a person wants to become a successful artist, businessman, dancer, housewife, or parent, it is greatly beneficial to possess good health. This is important so that the study, training, hard work, trials, and obstacles that one encounters can be met successfully. Optimum health will aid in the accomplishment of such goals. As Jennings, the biologist, has pointed out, the body can attend to only one thing at a time. If its attention is focused on a backache or an ulcer, it cannot be focused satisfactorily on essential work that must be done. Centering health attitudes or interests on life goals is dynamic because it represents an aid to accomplishment, achievement, and enjoyable living.

## Development of desirable health practices

Desirable health practices represent the application of desirable health habits to one's routine living. The health practices that a person adopts will determine in great measure the health of that person. Practices or habits that are harmful to optimum health, such as failure to obtain proper rest or exercise, overeating, overdrinking, and oversmoking or failure to observe certain precautions against contracting diseases, will usually result in poor health.

Knowledge does not necessarily ensure good health practices. An individual may have at his command all the statistics as to the results of speeding at seventy miles an hour, yet, unless this information is applied, it is useless. The health of an individual can be affected only by applying that which is known. At the same time, knowledge will not usually be applied unless an incentive, interest, or attitude exists that impels its application. Therefore it can be seen that in order to have a good school health program it is important to recognize the close relationship that exists among health knowledge, health attitudes, and health practices. Each contributes to the other.

## Development of health and safety skills

There are certain skills that should be learned through the health and safety education program in the schools. These include neuromuscular skills in first aid, home nursing, and safety and driver education. It takes skill to put splints on a broken leg or to administer artificial res-

*Oak Park and River Forest High School, Oak Park, Ill.*

Lifesaving—a phase of safety instruction.

*Pittsfield Public Schools, Pittsfield, Mass.*

Education for street traffic safety.

piration. It takes skill to read a thermometer or to care for a sick person. It takes skill to effectively put out a fire or help in the case of an accident. And it takes skill to drive in city traffic or to park on a steep hill. These skills are taught in various aspects of the school health and safety program and are outcomes that are expected from students who participate in these educational experiences. It should be remembered, however, that skill requires refresher training periodically in order that a person is always ready in the event of an emergency.

## INTERRELATIONSHIPS BETWEEN SCHOOL AND PUBLIC HEALTH PROGRAMS

The health of the school child is a major consideration of our educational systems. In 1918 it was placed first on the list of cardinal principles for education. In 1938 it was reemphasized by the Educational Policies Commission. Conferences have been held, legislation has been passed, personnel appointed, and programs planned for the express purpose of promoting the health of youth in our schools. This great emphasis focused on the health of the child and the happiness and fitness of future citizens of the United States means that every effort must be made to accomplish this objective in the most efficient and best way possible. Therefore, all the personnel and resources that are available in the community must be mobilized for this purpose. This is not a job for one agency. Instead, it requires the help and assistance of all organizations affecting the health of the child. Voluntary and official agencies, hospitals, boards of education, and interested individuals and organizations must pool their resources, facilities, equipment, and knowledge in order that the health of the child may receive utmost consideration.

In addition, the solving of community health problems outside the school needs the concerted effort of every agency. Public health programs are to a great degree based upon an enlightened public that understands the health problems of the community and gives its support to the solving of these problems. The school can play a major part in helping to educate the citizens of the community so that health progress may be realized. The school health program should fit into the total community health program in a well-coordinated manner so as to render utmost service to all concerned.

In discussing interrelationships between school and public health programs, it is important to consider the controversy between community health groups and the schools as to who is responsible for administering the various phases of the school health program.

There are primarily three points of view as to where the responsibility lies. One group believes that the board of education should be responsible, another group believes that public health officials should assume the responsibility, and a third group thinks that school health is a joint responsibility of both the board of education and public health officials. It is advisable to consider briefly some of the arguments in favor of each point of view.

Those individuals who advocate board of education control of the school health program set forth many pertinent arguments in their behalf. These arguments can be summed up in the following statements. They point to the fact that the Tenth Amendment to the Constitution of the United States places the authority for education in the hands of the states. The states delegate this authority to the local communities which, in turn, vest the authority in a board of education. The board of education, in the absence of legislation to the contrary, is responsible for all education, and therefore health education falls logically under their jurisdiction. They point to the fact that teachers, as a result of their training in such areas as psychology and methodology, are much better prepared to instruct children in health matters than are public health officials. They are better prepared to make health services meaningful educational experiences for all pupils. As another argument, they maintain that, if public health officials were responsible for the school health program, the teachers would have two bosses, thus making for inefficient administration.

Those individuals who advocate that the school health program should be controlled by public health officials also list many pertinent arguments in their favor. Public health supporters say that health is logically a province of the medical profession and should therefore be under the supervision of medical personnel such as those found in most public health departments. They point to the fact that the school is part of the total community and claim that therefore such an important thing as health is a responsibility of community health officials. Furthermore, the pupil is in school only five days a week and 180 days or so a year. The rest of the time he is in the larger community outside

the school environment. They argue that public health nurses, as a result of their training and experience, are the best qualified to develop and administer a health services program, especially in respect to home-school-community relationships. They maintain that according to law the control of communicable diseases is a prerogative of public health officials and that they can do the job much more efficiently than can the board of education.

Finally, there is a group of persons who maintain that the school health program should be controlled jointly by both the board of education and public health officials. They point out that there will be better utilization of personnel, facilities, and community resources and that, consequently, greater health progress can be made if there is joint control with both working together for the good of all.

There does not seem to be a simple solution to this controversy as to where the responsibility lies for school health. Probably the answer to this problem will vary according to the community. The solution would seem to depend upon how each community can best meet the health needs of the people who inhabit its particular geographical limits. The type of administrative setup that most fully meets the health needs and makes for greater progress should be the one that is adopted. Vested interests should not be considered, and the health interests of the consumer should be the primary concern. Health is everybody's business and everyone should strive for the best health program possible in his community, state, nation, and world.

## PROFESSIONAL PREPARATION OF HEALTH EDUCATORS*

Various individuals, committees, and surveys have stressed the need for more

**Who Administers School Health Services?**

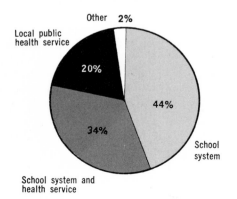

390 reporting school systems with 12,000 or more enrollment, 1965-66

*NEA Research Bulletin 44:107, Dec., 1966.*

*See also Chapter 21.

adequate preparation of those teachers who assume health education responsibilities.

Oberteuffer (1946), in a panel discussion before the College Physical Education Association, stressed the lack of adequate preparation in the field of health. He stated that the number of courses being offered in this area was highly insufficient and that to be good teachers of health, individuals must have training.

Langton has emphasized this same point, believing that at least 20% of the specialized area, in addition to the basic sciences, should be set aside for health education work. He further has pointed out that only through such a division is it possible for the prospective teacher to obtain adequate training in health education.

The Joint Committee on Physical Fitness of the American Medical Association and of the National Committee on Physical Fitness stated the need for the same kind of organized teaching of health that has been developed for the teaching of mathematics, English composition, history, and languages.

The National Committee on School Health Policies, formed in 1945 by the National Conference for Cooperation in Health Education listed the policies under which school health programs should operate and brought out the need for better qualified teachers in health education.

The results of one study, in which forty teachers and forty administrators participated, indicated that teachers are deficient in health education knowledge. The conclusion reached was that a teacher of health in the schools should be as well prepared as a teacher of any other subject.

In 1962 a major conference on the preparation of health, physical education, and recreation teachers and leaders was held in Washington, D. C. This conference, attended by many health leaders, stressed the need for adequate preparation of health teachers and outlined the requirements for such preparation. Furthermore, recommendations were made in the areas of student personnel, faculty, curriculum, laboratory experiences and facilities, and instructional materials.

As of 1965, there were forty-eight undergraduate programs that prepared health educators with a major emphasis, fifty at the master's level and twenty-six at the doctoral level. Students interested in taking further work in health education may wish to consult this list.*

The fact that a teacher needs more specialized training to teach health education is much in evidence. After coming to the conclusion that more training is needed, a next step would be to determine what knowledge and experience are most essential in the training of teachers for such responsibilities. Many recommendations have been made as to the content of the preparatory program. There are three recommendations that seem to stand out. First, the teacher education curriculum should provide for close cooperation with the health service program of the institution so that the prospective teacher may have the experience of having medical examinations, medical care, and medical advice. Second, instruction should be provided so that the student has a thorough scientific knowledge of such areas as the basic sciences, personal and community health, school health problems, and methods and materials of teaching health. Third, there should be a portion of the curriculum set aside for observation and practice teaching experiences so that the student may have contacts with child

---

*American Association for Health, Physical Education, and Recreation, Project of the Teacher Education Commission, Health Education Division: Institutions offering programs of specialization in health education at the undergraduate and graduate levels, Washington, D. C., 1965.

health services and health education programs.

A health educator has the job of improving health practices, attitudes, and knowledge of children and adults. He or she should be interested in community as well as personal health problems and devoted to encouraging and stimulating people to recognize the importance of good health for themselves and others. The health educator may act in the capacity of a teacher of concentrated courses in health education, a coordinator of a school or public health program, or a staff member of some voluntary health association such as the American Red Cross.

The personality of the health educator is of particular concern. This individual should be well adjusted and well integrated emotionally, mentally, and physically if he or she is to do a good job in developing these characteristics in others. Such a person must also be interested in human beings and possess skill and understanding in human relations so that health objectives may be realized.

It is very important that the health educator have a mastery of certain specialized health knowledge and skills and have proper attitudes. Such knowledge, skills, and attitudes will help the health educator to identify the health needs and interests of individuals with whom he comes in contact, provide a health program that will meet these needs and interests, and promote the profession so that human lives may be enriched. This means that many experiences should be included in the training of persons entering this specialized field. These experiences may be divided into general education, professional education, and specialized education.

General education experiences will constitute about one half of the total curriculum and include knowledge and skill in the communicative arts, understanding of sociological principles, and an apprecia-

tion of history of various peoples, with their various social, racial, and cultural characteristics, and the fine and practical arts which afford a means of expression, a means of releasing the emotions, a medium for richer understanding of life, and a medium for promoting mental health. The science area is very important to the health educator and should include such sciences as anatomy and kinesiology, physiology, bacteriology, biology, zoology, chemistry, physics, child and adolescent psychology, human growth and development, general psychology, and mental hygiene.

In professional education it is important for the health educator to have a mastery of the philosophies, techniques, principles, and evaluative procedures that are characteristic of the most advanced and best thinking in education. Professional courses in educational philosophy, methods of teaching, and practice teaching would come in this area.

The specialized health education area should include personal and community health, nutrition, family and child health, first aid and safety, methods and materials, organization and administration of school health programs, public health, including the basic principles of environmental sanitation and communicable disease control, and health counseling.

## Health education minor program

Although it is hoped that sometime in the future all persons who teach health will have a major in this special subject, this is not true at the present time. Therefore, in order to be realistic in terms of the need to improve the present quality of health teaching, a minor program is suggested. This, however, should be considered the minimum, and it is believed that physical educators who desire to teach health should have this minimum preparation. The prerequisites to the minor program should include biological, physical, and social sciences.

**Table 8-4.** *Vocational opportunities in the health sciences by states**

| | Public health work | | | | | | | School health educator | | | | | | Higher education | | |
|---|---|---|---|---|---|---|---|---|---|---|---|---|---|---|---|---|
| State | Private vol. health agency | City dept. | County dept. | State dept. | Federal agency | Hospital admin. | Safety director or coordinator | Elementary | Junior high | High school | School health coordinator | Public school safety director–coordinator | Teacher of driver educ. | Junior college | College | University |
| Alabama | x | | x | x | x | | | | | x | | | | | | |
| Alaska | x | | | x | | | | | | | | | | | | |
| Arizona | x | | x | x | | | | | x | x | | | x | | | |
| Arkansas | | x | | x | | | | | | | | | | | | |
| California | x | x | x | x | | | | | | | | | | | | |
| Colorado | x | x | x | x | | | x | x | x | x | x | | | x | | |
| Connecticut | | | | x | | | | | x | x | | | x | | | |
| Delaware | | | | | | | | | x | x | | | x | | | |
| Florida | x | | x | x | x | | | | x | x | | | x | x | x | |
| Georgia | | | x | x | | | | x | x | x | | | x | | | |
| Hawaii | x | | | x | | | | | | | | | | | | |
| Idaho | | | | x | | | | | | | | | | | | |
| Illinois | x | | | | | x | | x | x | x | | | x | x | x | |
| Indiana | x | x | x | x | | | | x | x | x | | | | x | x | |
| Iowa | x | | | x | | | | | | x | | | | x | x | |
| Kansas | | | | x | | | | | | x | | | x | | | |
| Kentucky | x | x | x | x | | x | x | | x | x | | | x | x | x | x |
| Louisiana | x | | | x | | x | x | | x | x | | | | | x | |
| Maine | x | x | | x | | | x | | x | x | | | x | x | | |
| Maryland | x | | x | x | | | | x | x | x | | | x | x | x | |
| Massachusetts | | | | | | | | | x | x | | | x | | | |
| Minnesota | x | | | x | x | | x | | x | x | | | x | x | | |
| Mississippi | | | | x | | | | | | | | | x | x | x | |
| Missouri | | | x | x | | | x | | | x | | | x | | | |
| Montana | x | | | x | | | | | | x | | | | | | |
| Nebraska | | | | x | | | | | | | | | | | | |
| Nevada | | | | x | | | | | | | | | x | | | |
| New Hampshire | x | | | | x | | | | | | | | | | | |

If no information is provided under one of the three major headings, this indicates that no response was received, rather than that no opportunities are available.

*From Rees, Floyd D.: Vocational opportunities in the health sciences, Journal of Health, Physical Education, and Recreation 36:70, Nov.–Dec., 1965.

*Continued.*

**Table 8-4.** *Vocational opportunities in the health sciences by states—cont'd*

| State | Private vol. health agency | City dept. | County dept. | State dept. | Federal agency | Hospital admin. | Safety director or coordinator | Elementary | Junior high | High school | School health coordinator | Public school safety director–coordinator | Teacher of driver educ. | Junior college | College | University |
|---|---|---|---|---|---|---|---|---|---|---|---|---|---|---|---|---|
| | Public health work | | | | | | | School health educator | | | | | | Higher education | | |
| New Jersey | x | x | x | x | x | x | x | | x | x | | x | | x | x | |
| New Mexico | | x | x | x | | | | | | x | | x | | | | |
| New York | x | x | | | | | | | | x | | | | x | | |
| North Carolina | x | | x | x | | x | | | | | | | | x | x | |
| North Dakota | x | | | | | | x | x | | | | | x | x | x | |
| Ohio | x | x | x | x | x | | x | x | x | x | | x | | x | x | x |
| Oklahoma | x | | x | | | | x | | | | | x | | | x | |
| Oregon | | | x | x | | | x | x | x | x | | x | x | x | x | |
| Pennsylvania | x | | x | | | | x | | x | x | | x | | | x | |
| Rhode Island | | | | | | | | | x | x | | x | | | | |
| South Carolina | x | | x | x | x | x | | | | | | | | | x | x |
| South Dakota | | | x | | | | | | | | | | | | | |
| Tennessee | | | | | | | | | | x | | x | | | | |
| Texas | | x | x | | | | x | | x | x | | x | | x | x | x |
| Utah | | | x | | | | | | x | x | | x | | | | |
| Vermont | | | | | | x | | | | | | x | | | x | |
| Virginia | x | | | | | | | x | x | x | | x | | | | |
| Washington | x | x | x | | | | | | x | x | | x | | x | x | x |
| West Virginia | x | x | x | x | | | x | | x | x | | | | | x | x |
| Wisconsin | | | x | | | | | | | | | x | | | x | |
| Wyoming | x | x | x | x | x | | | | | | | x | | | | |

Physical education majors, as part of their regular program, should take human anatomy, physiology, first aid and safety, body mechanics, physiology of exercise, health observation, and adapted physical education. The minor program should contain fifteen to twenty semester hours or twenty-two to thirty quarter hours in health education courses. This should include such subjects as personal and community health, first aid, nutrition, health problems of school children, accident prevention, environmental sanitation, methods and materials, safety education, and organization and administration of the school health program.

## CAREERS IN HEALTH EDUCATION

A physical educator with interest, training, and qualifications for health work may be interested in exploring the possibilities of a career in this field. In the years ahead there will be many positions available in the elementary and secondary schools and in colleges and universities. The expansion in school enrollments plus the increased emphasis given to health education augurs well for job opportunities in our community and educational programs throughout the country. Furthermore, some insurance companies, youth agencies, and organizations, such as the American Social Hygiene Association, National Tuberculosis Association, and Young Men's Christian Association, employ people trained in the health field. The attention being given to safety education means more positions for people with special training in this field in industry and government, as well as in the schools and other settings.

The physical educator, for professional as well as career purposes, should be familiar with such health organizations as the following:

*Selected educational health associations:*

1. American School Health Association
2. American Public Health Association
3. American Association for Health, Physical Education, and Recreation
4. Society of State Directors of Health and Physical Education

*Selected governmental health agencies:*
1. United States Public Health Service
2. State department of health
3. County health department
4. Local health department

*Selected professional health associations:*
1. American Medical Association
2. American Nurses' Association
3. American Dental Association

*Selected voluntary health agencies:*
1. American Cancer Society
2. National Tuberculosis Association
3. American Red Cross
4. National Association for Mental Health
5. National Society for Crippled Children and Adults
6. American Heart Association

*Selected international health organizations:*
1. World Health Organization

For those persons who are interested in specializing in safety education, several job opportunities prevail in schools, colleges, industry, transportation agencies, and other organizations and agencies. Safety educators devote their time to promoting safety considerations and reducing accidents. Jobs are available as supervisors of safety education and teachers of driver education in schools; as safety supervisors or safety directors in industry and government; as supervisors or consultants in community safety; or as teachers of safety and/or driver education in colleges and universities.

## QUESTIONS AND EXERCISES

1. Trace the history of health in the schools from the latter part of the nineteenth century to the present.
2. Define each of the following: (a) school health program, (b) school health services, (c) health appraisal, (d) school health counseling, (e) school health education, and (f) healthful school living.
3. Define and discuss each of the three main areas of the school health program.
4. What are the objectives of the school health program? Compare to the objectives of the physical education program.
5. What is the relationship of the school health program to the public health program?
6. What professional preparation does a health educator need? To what extent does this preparation overlap with that required in physical education?
7. What part can the physical educator play in the school health program?

## SELECTED REFERENCES

American Association for Health, Physical Education, and Recreation: Preparing the health teacher, Washington, D. C., 1961, The Association.

American Association for Health, Physical Education, and Recreation: Health concepts— guides for health instruction, Washington, D. C., 1967, The Association.

A Report of the National Conference on Coordination of the School Health Program: Teamwork in school health, Washington, D. C., 1962, American Association for Health, Physical Education, and Recreation.

A Statement From the Society of State Directors of Health, Physical Education, and Recreation: Guidelines for effective health planning by schools and voluntary health agencies, Journal of Health, Physical Education, and Recreation 34:26, Sept., 1963.

Bucher, Charles A.: Administration of school health and physical education programs, St. Louis, 1967, The C. V. Mosby Co.

Bucher, Charles A., Olsen, Einar A., and Willgoose, Carl E.: The foundations of health, New York, 1967, Appleton-Century-Crofts.

Byrd, Oliver E.: School health administration, Philadelphia, 1964, W. B. Saunders Co.

Cauffman, Joy G.: Evaluating a health education curriculum guide, Journal of Health, Physical Education, and Recreation 34:20, Oct., 1963.

Committee on Terminology in School Health Education: Report, Journal of Health, Physical Education, and Recreation 33:27, Nov., 1962.

Dukelow, Donald A., and Hein, Fred V., editors: Physicians and schools, Report of the Third National Conference on Physicians and Schools, Chicago, 1952, American Medical Association.

Grout, Ruth E.: Health teaching in schools, Philadelphia, 1963, W. B. Saunders Co.

Harris, William H.: Suggested criteria for evaluating health and safety teaching materials, Journal of Health, Physical Education, and Recreation 35:26, Feb., 1965.

Hein, Fred V.: Critical issues in health and safety education, The Journal of School Health 35:70, Feb., 1965.

Hoyman, Howard S.: An ecologic view of health and health education, The Journal of School Health 35:110, March, 1965.

Irwin, Leslie W., and Mayshark, Cyrus: Health education in secondary schools, St. Louis, 1964, The C. V. Mosby Co.

Joint Committee on Health Problems in Education, National Education Association and American Medical Association, Washington, D. C., National Education Association: The nurse in the school, 1955.

Healthful school living, 1957.
Health education, 1961.
School health services, 1961.
Suggested school health policies, 1962.

Joint Committee on Health Problems in Education, National Education Association and American Medical Association: The physical educator asks about health, Washington, D. C., 1951, American Association for Health, Physical Education, and Recreation.

Mayshark, Cyrus, and Shaw, Donald: Administration of school health programs, St. Louis, 1967, The C. V. Mosby Co.

Means, Richard K.: A history of health education in the United States, Philadelphia, 1962, Lea & Febiger.

Oberteuffer, Delbert, and Beyer, Mary K.: School health education, 4th ed., New York, 1966, Harper & Row, Publishers.

Oberteuffer, Delbert: Vital ties between health and education, NEA Journal 53:57, March, 1964.

Pollock, Marion B.: The significance of health education for junior college students, The Journal of School Health 34:333, Sept., 1964.

Report of the Study Committee on Health Education in the Elementary and Secondary School of the American School Health Association: Health instruction—suggestions for teachers, The Journal of School Health, vol. 34, Dec., 1964 (entire issue).

School Health Education Study: A summary report, Washington, D. C., 1964, School Health Education Study.

School Health Education Study: Health education: a conceptual approach, Washington, D. C., 1965, School Health Education Study.

Smith, Sara Louise: Implication of the report of the NEA project of instruction for health education, The Journal of School Health 34:432, Nov., 1964.

Smolensky, Jack, and Bonevchio, L. Richard: Principles of school health, Boston, 1966, D. C. Heath & Co.

Chapter 9

# Recreation

Recreation is concerned with those activities in which a person participates during hours other than work. It implies that the individual has chosen certain activities in which to voluntarily engage because of an inner self-motivating desire. Such participation gives him a satisfying experience.

To be more specific, the kind of recreation that education is advocating can be characterized by five descriptive terms:

1. *Leisure time.* To be recreation the activity must be engaged in during one's free time. From this point of view work cannot be one's recreation.

2. *Enjoyable.* The activity engaged in must be satisfying and enjoyable to the participant.

3. *Voluntary.* The individual must have chosen, of his own volition, to engage in this pursuit; there has been no coercion.

4. *Constructive.* The activity is constructive. It is not harmful to the person physically, socially, or in any other way. Conversely, it helps him to become a better integrated individual.

5. *Nonsurvival.* Eating and sleeping are not recreational activities in themselves. One may engage in a picnic where a wonderful dinner is involved, but other facets of the affair, such as the social games and fellowship, are important parts of the recreational activity.

## HISTORY

Recreation, to some extent, has always been a part of the lives of all people, of every race, nation, and creed. In many cases man has spent his leisure hours in a constructive and worthwhile manner by participating in such activities as music, dances, games, sports, painting, and other arts. In early history the Chinese, Hindu, Persian, Egyptian, Babylonian, and Greek peoples left evidence of these pursuits.

In the United States there have been many milestones in the progress of recreation to a place of national importance. The land that is now Central Park in New York City was purchased in 1853, and the Boston sand garden for children was opened by the Massachusetts Emergency and Hygiene Association in 1885. In 1889 playgrounds were opened in New York and in 1892 at Hull House in Chicago. The "playground" idea spread to other cities, which included Brookline, Massachusetts, Louisville, Kentucky, and Los Angeles, California. The Playground Association of America was founded in 1906 with Dr. Luther H. Gulick as president. This same association became known as the National Recreation Association and today it is part of the National Recreation and Park Association. The development of Community Houses, the Works

**249**

| AVERAGE LENGTH OF LIFE (ACTUAL YEARS) | | 40 | 70 | 75 |
|---|---|---|---|---|
| **DIFFERENT ERAS** | | 1885 | 1950 | 2000 |
| PERCENTAGE OF TOTAL LIFETIME SPENT IN ACTIVITIES SHOWN | SCHOOL | 5.6 | 4.0 | 4.8 |
| | WORK | 26 | 15.3 | 7.9 |
| | LEISURE | 7.8 | 20.7 | 27.1 |
| | EAT & SLEEP | 60.5 | 59.9 | 60.2 |

*Still, Joseph W.: Geriatrics 12:577, Sept., 1957.*

The use of time in three generations.

Progress Administration and the National Youth Administration of the depression years, and the large recreation program for service personnel of World War II have played an important part in the progress of recreation. In 1938 the word "recreation" was officially made a part of the title of the American Association for Health, Physical Education, and Recreation.

Since the turn of the century, recreation has been considered more and more to be a fundamental human need. More than 3,000 communities in this country are sponsoring public recreation programs under school and/or local government auspices. In addition, such volunteer and private organizations as the Boy Scouts, American Red Cross, camps, settlement houses, YMCA and YWCA, industry, and the armed forces have recreational programs. More than $1 billion are spent each year on community recreation and from $9 to $25 billion on recreation of all kinds.

The American people are becoming

Oakland Recreation Department,
Oakland, Calif.

Recreation—a fundamental human need.

recreation conscious, as shown by the following statistics* for a typical year:

1. 90% of the nation's population take part in some form of outdoor recreation.
2. 16.5 million Americans crowd the nation's campgrounds.
3. 100 million people participate in some form of water recreation.
4. $98 is spent, on the average, for recreation and recreation equipment by people earning less than $2,000 annually.
5. $513 is spent, on the average, for recreation and recreation equipment by people earning between $7,000 and $9,999 annually.
6. 33% of the population work around their yards and in their gardens.

---

*de Grazia, Sebastian: Of time, work and leisure, New York, 1962, The Twentieth Century Fund.

7. 14% of the population listen to records.
8. 10% of the population have such special hobbies as woodworking and knitting.
9. 5% of the population sing or play musical instruments.

In the last ten years the population of the United States has increased by 15%, and during the same period use of the national parks has increased 86%. In the future the population explosion will create an even larger market for recreation. In addition to population, income will jump skyward in the years ahead. Disposable consumer income will rise from $354 billion to $706 billion by 1976 and to $1,437 billion by the year 2000. Whereas the percentage of people with incomes of $10,000 is above 14% at the present, it is esti-

# AMERICANS WILL SEEK MORE OUTDOOR RECREATION...
## Because They Will Have More Money and Leisure Time

**ESTIMATED CHANGES IN POPULATION, INCOME, LEISURE, AND TRAVEL** FOR THE YEARS 1976 AND 2000, COMPARED TO 1960

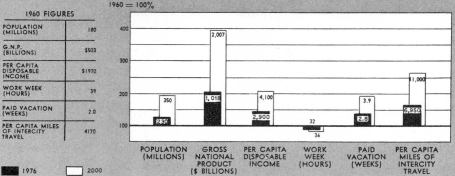

| 1960 FIGURES | |
|---|---|
| POPULATION (MILLIONS) | 180 |
| G.N.P. (BILLIONS) | $503 |
| PER CAPITA DISPOSABLE INCOME | $1970 |
| WORK WEEK (HOURS) | 39 |
| PAID VACATION (WEEKS) | 2.0 |
| PER CAPITA MILES OF INTERCITY TRAVEL | 4170 |

1960 = 100%

■ 1976   □ 2000

## Incomes Will be Higher . . .

**DISPOSABLE CONSUMER INCOME IN BILLIONS**
1960 AND PROJECTED, 1976 AND 2000

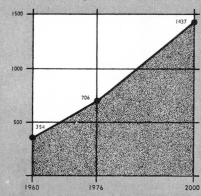

**PERCENT OF CONSUMER UNITS IN EACH INCOME CLASS**
1947, 1957, AND PROJECTED, 1976 AND 2000

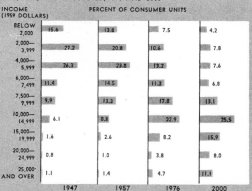

| INCOME (1959 DOLLARS) | 1947 | 1957 | 1976 | 2000 |
|---|---|---|---|---|
| BELOW 2,000 | 15.6 | 13.8 | 7.5 | 4.2 |
| 2,000—3,999 | 27.2 | 20.8 | 10.6 | 7.8 |
| 4,000—5,999 | 26.3 | 23.8 | 13.2 | 7.6 |
| 6,000—7,499 | 11.4 | 14.5 | 11.3 | 6.8 |
| 7,500—9,999 | 9.9 | 13.3 | 17.8 | 13.1 |
| 10,000—14,999 | 6.1 | 8.8 | 22.9 | 25.5 |
| 15,000—19,999 | 1.6 | 2.6 | 8.2 | 15.9 |
| 20,000—24,999 | 0.8 | 1.0 | 3.8 | 8.0 |
| 25,000 AND OVER | 1.1 | 1.4 | 4.7 | 11.1 |

## People Will Have More Free Time to Spend on Recreation

**AVERAGE SCHEDULED WORK WEEK FOR NONAGRICULTURAL WORKERS BY INDUSTRY**
1960 AND PROJECTED, 1976 AND 2000, HOURS

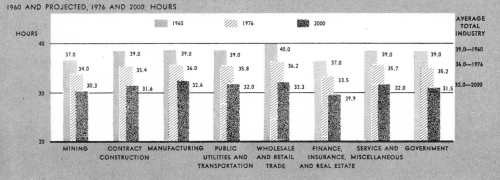

U.S. Department of Commer[ce]
A proposed program for scenic ro[ads]
and parkways, Washington, D. C., 19[...]

mated that the proportion will go to 40% by 1976 and to 60% by the year 2000. The increase in income will mean more leisure-time activities for most people.

The amount of free time available to people will increase. The standard scheduled workweek will decrease from thirty-nine hours to thirty-six hours by 1976 and thirty-two hours by the year 2000. Much of this additional leisure time will be devoted to recreational pursuits.

The future is bright for those persons who seek to guide the recreational destinies of human beings into constructive channels.

A great theologian, Peter Marshall, once said, "It is not the length of life that matters but how it is lived. That is the thing that counts. It is not how long, but how well." Constructive recreation adds to the quality of living. It contributes to a well-balanced life. It acts as a dash of fresh, cool water on the brow of the tired worker. It is refreshing and invigorating.

## OBJECTIVES OF RECREATION

There are many worthwhile objectives for the field of recreation. The American Association for Health, Physical Education, and Recreation states that this special field contributes to the satisfaction of basic human needs for creative self-expression; it helps to promote total health—physical, emotional, mental, and social; it provides an antidote to the strains and tensions of modern life; it provides an avenue to abundant personal and family living; and it develops good citizenship and vitalizes democracy.

According to George D. Butler, who spent more than a quarter of a century with the National Recreation Association, recreation contributes to human happiness, mental and physical health, character development, crime prevention, community solidarity, morale, safety, economy, and democratic living. These benefits are derived from a program that serves the entire population, including children and adults, boys and girls, men and women. Most programs are organized in respect to the needs and interests of those they serve.

One of the best statements of objectives has been discussed by The Commission on Goals for American Recreation.* The objectives are six in number:

1. *Personal fulfillment.* The need for each person to become all that he is capable of becoming and the contribution that recreation can make to this goal.

2. *Democratic human relations.* The recognition by recreation that it has goals that contribute to the individual as well as to the democratic society of which it is a part.

3. *Leisure skills and interests.* Recreation has the goal of meeting the interests of people and developing skills that will provide the incentive, motivation, and medium for spending free time in a constructive and worthwhile manner.

4. *Health and fitness.* Recreation recognizes the importance of contributing to the alleviation of such conditions as mental illness, stress, and physical inactivity that prevail in many segments of the American society.

5. *Creative expression and esthetic appreciation.* Recreation attempts to provide the environment, leadership, materials, and motivation where creativity, personal expression, and esthetic appreciation on the part of the participant exist.

6. *Environment for living in a leisure society.* Recreation plays an important role in encouraging such things as preservation of natural resources, construction of playgrounds and recreation centers, and awakening the population to an appreciation of esthetic and cultural values.

*The Commission on Goals for American Recreation: Goals for American recreation, Washington, D. C., 1964, American Association for Health, Physical Education and Recreation.

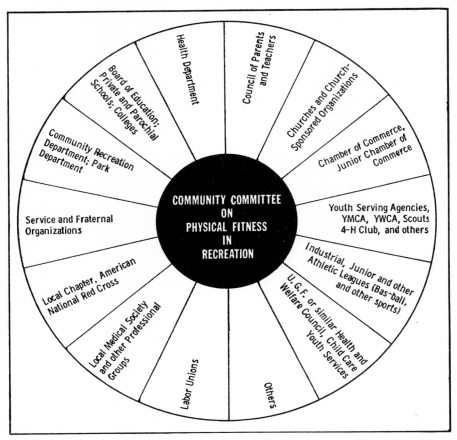

The wheel diagram shows:

COMMUNITY COMMITTEE ON PHYSICAL FITNESS IN RECREATION

Health Department

Council of Parents and Teachers

Churches and Church-Sponsored Organizations

Chamber of Commerce, Junior Chamber of Commerce

Youth Serving Agencies, YMCA, YWCA, Scouts 4-H Club, and others

Industrial, Junior and other Athletic Leagues (Bas-ball, and other sports)

U. G. F. or similar Health and Welfare Council, Child Care Youth Services

Others

Labor Unions

Local Medical Society and other Professional Groups

Local Chapter, American National Red Cross

Service and Fraternal Organizations

Community Recreation Department; Park Department

Board of Education; Private and Parochial Schools; Colleges

*President's Council on Youth Fitness: Physical fitness elements in recreation, Washington, D. C., 1962, U.S. Government Printing Office.*

A suggested community physical fitness organizational plan.

Four objectives that merit discussion are the health development objective, including physical fitness, human relations objective, civic development objective, and self-development objective.

### Health development objective, including physical fitness

Health development is an important objective in the field of recreation. Health, to a great degree, is related to activity during leisure hours as well as during hours of work. The manner in which a person spends his free time determines in great measure the quality of his physical, mental, emotional, and spiritual health. Through recreation, adaptive physical activity is available, which is conducive to organic, mental, emotional, and spiritual health. A wide range of activities exists that offer opportunities for every individual to promote his organic health. These activities provide relaxation, an escape from the tensions of work, and a chance to forget about problems; thereby they contribute to mental health. Activities are planned and conducted to provide enjoyment and pleasure and in this way contribute to emotional health. Activities are included that require the participation of

Recreation programs develop many individual qualities that contribute to good human relations.

many persons. This is conducive to better social relations and thus promotes spiritual health. Public recreation programs are designed to counteract the deteriorating effects of strenuous or routine work or study and thus complement the overall day-to-day tasks that a person follows. Recreation overcomes many of the shortages that exist when the man leaves the office, the child leaves school, or the housewife completes her work. In this way it contributes to the integration and development of the whole person.

It can be seen from the description of the health development objective that *recreation contributes to physical fitness.* The President's Council on Physical Fitness has prepared a special publication stressing the contribution that recreation programs can make to physical fitness of the population.* The chart on page 254

*President's Council on Youth Fitness: Physical fitness elements in recreation, Washington, D. C., 1962, United States Government Printing Office.

shows a community organizational plan for accomplishing this objective. The community committee on physical fitness in recreation, which represents the hub of this chart, should undertake to accomplish the following objectives:

1. Develop and carry out a community program of physical fitness involving all organizations and agencies having recreation interests
2. Provide opportunities for and encourage daily participation in vigorous physical activities adapted to all age groups
3. Provide year-round opportunities for the development of physical fitness
4. Utilize available leadership and facilities and strive for the enactment of state-enabling legislation and local ordinances authorizing use of public property or funds for recreation

## Human relations objective

The human relations objective represents a major contribution of recreation to enriched living. Recreational programs develop many individual qualities. Such attributes as courage, justice, patience, tolerance, fairness, and honesty are only a

few that can be developed while people
are playing and recreating together in the
many activities that comprise the total
recreation program. Attitudes are also developed that promote good human relations. Wholesome attitudes of social cooperation, loyalty to the group, recognition
of the rights of others, and the belief that
a person receives from the group in direct
proportion to what he gives make for
better relations and enable the accomplishment of worthy goals. The growth of
family recreation also helps to make for a
more unified home life. This is essential,
since the family group represents the
foundation on which good human relations are built. Furthermore, to develop
good social traits it is necessary to bring
people together in a situation where there
is a feeling of belonging and where each
individual is recognized. There are innumerable opportunities for such interaction
in the many recreational programs that
exist throughout the country.

## Civic development objective

The civic development objective is a
noteworthy goal for recreation. Recreation
contributes in many ways to the development of any community. It contributes to
community solidarity by uniting people in
common projects, regardless of race, creed,
economic status, or other discriminatory
factors. It helps to build the morale of the
members of the community. It is a contributing factor in alleviating crime in that
it provides settings and activities in which
youth and other individuals may engage
in constructive, worthwhile activities
rather than in destructive, antisocial activities. It helps to make the community a
safer place in which to live through adequate playgrounds and other recreational
centers which keep children and youth off
the streets. It helps to make the community more prosperous by contributing to
the health of the individual, by cutting
down on the dollar appropriation for

combating crime, and by increasing the
total work output of an individual. It
helps the growth and development of the
individual so that he becomes a more valuable citizen in the community and has
more to contribute in its behalf.

## Self-development objective

The self-development objective refers
to the potentialities that participation in
a program of recreation activities has for
developing the individual to his fullest
capacity. Recreation does this through a
variety of means. It contributes to the
balanced growth of a person. It allows for
growth in ways other than through the
production of material things for utilitarian purposes. In other words, it satisfies the human desire for creativity through
such things as music, art, literature, and
drama. It allows a person to create things
not for their material value but, instead,
for the joy, satisfaction, and happiness
that occur when producing something
through one's own efforts. It allows for
the development of skills and abilities
that are latent and dormant until they
are aroused by leisure hours with proper
settings and inspiration. These skills help
to make a better integrated person. They
provide an avenue for him to experience
joy and happiness through an activity
in which he has the desire to engage.
In this chaotic world of sorrows, heart-
breaks, and frowns, it is essential for
people to revitalize themselves through
the medium of activities that provide
smiles, hearty laughs, and release from
the tension associated with day-to-day routine. Such activities afford a place for
many to excel. Such an urge is many
times not satisfied in one's regular job or
profession. Recreation provides an opportunity to satisfy this desire. It provides an
educational experience. The participant
learns new skills, new knowledge, new
techniques, and develops new abilities. He
files away new and different experiences

that will be helpful in facing situations that he will encounter from day to day.

## NEED FOR RECREATION IN MODERN-DAY LIVING

Every individual should experience the joy that comes from engaging in recreation activities that fit his needs, interests, and desires. The Constitution of the United States sets forth a fundamental belief that the Creator endowed each individual with certain inalienable rights; among these are life, liberty, and the pursuit of happiness. Recreation can contribute to the attainment of such vital concepts.

The need for recreation in our changing society is increasing. History-shaking events have made this true. Paul F. Douglas, a leader in recreation, points out that two events which go hand in hand have happened since the turn of the century. In 1905 Albert Einstein set forth his famous formula $E = MC^2$. This represented the foundation for the atomic age. This new era of atomic energy brought increased leisure to man. A year later, in 1906, the National Recreation Association was founded. This organization was established to help man enjoy this leisure.

A shorter work week and more labor-saving gadgets have been the constant goal of many persons in our society. Man is given less work and more leisure. But, has increased leisure given man more happiness? Howard Mumford Jones says that this century has been one of increasing horror. The desire for life, liberty, and the pursuit of happiness is not being fulfilled for millions of Americans. A candid view of the public does not find an abundance of hearty laughs, happy smiles, and looks of satisfaction. People today are seeking all forms of escapes in sleeping pills, liquor, eating, cheap literature, and drugs. They are searching everywhere for happiness. Many people have not yet found the key to a happy life. However, they are beginning to realize that an accumulation of material things, a good job, power, and ample leisure do not in themselves ensure happiness. Happy people must be creative, have a feeling of belonging, and possess opportunities to direct their energies into constructive channels when the day's work is done.

A survey conducted at New York University included many thougsands of people, covering a wide range of occupations and including an age range of 4 to 80 years. This study pointed up the fact that the leading characteristics of happy people were (1) interest in work, (2) interest in hobbies, (3) interest in others, (4) lack of interest in material things, and (5) rendering a service to individuals and groups.

Dr. William Menninger, the famous doctor and psychologist, pointed out in a speech before the National Recreation Association that the happy and healthy person today is the one who has recreational pursuits. He participates in some recreational activity to supplement routine daily work. He further states that "good mental health is directly related to the capacity and willingness of an individual to play. Regardless of his objectives, resistances or past practice, any individual will make a wise investment if he plans time for his play and takes it seriously." However, too few persons know how to play. They lack skills, interest, and other motivating factors. They do not feel that it has an important place in their lives. Many think that when their mortarboards and commencement gowns are put away it is also time to cast off such things as tennis racquets, bathing suits, or paints and easels. Play is an important part of every person's life, and as Hjelte, a leader in recreation, pointed out, nothing is recreation in the full sense unless it is practiced in the spirit of play. Pleasure must come from engaging in the activity. It matters not if one is young or old, rich or poor, strong or weak, active or bedridden, man

*Youth Services Section, Los Angeles City Schools,*
*Los Angeles, Calif.*

An all-city chess tournament at Hollywood High School, Los Angeles, Calif. Every individual should experience the joy that comes from engaging in recreation activities that fit his needs and interests.

or woman, or boy or girl, recreation can contribute to better living. One recreation leader has stated that activities should range everywhere from the informal play of the child to highly competitive athletics for youth, from the make-believe play of the novice to the expertly staged dramatic presentation of the trained individual, from shaping a crude form in a sandpile to forming a beautiful object in marble, from discordant singing to classical composition, from the superficial reading of an average novel to the complete absorption in a literary masterpiece.

Recreation programs in communities from coast to coast are being challenged to provide all types of activities that cut across the needs, interests, and desires of human beings. Such activities must in-

clude arts and crafts, boating, nature study, gardening, all sorts of games and sports, literary activities, music, dramatics, nature study, camping, parties, and many others. In addition to offering a broad and varied program, it is a further essential that all the resources of a community be mobilized and coordinated so that the best possible program can be offered. Such groups as the church, YMCA, industry, business, schools, Camp Fire Girls, Boy Scouts, and labor unions must all do their share in providing for these essential human needs. Many communities across the country are providing broad recreation programs. These range from trips to museums in Sacramento to camping for handicapped children of the Butte County Schools in California, from dramatics in Natchitoches to fishing in Oregon.

| ASSUMING ADULT ROLE | | **43%** |
| --- | --- | --- |
| Helping at home, helping with chores | 19% | |
| Tasks with responsibility | 8% | |
| Adult roles at home | 6% | |
| School activities with responsibility | 6% | |
| Making plans, arrangements | 3% | |
| Other, adult role | 1% | |

| ACTIVITY | | **27%** |
| --- | --- | --- |
| Competing successfully | 22% | |
| Hobbies, crafts | 1% | |
| Other, activity | 4% | |

| PRIDE IN ACHIEVEMENT | | **25%** |
| --- | --- | --- |
| Doing well in school | 9% | |
| Making, fixing things | 6% | |
| Job well done | 3% | |
| Home run, winning point | 1% | |
| Other, pride in achievement | 6% | |

| GIVING HELP | | **14%** |
| --- | --- | --- |
| Helping others, general | 7% | |
| Helping with specific tasks | 5% | |
| Other, help | 2% | |

| PART OF A SOCIAL ORGANIZATION | | **12%** |
| --- | --- | --- |
| Part of a team | 6% | |
| Church activities | 2% | |
| Working together with friends | 1% | |
| Other, social organizations | 3% | |

| ACCEPTANCE BY PEERS | | **6%** |
| --- | --- | --- |
| Being liked | 3% | |
| Being with friends | 2% | |
| Other, peer acceptance | 1% | |

| NOTHING | **4%** |
| --- | --- |
| INDEPENDENCE (financial) | **3%** |
| RECOGNITION BY ADULTS | **3%** |

*Percentages total more than 100% because boys gave more than one response.*

*Needs and interests of adolescent Boys' Clubs members—
a national survey of members aged 14 to 18,
New York, 1960, Boys' Clubs of America.*

A variety of activities gives adolescents a sense of importance and usefulness.

Recreation program in Flint, Mich.

## NEW DEVELOPMENTS IN RECREATION IN A CHANGING SOCIETY AND WORLD

Some of the new developments in the field of recreation are as follows:

**The federal government is attempting to preserve and improve the beauty of America.** The national government recognizes that our growing population is swallowing up areas of natural beauty, and therefore is taking measures to provide for a beautiful America, such as making the Capitol the Nation's showcase, beautifying locations throughout the United States, planning land acquisition for conservation purposes, conducting research, preserving wildlife, retaining and improving scenic and historic sites, offering im- proved outdoor recreation to more people, improving water and waterways, and controlling pollution of streams and rivers.

**American communities are becoming recreation minded.** Many villages, cities, and communities from coast to coast are acquiring and developing their green spaces, restoring national shrines, rehabilitating depressed neighborhoods and ghettos, providing for "senior citizens," setting aside acreage for recreation, advocating "See America First," establishing neighborhood playgrounds, making provision for the physically handicapped and mentally ill and retarded to share in the benefits of recreational programs, stressing the performing arts, and developing sports programs.

**Community-school cooperation in rec-**

reation programs is being emphasized. Two examples will support this statement. In Flint, Michigan, as a result of the impetus provided by Charles Stewart Mott and the Mott Foundation, recreation programs exist in the schools. It brings people of all nationalities, economic status, and other types of backgrounds together on commonly owned property: the public schools. More than 12,000 visitors come each year to see the Flint program. The program includes all types of recreational activities ranging from roller skating to an international program that involves approximately 1,000 athletes and their families in Flint, Michigan, and Hamilton, Canada.

Another example of community-school connected recreation is in Los Angeles, California, where the city school district, through its Youth Services Section, sponsors a program where millions participate over the course of any one year. More than 550 recreation sites are utilized and more than 4,000 full-time and part-time personnel are involved in the leadership phase of the program. A year-round, 107-acre camp is utilized where outdoor education is carried on. A day camp is also in operation. The program utilizes the recreational experiences in the Youth Services Program as a laboratory experience for skills learned in the classroom.

**Religion is recognizing the value of recreation.** The puritan colonists encouraged the belief that recreation and spiritual teachings were not compatible. Today, however, religion and the church feel that it is their responsibility to help people make the most constructive and creative use of leisure. It is recognized that recreation can complement the church program and help to meet the needs of church members. As a result, many churches throughout the United States have gymnasiums and recreation centers as part of their facility complex. The Southern Baptists, for example, in one year spent approximately $150 million on facilities that are used primarily for recreation.

**The cultural explosion is leaving its impact on recreation.** The increased national interest in music, art, concerts, exhibitions, and other cultural interests is affecting recreation. Recreation programs are expanding their offerings to include specialists in the various arts. The public is encouraged to participate more. Opportunities are being increased for new forms of participation in the arts. Adtional appropriations of money are being made. As a result, recreation is being afforded the opportunity to meet the increased interest in cultural activities and thereby contribute to a better America.

**The National Recreation and Park Association is giving leadership to recreation.** This is a new association that combines the efforts of the leading recreation and park people who have joined together to further recreation in America and in the human environment. This agency is concerned with both natural and man-made beauty in America and the human environment. It is attempting to help people in this country have a better and healthier place in which to live, work, and enjoy their leisure. Its goal is to provide the populace with good parks and playgrounds and to instill the need for proper use of land and water. Better recreation programs and a better climate for recreation should evolve as a result of the formation of this new association.

## THE WISE USE OF LEISURE

James C. Charlesworth, Professor of Political Science, University of Pennsylvania, and President of the American Academy of Political and Social Science, proposes a comprehensive plan for the wise use of leisure.* This plan is a milestone in the professional literature, and

*The American Academy of Political and Social Science: Leisure in America: blessing or curse? Philadelphia, 1964, pp. 30-46.

# INCOME HAS A DECIDED INFLUENCE . . .

**TOTAL DAYS PARTICIPATION PER PERSON IN 17 OUTDOOR ACTIVITIES**
**BY FAMILY INCOME** JUNE-AUGUST, 1960, 12 YEARS AND OLDER

DAYS PER PERSON = 5 DAYS | NUMBER OF PERSONS IN EACH GROUP = 1 MILLION

| Income | Days per person | Persons (millions) |
|---|---|---|
| LESS THAN $3,000 | 18.5 | 29.8 |
| 3,000-4,499 | 33.5 | 22.2 |
| 4,500-5,999 | 33.3 | 26.6 |
| 6,000-7,999 | 40.5 | 21.1 |
| 8,000-9,999 | 42.4 | 11.8 |
| 10,000-14,999 | 44.2 | 11.0 |
| 15,000 AND OVER | 49.7 | 4.1 |

**TOTAL DAYS PARTICIPATION BY FAMILY INCOME** = 50 MILLION

| Income | Days participation |
|---|---|
| LESS THAN $3,000 | 552.0 |
| 3,000-4,499 | 744.7 |
| 4,500-5,999 | 887.1 |
| 6,000-7,999 | 853.6 |
| 8,000-9,999 | 498.2 |
| 10,000-14,999 | 488.0 |
| 15,000 AND OVER | 204.5 |

**PARTICIPATION IN SELECTED OUTDOOR ACTIVITIES BY FAMILY INCOME**
PERCENTAGE OF PERSONS 12 YEARS AND OVER, JUNE-AUGUST, 1960

PERCENTAGE PARTICIPATING

| Income | Boating | Camping | Horseback Riding | Walking for Pleasure | Fishing |
|---|---|---|---|---|---|
| LESS THAN $1,500 | 4 | 2 | 2 | 19 | 24 |
| $1,500 TO $2,999 | 21 | 9 | 4 | 3 | 28 |
| $3,000 TO $4,499 | 19 | 6 | 4 | 24 | 32 |
| $4,500 TO $5,999 | 28 | 8 | 6 | 32 | 36 |
| $6,000 TO $7,999 | 28 | 10 | 7 | 32 | 37 |
| $8,000 TO $9,999 | 33 | 13 | 7 | 31 | 37 |
| $10,000 TO $14,999 | 18 | 11 | — | 39 | 41, 37 |
| $15,000 AND OVER | 36 | 13 | 10 | 27 | 46 |

BOATING · CAMPING · HORSEBACK RIDING · WALKING FOR PLEASURE · FISHING

*U.S. Department of Commerce:*
*A proposed program for scenic roads*
*and parkways, Washington, D. C., 1966.*

# EDUCATION AFFECTS PARTICIPATION AS MUCH AS INCOME...

**PARTICIPATION IN SELECTED OUTDOOR ACTIVITIES BY YEARS OF FORMAL SCHOOLING**
PERCENTAGE OF PERSONS 25 YEARS AND OVER, JUNE-AUGUST, 1960          EACH SYMBOL = 5%

| | PLAYING OUTDOOR GAMES | SWIMMING | SIGHTSEEING | DRIVING FOR PLEASURE | WALKING FOR PLEASURE |
|---|---|---|---|---|---|
| ALL AGE 25 OR OVER | 20% | 35% | 41% | 50% | 29% |
| 4 YEARS OR LESS | 12% | 9% | 17% | 25% | 20% |
| 5-7 YEARS | 9% | 16% | 27% | 35% | 25% |
| 8 YEARS | 12% | 23% | 35% | 48% | 25% |
| HIGH SCHOOL: 1-3 YEARS | 22% | 36% | 36% | 54% | 29% |
| 4 YEARS | 25% | 49% | 51% | 58% | 32% |
| COLLEGE: 1-3 YEARS | 30% | 43% | 53% | 60% | 33% |
| 4 YEARS OR MORE | 36% | 56% | 57% | 56% | 39% |

# WHILE AGE HAS THE SHARPEST INFLUENCE...

**OLDER PEOPLE ENGAGE LESS IN MOST OUTDOOR ACTIVITIES**

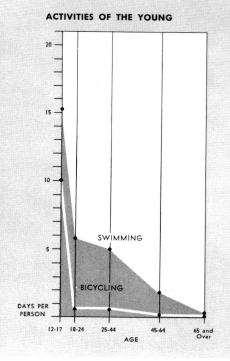

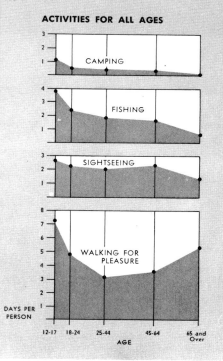

*U.S. Department of Commerce:*
*A proposed program for scenic roads*
*and parkways, Washington, D. C., 1966.*

as such, the reader will benefit from reading a few of the highlights that have implications for physical education and recreation.

### Charlesworth's categories of leisurites

The categories of persons who are in a position to make use of free time are: old people, children and teen-agers, wives, vacationers, week-enders, patients in mental and general hospitals, armed forces, prisoners, the unemployed, etc.

### A practical philosophy of leisure

1. *The wise use of leisure time is more creative, constructive, and wholesome than work.* The admonition that idle hands will do the Devil's work applies only to empty time.

2. *Programs for the wise use of leisure are a public and government responsibility.* Social dangers, including disease, illiteracy, crime, and mental disorders have implications for public and government responsibility for leisure.

3. *The present philosophy in this country of growth for growth's sake should be repudiated.* The desire to beat Russia and to prove the worth of capitalism is ill founded.

4. *One works in order to enjoy leisure.* The old adage that work is its own reward is outdated. People in recreation and education, however, must insist upon putting first things first.

5. *The leisure pattern in America must not be imitative.* It is interesting to read about the Greeks and the Romans, but a pattern of leisure in America should be based on its culture, economy, and other pertinent factors.

### Organization for leisure in government and education

*Organization plan for leisure.* This plan should provide for a department in state governments responsible for leisure. This department would give its attention to promoting the constructive use of leisure by inhabitants of its state.

*Instruction.* Activities for leisure should be compulsorily learned throughout school life and available throughout life. Emphasis should be on activities that evoke such qualities as pride, human understanding, and development of the mind and spirit. Softball leagues, for example, represent the elementary level of recreational thinking. Emphasis on championship records and sustained athletic practice is a low form of leisure objective. People should be taught self-fulfillment rather than encouraged to be spectators.

*Leisure program objectives.* Objectives should include intellectual development, aesthetic appreciation, social qualities, skill in nonathletic and athletic games, and in noncompetitive hobbies and sports, sight-seeing, nature study, and outdoor life, loafing, and resting.

*Administrative units for leisure activities.* Programs should be coordinated by governmental leisure agencies, but administered by such nongovernmental units as universities, churches and synagogues, clubs and organizations, neighborhood circles, housing developers, housing authorities, and settlement houses.

### RECREATIONAL ACTIVITIES

Activities that comprise the offerings for recreation programs may be classified into several groups. Some of the more common activities are as follows:

*Music activities*
  1. Instrumental
  2. Orchestral
  3. Community Sings
  4. Choral Groups
  5. Barber shop quartets
*Dance*
  1. Folk
  2. Square
  3. Social
  4. Modern

*Arts and crafts*
1. Plastics
2. Leathercraft
3. Graphic arts
4. Ceramics
5. Metalcraft
6. Photography
7. Stenciling and block printing
8. Sewing

*Sports and games*
1. Archery
2. Badminton
3. Bowling
4. Fencing
5. Golf
6. Hopscotch

*Dramatics*
1. Plays
2. Festivals
3. Clubs

*Outdoor activities*
1. Campfires
2. Outdoor cooking
3. Woodcraft
4. Camping
5. Canoeing
6. Conservation
7. Fishing
8. Orienteering

*Miscellaneous*
1. Horticulture
2. Forums
3. Cards
4. Hobby clubs

## AGENCIES THAT SPONSOR RECREATION PROGRAMS

The physical educator should be familiar with the various agencies that sponsor recreation programs. There are three major types of recreation agencies: public recreation agencies, private or voluntary agencies, and commercial agencies. Some examples of each type are as follows:

*Public agencies*
1. Municipal public agencies, such as the park department, recreation department, youth commission, education department, and other city or community departments
2. State public agencies, such as state park departments, state conservation departments, and state education departments
3. Federal public agencies, such as national parks, Forestry Service, Children's Bu-

reau, Fish and Wild Life Service, and the Tennessee Valley Authority

*Private voluntary agencies*
1. Youth-serving organizations, such as Boys' Clubs of America, Young Men's Christian Association, Young Women's Christian Association, Campfire Girls, Boy Scouts, and church centers
2. Organizations serving an entire population, such as museums, libraries, athletic clubs outdoor clubs, and granges
3. Private voluntary agencies organized around special interests of certain groups, such as music specialties, photographic specialties, and sports specialties

*Commercial agencies (operated for profit)*
Theaters, bowling alleys, art galleries, night clubs, and concert halls

## National Recreation and Park Association

Recently the American Institute of Park Executives, the American Recreation Society, the American Zoological Association, the National Council of State Parks, and the National Recreation Association were merged into a unified national organization known as the National Recreation and Park Association. Laurence S. Rockefeller was elected as the first president of this association. The merger was designed to bring together a single organization supported by private citizens and professional groups and dedicated to helping all Americans devote their free time to constructive and satisfying activities (for further discussion see chapter on Professional Organizations).

## THE PROFESSION AND RECREATION

The Recreation Division of the AAHPER has prepared a policy statement on what it feels are its contributions to the recreation program.* This statement was approved by the Board of Directors of the AAHPER. It envisions its concern with

*American Association for Health, Physical Education and Recreation: Recreation policy statement, Journal of Health, Physical Education, and Recreation 37:43, May, 1966.

recreation at the present time in five areas of endeavor:

1. *Education for leisure.* The profession has an important role to play in developing, communicating, and implementing a national philosophy of leisure and recreation.

2. *Professional preparation and personnel standards.* The profession has a concern for the recruitment and preparation of recreators, and for the improvement of personnel standards and practices.

3. *Research and evaluation.* The profession has a responsibility for proposing, formulating, and encouraging interdisciplinary and interagency exchange of information, and furthering the application of sound research concerned with recreation and leisure.

4. *Recreation services.* The profession has the responsibility of promoting the most productive relations possible between school and community recreation programs. Such relations may involve personnel, facilities, and other essentials to adequate recreational services. The profession supports the community–school concept in recreation.

5. *Planning and development.* The profession has the responsibility for encouraging greater participation by agencies at all governmental levels and other organizations in the process of coordinating, planning, developing, and financing resources and services for recreation.

## SCHOOL AND RECREATION

The school has a definite relationship to recreation. It has the responsibility of utilizing such resources as pupils, facilities, personnel, and programs to help in the attainment of recreation objectives, and it also has the responsibility of providing recreational experiences within the framework of the educational program. The cardinal principle of "worthy use of leisure time" can be fulfilled to a consider-

able extent if school authorities accept their responsibilities in achieving recreational objectives.

## School-centered recreation

Some recreation leaders have raised the question as to whether or not recreation should be school-centered. Hjelte and Shivers* list some arguments, pro and con, in respect to this issue. The reasons that they list *for* a school-centered program are as follows: The school possesses the facilities essential to a good recreation program, and duplicating these facilities results in waste and inefficiency. Schools are located within a community in much the same way as recreational centers are located—to meet the needs of the people within a particular geographical area. The school comes in contact with all the children, and therefore the consumer of recreation can best be met through this agency. The objectives of schools and the objectives of recreation are similar. The schools are a source of leadership for recreation programs.

Hjelte and Shivers' arguments listed as being *against* a school-centered recreation program are as follows: Education should restrict itself to intellectual training and not be concerned with experiences that are only indirectly related to intellectual training. Public schools have too many responsibilities without adding any more. Teachers are poorly paid and facilities are inadequate in many localities, and so a heavier burden should not be placed upon these resources. Recreation is hampered by the formality of the school environment and becomes regimented. Consequently, recreation is able to realize its potentialities to a greater extent through the establishment of a special agency. School facilities, equipment, and supplies are damaged through a recreation pro-

*Hjelte, George, and Shivers, Jay: Public administration of parks and recreational services, New York, 1963, The Macmillan Co.

gram and alterations are necessary, which raises the question as to whether other facilities might not be provided more economically. Finally, in attempting to join the forces of education and recreation, difficulties are encountered in securing financial aid for both. Greater public support can be gained if recreation is not grafted onto the educational program.

Regardless of the arguments for or against school-centered recreation, the schools should play a vital part in the field of recreation. At the present time they are contributing staff and facilities. The program of studies in the schools, however, has a long way to go before it realizes its potentialities for developing resources for leisure.

According to the report of the National Conference on School Recreation the responsibilities of the school in the area of recreation are fivefold*:

1. *Schools should educate for the*

*worthy use of leisure.* The schools must contribute their services in preparing young people for the increasing amount of leisure time they will have in an automated society. These services include the development of skills and appreciations and understandings in many educational areas, such as music and art, with which the school is concerned.

2. *Schools should achieve maximum articulation between instruction and recreation.* The articulation can be most effectively achieved by having an enlightened administration in charge of school affairs. By enlightened is meant an understanding and appreciation of the importance of constructive recreation in our society. Furthermore, this articulation can be achieved by providing leaders in the school-connected recreation program who develop effective teacher-pupil relationships, and plan and administer a dynamic educational program.

3. *Schools should develop cooperative planning of recreation programs and facilities.* School district officials should recognize and enthusiastically work toward

*Danford, Howard G., editor: School recreation, National Conference report, Washington, D. C., 1959, American Association for Health, Physical Education, and Recreation.

Oakland Recreation Department,
Oakland, Calif.

School playgrounds are the center for recreation activity.

the utilization of elementary schools, secondary schools, and community and junior colleges as centers for recreational activities. Such a goal should be implemented by cooperative planning between the school and officials representing the various agencies and organizations of the community.

4. *Schools should coordinate and mobilize total community resources for recreation.* The school should act as a hub around which recreation becomes an effective force throughout the community. School staffs, facilities, and a widely diversified program of recreation will help in achieving this goal.

5. *Schools should interpret recreation to the people.* The public should become aware of the need for recreation in today's world. Only as the need and importance of recreation are communicated to them will the proper support and participation accrue. There is a special need to interpret recreation to such key people as government officials, communication media officers, school leaders, parents, and students.

The Second National Conference on School Recreation* made the following recommendations, which included setting forth a series of principles and statements regarding school-centered recreation and municipal-school recreation. These principles and statements are presented in adapted form.

### School-centered recreation

1. Schools should accept, as a major responsibility, education for leisure.
2. Schools and colleges should provide their students with opportunities for participation in wholesome, creative activities.
3. The facilities and resources of a school

should be made available for recreation purposes when needed.
4. Where community recreation programs are missing or inadequate, the school should take the initiative and provide recreation programs for young and old alike.
5. The school should cooperate with community organizations and agencies interested in or already sponsoring recreation programs.
6. The school should appoint a person to act as a community school director who would be responsible for the recreation-education program in the school.
7. Recreation and education are not identical, but each has its own uniqueness and distinctive features.
8. The community-school director should provide in-service recreation education for his staff.
9. The federal level of government has a responsibility to stimulate recreation programs.
10. Recreation depends upon public understanding and support for its existence.
11. Recreation should be concerned with exploiting the interests of people.
12. The recreation program should consist of many varied activities.
13. Recreation should be concerned with contributing to the mental health of the individual.

### Municipal-school recreation

1. The school should accept the responsibility to educate for the worthy use of leisure, contribute to recreation in the instructional program, mobilize community resources, and cooperatively plan facilities for recreation. The college and university should promote research in recreation and provide professional preparation programs in this specialized area.
2. There should be joint planning of municipal school recreation based on stated principles and brought about by state departments of education and local boards of education.
3. School facilities should be available for recreational use.

*Report of the Second National Conference on School Recreation: Twentieth century recreation: Reengagement of school and community, November 7–9, 1962, Washington, D. C., 1963, American Association for Health, Physical Education, and Recreation.

## Ways in which the school program can develop resources for leisure

How people express themselves during their leisure hours will depend upon the

*Glencoe Public Schools,
Glencoe, Ill.*

The schools are a source of leadership for recreation programs.

resources they have developed for their free time. Human beings have a tendency to pursue during leisure hours those activities that are familiar to them and that are geared to their interests and abilities. Many want to spend their time doing something in which they have developed some skill and where they are recognized. A boy will go swimming in his free moments because he has learned how to swim or dive well. A girl will paint because she knows how to apply the principles of color dynamics. A man and woman will participate in dramatics because they have developed some acting ability and are recognized and accepted by the group. It is because these resources for leisure have been developed in these individuals that they engage in such activities. These activities in turn contribute to a more interesting, vigorous, and satisfying life. Other activities such as stealing, assaulting, gambling, or drinking also re-

flect the only type of resources that some individuals have to tap when they want to satisfy their leisure-time desires.

Although there is controversy over who should be responsible for leisure education, the schools seem best equipped to play a major role. Such essentials as leadership, facilities, and equipment are readily available. In addition, it is the center of community life and represents a common meeting ground for the entire population as well as the children who attend school. Furthermore, because of the many students who do not go on to college, the major part of this work must be done in the elementary and secondary schools. The ironical part of this whole problem of leisure-time education, however, is that, although the schools are best equipped to do the job, they are not accepting the challenge.

To a great degree school programs are still geared to preparation for college, to a mastery of the three R's, to an acquisition of subject matter content which is geared to some vocation or profession, and to what will help a person make more money or surpass his rival. Some time ago Dr. Paul Douglass, a former President of American University, conducted a survey. He discovered that only 3% of some 30,000 women graduates thought their education had been valuable for the development of resources for leisure-time pursuits. This is an indictment of our educational program in the United States. If schools are going to be practical and functional, then surely they should develop skills and other resources for leisure-time activities—especially in this age when leisure time is continually increasing. Yet, here are some illustrations of what is happening in some schools. A music teacher in one of our supposedly "better" schools would point to those students who could not carry a tune and ask them to please refrain from singing. This was a regular practice in her classes—only those who could sing well were allowed to join in. The others remained silent and were mere spectators. If the teacher is trying to develop in the child a resource for leisure, what difference does it make whether he has a good voice, can harmonize, or can hit the high notes? Another illustration points up a similar problem. A teacher of art used to say, "You must not draw a flower that way—draw it this way." The children were required to adhere to a fixed, rigid pattern which few of them were interested in or could master. Why should the child not be allowed to express himself? *If the flower looks beautiful to him and he enjoys himself, education for leisure has taken place.* It is important for teachers to realize that they are not developing star performers. Instead, they are working with individuals who vary in ability and skill. The important thing is to give them a satisfying experience and sufficient knowledge and skill so that they

will be motivated to do more of the same thing when they get away from the classroom and the teacher. This will not take place if the schoolroom becomes a place where only the most skilled youngsters can perform and where things have to be done in a rigid, prescribed pattern.

All subjects in the educational program have a contribution to make in developing resources for leisure. The science subjects, for example, should emphasize to a greater degree than they do at present a study of birds, trees, rocks, and flowers, as an incentive to forming hobbies. The art department should be concerned with making jewelry and artificial flowers, decorating furniture, and painting designs on materials, and painting as a hobby instead of turning out highly skilled work. English could do a better job with informal dramatics, storytelling, and creative writing. The social sciences could create a greater desire to participate in community activity and develop a better environment in which to live. They could also study the furniture of various periods of history as an incentive to antique collecting. Why not include more costume designing in home economics and stimulate to a greater degree the creative joy of cooking? Geography classes, while studying the various countries of the world, could obtain stamps from each, as an incentive to stamp collecting. Physical education could emphasize to a greater degree the individual activities such as fishing and tieing trout flies. When it is realized that only one out of approximately 1,000 persons ever plays football after leaving school, it can be seen that there should be at least equal stress on such activities as bait casting, swimming, bowling, and golf. Educators must realize that recreation is related not only to physical education but to all areas. Dr. Jay B. Nash, formerly of New York University, conducted a survey of 1,000 adults and found that only 2% utilized sports and games for their leisure-time activities. As one grows older there is a tendency to do other things.

The school with its wide and varied educational offering has infinite opportunities to develop resources for leisure. During this day and age of mass production, application of atomic energy to industry, and increasing amounts of leisure, the schools are being challenged to accept this responsibility.

Schools should help young people to adjust to the way of life that they will encounter after leaving school, aid them in solving the problems they will meet, and help them to become responsible citizens. Education most certainly must concern itself with leisure-time education. The day of the thirty-hour workweek is rapidly approaching. If one considers that eight hours a day are spent in sleeping and three hours for eating, this still leaves 61 hours a week for potential leisure-time activity, twice as much as for work. These leisure hours represent a challenge facing the nation's schools.

## PERFORMANCE OF RECREATION WORK BY PHYSICAL EDUCATORS

Physical education and recreation are not synonymous, but they are closely related, and physical education personnel can play a prominent part in recreation programs. The field of recreation utilizes not only physical education activities but also many other activities in which an individual desires to participate during his leisure hours. This means that, although games and sports play a prominent part, many other activities less physically active in nature, are utilized. However, physical education activities have implications for recreation. The skills that are developed and instruction that takes place in physical education classes have a definite carry-over value. People want to engage in activities in which they have mastered some skill. People like to excel.

A person trained in physical education has a great contribution to make to recreation. Many physical educators are playing prominent roles in this field today. When recreation was in its embryo state, the physical educator was usually the logical person to assume leadership for such a program. Today, however, in many of our large municipal recreation programs and in other areas, those with specialized training in recreation are providing much of the leadership. The physical educator, however, still plays a very prominent part in this work. Because of the nature of his training, the physical educator directs many recreation programs in communities where insufficient funds make it impossible to hire a full-time recreational leader; he or she acts as a specialist in the area of athletics and other physical education activities in large city, industrial, and other recreational programs; and he or she plays an important part in communities that utilize school facilities for the community recreation program. In the town of Great Neck, Long Island, for example, the head of the school health and physical education programs is also the head of the recreation program. The physical educator is also called upon to serve in many other recreational capacities such as playground director, supervisor, and camp director.

In discussing the relationship of physical education and recreation, one thing should be stressed above all others—there must be cooperation between the two. Both are primarily interested in furthering the health and happiness of people. In attempting to attain this objective, personnel must be utilized in a way that will be most advantageous in furthering the health and happiness of all. In many cases facilities must be utilized by both programs. Supplies and equipment must be shared. Programs must be planned cooperatively and the ultimate objective kept closely in mind. Each should help the other and follow practices that will result in the most benefits for the greatest number of people. Both should be well acquainted with the program in each area. Only in this way will the best interests of the people be served.

## QUALIFICATIONS FOR THE RECREATOR

The person who works in the field of recreation, whether full time or as a physical educator or other specialist, needs particular qualifications in order to carry out his or her responsibilities. Some qualifications that are of special importance are an interest in and liking for people, emotional maturity, enthusiasm and skill, desire to render a service, professional preparation, and professional mindedness.

### A recreation curriculum

#### FRESHMAN YEAR

| *First term* | *Hours* |
|---|---|
| English and American literature | 3 |
| English composition | 4 |
| Introduction to psychology | 3 |
| Introduction to mathematics | 4 |
| | 14 |

| | |
|---|---|
| English and American literature | 3 |
| Man and society | 3 |
| Educational psychology | 2 |
| Nature of matter | 4 |
| Introduction to music | 3 |
| | 15 |

| *Summer camp* | |
|---|---|
| Aquatics and land sports | 2 |
| Organization and supervision of camping or camp crafts | 2 |
| | 4 |

#### SOPHOMORE YEAR

| | |
|---|---|
| Philosophical analysis | 3 |
| Government and politics | 3 |
| Social psychology | 3 |
| Speech I | 2 |
| Introduction to anthropology | 3 |
| Introduction to human relations | 2 |
| | 16 |

| | |
|---|---|
| Man in a biological world | 4 |
| The American economy | 3 |
| Emotion and motivation | 3 |
| Group dynamics in the classroom | 2 |

| | |
|---|---|
| Man and society | 2 |
| Creative art experiments | 2 |
| | 16 |

| *Intersession* | |
|---|---|
| Activities for camp programs | 2 |

#### JUNIOR YEAR

| | |
|---|---|
| Culture and personality | 3 |
| Activities for social recreation | 2 |
| Crafts in recreation | 2 |
| Physical activities in recreation | 2 |
| Rhythms | 2 |
| First aid and safety procedures | 2 |
| Games | 2 |
| | 15 |

| | |
|---|---|
| Child psychology | 3 |
| Leadership in recreation | 2 |
| Folk dance | 2 |
| Organization and conduct of social recreation | 2 |
| Physical activities for recreation | 2 |
| Music in recreation | 2 |
| Recreational dramatics | 2 |
| Field work | 2 |
| | 17 |

#### SENIOR YEAR

| | |
|---|---|
| Psychology of adolescence | 3 |
| Crafts in recreation | 2 |
| Field work in recreation | 3 |
| Philosophy of recreation | 2 |
| Elective | 5 |
| | 15 |

| | |
|---|---|
| Field work in recreation | 3 |
| Introduction to social research | 2 |
| Social agencies in the community | 2 |
| Organization and administration of recreation | 2 |
| Elective | 5 |
| | 14 |

### Interest in and liking for people

The person who works in recreation must have faith in people and recognize the worth of each individual. The recreation leader should have qualifications that permit easy access to people of all races and creeds; he or she should be sympathetic and understanding in the many human associations related to work in the recreation program. People participate in the recreation program on a voluntary basis. They come of their own choice, and they can also leave of their own free will. Therefore it is important to provide all individuals with experiences that will satisfy the needs for which they attend.

### Emotional maturity

The person who works in recreation must be an adult in his or her outlook on life. He or she must have good mental and physical health, the ability to accept others' opinions and personalities for what they are, and a pleasing, friendly personality.

### Enthusiasm and skill

The person who works in recreation should be enthusiastic about recreation and the contribution such programs can make to human welfare. He or she should have skill in working with people and also in the organization and administration of particular activities or the program as a whole. The recreation leader should possess productive energy that can be channeled in the right directions.

### Desire to render a service

The person who works in recreation should be interested in rendering a service to mankind. He or she must like work and count rewards not in terms of material things but in terms of what he or she does for people.

### Educated

The person who works in recreation must be educated in the true sense of the word. The recreation leader should have a broad background of general education and, in addition, be well prepared in the activities taught and the particular specialized tasks performed.

### Professionally minded

The person who works in recreation should be interested in building the profession. He or she should maintain a high code of professional ethics, join professional associations and be active in them, conduct himself or herself in a manner that will bring credit to the profession, and continually try to work toward a better profession that renders greater services to humanity.

## PROFESSIONAL PREPARATION OF THE RECREATOR

The preparation of the recreation leader should be thorough and complete. The recreation curriculum on page 272 gives the requirements for a professional student in a large university. An examination of the courses and experiences required will show the extent to which the biological sciences, general education, social sciences, arts, humanities, and professional recreation courses are required over a four-year period. Although a physical educator will not want to pursue such an extensive curriculum, nevertheless he or she should attempt to become equipped with some of these experiences in order to do a good job in recreation work.

## OPPORTUNITIES IN RECREATION

There are many opportunities available in the field of recreation for qualified persons.

### Types of positions

The field of recreation has developed to the point where it offers a promising area of employment for individuals who have been trained in this specialized work. In recent years training institutions have developed curricula to provide the necessary leadership for the field of recreation. Many positions are open for the person who is qualified, including the following: superintendents, general supervisors, directors, play leaders, and supervisors of special activities in recreation departments; directors' assistants and area specialists in youth-serving organizations; consultants, executive officers, research work-

# *Choose a Career in* RECREATION

Choosing a career in Recreation, Parks, and Conservation is choosing a life of Leadership.

Few fields of endeavor offer the variety of experience and responsibilities as does the recreation, park, and conservation field. Administration, finance, public relations, planning, community action, group leadership, and personnel direction are all part of the daily life of the recreation leader. And, when the day is done, the personal satisfaction which results from the contributions you have made to the better life of the community and the enrichment of our nation is proof of the wise selection in choosing recreation as a career.

## PUBLIC

Public recreation includes administration, supervision and leadership in:

*Community Sponsored Programs.*
*School Sponsored Programs.*
*County Sponsored Programs.*
*State Sponsored Programs.*
*Federal Recreation Agencies*

(All public recreation is paid for by taxes through city, county, state or national government, depending upon the position described.)

## INDUSTRIAL

Industrial Recreation includes administration, supervision and leadership in:

*Management Sponsored Programs.*
*Employee Sponsored Programs.*
*Cooperative Programs Financed by Management;*
  *and (A) Operated by Employees or*
  *(B) Operated by Both Management and Employees.*
*Association or Institution Type Programs.*

## ILL and HANDICAPPED

Recreation for the Ill and Handicapped includes administration, supervision and leadership in medically approved recreation programs for hospitalized patients and for ill and handicapped persons in special schools and institutions. Recreation activities are used as a means of stimulating healthy response in patients, enriching their lives and in helping them achieve a better social adjustment.

## ARMED FORCES

Civilian positions with the Armed Forces include direction of clubs, libraries, hobby shops and entertainment (sports, drama and music) for active duty military personnel and their dependents.

## RECREATION EDUCATION

Recreation education is a basic responsibility of the home and school for preparing the individual for worthy use of leisure. Professionally it includes the continual responsibility on the part of the recreationist, as well as the teaching of recreation professional courses in a junior college, college or university.

## VOLUNTARY

Voluntary and youth serving programs include scouts, boy's and girl's clubs, Y's, and other agencies which derive support from public and private subscription.

## COMMERCIAL

Commercial recreation includes the operation and management of privately owned enterprises offering recreation and entertainment to the public for a set individual charge.

## PARKS

Parks management is closely allied with recreation as a result of a growing trend in government to join park management agencies with recreation agencies to better serve the total recreational needs of the people. Because recreationists are trained to plan for the effective use of facilities, as well as their care and upkeep, the recreation professional with the proper combination of training and experience will be the logical person to guide the total development and management of park and recreation facilities and programs for the public benefit.

Printed by
The Middle-Atlantic District Advisory Committee
of the
National Recreation and Park Association

ers, and assistants in government agencies; teachers in colleges, universities, and professional schools; administrative positions in commercial recreation; directors and area specialists for hospital recreation programs; positions with such organizations as 4-H clubs; and directors of church recreation programs.

Various types of recreation positions for which the aspiring student can prepare are as follows:

1. Superintendent of recreation
2. Assistant superintendent of recreation
3. Recreation director
4. Recreation supervisor
5. Recreation center director
6. Consultant in recreation
7. Field representative
8. Executive director
9. Hospital recreation supervisor
10. Camp recreation coordinator
11. Extension specialist
12. Service club director
13. Girls' worker or boys' worker
14. District recreation supervisor
15. Recreation leader
16. Supervisor of special activities
17. Recreation therapist
18. Recreation educator

## RECREATION SETTINGS

Recreation activities are conducted in many settings. These settings afford many job opportunities for the person with training in recreation. A few of these settings will be discussed.

**Villages, cities, and other communities.** Community recreation is provided by the local government. It is controlled, financed, and administered by the community. Community recreation departments and park departments, for example, sponsor recreation programs.

**Industries.** The nation's great industrial concerns, such as Lockheed Aircraft and Eastman Kodak Company, sponsor recreation programs for their employees.

**Hospitals.** Recreation programs are provided in many veterans, municipal, county, and other hospitals for the bene-

fit of patients. The therapeutic values have been well established.

**Schools and colleges.** Elementary and secondary schools and colleges and universities in some sections of the country provide recreation programs. School recreation is frequently provided by a board of education for the students and in some cases for the adult population.

**Home.** The family unit is becoming a center for much recreation.

**Commercial establishments.** Amusement parks, movie houses, bowling alleys, and many other forms of recreation abound from coast to coast.

**Service clubs for the armed forces.** The United Service Organization is a good example of a recreation program provided for individuals who serve in the armed forces.

**Churches and religious organizations.** Today, many churches and religious organizations, especially in large metropolitan areas, have extensive recreation programs for their parishioners.

**Voluntary youth-serving agencies.** Many agencies for young people such as the Boy Scouts and the Girl Scouts are interested in how these boys and girls spend their free time and therefore they sponsor recreation programs.

**State and federal agencies.** Various organs of the government at state and federal levels provide recreation programs. Examples of these government agencies are parks and forest preserves.

## OPPORTUNITIES FOR PLACEMENT AND SALARIES

The continued and expanded interest in recreation means many job openings in the years to come. The number of publicly sponsored local and county agencies engaged in recreation is approximately 3,000. Many more will be needed in the future. Thirty thousand companies now have recreation programs, and this number will expand considerably in the next decade. As people get more leisure time there will be a greater need for professional people to help them spend this leisure in as constructive a way as possible.

Salaries for recreation leaders now range from $4,000 to $7,000 to start and go to as high as $25,000 for key positions. As the cost of living increases and as teachers and other persons with comparable professional training find increased pay in their monthly envelopes, so will recreation leaders.

## Special opportunities in programs for mentally retarded, ill, and disabled

For those physical educators who would like to obtain positions in programs for the mentally retarded, ill, and disabled, some graduate recreation programs are available. This phase of recreation service is concerned with programs for the ill, disabled, handicapped, and aged persons who because of their condition are not able to participate in community recreation programs for the normal, physically active person. In addition to rendering direct services to such people there are also opportunities to supervise and administer programs in a variety of medical settings and other places that support such programs. Graduate courses taken in this area would include the usual research courses that are concerned with educational research and philosophy and, in addition, such courses as Survey of Physical Defects, Group Dynamics and Human Relations, Psychology of the Physically Handicapped, Abnormal Psychology, Recreational Crafts, Social Recreation, and Physical Rehabilitation.

### QUESTIONS AND EXERCISES

1. Define the term recreation. What is the history of the National Recreation and Park Association?
2. List and discuss each of the objectives of the recreation profession.
3. Survey your community to determine how many recreation activities are available for young people.
4. Why is there a need for good recreation programs in the space age in which we are living?
5. Select ten adults and find out how they spend their free time.
6. What part do physical education activities play in a recreation program?
7. What are the arguments for and against a school-centered recreation program?
8. How can the schools play a more important role in preparing for the student's leisure time?
9. For what jobs could a physical educator qualify in a municipal recreation program?

### SELECTED REFERENCES

American Association for Health, Physical Education, and Recreation: Recreation policy statement, Journal of Health, Physical Education, and Recreation 37:43, May, 1966.

Brightbill, Charles K.: Man and leisure, Englewood Cliffs, N. J., 1961, Prentice-Hall, Inc.

Bucher, Charles A., editor: Methods and materials in physical education and recreation, St. Louis, 1954, The C. V. Mosby Co.

Bucher, Charles A.: Administration of school health and physical education programs, St. Louis, 1967, The C. V. Mosby Co.

Carlson, Reynold E., and others: Recreation in American life, Belmont, California, 1963, Wadsworth Publishing Co., Inc.

Danford, Howard G., editor: School recreation, national conference report, Washington, D. C., 1959, American Association for Health, Physical Education, and Recreation.

de Grazia, Sebastian: Of time, work, and leisure, New York, 1962, The Twentieth Century Fund.

Dulles, Foster Rhea: A history of recreation, New York, 1965, Appleton-Century-Crofts.

Hunter, O. N., and Jensen, Clayne R.: Recreation and a changing world, Journal of Health, Physical Education, and Recreation 36:32, Sept., 1965.

Kleindienst, Viola, and Weston, Arthur: Intramural and recreation programs for schools and colleges, New York, 1964, Appleton-Century-Crofts.

Kraus, Richard: Which way—school recreation? Journal of Health, Physical Education, and Recreation 36:25, Nov.–Dec., 1965.

Kraus, Richard: Recreation today—program planning and leadership, New York, 1966, Appleton-Century-Crofts.

Larson, Leonard, and others: Leadership for leisure, Journal of Health, Physical Education, and Recreation **36**:34, March, 1965.

Lee, Robert: Religion and leisure in America, Nashville, 1964, Abingdon Press.

Meyer, Harold D., and Brightbill, Charles K.: Community recreation—a guide to its organization, Englewood Cliffs, N. J., 1964, Prentice-Hall, Inc.

President's Council on Youth Fitness: Physical fitness elements in recreation, suggestions for community programs, Washington, D. C., 1962, U. S. Government Printing Office.

Report to the President and Congress by the Outdoor Recreation Resources Review Commission: Outdoor recreation in America, Washington, D. C., Jan., 1962, U. S. Government Printing Office.

Saake, Alvin C.: Recreation is big in Hawaii, Journal of Health, Physical Education, and Recreation **37**:31, Nov.–Dec., 1966.

The American Academy of Political and Social Science: Leisure in America: blessing or curse? Philadelphia, 1964, The Academy.

Yukic, Thomas S.: Fundamentals of recreation, New York, 1963, Harper & Row.

# Chapter 10

# Camping and outdoor education

The out-of-doors is nature's laboratory. It is a setting that offers excellent opportunities to learn many knowledges and skills and develop wholesome attitudes. L. B. Sharp, one of the pioneers in the fields of camping and outdoor education, states it this way: "That which can best be learned inside the classroom should be learned there. That which can best be learned in the out-of-doors through direct experience, dealing with native materials and life situations, should there be learned."

Over the course of the last few years many experiments have been conducted based on the premise set forth by Sharp. These experiments have provided the evidence to show that boys and girls who use nature's classroom will learn more readily those things that directly relate to the out-of-doors and be more interested in doing so.

What L. B. Sharp stated several years ago was demonstrated by a kindergarten teacher who took her class out of the school to study the clouds in the sky, a third-grade class that utilized a compass to measure distances and determine directions preliminary to beginning a map for social studies, a sixth-grade class that went to a park and discovered fossils, and an eighth-grade class that found a spider web and related it to what they were doing on conservation. As pointed out time and time again, outdoor education is not just nature study, but represents a vital part of the educational program at all educational levels and in all subjects including art, social studies, mathematics, physical education, and industrial arts.

School camping and outdoor education are not synonymous. Outdoor education is education in the out-of-doors and also education about the out-of-doors. Outdoor education includes school camping. The camp provides a laboratory by which many facets of the out-of-doors can be studied firsthand. And the camp experience helps to develop qualities important to preparing young people for the lives they will live.

The worth of camping and outdoor education in the school program has been well established. The teacher of physical education, as well as all teachers at the elementary, secondary, and college levels, can benefit from studying the objectives, contributions, program, administration, and other aspects of these important fields. In the future, education will utilize these programs more and more, and the individuals who are trained in these areas will find many opportunities to apply their knowledge and experience.

Building trails through the state parks is a favorite project for school camp groups. The park manager (left) supervises the group in laying out this trail along the river.

## HISTORY

In May, 1948, representatives of such well-known organizations and agencies as the American Association for Health, Physical Education, and Recreation; United States Office of Education; National Secondary School Principals Association; American Association of School Administrators; and the American Council on Education made recommendations that camping experience should be a part of every child's educational experience, that cooperative arrangements should be worked out with conservation departments and other agencies directly related to natural resources, and that experimental camping programs, as a phase of the educational program, should be established in Michigan and any other states that were interested in trying out this educational trend.*

The state of Michigan led the way in this experiment to show the values that may be derived from making the camping experience a part of the regular school program. Twelve camps were set up in Michigan on an experimental basis. In one year alone they utilized 200 teachers and 1,000 students. There were also hundreds of educators and leaders in closely allied fields who visited these camps. The project was subsidized by the Kellogg Foundation. This was only the beginning of the school camping and outdoor education movement. Since that time it has grown rapidly. Schools all over the country are recognizing its value and importance in the educational program.

In 1962 one hundred leaders in education, conservation, and recreation participated in a National Conference on Outdoor Education. This Conference reaffirmed the importance of outdoor education and came to the following conclusions*:

*Smith, Julian W.: Journal of Health, Physical Education, and Recreation 26:8, 18, May–June, 1955.

*Professional Report from the National Conference on Outdoor Education: Journal of Health, Physical Education, and Recreation 33:29, Nov., 1962.

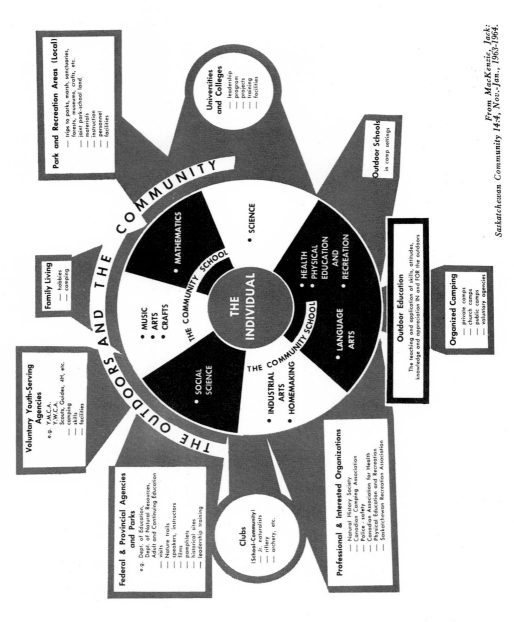

*From MacKenzie, Jack:*
*Saskatchewan Community 14:4, Nov.-Jan., 1963-1964.*

The world of outdoor education.

1. There is a greater need today than ever before for education in the out-of-doors.

2. Outdoor education needs to be stressed more in all schools and colleges and in conservation, recreation, and other agency programs.

3. All agencies and organizations concerned with outdoor education should work very closely together in order that such experiences can be provided for more boys and girls and also adults in our society.

4. The American Association for Health, Physical Education, and Recreation should provide strong leadership for the outdoor education program.

Outdoor education and camping have become firmly established in the American educational system. Schools are recognizing the values that relate to education that can take place in the out-of-doors and can be correlated closely to what is going on in the classroom. Also, the educators are becoming more aware of the importance of education about the out-of-doors and all the resources that are embodied in the world of nature. The years ahead will see further progress in this direction.

## OBJECTIVES OF CAMPING AND OUTDOOR EDUCATION

Many objectives have been listed for camping and outdoor education programs. Some of the more important objectives that have been enumerated over the years as being the reasons why such programs should exist in our schools are as follows:

1. Students learn to live democratically with other children and adults.

2. Students learn more about the physical environment and the importance of our vast wealth of natural resources.

3. An appreciation for the out-of-doors and the contributions it can make to enriched living is developed.

4. Those qualities that make for good citizenship, such as responsibility, leadership, teamwork, and honesty, are developed.

5. The contribution that the out-of-doors

*San Diego City Schools,*
*San Diego, Calif.*

Camping and outdoor education program.

can make to good health is more appreciated.

6. The love of adventure, which is a part of the makeup of children and youth, is satisfied.

7. Students are stimulated to learn about native materials and to see their relationship to the learning that takes place in the classroom.

8. Worthwhile skills in recreation such as map reading, fishing, and how to use a gun are developed.

9. Benefits are derived from wholesome work experiences.

10. Students learn to depend on personal resources in practicing the rules of healthful living.

11. Students learn some of the basic rules of safety.

These objectives are worthy goals and tie in closely with the social, intellectual, and health aims of general education. The child develops socially by learning to live democratically. Responsibilities for maintaining a camp are assumed by all. Each child, regardless of national origin, color, or other difference, is respected as an individual who can contribute to the group enterprise. He also develops intellectually as he satisfies his lust for adventure. He sees the wonders of nature firsthand. He learns about conservation, soil, water, and animal and bird life. A camping experience also promotes good health. The out-of-doors, together with healthful activity, interesting projects, and congenial classmates, improves the general fitness of the child. He usually leaves camp with a rugged glow to his cheeks, sparkling eyes that reflect the new things he has seen and learned, and an extra notch in his belt. If education is "preparation for life," then surely camping and outdoor experiences are an essential and worthwhile part of it.

Freeberg and Taylor* list four objectives for the outdoor education program: democratic group living, conservation edu-

*Freeberg, William H., and Taylor, Loren E.: Programs in outdoor education, Minneapolis, 1963, Burgess Publishing Co.

cation, leisure time education, and healthful outdoor living.

The Cleveland Heights, Ohio, public schools list as objectives for outdoor education the following:

1. To teach citizenship
2. To teach principles of natural science
3. To teach principles of conservation
4. To teach health and physical education
5. To teach other subject-matter aspects related to the camping situation

## PLACES AND ACTIVITIES FOR OUTDOOR EDUCATION

**School and community gardens and farms.** Experiences can be provided relating to such things as agriculture, bird and animal study, conservation, gardening, and milk production.

**School areas in general.** Experiences can be provided for studying such products of nature as plants, shrubs, birds, trees, and fish.

**School forests.** Where large wooded areas exist, experiences can be provided in relation to such things as reforestation, conservation, and the growth and wise use of forests.

**Museums.** Many different types of museums offer opportunities for experiences in such areas as archeological exploration, art appreciation, historical milestones, science accomplishments, and bird and animal life.

**Zoos.** These provide opportunities for experiences in the study of animals.

**Camps.** These offer opportunities for such things as group living, work experience, and development of outdoor skills.

Opportunities for outdoor education are available everywhere in the country. In addition to the fields, woods, and lakes, many private or public sanctuaries, museums, parks, camps, and zoos can be used for such purposes. Smith has outlined some common avenues of outdoor education through the following illustrations:

1. *Classroom-related experiences,* where the

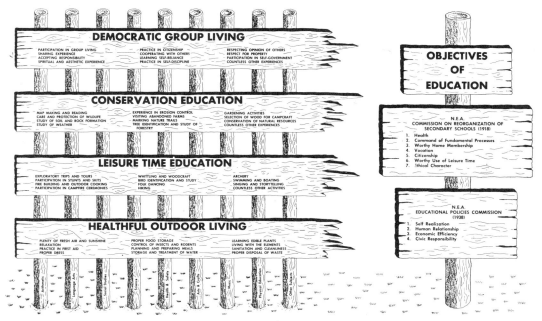

*From Freeberg, William H., and Taylor, Loren E.:
Programs in outdoor education,
Minneapolis, 1963, Burgess Publishing Co.*

roam over the wooded 'back forty.' As well as being a laboratory for science, gardening may be one of the most practical activities in outdoor education because of its recreational value.

3. *School camping*—one of the newest and most sensational developments in outdoor education—is the use of camps for an extended educational program by schools and colleges, whereby democratic social living is combined with learning about the natural environment and adventures in outdoor living. In school camping, children and teachers, together, have direct learning experiences related to many areas of the curriculum. Nearly one-half of the states now report programs ranging from pilot efforts to year-round operation. An increasing number of colleges have acquired camps whereby students have camping opportunities combined with teacher and leadership training.

4. *Day activities in outdoor areas,* sometimes called day camping is another pattern used by schools, colleges, recreation agencies, and youth-serving groups. Classes and organized groups have opportunities for field study combined with outdoor recreational skill.

5. *Outing and club activities,* usually considered a part of the curricular offerings, provide for organized special-interest groups. While usually conducted on an informal basis, such activities may be related to areas such as physical education, recreation, science, and others. Activities often include camping, hiking, and other interests of students, such as archery, shooting, fishing, arts and crafts, and bird study.

6. *Casting and fishing* are becoming more popular activities in schools and colleges. Fishing and allied activities, such as skish, spinning, bait and fly casting, which more nearly may be

called universal sports, are particularly significant in view of increased leisure time and the desire to seek the lakes and streams so prevalent in many parts of the country. Adaptable to all age groups, casting and fishing are closely related to camping, conservation and outdoor living skills. These activities fit well in the physical education, recreation, and adult education programs and have implications for science and other fields. Like other parts of an outdoor education program, training (including actual participation) is needed in order that those interested can derive the maximum benefits from the outdoor living that accompanies them. One needs only to observe the number of fishing licenses sold to realize the importance of this sport in American life today.

7. *Shooting and hunting,* like casting and fishing, are extensive and wholesome leisure-time activities in the American culture. More than 13 million hunting licenses are sold in the United States. More maximum satisfactions and values accrue in shooting and hunting when there is training in gun handling and safety, marksmanship, conservation, outdoor skills and woodmanship, care and use of public property, etc. Such activities as riflery, pistol shooting,

skeet, trap shooting, and archery, appropriately designed for the various age groups, fit well into physical education, clubs, recreation, adult education, and conservation activities in schools, colleges, and community organizations. In Michigan and New Hampshire, for example, state-wide institutes and clinics are conducted for school and college staff members in an effort to help develop sound educational activities centered around the natural interest of students in hunting and shooting. Assisting in these training ventures are such organizations and departments as the National Rifle Association, the Sporting Arms and Ammunition Manufacturers' Institute, state departments of conservation and education, colleges, sportsmen's clubs and police.

8. *Boating, sailing, canoeing, and other water activities* are becoming increasingly popular in some sections of the country and provide wholesome recreation pursuits for many people. These sports are also related to other interests such as fishing, hunting, and traveling, and should be related to safety, conservation, and outdoor skills.

9. *Winter sports,* including skating, skiing, tobogganing, snowshoeing, and others, are gain-

Learning how to saw trees properly is a form of outdoor education.

ing in popularity in states where the climate permits. Schools and colleges located in winter sports areas should consider offering appropriate training for participation in such activities. Like others mentioned, they are related to other outdoor skills and often can be included in programs.

10. *Community adult education and recreation* are offering a wide variety of activities in keeping pace with the public's great surge of interest in many outdoor activities . . . many can center about hobbies, such as making outdoor equipment and the training for advanced skills in outdoor sports.*

## PROGRAM

The San Diego City Schools utilizes its school camp experience to make studies in science and conservation more interesting and meaningful. Some of the learning experiences they describe are as follows:

*Astronomy.* Studying about stars and planets by looking at them through telescopes; visiting the Palomar Observatory and Museum

*Geology.* Digging into the earth to find rocks and minerals for study; reading the story of the soil profiles; studying soil and earth features

*Meteorology.* Observing and identifying weather; measuring weather phenomena at camp with accurate instruments; maintaining a weather station at camp

*Ecology.* Hiking to see and study the relationship of living things to their environment

*Conservation.* Learning about the problems of the land and working to help the land through soil erosion control, beetle control, tree planting, reduction of fire hazards, and forest improvement

*Botany and biology.* Studying birds, insects, animals, and plants in the field and pond; collecting specimens

*Forestry.* Learning woodmanship and the safe use of forestry tools and equipment

*Survival skills.* Using map and compass on hikes; considering problems of food, shelter, and safety on a "survival hike"

Many other school systems throughout the country have developed outdoor education and camping programs. The Uni-

---

*Smith, Julian W.: Journal of Health, Physical Education, and Recreation 26:8, 18, May-June, 1955.

versity School in Carbondale, Illinois involves their fourth, fifth, sixth, and seventh grade school children in such programs. Orange Local School District in Chagrin Falls, Ohio has access to Hirman House Camp. Stiles School in Rockford, Illinois has established a nature area. Snohomish County, Washington conducted a successful pilot outdoor education program. Long Beach, California schools provide valuable camping experiences for their school children at Camp Hi-Hill. Many other schools in other states have also had successful camping and outdoor education experiences.

Paul E. Harrison of Northern Illinois University has pointed out the contributions various departments in many schools are making in camping and outdoor education programs. These suggestions clarify the role of the total school offering in such an educational experience.

*Speech department*

Activities in speech and dramatics can take many forms:
1. Short plays, comedy, drama, etc.
2. Pageants
3. Folk festivals
4. Readings, recitations
5. Marionette and puppet shows

*Music department*

Campers can spend many happy hours with music:
1. Informal campfire sings
2. Pageants
3. Camp orchestra

*Mathematics*

Arithmetic is a must in many camp activities:
1. Food costs
2. Surveying and mapping
3. Camp stores and banks
4. Figuring land areas, elevation, tree heights, lumber footage, tree age

*Industrial arts*

Using appropriate tools and interesting natural materials where they are found:
1. Camp maintenance and repair
2. Building new camp equipment
3. Reading blueprints
4. Camp activities, dramatics, staging, etc.
5. Craft programs

*Homemaking*

Good food and appropriate clothing make for a happy camp:

1. Planning and preparing foods for cook-outs, camp-outs, and regular menus
2. Care of clothing and camp equipment
3. Social graces
4. Helping with camp food service

*English department*

The camp can provide an opportunity for the practice of effective communication and appreciation of literature:

1. Proper language usage
2. Writing letters, plays, poems
3. Storytelling
4. Reading

*Social science*

The history of the area—its land, its people, and its customs—is always an interesting problem for study:

1. A study of the area's industries
2. Indian lore and the lumber camps
3. Use of public property
4. Camp government

*Science, physical and biological*

A study of the land, water, and living things is always interesting and useful:

1. A study of forest and forest life
2. Experiences in botany
3. Activities in geology
4. Study of the skies, stars, constellations, weather stations, etc.
5. Soil
6. Sanitation
7. Rivers and lakes
8. Fish and fishing
9. Fire protection
10. Photography, aerial, etc.
11. Map development
12. Reforestation

*Physical education department*

Physical exercise is basic to camp happiness:

1. Hiking
2. Cook-outs and camp-outs
3. Swimming and boating
4. Snowshoeing
5. Archery
6. Bait casting and fishing
7. Hunting and tracking
8. Wood crafts
9. Camping out
10. Games and athletic events

*Art department*

The camper has a chance to study nature as it develops:

1. Creative drawing and sketching
2. Painting (dramatic-music pageants)

## SAMPLE STUDY UNITS IN OUTDOOR EDUCATION

The teachers and administrators of Clear Lake Camp, operated by Battle Creek Public Schools, Michigan, have developed an excellent program of study for outdoor education. In this course of study are listed such items as a statement of philosophy, suggestions to teachers and counselors, and more than forty units of study covering various aspects of camping and outdoor education. Two of these units are given to show the reader how camping and outdoor education can be made a functional part of general education.

### Bird hikes

I. Time—Varies with the purposes of various groups

II. Description of destination—May be one or more of the following: swamp, marsh, lake shore, woods, fields, home, or roadsides

III. Equipment—Binoculars or field glasses and cameras must be brought from home; bird identification books available at camp

IV. Learning possibilities
  A. Identification of birds
  B. Habitat of birds, and reasons
  C. Economic value or lack of value
  D. Enemies of birds
  E. Living habits of birds, their nests, their food, their family life
  F. Interdependence of birds and man
  G. Balance in nature
  H. How birds are or may be protected
    1. Game laws
    2. Reasons for game laws
    3. Sanctuaries
    4. Planting of trees
    5. International migratory laws
  I. Migration
    1. Routes
    2. Distances
  J. Why people "bird watch"
    1. Enjoyment of songs and actions and colors
    2. Feeling of at-homeness with nature
  K. Adaptation of body of bird to mode of life: claws, wings, beaks, etc.
  L. Evolution in bird families

V. Possible implications for curriculum
  A. Studies in science
  B. Studies in conservation

C. Studies in geography
D. Studies of grains

**Boating**

I. Place—Clear Lake
II. Safety precautions
  A. Safety is of prime importance in using the boats
  B. Children must be seated at all times while in a boat
  C. A teacher or counselor must be in the boat with the children
III. Equipment (available at camp)—Five boats with oars and anchors attached
IV. Learning possibilities
  A. Proper way to enter a boat
  B. How to shove off from shore
  C. How to sit in a boat and keep it balanced
  D. Identifying the stern, bow, gunnel or gunwale
  E. How to row
  F. How to turn
  G. Beaching a boat properly
  H. Why a boat floats (displacement of its own weight)
  I. Awareness of and practice of safety
  J. Uses of boats for recreation
  K. Uses of boats for making a living
V. Possible implications for curriculum
  A. Open up possibilities for thinking in terms of self-development and the place of recreation in balanced living
  B. Understanding more about water transportation
  C. Science learnings
    1. Displacement of weight causes an object to float
    2. Principle of leverage
    3. Principle of inertia
    4. Principle of momentum
    5. Principle of friction
VI. Resource materials
  Boy Scout Merit Badge Pamphlet on Rowing

## WORTH OF CAMPING AND OUTDOOR EDUCATION

The values of school camping and outdoor education are very much in evidence as a result of the many experiments that have been conducted throughout the United States. For purposes of discussion, it might be said that the values of such experiences are threefold. First, they meet the social needs of the child; second, they meet the intellectual needs of the child; and, third, they meet the health needs of the child.

A camping and outdoor education experience is an essential part of every child's school experience because it helps to develop the child socially. In a camp setting children learn to live democratically. They mix with children of various creeds, national origins, races, economic status, and abilities. They aid in planning the program that will be followed during their camp stay; they assume part of the responsibility for the upkeep of the camp, such as making their own beds, helping in the kitchen, sweeping their cabins, and fixing the tennis courts; and they experience cooperative living. The children get away from home and from their parents. They lose their feeling of dependency upon others and learn to do things for themselves. This is especially necessary in modern-day society where divorce, separations, and the desire of the mothers to seek careers of their own are so prevalent. The child learns to rely on his own resources. The camp experience also provides an enjoyable experience for the child. A child is naturally active and seeks adventure. This experience provides the opportunity to release some of this adventure and satisfy the "wanderlust" urge.

A camping and outdoor education experience is an essential part of every child's school experience because it helps to develop the child intellectually. While living in a camp or in another outdoor education setting, the child learns about such things as soil, forests, water, and animal and bird life. He learns about the value of the nation's natural resources and how they should be conserved. He learns by doing rather than through the medium of textbooks. Instead of looking at the picture of a bird in a book, he actually sees the bird chirping on the branch of a tree. Instead of reading about soil erosion

Camping and outdoor education in New Zealand.

in a textbook, he sees how it really occurs. Instead of being told about the four basic groups of food, he has the opportunity to live on a diet that meets the right standards. Instead of reading about the values of democratic living, he actually experiences it. The child experiences many new things that he cannot possibly experience at home or within the four walls of a school building. Camping is also of especial value to children who do not learn easily from books. In many cases the knowledge accumulated through actual experience is much more enlightening and beneficial.

A camping and outdoor education experience is an essential part of every child's school experience because it helps to meet the health needs of the child. Camps are located away from the turmoil,

confusion, noise, and rush of urban life. Children experience having their meals at a regular time, obtaining sufficient sleep, and participating in wholesome activity in the out-of-doors. They wear clothing that does not restrict movement, that permits the absorption of healthful sun rays, and that they are not afraid to get dirty. The food is good. They are doing things that are natural for them to do. It is an outlet for their dynamic personalities. It is much more healthful, both physically and mentally, than living in a "push-button" existence with its lack of recreation, relaxation, and opportunity for enjoyable experiences. It is like living in another world, and children come away refreshed from such an experience.

Another way to determine the worth of camping and outdoor education is to eval-

CLAY MODELING

WHAT IS CLAY ?

HOW IS CLAY MOLDED ?

*San Diego City Schools,*
*San Diego, Calif.*

Utilizing clay modeling as a medium for outdoor education.

uate the comments of students, teachers, school administrators, and parents who have experienced these programs. The Long Beach Unified School District in Long Beach, California, has compiled a sampling of such statements, a few of which are as follows:

*What the students say:*

"I like being in the out-of-doors because I feel I understand wildlife better than reading a book about it or having someone tell me about it. I feel happy and carefree when I am around wildlife. Wildlife is something more to me than words on a paper. I hope you will understand how I feel about conservation."

"I like playing and working with others because it helps me to get along with my schoolmates and to be a better person. Because of this I have done much better in all my work and play."

"I felt that I could take care of myself because I didn't have to depend upon my mother, and I had a lot of fun trying to prove it to myself."

"I learned how all living things depend upon each other for something. Man depends on certain insects to carry pollen from one plant to another. Insects, in turn, depend on certain flowers to help them with their food supply, nectar. It all keeps revolving in this way to make life possible."

"Before I went to camp I didn't care about stars, plants, rocks, trees, or animals. Now I want to know more about them. Since camp I have read several books and seen several nature movies."

*What the teachers say:*

"The class has a much better understanding and interest in the ways and means of conserving our natural resources."

"For many, camp has opened a world which they have read about or studied but never experienced. A knowledge of and an appreciation of nature are clearly evident in the children and will provide them a richer life."

"Quietness of the evening and the campfire has excellent spiritual value." "I went to camp in doubt. I came back completely sold."

*What the parents say:*

"It is the grandest thing that has ever been presented by our schools."

"I consider it a very necessary part of the curriculum, and the experience gained is a necessary part of growth."

"I sincerely hope the camp program will be continued and in my opinion should be made compulsory for all children. I can't begin to express my appreciation."

"One of the finest projects the city schools have ever undertaken. A rare treat and privilege."

"They learned so much in so short a time."

*What the school administrators say:*

"Space does not permit saying all that might

be said in praise of this fine educational experience provided for sixth graders, but I feel that it represents a very rich addition to our program."

"It was my privilege to see two groups in action and I have every confidence that we have in this phase of our educational program something that will grow in popularity and usefulness as it becomes better known by our community."

"They [the children] themselves seemed to feel that this was one of the most important and enjoyable experiences of their lives and one which really gave them some new values. They evidenced this in improved attitudes and habits, new appreciations and interests."

## IMPLICATIONS FOR PHYSICAL EDUCATION TEACHER

If camping and outdoor education are to render their greatest service to the pupil, good leadership must be present. Regardless of how elaborate the camping facilities, the size of the budget, and the number of opportunities available for educational trips, true education will not take place unless the teachers, counselors, and leaders can interpret, discuss, guide, and educate the student. Physical education teachers can provide much of this leadership. The close alliance that exists between their field and that of camping, through a common interest in such things as the out-of-doors, sports, and other activities, makes it possible for them to take a leading role in this movement. Persons must be trained as camp administrators, camp counselors, and instructors. Classroom teachers must receive special instruction to orient them to the camping program. School administrators must be informed and their cooperation and support enlisted. These are only a few of the opportunities and challenges facing leaders in camping

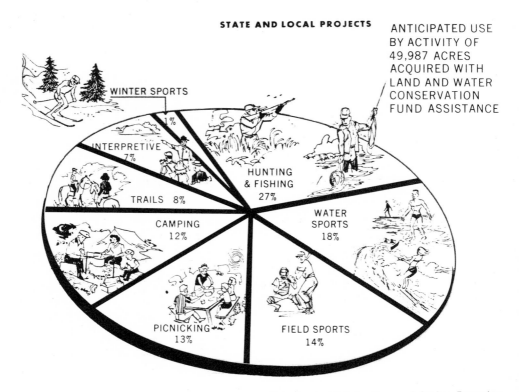

**STATE AND LOCAL PROJECTS**

ANTICIPATED USE BY ACTIVITY OF 49,987 ACRES ACQUIRED WITH LAND AND WATER CONSERVATION FUND ASSISTANCE

WINTER SPORTS 1%

INTERPRETIVE 7%

TRAILS 8%

CAMPING 12%

HUNTING & FISHING 27%

WATER SPORTS 18%

PICNICKING 13%

FIELD SPORTS 14%

*Department of Interior, Bureau of Outdoor Recreation: Expanding America's outdoor recreation estate, 1966.*

and outdoor education. Physical education personnel should play a major role in meeting these opportunities and challenges.

Those interested in becoming active in the camping and outdoor education movement should have special preparation in this area. Such courses as camp counseling, camp administration, crafts, guidance, and psychology, together with an actual camp experience, will prove helpful.

Smith has outlined three essential features of training for outdoor education: (1) an understanding of human beings, (2) the ability to interpret the outdoors, and (3) skills and techniques to teach and guide in the out-of-doors. He goes on

to give his suggestions for leadership in this important area.

Colleges and universities will need to provide more actual and direct experiences in the outdoors along with methods and techniques adapted to teaching in informal situations. A multidisciplinary approach is needed, involving all appropriate fields and departments, to provide adequate training. Preparation must include realistic outdoor field experiences with children and teachers in communities.

The interdisciplinary approach, as the diagram on page 292 suggests, is an ideal way to prepare leaders for outdoor education. In this way the pertinent disci-

*John Goss.*

Camping and outdoor education at Westchester County Recreation Camp, Croton, N. Y.

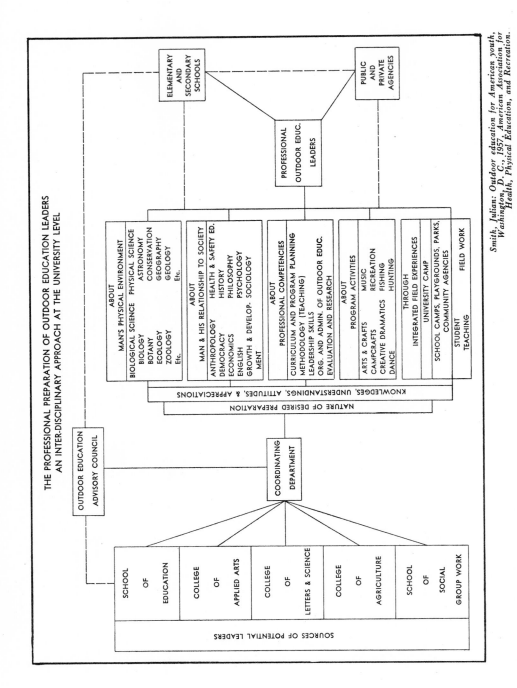

Professional preparation of outdoor education leaders—an interdisciplinary approach at the university level.

Smith, Julian: *Outdoor education for American youth,* Washington, D. C., 1957, American Association for Health, Physical Education, and Recreation.

plines and departments of the university are coordinated to supply the comprehensive preparation needed.

The interested physical educator can contribute to camping and outdoor education by preparing himself through study as well as experience for leadership in these fields. Furthermore, all physical educators can do much to contribute to the objectives of these specialized areas by stressing outdoor activities. There is a need for more teaching of swimming, archery, tennis, boating, skin and scuba diving, water skiing, skating, bicycling, hiking, and many other activities conducted in the out-of-doors. These activities can be enjoyed at all ages. They are important parts of physical education programs. For those undergraduate students, as well as the physical education leaders in the field whose interests and desires tend toward camping and the out-of-doors, this is a field where participation has vast possibilities. It deserves special consideration by those who wish to pioneer in a new field of endeavor, render an outstanding contribution to children, youth, and adults, help in the achievement of educational objectives, and build a healthier and better society.

## QUESTIONS AND EXERCISES

1. How do camping and outdoor education contribute to the goals of general education?
2. Compile a list of objectives for camping and outdoor education programs.
3. List ten outdoor education experiences that every child should have.
4. What contributions can each of the subject-matter departments in the school make to camping and outdoor education programs?
5. Consult several authoritative camping books and draw up what you feel would constitute a desirable camp program.
6. What is the relationship of physical education to camping and outdoor education?
7. What contributions can the physical educator make to camping and outdoor education programs?

## SELECTED REFERENCES

Bucher, Charles A.: Administration of school health and physical education programs, St. Louis, 1967, The C. V. Mosby Co.

Bucher, Charles A., and Reade, Evelyn M.: Physical education in the modern elementary school, New York, 1964, The Macmillan Co.

Bureau of Outdoor Recreation, U. S. Department of the Interior: Outdoor recreation action, published regularly by the Department of the Interior, Washington, D. C.

Donaldson, George W.: Journal of Outdoor Education, Northern Illinois University, DeKalb, Illinois (back and current issues).

Freeberg, William H.: Programs in outdoor education, Minneapolis, 1963, Burgess Publishing Co.

Harrison, Paul E.: Education goes outdoors! Journal of Health, Physical Education, and Recreation 24:20, Dec., 1953.

Outdoor education, Journal of Health, Physical Education and Recreation 36:75, April, 1965.

Report to the President and Congress by the Outdoor Recreation Resources Review Commission: Outdoor recreation in America, Washington, D. C., Jan., 1962, Government Printing Office.

Singer, Robert N.: Education and camping, The Physical Educator 21:75, May, 1964.

Smith, Julian W., and others: Outdoor education, Englewood Cliffs, N. J., 1963, Prentice-Hall, Inc.

Smith, Julian W.: Outdoor education for American youth, Washington, D. C., 1957, American Association for Health, Physical Education, and Recreation.

Smith, Julian, et al.: Outdoor education, Englewood Cliffs, N. J., 1963, Prentice-Hall, Inc.

The plunger

*Works of R. Tait McKenzie.*
*Courtesy Joseph Brown,*
*School of Architecture, Princeton University.*

**PART FOUR**

# Changing concepts of physical education

**Chapter 11**

# Changing concepts from early times to modern European period

It is interesting to note the various purposes for which physical education has existed in the lives of people of various countries and cultures. From the time of primitive man to the present, either directly or indirectly, physical activity has played a part in the lives of all people. Sometimes this activity has been motivated by such a factor as the necessity for earning a livelihood, whereas in other instances it has resulted from a desire to live a fuller life. Furthermore, it is clear that the objectives of physical education have changed over the course of history, so that at the present time they are directed at the better development of man, not only physically but also emotionally, socially, and intellectually. These changing concepts of physical education have come about only as a result of many years of experience and study in regard to the values inherent in participating in physical activity under qualified leadership. This chapter proposes to briefly review the concepts of physical education in leading ancient and medieval civilizations.

*The principal aim of gymnastics is the education of all youth and not simply that minority of people highly favored by Nature.*

—Aristotle (350 B.C.)

*Lack of activity destroys the good condition of every human being, while movement and methodical physical exercise save it and preserve it.*

—Plato (380 B.C.)

*Intellectual progress is conditioned at every step by bodily vigor. To attain the best results, physical exercises must accompany and condition mental training.*

—Comenius (1650)

*If you would cultivate the intelligence of your pupil, cultivate the power that it is to govern. Give his body continual exercise.*

—Rousseau (1750)

*The greatest of follies is to sacrifice health for any other advantage.*

—Schopenhauer (1850)

*We do not yet sufficiently realize the truth that as, in this life of ours, the physical underlies the mental, the mental must not be developed at the expense of the physical....*

—Herbert Spencer (1860)

*I hope that here in America more and more the ideal of the well-trained and vigorous body will be maintained neck and neck with that of the well-trained and vigorous mind.*

—William James (1890)

*The young child perhaps learns more and develops better through his play than through any other form of activity.*

—Herbert S. Jennings (1917)

*Failure to develop good muscular coordination puts a very definite ceiling on genius.*

—Dr. Leslie N. Nason (1958)

*There is danger at the present time in the enthusiasm for the cramming of the brains of our young people with facts, scientific or otherwise, that there will be inadequate time for the establishment and perpetuation of physical fitness, which should never stop.*

—Dr. Paul Dudley White (1960)

## HISTORY OF PHYSICAL EDUCATION

Let's roll back the years and let our minds
    wander
Back to the days of the Great Alexander,
When the Greeks' concern for strength and
    speed
Was geared to the objective of the nation's
    need.
There was reasonable pride in masculine
    muscle
And no person sneered at the concept of
    bustle,
And Demosthenes and Aristotle
Were pressing with logic the national throt-
    tle
The Grecian leaders in education
Had never heard of integration.
The Norsemen and Gauls had not yet
    bowed
To the power of Caesar and his Roman
    crowd.
Jousts and skill with the sword and bow
Were the accepted routine of the weekend
    show.
Came the Renaissance with its freedom
    newborn
Which sneered at the medieval as out-
    moded corn,
Jahn and Ling and old Guts Muths
Suddenly discovered the startling truths,
That the proper road to physical education
Could be trod only by regimentation.
And the Turnverein with emphasis formal
Was considered to be the training most nor-
    mal.
Then Catherine Beecher and her calisthen-
    ics
Were accepted as the acme of rhythm me-
    chanics,
Came Sargent's concept that human
    strength
Could be measured best by weight and
    length
But suddenly out of the routine and drill
The voice of free play arose with a shrill
Demand for concomitant outcome and aims
That could only be reached by a program
    of games.
Williams urged activities informal,
Obedience to command was considered ab-
    normal,
Disciples were enlisted throughout the na-
    tion
Against the "whistle-blowers" and regimen-
    tation.
Williams held court in old York State

Along the Hudson with Nash, his mate.
Assisted by Brownell, Cassidy and others
They dried the sweat from their muscular
    brothers.
Then mental hygiene and safety and sex
Were solved at conventions so they'd no
    longer vex
The disciples of the new inanimation
Which some claimed was withering the legs
    of the nation.
Elmer Mitchell favored another variation
In the fields of intramurals and recreation.
The happy student found there was no
    need
To move around at the former high speed.
He could shoot has arrows and cast his flies
In a program which claimed to humanize.
But suddenly the Axis war machine
Challenged the disciples of the new routine,
The American youth who had trained in
    cars
And purportedly absorbed their rhythms in
    bars,
Were transformed o'ernight into Army sad-
    sacks
Trudging on foot with rifles and packs,
Thousands of miles all over the world
Wherever the Stars and Stripes were un-
    furled.
The scions of this soft and decadent nation
Which had taken the muscles out of edu-
    cation
Out-stouted, outfought, outlasted the men
Trained from the cradle in drill regimen.
Mussolini, then Hitler, then Tojo were
    taken,
Our boys lived on Spam and brought home
    the bacon.
Back from the wars to school and college
Once again in search of knowledge,
Where philosophers talk themselves into
    condition
And shudder at the evils of competition,
Youth continues to fight and to play,
To develop and grow in the time-honored
    way.
And the members of the world's greatest
    profession
By precept and deed in daily session,
Inspire and lead the youth of the nation
To prepare for citizenship and vocation.
The methods are varied, but the goal's
    within reach
So long as the teachers continue to teach.*

*Gary, M. J.: Bulletin of Connecticut Association for Health, Physical Education, and Recreation, June, 1956.

These statements on health and physical education by great leaders emphasize the importance placed on physical activity throughout the centuries.*

## PHYSICAL EDUCATION IN ANCIENT ORIENTAL NATIONS

Primitive society did not think of physical education as people do today. There was no organized physical education program in primitive society nor in the cultures of any of the ancient oriental nations. From the physical point of view, primitive man did not need to set aside a period during the day when he could participate in various forms of activity— activity was a part of his daily regimen. Well-developed bodies and sound organic systems were commonplace among primitive people. Their physical activity was obtained in the search for food, such as berries, fish, and wild game, in erecting shelters from the adverse elements, and in protecting themselves from a hostile environment.

History has shown that there are certain tendencies in man that have been responsible for his formal and informal participation in physical activity. Some of the more important of these throughout history have been the search for food to satisfy hunger, the desire for protection against enemies, innate drives for mating and propagation, the urge to manipulate brain and brawn, fear of the strange and unknown, and man's gregarious nature. Hunting, fishing, warfare, dancing, and play evolved as a result of these general tendencies exhibited by man. These explain to some extent why primitive man and all men in general have been prone to engage in motor activities whether they wanted to or not. Whether or not these activities should be characterized as "work" or as "play" depends upon the

psychology behind the participation in the activity. "Work" is characterized by need, necessity, and is more or less compulsory. On the other hand, "play" is spontaneous, internally driven, and is utilized for fun and relaxation.

Civilization has brought the need for an organized physical education program. As a result of laborsaving devices, sedentary pursuits, and security, the need has arisen for some type of planned program whereby individuals may realize the physical benefits that were a part of early man's daily routine, as well as many emotional, sociological, psychological, and intellectual benefits. Therefore it is interesting to examine certain of these ancient countries in order to determine the part physical education played in the lives of their people. Through an understanding of the past or history of physical education, a person is better able to understand and interpret present-day physical education.

### China

Ancient China followed a policy of isolation. It did not care to associate with the rest of the world but, instead, desired to live unto itself. At first, the topography of the land provided China with the necessary protection against invaders. When the Himalaya Mountains no longer served this purpose, the Great Wall was built; and when the wall became obsolete, laws were passed to keep invaders out of the country.

The fact that ancient China lived an isolated existence was detrimental in many ways to a belief in physical education. Since China did not fear aggression, it lacked the military-motivating factor of being physically strong. Furthermore, the teachings of the people of ancient China were mainly concerned with memorizing the works of Confucius. Ancestor worship was also an important part of their religious life. Individuality was suppressed, and all persons were destined to live a

---

*Quoted on a wrestling tournament program, January 29, 1963, Health and Physical Education Department, Norfolk, Virginia.

rigid and stereotyped existence. In a country where such beliefs held sway, there was little room for organized physical education. Physical activity stressed the importance of the body and individual freedom of expression, which were contrary to the teachings in this ancient country. China felt secure behind its natural and man-made barriers and did not have an incentive to be physically strong, as was found in many of the ancient countries.

There were certain evidences of participation in physical education activities in China, however, despite the emphasis on intellectual excellence and the influences of Taoism, Confucianism, and Buddhism, all of which emphasized a studious, quiet, and contemplative life. In many Chinese classics there abound discussions of how sons of rich families engaged in music, dancing, and archery. Dancing especially was popular, with such special dances as "split-feather dance," "whole-feather dance," "regulating dance," "tail dance," "shield dance," "battle-axe dance," and the "humanity dance" being engaged in. Wrestling, jujitsu, boxing, football (ts' u chu), polo, tug-of-war, water games, ch' ui wan (in many respects similar to golf), shuttlecock, and flying kites were also popular.

It is interesting to note that the Chinese felt certain diseases were caused from inactivity. As a result, history discloses that the "Kong Fu" gymnastics were developed in 2698 B.C. and practiced since that time. These were medical gymnastics intended to keep the body in good organic condition. It was believed that illnesses were due to internal stoppages and to malfunctioning of organs. Therefore, if certain kneeling, bending, lying, and standing exercises could be taken, together with certain types of respiratory training, the illness could be helped.

Although there does not seem to have been much participation in the various physical activities by the masses in early China, play was engaged in by the more favored classes.

## India

Ancient India in many ways was similar to ancient China. People in this country lived an existence that was very religious in nature. Hinduism stressed the fact that man's soul passed through several reincarnations before being united with Brahma, the supreme goal. The quickest and most certain way to attain this goal was to refrain from catering to the body and enjoying worldly things. The person who desired to be holy ignored the physical needs of his body and concentrated solely on his spiritual needs. It can readily be seen that physical activity had little place in the culture of this religious people.

Buddha's prohibitions of games, amusements, and exercises in ancient India did not totally prevent participation in such activities. Evidence is available as to such pastimes as dice, throwing balls, plowing contests, tumbling, chariot races, marbles, riding elephants and horses, swordsmanship, races, wrestling, boxing, and dancing. Yoga, an activity common in India and involving exercises in posture and regulated breathing, was very popular. This disciplining of mind and body required the instruction of experts, and a person fully trained in this activity followed a routine involving eighty-four different postures.

## Ancient Near East

The civilizations of ancient Egypt, Assyria, Babylonia, Syria, Palestine, and Persia mark a turning point in the history of physical education. Whereas the objectives in China and India had been confined mainly to religious and intellectual matters, these countries were not restricted by a static society and religious ritual. On the contrary, they believed in living a full life. Therefore all sorts of

*Text continued on p. 304.*

*Courtesy Dr. Gunsun Hoh, Republic of China.*

Track and field training in a girls' school in Tainan, Taiwan.

*Courtesy Dr. Gunsun Hoh, Republic of China.*

Chinese students chin themselves during physical education class.

Physical education activity in India.

Modern-day Israel emphasizes mass recreational activities. Five thousand swimmers participate in a popular crossing of the Sea of Galilee.

physical activity contributed to this objective. It is in these countries that physical education also received an impetus from the military, who saw in it an opportunity to build stronger and more powerful armies.

Egyptian youths were reared in a manner characterized by much physical activity. While yet young boys, they were instructed in the use of various weapons of war, such as bow and arrow, batttle-axe, mace, lance, and shield. They were required to participate in exercises and activities designed to make the body supple, strong, and capable of great endurance and stamina. These activities included considerable marching, running, jumping, wrestling, pirouetting, and leaping. Before their military training started they also had numerous opportunities to engage in many sports and gymnastic exercises. They found great enjoyment in going on hunting and fishing expeditions.

In the countries between the Tigris and Euphrates rivers there was also great stress placed upon physical education activities. This was especially true of the upper classes. Whereas the lower elements of the population found few opportunities for recreation and play, although they participated when possible, the upper classes seem to have indulged themselves in these pastimes at regular intervals. Horsemanship, use of bow and arrow, water activities, and training in physical exercises were considered on a par with instruction that was more intellectual in character.

Persia is a good example of a state that had as its main objective the building of an empire through military aggression. A strong Persian army meant a healthy and physically fit army. Under King Cyrus the Great the imperialistic dreams of Persia were realized. At the end of his rule in 529 B.C., the Persian Empire encompassed the area that we refer to today as the Near East. The success of King Cyrus' campaigns was largely due to the moral and physical conditioning of his soldiers. At the age of 6 years, the state took all boys away from their homes for training. This training consisted of such events as running, slinging, shooting with a bow, throwing the javelin, riding, hunting, and marching. The soldier had to be able to travel without much food and clothing and was compelled to endure all sorts of hardship. Intellectual training was thought useless in a state that depended upon a strong army to realize its ambitions. Here we see an example of physical education turned toward imperialistic ends. The program of physical activity was directed toward building strength and power in each member of the armed forces, with the major objective of destruction, conquest, and aggrandizement. Strength, endurance, stamina, agility, and other physical characteristics were not developed so that the individual could live a full, vigorous, and more interesting life but, instead, so that the state could utilize these physical attributes in achieving its own selfish aims. In directing physical education toward such ends, this profession loses one of its most vital potentialities—that of helping to build a peaceful world characterized by objectives aimed at the development of each individual's capacities to their fullest extent.

## PHYSICAL EDUCATION IN GREECE

Physical education experienced a "golden age" in ancient Greece. The Greeks strove for physical perfection, and this objective affected all phases of their life. It had its influence on the political and educational systems, on sculpturing and painting, and in the thinking and writings of that day. It was a unifying force in Greek life, played a major part in the national festivals, and helped in building strong military establishments. No country in history has held physical education in such high respect as did the ancient Greeks.

As early as 3000 B.C. there were evidences of physical education activities being popular in Cretan culture. Archaeological investigations at Mycenae and other centers of Aegean civilization have unearthed buildings, pottery, and other materials that point to the important place of physical education in this ancient culture. Literature such as Homer's *Iliad* and *Odyssey* also is a source of this information. Hunting seems to have been one of the most popular pastimes in this era. Lion hunting, deer hunting, bull grappling, boxing, wrestling, dancing, and swimming are commonly referred to by historians who have written about these ancient civilizations.

Physical education was a vital part of the education of every boy in Greece. Gymnastics and music were considered the two most important subjects. Music was for the intellect and gymnastics was for the body. "Exercise for the body and music for the soul" was a common pronouncement. Gymnastics, it was believed, contributed to courage, discipline, and physical well-being. Furthermore, gymnastics stressed a sense of fair play, development of the individual, aesthetic values, amateurism, and the utilitarian values inherent in the activity. Professionalism was frowned upon. An individual ran, wrestled, jumped, danced, or threw the javelin not for reward but for what it would do for his body. Beauty of physique was stressed, and everyone participated in the nude, which motivated development of the "body beautiful."

Because of the topography of the land and for various political reasons, Greece was composed of several city-states, each exercising its own sovereignty and existing as a separate entity. It waged war and conducted all of its affairs separately from the other city-states. This situation had an influence not only on the political aspects of each city-state, but also on the objectives of physical education within each

state. Sparta and Athens exemplify two such city-states.

In Sparta, a city-state in the Peloponnesus district of Greece, the main objective of physical education was to contribute to a strong and powerful army. The individual in Sparta existed for the state. He was subservient to the state and was required to help defend it against all enemies. Women as well as men were required to be in good physical condition. It was believed that healthy and strong mothers would bear healthy and strong sons, which in turn would strengthen the state. It is believed that Spartan women may have begun their physical conditioning as early as 7 years of age and continued gymnastics in public until they were married. Newborn infants, if found to be defective or weak, were left on Mount Taygetus to die. Only strong and vigorous babies were welcome in this military state. Woody points out that mothers bathed babies in wine to test their bodies and to temper them for future ordeals. A boy was allowed to stay at home only for the first six years of his life. After this he was required to stay in the public barracks and entered the agoge, a system of public, compulsory training, where he underwent a very vigorous and rigid training schedule. If he failed in this ordeal, he was deprived of all future honors. A major part of this training consisted of such physical activities as wrestling, jumping, running, throwing the javelin and discus, marching, horseback riding, and hunting. This conditioning program secured for Sparta a strong army that was second to none. However, it was developed at the expense of personal freedom.

Athens was a city-state in eastern Greece which was the antithesis of Sparta. Here, the democratic way of life flourished, and consequently it had a great bearing on the objectives of physical education. Here the state did not control and regulate the individual's life as rigidly as in Sparta. In

Athens the people enjoyed the freedom that is characteristic of a truly democratic government. Although the military emphasis was not as strong in Athens as in Sparta, the emphasis on physical education was just as great or greater. Athenians engaged in physical activity to develop their bodies, for the aesthetic values, and to live a fuller and more vigorous life. An ideal of Athenian education was to achieve a proper balance in moral, mental, physical, and aesthetic development. To the Hellenes, man was a whole, and he was as strong as his weakest part. One part of him could not be sound if the other parts were not also sound.

Gymnastics for the youth were practiced in the palaestra, a building that provided rooms for various physical activities, for oiling and sanding their bodies, and an open space for such activities as jumping and wrestling. The proprietor of the palaestra was called a paidotribe (from the Greek word *paidotribes,* meaning boy rubber). He was responsible for directing the exercises and games of the Greek youth. He also had the assistance of flute players, since many activities were conducted with music. Some of the more noted palaestras were those of Taureas, Timeas, and Siburtios. The paidotribe was similar to a present-day physical educator. He taught many activities, understood how certain exercises should be adapted to various physical conditions, knew how to develop strength and endurance, and was an individual who could be trusted with children in the important task of making youthful bodies serve their minds. As a boy approached manhood, he deserted the palaestra and attended the gymnasium. Gymnasiums became the physical, social, and intellectual centers of Greece. Although the first use was for physical activity, such men as Plato, Aristotle, and Antisthenes were responsible for making such gymnasiums as the Academy, Lyceum, and Kynosarges outstanding intellectual centers as well. Youth usually entered the gymnasium at from about 14 to 16 years of age. Here special sports and exercises received the main attention under expert instruction. Although activities that had been engaged in at the palaestra were continued, other sports such as riding, driving, racing, and hunting were added. Instruction in the gymnasium was given by a paidotribe and also a gymnast. The paidotribe had charge of the general physical training program, whereas the gymnast was a specialist responsible for training youth in gymnastic contests. The chief official at the gymnasium, in over-all charge of the entire program, was called a gymnasiarch. In keeping with the close association between physical education and religion, each gymnasium recognized a particular deity. For example, the Academy recognized Athena; the Lyceum, Apollo; and the Kynosarges, Hercules.

The national festivals were events that were most important in the lives of the Greeks and were also very important in laying the foundation for our modern Olympic games, which are conducted every fourth year in various parts of the world. These national festivals were in honor of some hero or divinity. They consisted of feasting, dancing, singing, and events of physical prowess. Although there were many of these national festivals conducted in all parts of Greece, four of them are of especial importance and attracted national attention. The first and most famous of the four was the Olympia festival in honor of Zeus, the supreme god, and was held in the western Peloponnesus district. Another was the Pythia festival in honor of Apollo, the god of light and truth, and was held at Delphi which was located north of the Corinthian Gulf. A third was the Nemea festival held in honor of Zeus at Argolis near Cleonae. The fourth was the Isthmia festival in honor of Poseidon, the god of the sea, and was held on the isthmus of Corinth. Athletic events were the main attraction and drawing force in each. People came from all over Greece to see the games. At Olympia the stadium provided standing space for approximately 40,000 spectators.

During the time the games were held, a truce was declared by all the city-states in Greece, and it was believed that if this truce were broken the wrath of the gods would be visited upon the guilty. By the middle of the fifth century this truce had probably lasted for three months. A rigid set of requirements had to be met before anyone could participate as a contestant. For example, the contestant had to be in training for ten months; he had to be a freeman; he had to be of perfect physique and of good character; he could not have any criminal record; and he had to compete in accordance with the rules. An oath also had to be taken that he would not use illegal tactics to win, to which fathers, brothers, and trainers also had to swear. Once enrolled for a contest, the athlete had to compete. Physical unfitness was not a good excuse. Events consisted of such feats as foot racing, throwing the javelin, throwing the discus, wrestling, high jumping, broad jumping, weight throwing, boxing, and horse racing. The victor in these events did not receive any material reward for his victory. Instead, a wreath of olive branches was presented. However, he was a hero in everyone's eyes and had many receptions given in his honor. Furthermore, he had many privileges bestowed upon him by his home city-state. To be crowned a victor in an Olympic event was to receive the highest honor that could be bestowed in Greece. The Olympic games were first held in 776 B.C. and continued every fourth year thereafter until abolished by the Romans in A.D. 394. However, they have since been resumed and today are held every fourth year in a different country.*

---

*For an evaluation of Olympic games, see Bucher, Charles A.: Sports Illustrated, Aug. 8, 1955; Reader's Digest, Sept., 1955.

Physical education in ancient Greece will always be looked upon with pride by members of this profession. The high ideals that motivated the various gymnastic events will always be objectives that all should try to emulate. Such great men of history as Socrates, Plato, Aristotle, Hippocrates, and Galen proclaimed their value for all. The large expanse of ruins excavated at Olympia and the relics, sculptures, and statues, especially the one of Hermes by Praxiteles, are evidence of the emphasis on physical perfection and pride in Hellenic culture that exalted Greek civilization.

Another aim of physical education was held by the Greeks. In addition to serving as a recreational pursuit and as an aid to aesthetic development, physical education was also utilized as therapy for the infirm and for the diseased. The growth of this phase of physical education was stimulated as a result of increased medical knowledge and also a result of a social trend in later Greek history. Many individuals, because of wealth and idleness, obtained inadequate exercise and indulged in luxurious living at the expense of their health. Adapted physical exercise proved to have therapeutic value in many such cases. By paying attention to diet and exercise, evil consequences to health could be avoided.

The use of physical education as an aid to medicine can be identified as early as Herodotus and about the middle of the fifth century B.C. Its worth was emphasized by outstanding Greeks at later dates. Galen stated that physical education is a part of hygiene and subordinate to medicine. Hippocrates proclaimed the law of use, stating that through use all parts of the body are kept in health, whereas disuse results in imperfect development and ill health. He also pointed out that some exercises are natural, whereas others are violent, and that many should be engaged in on a progressive basis. Hippocrates divided the year into the four seasons and recommended suitable diet and exercise for each. For example, in the winter one should eat lightly, and exercise should be procured by engaging in many kinds of activity. He listed running on the double, wrestling, and brisk walks as possible sources of activity.

In concluding this section on Greek physical education it is interesting to point out the views of certain outstanding philosophers and Greek leaders to whom the world today turns for a great deal of its thinking.

*Socrates* stressed the general utility of physical education and the importance of health in achieving life's purposes. He pointed out that even in thinking, where it seems the body is used very little, bad health can contribute to grave mistakes.

*Plato* recognized the importance of physical education for both men and women. He thought that both physical education and music were important phases of education.

*Aristotle* held that the body and soul are closely interrelated and that mental faculties are affected by bodily movement and conditions of body health. He thought that one should engage in lighter exercises such as dancing, running, jumping, and throwing until 14 or 15 years of age. Heavier exercises could be engaged in later and they would not impair the body. Excessive or deficient exercise is similar to excessive or deficient food and drink; both result in harm to the body. Physical education should help one to live a virtuous life and not one of conquest.

*Xenophon,* a contemporary of Plato, thought of physical education as important for the building up of a strong army. He felt that soundness of body and of mind was essential to success in life. However, Xenophon's main thoughts were of war, and his thinking in regard to physical education was mainly in terms of the military.

## PHYSICAL EDUCATION IN ROME

While the Hellenes were settling in the Grecian peninsula about 200 B.C., another Indo-European people was migrating to Italy and settling in various central and southern parts of this country. One of these wandering tribes, known in history as Latins, settled near the Tiber River, a settlement that later became known as Rome. The Romans were to have a decided effect not only upon the objectives of physical education in their own state but also upon that of the Greek world which they conquered.

The Romans, through their great leaders and well-disciplined army, extended their influence throughout most of the Mediterranean area and the whole of Europe. However, this success on the battlefield brought influences into Roman life that affected Roman ideals. The average Roman became interested in material things as a result of the conquests. He was not truly interested in the cultural aspects of life, although sometimes some of the finer aspects of Hellenic culture were taken on as a means of show. Wealth became the objective of most citizens, and vulgar display became the essence of wealth. Luxury, corruption, extravagance, and vice became commonplace in the various phases of Roman living.

In respect to physical education, the average Roman believed that exercise was good only for health and military purposes. He did not see the value of play as an enjoyable pastime. During the period of conquest, when Rome was following its strong imperialistic policy and before the time of professional troops, citizens were liable for military service from 17 to 60 years of age. Consequently, during this period of Roman history, army life was considered very important, and the various types of physical activity were considered essential in order to be in top physical shape and ready to serve the state at a moment's notice. All soldiers followed a rigid training schedule which consisted of such things as marching, running, jumping, swimming, and throwing the javelin and discus. However, during the last century of the Republic, mercenary troops were used, with the result that the objectives of physical training were not considered as important for the average Roman. As a spectator, he could enjoy life without all this waste of time building up the body.

After the conquest of Greece, Greek gymnastics were introduced to the Romans, but they were never well received. The Romans lacked the drive for clean competition. They did not believe in developing the "body beautiful." They did not like nakedness of performers. They preferred to be spectators rather than participants. They preferred cruel, gory, gruesome games to clean, wholesome events that were played for the benefit of the participants. They preferred professionalism to amateurism.

The Roman's dislike of Greek physical education was voiced in numerous ways. Cicero thought the physical exercises performed by the Greeks were absurd. Scipio was criticized for going to the palaestra. Horace felt the Greek system did not develop endurance and stamina enough for the Roman. Martial referred sarcastically to the wrestling grounds of Greece. Tacitus criticized the habit of taking off one's clothes to exercise.

Athletic sports were not conducted on the same high level as in ancient Greece. The Roman wanted something exciting, bloody, ghastly, and sensational. At the chariot races and gladiatorial combats, excitement ran high, and men were pitted against wild animals or against one another and fought to the death in order to satisfy the craving of the Roman for excitement and brutality. Frequently large groups of men fought each other in mortal battle before thousands of pleased spectators.

The rewards and incomes of some individuals who engaged in the chariot races were enormous. Diocles of Spain retired at 42 years of age, having won 1,462 of 4,257 races and rewards totaling in the neighborhood of $2 million. Other famous contestants were Thallus, Crescens, and Scorpus.*

The thermae and the Campus Martius in Rome took the place of the gymnasium in Greece. The thermae were the public baths, where provision was also made for exercise, and the Campus Martius was an exercise ground on the outskirts of the city. Most of the exercise was recreational in nature.

Many leaders in physical education have drawn parallels between Roman conditions and those that prevail in present-day United States. In making these comparisons, they raise the question as to whether the United States is following the same road that Rome followed. They point to the influence of wealth and materialism on our way of life, the political corruption that exists, the class struggle, the passing out of doles, the cry for "bread and games," the professionalism in the world of athletics, the desire of thousands of Americans to see pugilists knock each other into unconsciousness, the growing habit of being a spectator rather than

---

*At the site where once the inhabitants of Rome yelled with delight at the skill and daring of their favorite charioteers and gladiators, Romans of today are applauding the expoits of the soccer players who have replaced the chariot drivers and slaves in the public estimation.

The Circus Maximus, the oldest and greatest of the Roman circuses, was situated at the foot of the Palatine Hill and dated back to the last king of Rome, Tarquinius the Younger (534-510 B.C.). It reached its greatest splendor in imperial times and seated as many as 200,000 persons. It reached its final form under Trajan (A.D. 53-117). The Rome Municipal Council decided that this unusual site, formerly occupied by the Circus Maximus, should be transformed into a sports center.

a participant, and the desire to please and help the individual in the gallery rather than the individual on the field.

## PHYSICAL EDUCATION
## DURING THE DARK AGES

The fall of the Roman Empire in the West about A.D. 476 resulted in a period of history that is frequently referred to as the Dark Ages. This period, however, was anything but dark in respect to the physical rejuvenation brought about by the overrunning of the Roman Empire by the Teutonic barbarians.

Before considering the Dark Ages, it is interesting for the student of physical education to note a cause of the fall of Rome which brought on this new period in history. Historians list many causes for the breakdown of the Roman Empire, but the most outstanding cause was the physical and moral decay of the Roman people. The type of life the Romans led, characterized by divorce, games, and suicide, caused a decrease in population. Extravagance, doles, slave labor, and misuse of public funds caused moral depravity and economic ruin; and luxurious living, vice, and excesses caused poor health and physical deterioration. The lesson is borne out in Rome, as it has been in many civilizations that have fallen along the way, that in order for a nation to remain strong and endure it must be physically as well as morally fit.

As a morally and physically weak Roman Empire crumbled, morally and physically strong Teutonic barbarians overran the lands that once were the pride of the Latins. The Visogoths overran Spain, the Vandals overran North Africa, the Franks and Burgundians overran Gaul, the Angles and Saxons overran Britain, and the Ostrogoths overran Italy. These invasions brought about the lowest ebb in literature and learning known to history. The so-called cultural aspects of living were disregarded. Public works projects were neglected. Bridges and buildings were allowed to collapse. In the area of government, centralization of authority began to be abandoned, and in its place, tribes looked to their chieftains or lords for protection.

Despite all the backwardness that accompanied the invasions in respect to learning, public works, and government and that resulted in the name "Dark Ages" being attached to this period of history, the entire world still received physical benefits. The Teutonic barbarians were a nomadic people who lived out of doors on simple fare. They were mainly concerned with a life characterized by hunting, caring for their cattle and sheep, and participating in vigorous outdoor sports and warfare. A regimen such as this built strong and physically fit bodies and well-ordered nervous systems. The Teutonic barbarians came at a time when the physical deterioration caused by the excesses in Rome needed a change. They helped to guarantee a stronger, healthier, and more robust stock of future generations of people.

Although the Teutonic invasions of the Dark Ages supported the value of physical activity, two other movements during approximately this same period in history worked to its disadvantage—asceticism and scholasticism.

Out of pagan and immoral Rome, Christianity and asceticism grew and thrived. Certain individuals in ancient Rome became incensed with the immorality and the worldliness that existed in Roman society. They believed in "rendering unto Caesar the things that are Caesar's and unto God the things that are God's." They would not worship the Roman gods, attend the baths, or visit the games. They did not believe in worldly pleasures and catered to the spirit and not to the body. They believed that this life should be used as a means of preparing for the next world. They thought that all sorts of physical activity were foolish pursuits in that they were designed to improve the body. The body was evil and should be tortured rather than improved. They preached that the mind and body were distinct and separate entities in man and that one had no bearing on the other. A Christian emperor, Theodosius, abolished the Olympic games in A.D. 394 as being pagan.

The spread of Christianity resulted in the rise of asceticism. This was the belief that evil exists in the body, and therefore it should be subordinated to the spirit which is pure. Worldly pursuits are evil, and one should spend his time by being alone and meditating. The body is possessed of the devil and should be tortured. Individuals wore hair shirts, walked on hot coals, sat upon thorns, carried chains around their legs, and exposed themselves to the elements so that they might bring their worldly body under better control. Such practices led to poor health and shattered nervous systems on the part of many.

As Christianity spread, there also developed monasteries where Christians could isolate themselves from the world and its evils. Later, schools were attached to these monasteries, but it can be readily understood that any institution so clearly associated with early Christianity would not allow physical education to become a part of the curriculum. The medieval university also frowned upon physical education, thinking it unimportant in the lives of students.

Another influence that has had a tremendous effect on the history of physical education has been scholasticism. This is the belief that facts are the most essential items in one's education. If one knows the facts, if one has developed his mental and intellectual powers, he will have the key to a successful life. It deemphasized the physical as being unimportant and unnecessary. This movement, developed

among the scholars and universities of the Middle Ages, has been passed down from generation to generation and still plagues physical educators today. In many leading universities and among many outstanding scholars, there still is a tendency to disregard the physical and to play up the mental. A dean of a famous college in the East recently referred to the gymnasium as a "muscle factory," and from his speech one could readily discern that for him it existed only as a necessary evil. Scholasticism presents a challenge to physical education. Only through a true interpretation of the values inherent in physical education under proper guidance can a respected position for physical education be secured in the schools of this country.

## PHYSICAL EDUCATION DURING THE AGE OF FEUDALISM

As a result of the decentralization of government during the period of the Dark Ages, the period of feudalism came into being. Although Charlemagne established an empire over which he ruled effectively for some time, his death in 814 marked the disintegration of his empire, and it crumbled almost immediately. For the next few centuries effective, centralized leadership was lacking. A new social order was established. The period during which this social order existed is called the period of feudalism and extended between the ninth and fourteenth centuries. The type of government, the judicial system, human relations, methods of waging warfare, land ownership, industry, and social life were all affected by feudalistic practices.

The feudalistic period appeared because man needed protection, and since there was a shortage of strong monarchs and governments that could supply this protection, individuals turned to noblemen and others who built castles, had large land holdings, and made themselves strong. It could be said that feudalism was a system of land tenure based upon allegiance and service to the nobleman or lord. The lord who owned the land, called a fief, let it out to a subordinate who was called his vassal. In return for the use of this land the vassal owed his allegiance and certain obligations to his lord. The large part of the population, however, was made up of serfs, who worked the land and shared little in the profits. They were attached to the land and, as it was transferred from vassal to vassal, they were also transferred.

The lord lived on a large estate or manor which was a self-sufficient community in itself. The house or castle was usually erected on a site that was easily defensible and quite frequently surrounded by high walls and a moat.

There were two careers open to sons of noblemen during feudalistic times. They might enter training for the church and become members of the clergy, or they might enter chivalry and become knights. If they decided in favor of the church, they pursued an education that was religious and academic in nature, and if they decided in favor of chivalry, they pursued an education that was physical, social, and military in nature. To the average boy, chivalry had much more appeal than the church.

The training that a boy experienced in becoming a knight was long and thorough. Physical training played a major role during this period. At the age of 7 years a boy was usually sent to the castle of some nobleman for training and as preparation for knighthood. First, he was known as a page, and his instructor and teacher was usually one of the women in the lord's castle. During his tenure as a page, a boy learned court etiquette, waited on tables, ran errands, helped with household tasks, and during the rest of the time participated in various forms of physical activity which would serve him well as a knight and which would harden

and strengthen him for the arduous years ahead. He practiced for such events as boxing, running, fencing, jumping, and swimming.

At the age of 14 years the boy became a squire and was attached to some knight. His duties included keeping the knight's weapons in good condition, caring for his horses, helping him with his armor, attending to his injuries, and guarding his prisoners. During the time the boy was a squire, there was more and more emphasis placed on physical training. He was continually required to engage in vigorous sports and exercises, such as hunting, scaling walls, shooting with the bow, runing, swordsmanship, horsemanship, and climbing.

If the squire proved his fitness, he became a knight at 21 years of age. The ceremony through which he passed to become a knight was very solemn and memorable. The prospective knight took a bath of purification, dressed all in white, and spent an entire night in meditation and prayer. In the morning the lord placed his sword on the knight's shoulder, a ceremony known as the accolade, which marked the conferring of knighthood.

Jousts and tournaments were two special events in which all knights engaged several times during their lifetime. These special events served both as amusement and as training for battle. In the jousts, two knights attempted to unseat one another from their horses with blows from lances and by skill in horsemanship. In tournaments many knights were utilized in a program that was designed to exhibit the skill and showmanship that the knights had gained during their long period of training. They were lined up as two teams at each end of the lists, as the grounds were called, and upon a signal they attempted to unseat the members of the opposing team. This melee kept on until one team was declared the victor. Many of the knights wore their lady's colors on their armor and attempted with all their strength and skill to uphold her honor. During these tournaments death often resulted for many participants. It was during these exhibitions that a knight had the opportunity to display his personal bravery, skill, prowess, strength, and courage.

Physical education played a major part in preparing for chivalry. The objective of physical education, however, was for the purpose of self-preservation only. There were no objectives as worthy as those in Greece, which collectively aimed at total individual development. Before the invention of gunpowder and while there was no centralized government, men had to depend on physical strength, endurance, stamina, and skill to keep them alive. Consequently, physical education was a contributing factor to their day-to-day living.

## PHYSICAL EDUCATION DURING THE RENAISSANCE

The transitional period in history between the dark years of the medieval period and the beginning of modern times, the fourteenth to sixteenth centuries, was known as the period of the Renaissance and was an age of great progress for mankind.

During the medieval period men lacked originality. Individuality was a lost concept, and interest in the hereafter was so prevalent that men did not enjoy the present. The Renaissance caused a change in this way of life. There was a revival or rebirth of learning, a belief in the dignity of man, a renewed spirit of nationalism, an increase of trade among countries, and a period of exploration. Scientific research was used to solve problems; books were printed and thereby made available to more people; and there was a renewed interest in the classics. This period is associated with such names as Petrarch, Boccacio, Michelangelo, Erasmus, DaVinci, DaGama, Columbus, Galileo, and Harvey.

The Renaissance period also had an impact upon physical education. With more attention being placed on enjoyment of the present and the development of the body, asceticism lost its hold on the masses. During the Renaissance the theory that the body and the soul were inseparable, that they were indivisible, and that one was necessary for the optimum functioning of the other became more popular. It was believed that learning could be promoted through good physical health. A person needed rest and recreation from study and work. The body needed to be developed for purposes of health and for preparation for warfare.

Some outstanding leaders in the Renaissance period who were responsible for spreading these beliefs concerning physical education are mentioned briefly.

*Vittorino Da Feltra* (1378–1446) taught in the court schools of northern Italy and was believed to be one of the first teachers to combine physical and mental training in a school situation. He incorporated daily exercises in the curriculum, which included dancing, riding, fencing, swimming, wrestling, running, jumping, archery, hunting, and fishing. His objectives of physical education emphasized that it was good for disciplining the body, for preparation for war, for rest and recreation, and that good physical condition helped children learn other subject matter much better.

*Pietro Vergerio* (1349–1428) of Padua and Florence wrote a treatise entitled *De Ingenius Moribus,* in which the following objectives were emphasized: physical education is necessary for the total education of the individual, as preparation for warfare, to better undergo strain and hardship, as a means of fortifying the mind and body, as an essential for good health, and as a means of recreation to give a lift to the spirit and the body.

*Pope Pius II's* (1405–1464) objectives of physical education were for a good posture, body health, and as an aid to learning.

*Sir Thomas Elyot* (1490–1546) of England wrote the treatise on education entitled *The Governor,* which elaborated on such objectives of physical education as recreation and physical benefits to the body.

*Martin Luther* (1483–1546), the leader of the Protestant Reformation, did not preach asceticism as a means of salvation. He saw in physical education a substitute for vice and evil pursuits during leisure hours such as gambling and drinking, a means of obtaining elasticity of the body, and a medium of promoting one's health.

*Francis Rabelais* (1490–1553), a French educational theorist, emphasized the objectives of physical welfare, the fact that physical education is an important part of education and aids in mental training, and that it is good preparation for warfare.

*Roger Asham* (1515–1568), professor at Cambridge in England, proclaimed the value of physical education as a preparation for war and as a means of resting the mind.

*John Milton* (1608–1674), the English poet, expressed his views on physical education in his *Tractate on Education.* In this treatise he discussed how physical education helps in body development, is a means of recreation, and is good preparation for warfare.

*John Locke* (1632–1704), famous English philosopher and a student of medicine, supported physical education in a work entitled *Some Thoughts Concerning Education.* His objectives could be summed up under health as a means of meeting emergencies involving hardships and fatigue and as a means of having a vigorous body at one's command.

*Michel de Montaigne* (1533–1592), a French essayist, stressed that physical education was necessary for both body and soul and that it was impossible to divide an individual into two such components since they are indivisible and together comprise the human being that is being trained.

*John Comenius* (1592–1671), a Bohemian educational reformer, and *Richard Mulcaster* (1530–1611), an English schoolmaster, had as their objectives of physical education a means of maintaining health and physical fitness and a means of obtaining rest from study.

*Jean Jacques Rousseau* (1712–1778), a French writer, in his book *Emile* points out what he considers to be an ideal education. In this education, physical education would contribute to the objectives of health and a vigorous body. He stressed that the mind and body are an indivisible entity in man and that both are bound together.

The Renaissance period helped to interpret the worth of physical education to the public in general. It also demonstrated how a society that promotes the dignity and freedom of the individual and recognizes the value of human life will also place in high respect the development and maintenance of the human body. The belief became prevalent that physical education is necessary for health, as a preparation for warfare, as a means of developing the body, and as a means of providing recreation for the wealthier classes. However, at that point in history, society failed to recognize universally, to any degree, the important contributions that physical education can make to the aesthetic, social, and moral life of society.

## SOME POPULAR SPORTS AND THE COUNTRIES OR CULTURES MOST OFTEN CREDITED WITH THEIR ORIGIN OR MODERN FORM OF PLAY

| Sport | Origin |
| --- | --- |
| Archery | England |
| Badminton | India |
| Baseball | United States |
| Basketball | United States |
| Billiards | Egypt |
| Bowling | Egypt |
| Boxing | Sumeria |
| Canoeing | North American Indians |
| Cricket | England |

| | |
|---|---|
| Croquet (roque) | France |
| Curling | Scotland |
| Fencing | Germany |
| Field events | Greece |
| Field hockey | Greece and Persia |
| Fives (handball) | Ireland |
| Football | England |
| Golf | Scotland |
| Gymnastics | Greece |
| Horseracing | England |
| Horseshoes | Greece |
| Hurling | Ireland |
| Ice hockey | Canada |
| Ice skating | Scandinavia |
| Jai alai | Spain |
| Judo | Japan |
| Jujitsu | China |
| Lacrosse | North American Indians |
| Lawn bowls | England |
| Paddle tennis | England |
| Platform tennis | United States |
| Polo | India |
| Quoits | England |
| Shuffleboard | Persia |
| Skiing | Scandinavia |
| Skin diving | South Sea Islands |
| Soccer | Rome |
| Softball | United States |
| Speedball | United States |
| Squash rackets | England |
| Squash tennis | United States |
| Surfing | Polynesia |
| Swimming | England |
| Table tennis | England |
| Target rifle shooting | British Isles |
| Tennis | France |
| Track events | Greece |
| Volleyball | United States |
| Water polo | England |
| Water skiing | France |
| Weight lifting | Egypt and Japan |
| Wrestling | Sumeria |
| Yacht racing | England |

## ORIGINS OF WORDS AND TERMS COMMONLY USED IN PHYSICAL EDUCATION*

Although our language and speech comes from all over the world, it is very interesting how various terms and words

---

*I am indebted to Robert N. Kasper, teacher of health and physical education at Macomb's Junior High School, New York, N. Y., for his research concerning the origin of the words and terms listed.

have entered the field of physical education. Many words and terms have passed through languages from all corners of the globe before reaching the United States. It is hoped that the reader will find the origins of these words and terms useful as well as interesting reading and study. For further information, consult the references at the end of this chapter.

**Amateur** (ăm á tûr; ăm á tûr). Amateur comes from the Latin meaning lover *(amator)*. The term was first used to indicate those athletes who won events in the Olympic games but refused to capitalize commercially on their fame. The present Anglo-Saxon spelling was given to the word in the late eighteenth century. The term was used to distinguish "Gentleman Jack Jackson" from the fighters of his time who fought for money. He was an amateur since he would not fight for profit.

**Archer** (är'chor). From the Latin *arcus*, or bow, referring to a person who uses a bow and arrow.

**Arena** (à rē'na). Arena is the Latin word for sand. There was so much bloodshed in the gladiatorial contests in the Roman amphitheaters that sand was liberally distributed on the ground to soak up the blood. The place of combat obtained its name from the sand.

**Athlete** (ăth'lēt). Athlos referred to a Greek contest and Athlon to a prize. An athlete was one who contended for a prize in a contest. The meaning for this term therefore has been used since the time of the Greeks and the Olympic games.

**Ball** (bôl). Originally, a voter put a black or white ball into a special box when he cast a secret ballot. Now the word refers to any spherically shaped object, and is derived from the Middle English word *bal*.

**Bowl** (bōl). A bowl is a weighted ball that is used for the game called bowling. The phrase "to throw" refers to the release of the spherical object known as a bowl.

**Box** (bŏks). This word is derived from the Greek *pyxos*, or box tree. In the sport of boxing, the ring is box shaped, and the clenched fist blows of the combatants are "boxes" or cuffs.

**Canoe** (kȧ'nōō'). The canoe was used in China, Polynesia, Africa, and other places. It did not originate with the American Indian. Some of the members of Christopher Columbus' crew borrowed the word from the

Haitian *kanoa* and took it back to Spain. The term came to America from Spain and originally referred to a dugout made from a hollowed log.

**Coach** (kōch). The word *coach* comes from the vehicle also called coach. The maker of the first coach vehicle lived in a town in Hungary called Koszi or Kocsi. The word comes from the name of this town. A coach in the sports sense is one who carries the athlete along.

**Contest** (kŏn test′). The word *contest* comes from the Latin *contestari,* meaning to call witness. When we break this down further, we have (*con + testari,* to be a witness). When you have witnesses arraigned on both sides, you have a contest.

**Circus** (sûr kŭs). The word *circus* comes from the Latin *circulus,* meaning a small ring. The Romans had a very large building in Rome that housed a large ring. This structure was called the Circus Maximus. The great shows and spectacles were held in the Circus Maximus during Roman times. The enclosure had a track or large ring laid out for chariot races, games, and other activities.

**Drill** (drĭl). It is through a pun on the word *bore* that the word has been applied to the exercises in which soldiers engage. The word is derived from the Dutch *drillen,* meaning to pierce or to bore. All drills turn round and round and bore, as do soldiers in many of their exercises turn in various formations.

**Exhibition** (ĕk′sĭ bĭsh′ŭn). The word *exhibition* is from the French and Latin *exhibeo; ex,* meaning out, and *habeo,* meaning hold. This takes its meaning from the fact that at exhibitions the artist holds out his pictures so that others may see them.

**Exercise** (ĕk′ser sīz). To exorcise is to chase out the demons and to exercise is to let out the animals (to keep them at work). This is from the Latin *ex,* meaning out, and *arcere,* meaning to confine, enclose. The original sense of the word is expressed in the statement. "Don't get exercised" or all worked up.

**Fan** (făn). A *fan* is one who goes into a frenzy about a particular sport or interest. He is an ardent admirer and devotee. During Roman times some priests were so inspired by religious frenzy that they would tear their robes aside and cut their bodies so that blood spurted in all directions. These priests were believed to be so inspired because of the goddess who worshiped in the fane or temple. This zeal was referred to by the Romans as fanaticus. Our word fa-natic is derived thus. The literal meaning is "inspired by the fane."

**Forfeit** (fôr′fĭt). The word originates from the French. It is a compound of the French words *fors,* meaning outside, and *fait,* meaning done. It means that it is something that is done outside the law. In early days in England and France *forfaite* was a crime, and a person was arrested when he was so discovered. Today, it refers to a penalty applied in games and sports.

**Game** (gām). The old English term *gamen* meant fun. It had a very broad meaning, embracing all forms of amusement. Today, it relates primarily to a contest.

**Gymnast** (jĭm năst). **Gymnasium** (jĭm nā′zĭ ŭm). From the Greek words *gymnos* meaning naked, and *gymnazo,* meaning to train naked. A literal interpretation of gymnast is the performer who is naked while performing and of gymnasium, a place where such a performance takes place. A custom in ancient Greece was to exercise in the nude since the body was considered to be a thing of beauty and something that should be exhibited for all to see.

Three intellectual centers of Athens in ancient Greece were the Academy where Plato resided, the Lyceum, attended by Aristotle, and Kynosarge, attended by Antisthenes. The gymnasium was a place where much learning also took place and where a person attended when he achieved manhood.

**Intramurals** (in′trà mūrals). The word is derived from the Latin *intra,* meaning within, and *murus,* meaning wall. In this sense it means sports that are played within the walls or a school, not with other schools.

**Marathon** (mâr′a thŏn). Marathon comes from the time in 490 B.C. when the Athenians defeated the Persians at the battle of Marathon. Since that time it has been used to name a long-distance running event over a course approximately twenty-six miles long.

**March** (märch). The word comes from the French *marcher,* meaning to walk. Originally the word had a slightly different meaning and included treading or tramping.

**Match** (măch). This word is derived from the Anglo-Saxon *gemaecca,* referring to husband and wife or male and female animal. The German influence added the meaning "to bring together."

**Net** (nĕt). Net comes from the Latin word *nassa* which meant a fishnet. Our tennis net and other sports nets such as in volleyball and badminton resemble the fishnet.

**Novice** (nŏv'ĭs). Novice comes from the French *novice* and the Latin *novititius* or *novus,* meaning new. A person just taking up a game or sport is a novice or somebody just beginning—new to the game.

**Olympiad** (ō lĭm'pĭ ăd). This was the period of four years between the celebrations of the Olympic games. It started out this way in Greece and has been passed down from 776 B.C.

**Olympic games** (o lĭm'pĭk). This was the name given to the most widely known of the four sacred festivals held in ancient Greece. The Olympic games were held at Olympia every fourth year in the month of July. The festival began with sacrifices and included racing, wrestling, and other contests and ended on the fifth day with processions, sacrifices, and banquets to the victors, who were given olive leaves to wear as garlands to symbolize their victory.

**Racket** (răk'ĕt). The word *racket* is originally from the Arabic *rahat,* meaning palm of the hand. A racket is usually held in the palm of the hand and is used in many games, including tennis, badminton, and squash.

**Race** (rās). The word *race* comes from the Old English word *raes,* meaning hurry or rush. A race is an event in which the contestants hurry as fast as they can to cross a goal or reach some other objective.

**Relay** (rē'lā). The word *relay* comes from the French verb *relayer,* meaning to lose the hounds. As it was originally used, a relay meant to hold some fresh hounds in reserve during a hunt. These fresh hounds were released at the strategic moment so that the scent was not lost. Of course, as it is used today it means a number of runners or contestants who relieve another group in a track event or other activity.

**Score** (skōr). The word *score* comes from the word *scoru,* which was borrowed by the English from the Old Norse *skor,* meaning notch. This was the way a score of a game was recorded—by making notches on a stick. The same practice was followed in American history by pioneers who notched their guns. Items are still scored by marking them with grooves, cuts, and other designs.

**Scout** (skout). The word *scout* comes from the Old French *escoute,* meaning a person who was a spy or an eavesdropper. It is now used in sports to refer to one who watches another team to obtain information of importance to his own team.

**Shuttlecock** (shŭt'l kŏk'). The Anglo-Saxon word *scytel,* referring to the back-and-forth

motion of a weaver's tool gave rise to the word shuttlecock, now a cork and feather object that is batted back and forth.

**Ski** (skē). In Norwegian, the word *ski* means snowshoe, or a slender wooden runner that is used in snow, the modern ski.

**Sport** (spōrt). The word *sport* is derived from the Latin words, *des,* meaning away, and *porto,* meaning carry. In other words, in its original meaning it meant to carry away or to carry away from one's work or business. It also is an abbreviation of the word *disport,* meaning to amuse oneself.

**Strategy** (străt'e jĭ). The word *strategy* comes from the Greek word *Strategos* or general, which broken down combines *Stratos,* army, + *agein,* to lead. This refers to the plan or strategy by which the general leads his forces to victory.

**Stunt** (stŭnt). The origin of the word *stunt* is rather cloudy. Some persons trace its origin to a trick done by a stunted acrobat, as opposed to a full-sized acrobat. Others suggest it comes from the word *stint,* meaning a task, and also from the German *Stunde,* meaning an hour or period of time. As part of early college athletic slang, it was used to refer to any feat or performance.

**Team** (tēm). The derivation of this term is very interesting since the earlier form was the Old English *tem,* which pertained to a set, a brood, or litter, or a number of animals harnessed in a row. From this early beginning it gradually became associated with a closely associated group of individuals or animals, such as a team of horses or a basketball team.

**Tournament** (tŏur'na ment). The derivation dates back to the Old French and the words *tournoi* and *tournoment,* referring to its basic concept—to turn. The English used it as *tourney* and *tournament,* particularly in the days of feudalism when knights dressed in armor rode away from each other and then turned and charged each other.

**Trophy** (trō fy). The word *trophy* comes from the Greek word *trope,* meaning putting to flight or a turning point in a battle or contest The word *tropaion* referred to a monument that was erected at the exact spot where the enemy was stopped and turned back. It later came to mean any monuments that were erected. A trophy now means a cup or other ornament that is conferred for winning a contest or to signify some other accomplishment.

**Umpire** (ŭm'pīr). The word originates from the Latin words *non per,* meaning not equal, that is, uneven or third person. This means that the umpire is an odd man who decides the dispute.

**Varsity** (var′sĭ tĭ). Varsity refers to a shortened form of university, that is, varsity baseball team, etc.; the varsity team selected to represent a college or a school.

**Volley** (vŏl′ĭ). The Latin word *volare*, "to fly" gives rise to volley, or keeping a ball in motion without allowing it to strike the ground.

**Yacht** (yŏt). A yacht is now a pleasure craft that is often used for racing. The Dutch word *jagt*, to speed or hunt, gave the yacht its original purpose. It was used by privateers to quickly hunt and overtake other ships to raid.

**Specific activities**

**Badminton** (băd′mĭn′ tn). In India badminton was known as *Poona*. This was where the game was first observed by English army officers in the 1860's. It was adopted by the English and formally introduced at a party given in 1873 by the Duke of Beaufort at his country place, which was called "Badminton in Gloucestershire." The game was referred to after this as "The Game at Badminton." As a result, *badminton* became the official name.

**Baseball** (bās′bâl). It is believed that baseball originated from the fifteenth century game of prisoners' base; prisoners' base was originally known as prisoners' bars, but the letter "r" was later dropped.

**Cricket** (krĭk′ĭt). The Old French word *criquet* referred to a curved bat. Now, the game of cricket is played by two teams of eleven men each.

**Curling** (kûr′lĭng). The Middle English word *crul*, which described the curving path of a stone gave rise to this word. The game of curling is played on ice, and heavy smooth stones are pushed toward a marker for score.

**Golf** (gŏlf). The origin of golf is somewhat obscure. However, most scholars believe it comes from the Dutch word *kolf*. *Kolf* is the term used for a club used in such games as hockey and croquet. Although most of the early accounts of the game of golf are associated with Scotland, many persons feel it is a Dutch game and to prove their point show that the Scotch imported their best golf balls from the Dutch.

**Hockey** (hŏk′ĭ). The word *hockey* probably took its name from the Old French word *hoquet*, meaning a crook or shepherd's staff.

Hockey is a very old game, having been played by the Greeks and the Persians.

**Hurling** (hûr′lĭng). This is the Irish name for a game that is almost identical to field hockey. It comes from the Old French word *houler*, "to hurl."

**Jujitsu** (jōo jĭt′sōo). Originally from the Chinese word *jiu-shu*, meaning to defeat an opponent by using his own strength and size against him, rather than resorting to weapons.

**Lacrosse** (là krôs′). The Indians played this game called baggataway, with sometimes hundreds of players on a side. The French formalized the game and named it from the stick used which they asserted resembled the "crozier's staff." (Old French *crossier*, meaning bearer of the crosse, bishop's crook.)

**Polo** (pō′lō). The Tibetan word *pulu* means ball. This game was invented by an Englishman living in India, and resembles hockey played on horseback.

**Quoits** (kwoits). The verb "to quoit" means to make an object slide. In its early form the game of quoits was a sliding rather than a throwing game. It comes from the Anglo-French word *jiu de coytes*.

**Soccer** (sŏk′ẽr). The game soccer is sometimes called association football. It is claimed that the word soccer originated by shortening the word *association* to *assoc* and then eliminating the first two letters of the latter term, leaving "soc." The game is very popular in England.

**Tennis** (tĕn′ĭs). Some scholars suggest that the word *tennis* comes from the city of Tinnis in the Egyptian Delta, which during the Middle Ages was noted for its fine linen and where the best tennis balls were made.

**Tumbling** (tŭm′blĭng). The word *tumbling* comes from the Anglo-Saxon word *tumbian* which meant to dance.

**QUESTIONS AND EXERCISES**

1. Discuss in approximately 500 words the history of physical education from the time of primitive man until the start of the modern European period.
2. From the physical point of view, why was the need for a planned physical education program not as great in the time of primitive man as it is today?
3. What was the attitude toward physical education in ancient China?
4. What are the forces that directly or indirectly drive men into physical activity?
5. What was the effect of Hinduism upon physical education in ancient India?

6. Contrast the attitude toward physical education in ancient China and India with that in Egypt, Assyria, Babylonia, Syria, Palestine, and Persia.
7. Describe the routine you would have followed if you had grown up in Persia during the reign of King Cyrus.
8. How do many countries utilize physical education for destructive purposes?
9. Compare physical education in ancient Greece with that prevalent today in the United States.
10. What were the objectives of physical education during the "golden age" in ancient Greece?
11. Compare the roles of physical education in the city-states of Sparta and Athens.
12. What were the palaestra and the gymnasium? What kind of activities did each provide?
13. What were the names of some of the outstanding national festivals in Greece and what gods did they honor?
14. Describe the games held at Olympia, bringing out the following points: (a) requirements for contestants, (b) events, (c) rewards, and (d) attitude of Greeks toward these games.
15. What was the attitude of each of the following toward physical education: (a) Socrates, (b) Plato, (c) Aristotle, and (d) Xenophon?
16. Compare the Greeks and the Romans in their attitudes toward physical education.
17. In approximately 250 words discuss the statement that America is going the way of the Romans.
18. What were the Dark Ages? Was this a dark period in history for physical education? Explain.
19. Discuss asceticism and scholasticism and show how they still exist in many forms in twentieth century society.
20. What was the influence of the feudalistic period upon physical education?
21. How did each of the following contribute to physical education: (a) Da Feltra, (b) Vergerio, (c) Pope Pius II, (d) Sir Thomas Elyot, (e) Martin Luther, (f) Rabelais, (g) Asham, (h) John Milton, (i) Locke, (j) Comenius, and (k) Rousseau?

## SELECTED REFERENCES

Abbott, E. A.: Society and politics in ancient Rome, New York, 1909, Charles Scribner's Sons.

Allier, R.: The mind of the savage, New York, 1929, Harcourt, Brace & Co., Inc.

Barnes, H. E.: The history of western civilization, New York, 1935, Harcourt, Brace & Co., Inc.

Bauer, L.: Chinese dances for children, Journal of Health and Physical Education 4:22, Sept., 1933.

Bennett, Bruce L.: Improving courses in the history of physical education, Journal of Health, Physical Education, and Recreation 37:26, Feb., 1966.

Botsford, G. W., and Sihler, E. G.: Hellenic civilization, New York, 1915, Columbia University Press.

Bowra, C. M.: Xenophanes and the Olympic games, American Journal of Philology 59: 257, 1938.

Brink, D. B., and Smith, P.: Athletes of the Bible, New York, 1914, Associated Press.

Bucher, Charles A.: Are we losing the Olympic ideal? Sports Illustrated, Aug. 8, 1955.

Bucher, Charles A.: Let's put more sportsmanship into the Olympics, Reader's Digest, Sept., 1955.

Bucher, Charles A.: Scorekeepers vs. first principles, Journal of Health, Physical Education, and Recreation 35:26, Sept., 1964.

Bury, J. B.: The invasion of Europe by the barbarians, London, 1928, The Macmillan Co.

Butler, A. J.: Sport in classic times, London, 1930, Ernest Benn, Ltd.

Buttree, J. M.: The rhythm of the Redman, New York, 1930, A. S. Barnes & Co.

Caillois, Roger: Man, play, and games, New York, 1961, The Free Press of Glencoe, Inc. (translated from the French).

Carcopino, J.: Daily life in ancient Rome (translated by E. O. Lorimer), New Haven, 1940, Yale University Press.

Chryssafis, J.: Aristotle on physical education, Journal of Health and Physical Education 1: 3, Feb., 1930.

Chryssafis, J.: Aristotle on kinesiology, Journal of Health and Physical Education 1:14, Sept., 1930.

Clark, Ellery H.: The Olympic games and their influence upon physical education, Journal of Health, Physical Education, and Recreation 35:23, Sept., 1964 (reprinted from The American Physical Education Review).

Coomaraswamy, A.: The dance of Siva, New York, 1918, Sunrise Turn.

Cubberly, E. P.: Readings in the history of education, Boston, 1920, Houghton Mifflin Co.

Dulles, Foster Rhea: A history of recreation—

America learns to play, New York, 1965, Appleton-Century-Crofts.

Falkener, E.: Games ancient and oriental and how to play them, London, 1892, Longmans.

Fuld, L. F.: Physical education in Greece and Rome, American Physical Education Review **12:**1, March, 1907.

Gardiner, E. N.: Athletics of the ancient world, Oxford, 1930, Clarendon Press.

Genasci, James E., and Klissouras, Vasillis: The delphic spirit in sports, Journal of Health, Physical Education, and Recreation **37:**43, Feb., 1966.

Gray, J. H.: Physical education in India, American Physical Education Review **24:**373, Oct., 1919.

Hackensmith, C. W.: History of physical education, New York, 1966, Harper & Row.

Hoh, G.: Physical education in China, Shanghai, 1926, Commercial Press.

Lee, J.: Play in education, New York, 1922, The Macmillan Co.

Leonard, F. E.: A guide to the history of physical education (edited by R. T. McKenzie), Philadelphia, 1923, Lea & Febiger.

Leonard, F. E., and Affect, G. B.: A guide to the history of physical education, Philadelphia, 1947, Lea & Febiger.

Lucas, John A.: Coubertin's philosophy of pedagogical sport, Journal of Health, Physical Education, and Recreation **35:**26, Sept., 1964.

Means, Richard K.: A history of health education in the United States, Philadelphia, 1962, Lea & Febiger.

Monograph IV. Quest, The National Association for Physical Education of College Women and The National College Physical Education Association for Men, April, 1965.

Rice, Emmett A., Hutchinson, John L., and Lee, Mabel: A brief history of physical education, New York, 1958, The Ronald Press.

Schleppi, J. R.: Architecture and sports, The Physical Educator **23:**123, Oct., 1966.

Trekell, Marianna: Speaking to the future, Journal of Health, Physical Education, and Recreation **37:**29, Feb., 1966.

Van Dalen, Deobold B., Mitchell, E. D., and Bennett, B. L.: World history of physical education, New York, 1953, Prentice-Hall, Inc.

Weston, Arthur: The making of American physical education, New York, 1962, Appleton-Century-Crofts.

Woody, Thomas: The fair sex in Greek society, Research Quarterly **10:**57, May, 1939.

Woody, Thomas: Life and education in early societies, New York, 1949, The Macmillan Co.

*References for word origins*

Brewer, Ebenezer: Dictionary of phrase and fable, New York, 1952, Harper & Brothers.

Funk, Charles E.: Thereby hangs a tale, New York, 1950, Harper & Brothers.

Funk, Wilfred: Word origins and their romantic stories, New York, 1950, Wilfred Funk, Inc.

Holt, Alfred H.: Phrases and word origins, New York, 1961, Dover Publications, Inc.

Menke, Frank G.: The encyclopedia of sports, New York, 1961, A. S. Barnes & Co.

Shipley, Joseph T.: Dictionary of word origins, New York, 1945, The Philosophical Library, Inc.

Weekley, Ernest: Concise, etymological dictionary of modern English, New York, 1952, E. P. Dutton & Co., Inc.

# Chapter 12

# Changing concepts from beginning of modern European period to present

A study of physical education in the modern European period shows many reasons why special programs in this area were established and the nature of such programs in the various countries of Europe. The spirit of nationalism and the necessity of being prepared for warfare were two leading causes for instituting programs of physical activity on the Continent. Physical education was increasingly being recognized for its therapeutic value. Stress was placed on physical education as a science, requiring more study in anatomy, physiology, and other foundational sciences. There was a trend toward a games and sports program to supplement the rigid and formal type of gymnastics. The public was becoming cognizant of a need for incorporating a planned program of physical activity in the schools. It was being more fully recognized that the physical and the mental go hand in hand and give support to each other and that exercise is necessary for optimum growth and development. It is interesting to note in passing that the potentialities of physical education as a

means of developing acceptable social and moral traits still were not fully realized. Education *of* the physical was to a great extent the predominant objective, with less regard for education *through* the physical.

## PHYSICAL EDUCATION IN EUROPE

A study of the various men and countries that influenced physical education the most during the modern European period shows what each contributed to the growth and advancement of this field.

### Germany

Physical education in Germany during the modern European period is associated with such names as Basedow, Guts Muths, Jahn, and Spiess.

*Johann Bernhard Basedow* (1723–1790) was born in Hamburg and early in life went to Denmark as a teacher. Here he witnessed physical education in practice as part of a combined physical and mental training program. After gaining a wealth of experience in Denmark, he went back to Germany and decided to spend all of his time in the reform of educational methods. In 1774 he was able to realize his objective of establishing at Dessau a school which he called the Philanthropinum. In this model school physical education played an important part in the daily program of all students. The activities included such items as dancing, fencing, riding, running, jumping, wrestling, swimming, skating, and marching. This was the first school in modern Europe that admitted children from every class in society and that offered a program where physical education was a part of the curriculum. Such an innovation by Basedow did much to influence the growth of physical education in Germany as well as in the rest of the world.

*Johann Christoph Friedrich Guts Muths* (1759–1839) brought his influence to bear upon the field of physical education through his association with the Schnepfenthal Educational Institute, which had been founded by Christian Gotthilf Salzmann (1744–1811). Guts Muths succeeded Christian Carl Andre as the instructor of physical education at this institution and remained on the staff for fifty years. His beliefs and practices in physical education were recorded for history in various books, two of which are of special importance, *Gymnastics for the Young* and *Games*. These books give such information as illustrations of various exercises and apparatus, arguments in favor of physical education, and the relation of physical education to educational institutions. Because of his outstanding contributions, Guts Muths is often referred to as one of the founders of modern physical education in Germany.

*Friedrich Ludwig Jahn* (1778–1852) is a name that is associated with the Turnverein, an association of gymnasts which has been in evidence ever since its innovation by Jahn. Jahn's incentive for inaugurating the Turnverein movement was love of his country. It was during his life-

time that Napoleon overran Germany and caused it to be divided into several independent German states. Jahn made it his life's work and ambition to help in bringing about an independent Germany free from foreign control. He felt that he could best help in this movement by molding German youth into strong and hardy citizens who would be capable of throwing off this foreign yoke.

To help in the achievement of his objective, Jahn accepted a teaching position in Plamann's Boys School. In this position he worked regularly with the boys in various outdoor activities. He set up an exercise ground outside the city called the Hasenheide. Before long Jahn had erected various pieces of apparatus which included equipment for jumping, vaulting, balancing, climbing, and running. The program grew in popularity, and soon hundreds of boys were visiting the exercise ground or turnplatz regularly and more apparatus was added.

Jahn's system of gymnastics was recognized throughout Germany, and in many cities Turnvereins were formed, using as a guide the instructions that Jahn incorporated in his book *Die Deutsche Turnkunst*. When Jahn died, his work carried on and turner societies became more numerous. In 1870 there were 1,500 turner societies, in 1880 there were 2,200, in 1890 there were 4,000, in 1900 there were 7,200, and in 1920 there were 10,000. Turnvereins are still in existence in many parts of the world.

The objectives of Jahn's work in physical education were tied up with his desire for an independent Germany. He believed that through physical education his country could be made strong. Despite the overwhelming political motive, Jahn saw in physical education a means of aiding the growth and development of children, social equality, and its importance in the curriculum of the school. Many persons have disagreed with Jahn's gymnastics.

The turnplatz.

They argue that they were not founded on the sciences of physiology and anatomy, were too heavy for children, were too rigid and formal, and did not provide a program for the women.

Although there may be some disagreement as to Jahn's motives and methods, he has had a great influence on physical education in Germany, as well as throughout the world. He instilled in the German people a love for gymnastics which has been passed down for several generations.

*Adolph Spiess* (1810–1858) was the founder of school gymnastics in Germany, and, more than any other man in German history, he helped to make physical education a part of school life. Spiess was proficient in physical education activities himself and was well informed as to the theories of such men as Guts Muths and Jahn. His own theory was that the school should be interested in the total growth of the child—mental, emotional, physical, and social. Physical education should receive the same consideration received by the important academic subjects such as mathematics and language. It should be required of all students, with the possible exception of those a physician would excuse. There should be provisions for an indoor as well as an outdoor program. Elementary school children should have a

minimum of one hour of the school day devoted to physical education activities, which should be taught by the regular classroom teacher. The upper grades should have a progressively smaller amount, which should be conducted by specialists who were educators first, but who were also experts in the field of physical education. The physical education program should be progressive, starting with simple exercises and proceeding to the more difficult. Girls as well as boys need an adapted program of physical activity. Exercises combined with music offer an opportunity for the individual to express himself more freely. Marching exercises aid in class organization, discipline, and posture development. Formalism should not be practiced to the exclusion of games, dancing, and sports.

Many of Spiess' theories and practices have been incorporated in school programs of physical education the world over. Spiess recognized the valuable contribution physical education could make in the education of boys and girls. He appreciated the values of such a program in developing the body and in developing an individual socially and morally.

There are other outstanding individuals in modern German history who have influenced physical education, including Eiselen, Koch, Hermann, and Von Schenck-endorff. However, the names of Basedow, Guts Muths, Jahn, and Spiess stand out as the ones who, in large part, have influenced physical education the most.

### Sweden

The name of *Per Henrik Ling* (1776–1839) is symbolic of the rise of physical education to a place of importance in Sweden. The "Lingaid," held at Stockholm, in which representatives of many nations of the world participate, is a tribute to this great man.

Ling's greatest contribution is that he strove to make physical education a science. Formerly it had been conducted mainly on the premise that people believed it was good for the human body because it increased the size of one's musculature, contributed to strength, stamina, endurance, and agility, and left one exhilarated. However, this had never been proved scientifically. Ling approached the field with the mind of a scientist. Through the sciences of anatomy and physiology,

he examined the body to determine what was inherent in physical activity to enable the body to function in a more nearly optimum capacity. His aims were directed at determining such things as the effect of exercise on the heart, on the musculature, on the various organic systems of the body, and the like. He felt that through such a scientific approach, he would be better able to understand the human body and its needs and would be better able to select and apply activity intelligently.

Ling is noted for establishing the Royal Central Institute of Gymnastics at Stockholm where teachers of physical education received their preparation in one of three categories—educational gymnastics, military gymnastics, or medical gymnastics.

Ling believed that physical education was necessary for the weak as well as the strong, that exercise must be prescribed on the basis of individual differences, that the mind and body must function harmoniously together, and that teachers of physical education must have a founda-

The Idla Girls, the famous Swedish group of amateur women gymnasts, displaying their graceful program in front of the seventeenth century Royal Palace of Drottningholm.

tional knowledge of the effects of exercise on the human body.

Ling's objectives for physical education included the desire to see each person develop his body to the fullest extent, to restore health to individuals with weaknesses and afflictions, and to make the country strong against aggressors.

In 1839 *Lars Gabriel Branting* (1799–1881) became the director of the Royal Central Institute of Gymnastics upon the death of Ling. Branting spent the major part of his time in the area of medical gymnastics. His teachings were based on the premise that activity causes changes not only in the muscular system of the body but also in the nervous and circulatory systems as well. Branting's successor was *Gustaf Nyblaeus* (1816–1902), who specialized in military gymnastics. An innovation during his tenure was the inclusion of women in the school.

The incorporation of physical education programs in the schools of Sweden did not materialize as rapidly as many leaders in the field had hoped. As a result of the teachings of Ling and other leaders, a law was passed in 1820 requiring a course of physical education on the secondary level. More progress was made in education when the values of physical education to the growth and development of children became apparent in Sweden. To *Hjalmar Fredrik Ling* (1820–1886) most of the credit is due for the organization of educational gymnastics in Sweden. He was largely responsible for physical education becoming an essential subject in all schools for both boys and girls and on all institutional levels. Today, most schools in Sweden require a period a day for physical education, which is devoted to a program of games and Swedish exercises.

### Denmark

Denmark has been one of the leading European countries in the promotion of physical education. *Franz Nachtegall* (1777–1847) was largely responsible for the early interest in this field. He had a direct influence in introducing physical education into the public schools of Denmark and in preparing teachers of this subject.

Franz Nachtegall had been interested in various forms of physical activity since childhood and had achieved some degree of skill in vaulting and fencing. He began early in life to teach gymnastics, first to students who visited his home and then in 1799 in a private outdoor gymnasium, the first to be devoted entirely to physical training. In 1804 Nachtegall became the first director of a Training School for Teachers of Gymnastics in the Army. For a time, only service personnel were allowed to pursue the course; later, however, civilians were also given permission. The need was great for instructors in the public schools and in teachers' colleges, so that graduates readily found employment. In 1809 the secondary schools and in 1814 the elementary schools were requested to provide a program of physical education with qualified instructors. It was shortly after this that Nachtegall received the appointment of Director of Gymnastics for all Denmark.

The death of Nachtegall in 1847 did not stop the expansion of physical education throughout Denmark. Some of the important advances since his death have been the organization of Danish Rifle Clubs or gymnastic societies, the introduction of the Ling system of gymnastics, complete civilian supervision and control of programs of physical education as against military supervision and control, greater provision for teacher education, government aid, the incorporation of sports and games into the program, and the work of Niels Bukh.

One of the innovations in the field of physical education has been the contribution of Niels Bukh with his "Primitive Gymnastics." Patterned to some ex-

Danish performers at New York University.

tent after the work of Ling, they attempted to build the perfect physique through
a series of exercises that were performed
without cessation of movement. His routine included exercises for arms, legs, abdomen, neck, back, and the various joints.
In 1925 he toured the United States with
some of his students, demonstrating his
"Primitive Gymnastics."

### Great Britain

Great Britain is known as the home of
outdoor sports, and her contribution to
this field has influenced physical education the world over. When other European countries were utilizing the Ling,
Jahn, and Guts Muths systems of gymnastics, England was utilizing a program
of organized games and sports.

Athletic sports are a feature of English
life. As early as the time of Henry II,
English youth were wrestling, throwing,
riding, fishing, hunting, swimming, rowing, skating, shooting the bow, and participating in various other sports. The
games of hockey and quoits, for example,
were played in England as early as the
fifteenth century, tennis as early as 1300,
golf as early as 1600, and cricket as early
as 1700. Football is one of the oldest of
English national sports. Games were
played in all parts of England from the
earliest of times.

In addition to outdoor sports, England's
chief contribution to physical education
has been through the work of *Archibald
Maclaren* (1820–1884). Maclaren at an
early age enjoyed participating in many

*Acme Photo.*

Danish gymnastic team performing at New York University.

sports, but especially fencing and gymnastics. He also studied medicine and was eager to make a science of physical training. In 1858 he opened a private gymnasium where he was able to experiment. In 1860 Maclaren was designated to devise a system of physical education for the British Army. As a result of this appointment, he incorporated his recommendations in a treatise entitled *A Military System of Gynmastic Exercises for the Use of Instructors.* This system was adopted by the military, and Maclaren undertook the responsibility of training a cadre of Army and Navy men in his system of exercises.

Maclaren contributed several other books to the field of physical education.

Some of these were *National Systems of Bodily Exercise, A System of Fencing, Training in Theory and Practice,* and *A System of Physical Education.* In his works he points out that the objectives of physical education should take into consideration that health is more important than strength; that the antidote for tension, weariness, nervousness, and hard work is physical action; that recreative exercise as found in games and sports is not enough in itself for growing boys and girls; that physical exercise is essential to optimum growth and development; that physical training and mental training are inseparable; that mind and body represent a "oneness" in man and sustain and support each other; that exercises must

**Table 12-1.** *Chronological distribution of established dates of origins**

| Sport | Date of origin† | Sport | Date of origin† |
|---|---|---|---|
| Wrestling | (2160) 1788 B.C. | Field hockey | (B.C.?) 1886 |
| Boxing | (2160?) 850 B.C. | Polo | (475?) 1596 |
| Field events | (900 B.C.?) 776 B.C. | Curling | 1607 |
| | | Ice skating | (500) 1659 |
| Track events | (900 B.C.?) 776 B.C. | Cricket | (1600) 1744 |
| | | Fives | 1746 |
| Hunting | (2357) 400 B.C. | Yacht racing | (1675) 1775 |
| Kite flying | (1121) 221 B.C. | Pedestrianism | (1610) 1792 |
| Coursing | 7 A.D. | Racquets | (1555) 1799 |
| Cock fighting | 77 | Horseshoes | (1750?) 1801 |
| Angling | 200 | Coaching | (1590) 1807 |
| Falconry | 350 | Steeplechasing | (1740) 1810 |
| Horse racing | (648 B.C.) 1174 | Mountaineering | (1780?) 1811 |
| Tennis | 1230 | Gymnastics | (1790) 1816 |
| Lawn bowls | 1366 | Pigeon racing | (1800) 1818 |
| Quoits | (450 B.C.) 1409 | Harness racing | 1825 |
| Golf | (1380?) 1457 | Sculling | (1715) 1839 |
| Target rifle shooting | 1498 | Lacrosse | (1400) 1839 |
| Fencing | 1517 | Rowing | 1839 |
| Hurling | 1527 | Bowling (ten pins) | (1600) 1840 |
| Shuffleboard | 1532 | Croquet | 1840 |
| Archery (target) | (1530) 1585 | Handball | (1500?) 1840 |
| Billiards | (1520?) 1590 | Birling | 1888 |
| Fowling | (2475 B.C.) 1596 | Table tennis | 1889 |
| Baseball | (1750) 1846 | Darts | (1850?) 1890 |
| Rugby | 1846 | Rope spinning | (1850?) 1890 |
| Iceboating | (1720) 1850 | Squash tennis | 1890 |
| Weight lifting | (1720) 1854 | Basketball | 1891 |
| Canoe racing | (1790?) 1859 | Automobile racing | 1895 |
| Soccer | 1859 | Volleyball | 1895 |
| Squash raquets | 1859 | Jai alai | 1896 |
| Swimming | (1530) 1859 | Paddle tennis | 1898 |
| Roller skating | 1863 | Motorcycle racing | 1902 |
| Trap shooting | 1866 | Corkball | 1904 |
| Field trials | 1866 | Motorboat racing | 1904 |
| Bicycle racing | 1868 | Model airplane flying | 1905 |
| Badminton | 1870 | Airplane flying | 1907 |
| Skiing | (1750) 1870 | Soaring | 1909 |
| Target pistol shooting | 1871 | Speedball | 1920 |
| Model sailboat racing | 1872 | Softball | (1890) 1923 |
| Lawn tennis | 1873 | Miniature golf | (1860) 1927 |
| Football (American) | 1874 | Soapbox racing | 1927 |
| Dog racing | (1810?) 1876 | Six man football | 1933 |
| Roque | 1879 | Skin diving | 1934 |
| Ice hockey | (1810) 1880 | Miniature auto racing | 1936 |
| Rodeo | (1830) 1880 | Water skiing | 1939 |
| Judo | 1882 | Skish | (1880?) 1939 |
| Tobogganing | (1837?) 1883 | Flickerball | 1948 |
| Water polo | 1885 | | |

*Eyler, Marvin H.: Research Quarterly, AAHPHR **32**:484, Dec., 1961.

†The date given after each sport is that of the earliest documented evidence of its origin in organized form. Dates shown in parentheses are those of documented evidence of previous existence, as unorganized or noncompetitive activity. A date in parentheses with a question mark indicates that reputed evidence previous to this date may not actually refer to this specific sport.

be progressive in nature; that exercises should be adapted to an individual's fitness; that physical education should be an essential part of any school curriculum; and that physical education should be organized and administered effectively so that all of its potentialities will be realized.

Since the time of Maclaren the Swedish system of gymnastics has been introduced into England and has been well received. Many ideas were also imported from Denmark. Leaders came from Denmark and Sweden in the persons of Knudsen, Langkilde, and Osterberg. Training schools for teachers were established, and educational laws were passed promoting physical education in the schools. There was more emphasis on the health movement, and laws were passed providing for health services, healthful school living, and health instruction.

• • •

Germany, Sweden, Denmark, and England have led Europe in the promotion of physical education. Other countries of

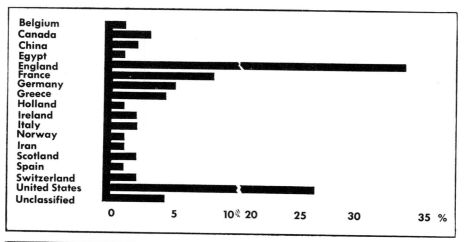

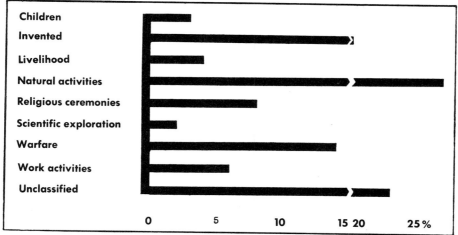

*Eyler, Marvin H.: Research Quarterly,*
*AAHPHR 32:483, Dec., 1961.*

Origins of contemporary sports. **A,** Percentage distribution of place of origin for ninety-five sports. **B,** Percentage distribution of activities from which the ninety-five sports evolved.

Europe as a rule imported the various systems of Jahn, Guts Muths, and Ling. There are persons from other countries who have also contributed much to the field of physical education and should be mentioned. From Switzerland, Pestalozzi with his educational theories, Dalcroze and his system of eurythmics, and Clias did a great deal to advance the field of physical education; Colonel Amoros from France inaugurated a system of gymnastics; and Baron Pierre de Coubertin was instrumental in reviving the Olympic games in 1896 at Athens, Johann Happel from Belgium was outstanding in physical education and was director of a normal school of gymnastics. Dr. Tyrs from Czechoslovakia organized the first gymnastic society in his country.

The origins of some common sports are given in Table 12-1.

## PHYSICAL EDUCATION IN AMERICA

Physical education in America has experienced a period of great expansion from the colonial period, when little regard was had for any planned program of activity, until today, when programs are required in the public schools of most of our states and when physical education is becoming a respected profession.

### Colonial period

During the colonial period in America conditions were not conducive to organized physical education programs. The majority of the population lived an agrarian existence and felt that they received enough physical exercise working on the farms. Also, there were few leisure hours during this period that could be devoted to various forms of recreational activities. In certain sections of the country, such as New England, religious beliefs were contrary to participation in play. The Puritans, especially, denounced play as the work of the devil. Participation in games was believed just cause for external

damnation. Pleasures and recreation were banned. Stern discipline, austerity, and frugality were thought to be the secrets to eternal life and blessedness.

People of some sections of the nation, however, brought with them from their mother countries the knowledge and desire for various sports. The Dutch in New York liked to engage in such sports as skating, coasting, hunting, and fishing. However, the outstanding favorite was bowling. In Virginia many sports were popular, such as running, boxing, wrestling, horse racing, cockfights, fox hunts, and later cricket and football.

During the colonial period little emphasis was given to any form of physical activity in the schools. The emphasis was on the three R's on the elementary level and on the classics on the secondary level. The teachers were ill prepared in the methodology of teaching. Furthermore, on the secondary level students were prepared mainly for college, and it was thought that physical activity was a waste of time in such preparation.

### National period*

During the national period of the history of the United States physical education began to assume an important place in American society.

The academies, as many of the secondary schools were called, provided terminal education for students, and instead of preparing for college, they prepared for living. These educational institutions utilized games and sports as after-school activity. They had not reached the point, however, where they thought its value was such that it should occupy a place in the daily school schedule. They encouraged participation during after-school hours on the premise that it promotes

*The period from the American Revolution to the Civil War.

*Los Angeles Public Schools, Los Angeles, Calif.*

During the colonial period in America conditions were not conducive to organized physical education programs such as exist today.

health and rest from the mental phases of school life.

The United States Military Academy was founded in 1802 and gave physical training an important place in its program of activities. Through history, this training school has maintained such a program, and today it is considered one of the best in existence.

It was during the national period that German gymnastics were introduced to America. Charles Beck introduced Jahn's ideas at the Round Hill School at Northampton, Massachusetts, in 1823; and Charles Follen introduced them at Harvard University and in Boston. Both Beck and Follen were turners and proficient in the execution of German gymnastics. Their attempt to introduce German gymnastics into the United States, however, was not successful at this time. A few years later they were introduced with more success in such German settlements

as Kansas City, Cincinnati, St. Louis, Davenport, and others. Turnverein associations were organized, and gymnastics were accepted with considerable enthusiasm by the residents of German extraction. As for native Americans, the majority of them felt that the formal type of gymnastic program was not suitable for their purposes.

The Turnverein organizations spread, and by 1852 there were twenty-two societies in the North. The oldest Turnverein in the United States, which flourishes to the present day, is the Cincinnati Turnverein founded November 21, 1848. The Philadelphia Turnverein, one of the strongest societies today, was founded on May 15, 1849. A national organization of Turnvereins, now known as the American Turnerbund, was established in 1850 and held its first national turnfest in Philadelphia in 1851. Societies from New York, Boston, Cincinnati, Brooklyn, Utica, Philadelphia, and Newark were represented. There were 1,672 turners in the United States in 1851. At the outbreak of the Civil War there were approximately 150 Turnverein societies and 10,000 turners in the United States. After the Civil War these organizations continued to grow and exercised considerable influence on the growing physical education profession. The Turnverein organizations led to the establishment of the Normal College of the American Gymnastic Union. Many outstanding physical education leaders graduated from this school.

There were notable advances in physical education prior to the Civil War. In 1828 a planned program of physical education, composed mainly of calisthenics done to music, was incorporated by Catherine E. Beecher in the Hartford Female Seminary in Connecticut, a famous institution of higher learning for women

and girls. The introduction of the Swedish Movement Cure in America, the building of gymnasiums in many large cities, the formation of gymnastic and athletic clubs by many leading institutions of higher learning, and the invention of baseball were all events of importance in the progress of physical education in America during this period.

## Physical education in America from Civil War until 1900

Many outstanding leaders and new ideas influenced physical education in America in the period from the Civil War to 1900.

After the Civil War the Turnverein societies were established for both boys and girls. The members of these associations gave support to various phases of physical education and especially encouraged the program in the public schools. The ob-

*The J. Clarence Davies collection, Museum of the City of New York.*

Dr. Rich's Institute for Physical Education.

jectives of the turners were of the highest type. They disapproved of too much stress being placed on winning games and professionalism. They felt that the main objectives should be to promote physical welfare and provide social and moral training. They opposed military training in the schools as a substitute for physical education and supported the playground movement.

From 1859 to the early 1870's, Dr. George Barker Winship gained considerable publicity by emphasizing gymnastics as a means of building strength and large muscles.

In 1860 Dr. Dio Lewis devised a new system of gymnastics and introduced it in Boston. As opposed to Winship, Lewis was not concerned with building muscles and strength. He was more interested in the weak and feeble persons in our so-

ciety. Instead of large muscles, he aimed at developing agility, grace of movement, flexibility, and improving one's general health and posture. He also stressed that teachers should be well prepared, and in 1861 he established a normal school of physical education in Boston for training teachers. Lewis opposed military training in our schools. He felt that sports in themselves would not provide an adequate program but that gymnastics should also be included. Through lectures and written articles, Lewis became a leading authority on gymnastics used in the schools and the public in general. He is noted for advancing physical education to a respected position in our society. Several leading educators, after hearing Lewis, set up planned physical education programs in their school systems.

In the 1880's the Swedish Movement

*Los Angeles Public Schools, Los Angeles, Calif.*

Many outstanding leaders and new ideas influenced physical education in the period since the Civil War in America so that today it is generally recognized as having essential contributions to make to all who participate in its programs.

Cure was made popular by Hartvig Nissen, head of the Swedish Health Institute in Washington. This system was based on the Ling or Swedish gymnastics so well known in Europe and recognized in America for inherent medical values. Also in the 1880's Mrs. Hemenway and Amy Morris Homans added their contributions to physical education. They stimulated the growth of Swedish gymnastics, founded a normal school for teachers at Framingham, Massachusetts, contributed to

---

To the members of the Athletic Club:

MISGUIDED MORTALS—Dwell as I do in the atmosphere of piety with which my father's home is always pervaded, and separated as I am from the vanities of this wicked world, it is not often that I receive tidings from the valley of worldliness which stretches out far below me.

But I have been made acquainted with that zeal for a fleshly gospel, and for a merely muscular grace, which has unhappily broken out in our once religious village.

It was a sufficiently mournful token of the decay of Zion that so many professors fell from their allegiance and built that temple to Baal, which, I think, you call a Club House—an edifice erected to frivolity, and unconsecrated by one prayer or psalm.

But my cup of spiritual grief was filled, when I learned that even the handmaidens of our village are also bowing down to this pagan fashion, and are learning the unscriptural practice of gymnastics, and having heard that you are this night to discuss formally the subject of women's part in your gymnasium, I write unto you this letter of counsel, warning, and reproof. Where in the Bible can you find the least authority for gymnastics? Echo answers, where?

That pagan name does not occur anywhere in the sacred volume, from Genesis to Revelation. But while gymnastics are not mentioned by name, they are referred to, and that with the severest censure. The Apostle Paul (I Tim. iv. 7, 8) says to Timothy: Exercise thyself rather unto Godliness. For bodily exercise profiteth little; but Godliness is profitable unto all things.

Also, is it not a great shame and a scandal, that young ladies should be so negligent of propriety as to take part in diversions which must cause an unseemly exposure of their feet, and even of their ankles?

The Apostle Paul would not allow women to appear in public with their heads uncovered. What would he have said to you who are willing not only to show your heads, but your ————? I am too much shocked to finish the sentence.

The Scripture teaches also that woman was intended to be weak. But your gymnastics oppose the will of Providence, and the words of Scripture, by making woman strong.

It is the duty of woman to stay at home and comfort her husband (here there were smiles and profuse whisperings among the ladies) and take care of his house. But how can she properly discharge this duty if she goes to the gymnasium?

We are also told in the Scripture that it is the will of God that the great duty of woman should be attended with suffering; "In sorrow shall thou bring forth children." But so profane has the world grown, that you gymnastic people openly boast that woman can be so strengthened as to bear children without great pain, and thus thwart the righteous will of Heaven. Need I say more to prove to you the error of your present course? I pray that you may see the wickedness of your way, and turn your unscriptural Club House into a temple of the living God.

Yours sorrowfully,
"JERUSHA SNIPP"

Excerpt from The Brawnville Papers
by Moses Coit Tyler
(Fields, Osgood & Co., Boston, 1869)

---

A letter written in the 1860's reflects how some people felt about physical education.

the school children of Boston, Massachusetts, by offering courses of instruction in Swedish gymnastics to schoolteachers, and were influential in the establishment of the Boston Normal School of Gymnastics.

In the 1890's the Delsarte System of Physical Culture was introduced by Francois Delsarte. His system was based on the belief that by contributing to poise, grace, beauty, and health certain physical exercises were conducive to better dramatics and better singing.

During this period American sports began to achieve some degree of popularity. Tennis was introduced in 1874, and in 1880 the United States Lawn Tennis Association was organized. Golf came to America in the late 1880's and in 1894 the United States Golfing Association was formed. Bowling had been popular since the time of the early Dutch in New York,

but it was not until 1895 that the American Bowling Congress was organized. Basketball, one of the few sports originating in the United States, was invented by James Naismith in 1891. Some of the other sports that became popular during this period were wrestling, boxing, volleyball, skating, skiing, lacrosse, handball, archery, track, soccer, squash, football, and swimming. In 1879 the National Association of Amateur Athletics of America was developed. The American Athletic Union developed out of this organization.

Physical education has played a large part in the Young Men's Christian Association, an organization that is worldwide in scope and that is devoted to developing Christian character and better living standards. Robert J. Roberts was an outstanding authority in physical education for the Young Men's Christian As-

*Los Angeles Public Schools, Los Angeles, Calif.*

Physical education made big advances in colleges and universities with the construction of facilities and the development of departments in this area. A junior college swimming program in action.

*The J. Clarence Davies collection, Museum of the City of New York.*

Skating in Central Park, New York, 1885.

# RECREATION AND STUDY

Chautauqua Affords Opportunity for Instruction Under the Best Instructors. Together with Abundant Outdoor Recreation and an Attractive Program of Concerts, Popular Lectures and the Best Entertainments.

THE CHAUTAUQUA CREW

*Courtesy Harold L. Ray, Western Michigan University, Kalamazoo, Mich.*

Boating on Lake Chautauqua.

Photographs of the Chautauqua institution—early showcase for physical education in the late 1800's and early 1900's. It was located on Lake Chautauqua in southwestern New York State. William G. Anderson, founder of the American Association for Health, Physical Education, and Recreation, was active at this institution.

sociation in the late 1800's. In 1885, an International Training School of the Young Men's Christian Association was founded at Springfield, Massachusetts. Roberts became an instructor there, as did Luther Gulick, who later became Director of Physical Training for the New York City Public Schools. After Gulick left Springfield, Dr. McCurdy became head of the physical education department.

The first Young Women's Christian Association was founded in Boston in 1866 by Mrs. Henry Durant. This organization is very similar to the Young Men's Christian Association in nature and has a broad physical education program for its members.

Physical education made major advances in colleges and universities with the construction of gymnasiums and the development of departments in this area. Two of the great leaders in physical education during the last half of the nineteenth century were Dr. Dudley Allen Sargent, who was in charge of the physical education work at Harvard, and Dr. Edward Hitchcock, who was head of the physical education department at Amherst. Sargent is known for his work in teacher preparation, remedial equipment, exercise devices, college organization and administration, anthropometric measurement, experimentation, physical diagnosis as a basis for activity, and scientific research. Some of the schools that constructed gymnasiums were Harvard, Yale, Princeton, Bowdoin, Oberlin, Wesleyan, Williams, Dartmouth, Mt. Holyoke, Vassar, Beloit, Wisconsin, California, Smith,

*Courtesy Harold L. Ray, Western Michigan University, Kalamazoo, Mich.*

The staff and first normal class in physical education of the Chautauqua school, dated 1886. Pioneers in the field who taught this first operational summer school of physical education are identified by numbers, as follows: 1, Dr. Eliza M. Mosher, Brooklyn; 2, Dr. Jay W. Seaver, Yale; 3, Hope Narey, Holyoke; 4, Dr. Julius King, Cleveland; 5, Dr. Claes Enebuske, Boston; 6, Dr. Henry Boice, Trenton; 7, Henry S. Anderson, Yale and Brooklyn; 8, Emily M. Bishop, Jamestown and New York City; 9, Dr. William G. Anderson; 10, Lee Pennock, Jamestown and New York City; 11, Dr. Louis Collin, Boston; 12, Gertrude Jeffords, Jamestown, accompanist. Those persons not identified by numbers were students.

*Courtesy Harold L. Ray, Western
Michigan University, Kalamazoo, Mich.*

The wand drills were an important part of program activities in the 1890's.

*Courtesy Harold L. Ray, Western
Michigan University, Kalamazoo, Mich.*

Exhibition on the parallel bars by the men's physical education class.

and Vanderbilt. Intercollegiate sports also began to play a prominent part, with the first intercollegiate meet in the form of a crew race between Harvard and Yale in 1852. Williams and Amherst played the first intercollegiate baseball game in 1859, and Rutgers and Princeton the first football game in 1869. Other intercollegiate contests in such sports as tennis, swimming, basketball, squash, and soccer were soon to follow.

Organized physical education programs as part of the curriculum began to appear early in the 1850's in elementary and secondary schools. Boston was one of the first communities to take the step under the direction of Superintendent of Schools, Nathan Bishop. The cities of St. Louis and Cincinnati followed soon afterward. During the next two decades there were only a few instances in which physical education was made part of the school program. However, in the 1880's there was a renewed drive in this direction, with the result that physical directors were appointed in many of the larger cities, and many more communities recognized the need for planned programs in their educational systems.

In 1885, in Brooklyn, the American Association for the Advancement of Physical Education was organized with Edward Hitchcock as the first president and Dudley Sargent, Edward Thwing, and Miss H. C. Putnam as vice-presidents. William G. Anderson was elected secretary and J. D. Andrews, treasurer. This association later became the American Physical Education Association and at the present time is known as the American Association for Health, Physical Education, and Recreation. The purpose of this organization is to keep the standards of the profession high, interpret physical education to the public, promote physical education so as to secure adequate programs for the entire country, and to provide well-trained teachers.

A struggle between the Swedish, German, and other systems of gymnastics developed in the 1890's. Advocates of each system did their best to spread the merits of their particular program and attempted to have them incorporated as part of school systems. In 1890 Baron Nils Posse introduced the Swedish system in the Boston schools, where it proved popular, and it was later adopted through-

---

## A SCHOOL PRINCIPAL'S INSTRUCTIONS TO HIS TEACHERS IN THE YEAR 1872

1. Teachers each day will fill lamps, clean chimneys, and trim wicks.
2. Each teacher will bring a bucket of water and scuttle of coal for the day's sessions.
3. Make your pens carefully. You may whittle nibs to the individual tastes of the pupil.
4. Men teachers may take one evening each week for courting purposes, or two evenings a week if they go to church regularly.
5. After ten hours of school, the teachers should spend the remaining time reading the Bible or other good books.
6. Women teachers who marry or engage in other unseemly conduct will be dismissed.
7. Every teacher should lay aside from his pay a goodly sum of his earnings for his benefit during his declining years so that he will not become a burden to society.
8. Any teacher who smokes, uses liquor in any form, frequents pool or public halls, or gets shaved in a barber shop will give good reason to suspect his worth, intentions, integrity, and honesty.
9. The teacher who performs his labors faithfully and without fault for five years will be given an increase of twenty-five cents per week in his pay providing the Board of Education approves.

1851  1866

1910  1920

1927

yesterday
today
tomorrow...
the right costume
for gymnasium,
pool & dance

*Courtesy Aldrich & Aldrich.*

Physical education costumes for American women in previous years.

out the schools of Massachusetts. The Swedish system had more popularity in the East, and the German system was more prevalent in the Middle West. A survey in the 1890's points out not only the prevalence of the various systems of gymnastics but also the prevalence of physical education programs in general throughout the country. It was reported, after a study of 272 cities, that 83 had a director of physical education for their school systems, 81 had no director, but teachers were responsible for giving the exercises to the students, and in 108 cities the teachers could decide for themselves whether exercises should be a part of their daily school programs. A report on the dates the physical education programs were established in the schools surveyed show 10% were established before 1887, 7% from 1887 to 1888, 29% from 1889 to 1890, and 54% from 1891 to 1892. In respect to the system of gymnastics used, the report showed 41% used the German type of gymnastics, 29% Swedish, 12% Delsartian, and 18% eclectic.* Only 11 cities had equipped gymnasiums. It was not long, however, before there was greater expansion in gymnasiums, equipment, trained teachers, and interest in physical education. Ohio in 1892 was the first state to pass a law requiring physical education in the public schools. Other states followed and there were 33 in 1925. Today there are only a very few which have not provided such legislation.

## Physical education in early twentieth century

Some of the great names that should be mentioned in any discussion of the history of physical education during the early part of the twentieth century will be discussed. *Thomas Dennison Wood* was one who made an outstanding contribu-

tion to the field of physical education. A study of his career shows that he attended Oberlin College, was the first director of the physical education department at Stanford University, and later became associated with Teachers College, Columbia University. He believed there should be more emphasis on games and game skills and introduced his new program under the name of Natural Gymnastics.

*Clark Hetherington* is also well known to physical educators. His thinking was influenced by his close association with Thomas D. Wood, who chose Hetherington as his assistant while he was at Stanford. Hetherington's contributions resulted in a clearer understanding of children's play activities in terms of survival and continued participation. This was also true of athletics and athletic skills. Hetherington became head of the physical education department at New York University and along with his successor, *Dr. Jay B. Nash,* was responsible for its becoming one of the leading teacher-training schools in the nation.

*Robert Tait McKenzie,* a physical educator, surgeon-scientist, and artist-sculptor, served distinguished periods at McGill University and the University of Pennsylvania. He was known for his great contribution to sculpture, for his dedication to helping physically underdeveloped and atypical individuals overcome their deficiencies, and for his writings of such books as *Exercise in Education and Medicine,* published in 1910.

*Jessie H. Bancroft,* a woman pioneer in the field of physical education, taught at Davenport, Iowa, Hunter College, and Brooklyn and New York City Public Schools. She greatly influenced the development of physical education as a responsibility of homeroom teachers in elementary schools. She also contributed much to the field of posture and body mechanics, was the first living member of

---

*A combination of the various systems of gymnastics.

the AAHPER to receive the Gulick Award, and was well known for her book *Games for the Playground, Home, School, and Gymnasium.*

*Delphine Hanna,* an outstanding woman leader of physical education, developed a department of physical education at Oberlin College, which sent outstanding graduates all over the country. She was instrumental in motivating not only many outstanding leaders in the female ranks, but also such outstanding men as Thomas Wood, Luther Gulick, and Fred Leonard to follow illustrious careers in physical education.

*James H. McCurdy* studied at the Training School of Christian Workers at Springfield Medical School of New York University, Harvard Medical School, Springfield College, and Clark University. He was closely associated with Springfield College where he provided outstanding leadership in the field of physical education. He published such works as *The Physiology of Exercise* and was editor of the *American Physical Education Review.*

*Luther Gulick,* born in Honolulu, was director of physical education at Springfield College, principal of Pratt High School in Brooklyn, Director of Physical Education for Greater New York City Public Schools, president of the American Physical Education Association, taught philosophy of play at New York University, helped to found and was the first president of the Playground Association of America (later to become the National Recreation Association), was associated with the Russell Sage Foundation as director of recreation, and was president of Camp Fire Girls, Inc.

Health education and recreation, branches of what were formerly phases of the physical education program, grew during the early twentieth century to the extent that specialists and programs were utilized in many communities which were distinct and separate from those of phys-ical education. Health education proved its value in educating the public about the health services that were available, in respect to scientific health knowledge, and in respect to healthful living. Recreation came to the front in helping the public better utilize their increased leisure, which resulted from a higher standard of living. Through programs that dealt with such activities as arts and crafts, athletics, dramatics, and music, mental and physical dividends resulted for many persons.

The playground movement had a rapid period of growth after the first sand garden was set up in 1885 in Boston. In 1888, New York passed a law that provided for study of places where children might play out of doors. In New York the name of Jacob A. Riis was symbolic of the playground movement in that city. In Chicago a playground was managed by Hull House. In 1906 the Playground and Recreation Association of America was established to promote the development of rural and urban playgrounds, with Dr. Gulick as president. Since that time playgrounds have been established in many cities and smaller communities throughout the country.

In the field of teacher education in physical education, higher standards were established and better trained leaders were produced. The two-year normal school became a thing of the past, with four years of preparation being required. The trend in professional preparation required of students a broad general education, a knowledge of child growth and development and the psychology of learning, and specialized training in physical education, including a knowledge of the foundational sciences, curriculum materials, methodology, and the like.

## Physical education at mid-twentieth century

Physical education progressed in the twentieth century to a point where it is increasingly recognized and an important part of American culture, with several new trends in evidence. Sports, athletics, and team games have become more important, with broad and extensive programs being established in schools, recreational organizations, and other agencies. The National Collegiate Athletic Association, National Association of Intercollegiate Athletics, and other leagues, organizations, and associations have been formed to keep a watchful eye on competitive sports. Nevertheless, the emphasis on gate receipts and winning games has resulted in many problems that threaten the entire physical education structure of a few educational organizations. Some schools have abolished or deemphasized athletics as a means of coping with this problem. The struggle between the formal and informal types of physical education programs continues to exist. World Wars I and II opened up countless opportunities for physical education. The church, industry, and society in general reflect the

national interest in all kinds of recreational pursuits; intramural sports are increasingly being advocated as an excellent form of competition; work in rehabilitation and physical therapy is receiving more and more emphasis, with an attempt to conserve human resources; and work in dance is becoming an integral part of physical education programs.

During the twentieth century a new physical education has been evolving. With a scientific basis, it is attempting to discover the physical needs of individuals and the part that a planned physical education program can play in meeting these needs. It recognizes that education is a "doing" process and that the individual learns through doing. It stresses good leadership, in which exercises and activities will not be a matter of mere physical routine but, instead, will be meaningful and significant to the participant. It stresses a varied program of activities which include the fundamental skills of running, jumping, climbing, car-

---

**OUR PRESIDENTS ARE SPORTSMEN**

George Washington was a master woodsman and horse-lover.

John Quincy Adams was an expert in billiards.

Andrew Jackson was fascinated by horse racing and owned several thoroughbreds.

John Tyler was playing marbles when he received the news that Benjamin Harrison had died and that he was now President.

Abraham Lincoln was an excellent wrestler.

Ulysses Grant was a gifted horseman.

Grover Cleveland enjoyed fishing and hunting.

Theodore Roosevelt developed skill in riding, wrestling, and boxing.

Woodrow Wilson coached football.

Warren G. Harding's forte was golfing.

"Silent Cal" Coolidge was a fisherman and a horseman.

Herbert Hoover possessed expertise in fishing. President Hoover pointed out on one occasion that "Presidents have only two moments of personal seclusion, one is prayer. The other is fishing—and they can't pray all the time."

Franklin D. Roosevelt enjoyed fishing.

Harry Truman went swimming and also fished.

Dwight D. Eisenhower established himself as the best golfer among presidents.

John F. Kennedy participated in many sports, including golf, swimming, and sailing.

Lyndon B. Johnson enjoys riding.

*Gould Academy, Bethel, Maine.*

Twentieth-century physical education stresses a varied program of activities.

rying, throwing, and leaping; camping activities; self-testing activities; "tag" and "it" games; dancing and rhythmical activities; dual and individual sports; and team games. It stresses the need for more research and investigation into what type of physical education program will best serve the needs of children and adults. It stresses the need for a wider use of measurement and evaluation techniques to determine how well we are attaining our objectives. It stresses getting at the "why" of the activity as well as the activity itself. Finally, it is interested in providing a program that will better serve to adapt individuals to the democratic way of life.

Since the publication in 1918 of the *Cardinal Principles of Secondary Education* by the Bureau of Education of the United States, physical education has taken on new meaning. This report of a committee of the National Education Association listed the seven cardinal principles of secondary education and placed health at the top of the list. In elaborating on health needs of children, the committee stressed the importance of a program of physical activity.

World Wars I and II and later events focused attention on the physical fitness of the American population. Selective Service data showed the poor physical condition of the youth of our country and brought out the need for a nationwide program of physical activity that could do much in developing the essential health and physical characteristics so necessary to a strong democratic society.

Other significant developments in physical education during the twentieth century have included a national concern for state and federal legislation. Nearly all of the fifty states have legislated required programs, together with a state director or some other person responsible for the supervision and upgrading of these programs. Teacher preparation has been strengthened as a result of many professional-preparing conferences, with higher standards established. Also, the accreditation movement has moved ahead with the participation of the National Council for Accreditation of Teacher Education in the field of physical education. Scientific progress has been made in research and in the fields of tests and measurements. Professional literature has increased in volume. Greater national interest, partly because of increasing television coverage, has been demonstrated in sports, games, and competitive athletic activities. More emphasis has been placed on the dance in education. Greater stress has been made on camping and outdoor education. Increased concern has been felt for adaptive physical education with more programs for atypical individuals. Probably the most popular development in physical education, however, has been the physical fitness movement initiated during President Eisenhower's administration and continued under President Kennedy and President Johnson.

## PHYSICAL EDUCATION MILESTONES
### Period I: Developments at the turn of the century

Many new developments were taking place at the turn of the century in the area of general education that were to leave their impact upon physical education.

**Professional education was given increased attention.** Teachers College, Columbia University, was organized. A School of Education was established at the University of Chicago and a Graduate School of Education came into being at Harvard. The first junior college was founded in Joliet, Illinois, in the year 1902.

**Psychology was influencing educational thinking.** In 1878, *Wilhelm Max Wundt* (1832–1920), a German physiologist, founded a psychological laboratory in

Leipzig which many American students attended. Wundt's studies in the area of play interest of animals and humans stimulated much interest at home and abroad. *William James* (1842–1910), a follower of Wundt, proclaimed many pragmatic theories, and was known particularly for his research into such things as habit formation, mental discipline, transfer of training, and instincts. *E. L. Thorndike* (1874–1949), who studied under William James, a specialist in the area of educational psychology, made contributions in such areas as the learning process, mental testing, and child psychology. He was particularly well known for his introduction of the stimulus–response (S–R) theory of learning.

**Sociology was influencing educational thinking.** *George H. Mead* (1863–1931), expounded on the theory that man is the product of his social interaction with other men. *John Dewey* (1859–1952) interpreted the impact of industrial and social changes upon education.

**The importance of child study gained great emphasis.** *G. Stanley Hall* (1845–1924) was the leader of the Child-Study Movement and advocated the "Recapitulation" theory (see chapter on Sociologic Foundations) of play. Hall was particularly interested in play and games as a means of fulfilling the health needs of children and youth. Much of the emphasis upon rhythms and dancing, he felt, should take place during the adolescent period. He stressed that informal play and games were superior to the formal calisthenic type of exercise. *Luther H. Gulick* (1865–1918) also stressed the natural activities for children and advocated play and games as opposed to formal calisthenics. *John Mason Tyler* (1851–1929), a biologist, stressed the need to know the biologic characteristics of children in order to prescribe the physical activities that were best suited to their needs. He stressed gymnastics as well as play and games. Such physical educators as

*Thomas Denison Wood* (1865–1951), of Columbia and Stanford Universities, *Clark W. Hetherington* (1870–1942), of California, Missouri, Wisconsin, Columbia, and New York Universities, also had great impact during this era when educators became increasingly aware of the relationship of the mind and the body and the need to provide physical education programs in our schools and colleges.

**Youth-serving programs were initiated in greater number.** Scouting, Camp Fire Girls, Girl Scouts of America, playground activities, and outdoor activities were given much greater attention by the American public and educators in general.

**Physical education programs in schools and colleges gained momentum.** A survey by the North American Gymnastic Union of physical education programs in 52 cities showed that gymnastic programs averaged 15 minutes in the elementary schools and two periods weekly in the secondary schools. Cities that were surveyed showed 323 gymnasiums in existence and many more under construction. Extensive interscholastic programs also existed, as a survey of 290 high schools in 1907 showed that 28% of the students engaged in one or more sports. The controversy over interscholastic athletics for girls was very pronounced, with such people as *Jessie Bancroft* and *Elizabeth Burchenal* stressing the importance of intramural games for girls rather than interscholastic competition. A majority of colleges and universities had departments of physical education and most institutions of higher learning provided some program of gymnastics for their students. A survey by *Thomas D. Storey* in 1908 gave an indication of the leadership in physical education. It showed that of the institutions surveyed, 41% of the directors of physical education possessed medical degrees, 3% of the directors held doctor of philosophy degrees, and the remaining possessed a bachelor's degree. Intercollegiate athletics were brought under more rigid academic control as the abuses mounted. Intramural athletics gained in prominence as the emphasis on athletics for all gained momentum.

At the turn of the century increased interest was also displayed in playground and camping movements and school health programs. Also, the rise of new educational philosophies was evidenced. Other significant events during this period included the following:

1. The Athletic Research Society was founded in 1907 by Dr. Sargent and Dr. Gulick.
2. Football was abolished in New York City Public Schools in 1910 because of unfavorable conditions.
3. The Athletic Research Society, backed by the American Physical Education Association, established a committee to aid in the development of intramural sports within the schools.
4. The American Physical Education Association provided time for dance sessions at annual meetings—folk dancing was stressed.
5. The American Physical Education Association established sections in their organization for anthropometry, elementary schools, normal schools, college directors, nonschool groups, private secondary schools, and medical gymnastics.
6. The Woman's Section of the American Physical Education Association was recognized for the first time on a convention program in 1914.
7. District associations of the American Physical Education Association came into being.
8. National headquarters of the American Physical Education Association was transferred from Boston to New York.
9. There were forty-seven foreign members of the American Physical Education Association by 1910.

## Period II:
## World War I (1916–1919)

World War I started in 1914, and America's entry in 1918 had a critical impact on the nation and education. The Selective Service Act of 1917 called to service all men between the ages of 18 and 25 years. Health statistics gleaned from Selective Service examinations aroused considerable interest in the nation's health. Discussions were held on the most feasible manner for achieving top physical condition.

Social forces were also at work during this period. The Eighteenth Amendment was passed, which had to do with the prohibition of selling alcoholic beverages. This opened up the period of the "rum runners" and "speak-easies." Out of this movement came the Anti-Saloon League and the Woman's Christian Temperance Union, which were in later years to have a great impact on the introduction of health teaching into the schools. The emancipation of women was furthered by the passage of the Nineteenth Amendment. Women also began to show interest in sports and physical education, as well as in other fields formerly considered to be "off-limits."

During World War I many physical educators provided leadership for physical conditioning programs for the armed forces and also for the people on the home front. Such persons as Dudley Sargent, Luther Gulick, Thomas Storey, and R. Tait McKenzie contributed their services to the armed forces. The Commission on Training Camp Activities of the War Department was created and Raymond Fosdick was named as the head of this program. Joseph E. Raycroft of Princeton University and Walter Camp, the creator of "All-Americans," were named to head the athletic divisions of the Army and the Navy respectively. Women physical educators were also active in conditioning programs in communities and in industry at home.

After the war was over and the public had an opportunity to study the medical examiner's report for the men who had been called to military duty, pressure built up for the government and education to do something about the fact that one third of our men were found physically unfit for armed service, and that many more were physically inept. Also a survey by the National Council on Education in 1918 showed that children in the elementary and secondary schools of the nation were woefully physically subpar. The survey indicated as many as three fourths of them could be placed in this category. The result was the passing of much legislation in the various states to upgrade physical education programs in the schools. The following states listed laws enacted between 1917 and 1919: Alabama, California, Delaware, Indiana, Maine, Maryland, Michigan, Nevada, New Jersey, Oregon, Pennsylvania, Rhode Island, Utah, and Washington. To provide supervision and leadership for the expanded programs of physical education, state departments of public instruction established administrative heads for their states in many sections of the country.

Significant events during this period also included the following:

1. Fourteen states enacted laws regarding physical education.
2. Draft statistics aroused popular interest in health and physical education.
3. New York appointed the first state director of physical education.
4. Many colleges established departments of physical education.
5. Dr. William Burdick, President of the American Physical Education Association, appointed a Committee on Women's Athletics.
6. Dr. Elmer Mitchell helped to develop intramural sports.
7. Seven "cardinal principles" of education developed.
8. Ernest H. Arnold of the New Haven Normal School was active in the work of the American Physical Education Association as president and in other positions.
9. The National Recreation Association established the National Physical Education Service.

## Period III:
## Golden twenties (1920–1929)

The "golden" or "roaring" twenties ushered in a period when people wanted to relax, have a good time, and forget the tragic war that had just passed. The period was an opportune moment for the growth of "big-time" athletics and an era of spectator sports.

The twenties showed the way for a new physical education—advocated by such leaders as Hetherington, Wood, Nash, and Williams. The move away from the formal gymnastic systems of Europe was well received. The temperament of the times seemed to emphasize a less formal type of program. More games, sports, and free play were the order of the day.

The feeling that physical education had greater worth than building strength and other physical qualities, as incorporated in the thinking of the "New Physical Education," aroused much discussion. Franklin Bobbit, a University of Chicago educator, commented, "There appears to be a feeling among physical educationists that the physical side of man's nature is lower than the social or mental, and that . . . they, too, must aim primarily at those more exalted nonphysical things of mental and social type." William Burnham, of Clark University, felt that physical education could contribute to the whole individual. Clark Hetherington felt that physical education had different functions in a democratic society than in Europe, where some of the gymnastic systems prevailed. Jesse Feiring Williams stressed the importance of physical education in general education.

Thomas D. Wood, Rosalind Cassidy, and Jesse Feiring Williams published their book, *The New Physical Education,* in 1927; it stressed the biologic, psychologic, and sociologic foundations of physical education.

Another development during this period included the stress on measurement in physical education by such persons as David K. Brace and Frederick Rand Rogers, as a means of grouping pupils, measuring achievement, and motivating performance.

Programs of physical education continued to expand in schools and colleges. The elementary school program of physical education stressed mainly formal activities. The secondary school program also felt the influence of the formalists. In addition, there were periodic lectures on hygiene. Interscholastic athletics continued to grow in popularity with the need being felt to institute controls. The National Federation of High School Athletic Associations was established in 1923. At the college and university level a study by George L. Meylan, reported in 1921, that of 230 institutions surveyed, 199 had departments of physical education presided over by administrative heads and an average of four staff members per institution. Many of the staff members had professorial rank. More than three-fourths of the institutions required physical education for their students, with the most general requirement being for two years in length. The twenties also saw a boom in the area of stadium construction.

Many problems arose in respect to college athletics. As a result, the Carnegie Foundation provided a grant in 1923 for a study of intercollegiate athletics in certain institutions in the South by a Committee of the Association of Colleges and Secondary Schools. Later, a study was conducted of athletic practices in American colleges and universities. The report of this study was published in 1929 under the title *American College Athletics*. The report denounced athletics as being professional, rather than amateur in nature, and as a means of public entertainment and commercialization. Problems such as recruiting and subsidizing athletics also were exposed.

During this period there was an increase in the intramural athletic programs in colleges and universities. Women's departments of physical education also showed a great growth over the previous period discussed. Women's programs experienced an increase in the number of staff, hours required for student participation, activities offered, and physical education buildings in use.

Some significant happenings during this period were the following:

1. A spectator boom in athletics was observed.
2. The new physical education was accepted.
3. Social education was recognized as an objective of physical education.
4. Intramural programs were expanded.
5. Growth of the recreation and playground movements was encouraged.
6. More emphasis was placed on sports that could be played in adult life.
7. Dancing was introduced into many school programs.
8. The number of institutions preparing physical education personnel was increased from 20 in 1918 to 139 in 1929.
9. Corrective physical education was made a part of many university programs.
10. Laws regarding physical education were enacted by more than twenty states.
11. The National Federation of State High School Athletic Associations was established.
12. The Women's Division of National Amateur Athletic Federation was established.
13. Doctoral programs were offered at Teachers College, Columbia University, and New York University.

## Period IV:
## Depression years (1930–1939)

The 1929 stock market crash ushered in the great depression which affected education. The golden twenties had seen an era of plenty. Now unemployment and poverty reigned. Health and physical education had a difficult time surviving in many communities. The numbers on the unemployed list brought about the program of leisure-time education. This was also the era when the government subsidized the Works Progress Administration and other agencies which were used to construct recreation and other facilities.

During the period of the economic depression in the United States many of the gains achieved by physical education in the schools of the nation were lost. Budgets were cut back and programs in many cases were either dropped or downgraded. In the 1932–1934 period an estimated 40% of the physical education programs were dropped completely. There were legislative moves in several of the states, such as Illinois and California, to do away with the physical education requirement.

Another development during the depression years was that the physical educator became more involved in recreation programs in the agencies and programs concerned with unemployed persons. These later programs were being subsidized through special governmental assistance. The national association, taking cognizance of the increased interest in recreation, voted to change its title to include the word "Recreation,"—the American Association for Health, Physical Education, and Recreation.

A new interest captivated many physical educators, namely that of facilities concerned with programs of physical education, athletics, and recreation. Several publications appeared before the end of the 1920's on this subject.

The trend in physical education programs was away from the formal type to an informal games and sports approach. Also, what constitutes an acceptable program of physical education at various school and college levels was outlined by William R. LaPorte of the University of Southern California in his publication *The Physical Education Curriculum—A National Program,* published in 1937. This publication, which is still in use today, left a deep imprint upon elementary and secondary physical education programs.

Interscholastic athletic programs continued to grow and in some situations dominated physical education programs and created many educational problems. The collegiate athletic program received a temporary setback from the Carnegie Report but then started to grow again.

The National Association of Intercollegiate Basketball was established in 1940 for the purpose of providing an association for the smaller colleges. It later changed its name to National Association of Intercollegiate Athletics in 1952. In 1937, representatives of the Junior Colleges of California met for the purpose of forming the National Junior College Athletic Association.

Intramural athletics continued to grow in colleges and universities. Women's athletic associations also increased in number. The principles that guided such programs were established largely by the National Section on Women's Athletics, now called the Division of Girls and Women's Sports.

Some significant happenings during this period are as follows:

1. The objective of leisure-time education became important to the field of physical education.
2. Civilian Conservation Corps was used for recreation projects.
3. WPA proved a boost for recreation.
4. Many more states added state directors to their rosters.
5. Women's Athletic Section of APEA was organized.
6. Health and Recreation were added to the title of the American Physical Education Association.
7. Educational Policies Commission formulated educational objectives.
8. APEA became a department of the National Education Association.
9. First woman president of national association, Mabel Lee of the University of Nebraska was elected.
10. First issues of *Journal of Health and Physical Education* and the *Research Quarterly* were published.

## Period V: World War II and adjoining years (1939–1946)

The country was jolted from the depression by World War II. Physical education received a tremendous impetus as physical training programs were established under Gene Tunney in the Navy,

Hank Greenburg in the Air Force, and sports leaders in other branches of the armed forces. Schools and colleges were urged to help develop physical fitness in the youth of the nation. A return to more formalized conditioning programs resulted.

The need for a national program of physical fitness was evident as a result of selective service examinations and other indications that American young people were not in good physical shape. Several steps were taken in this direction. President Roosevelt appointed John B. Kelly, of Philadelphia, National Director of Physical Training. In 1941, Mayor Fiorello LaGuardia, of New York City, was appointed by President Roosevelt as Director of Civilian Defense in Charge of Physical Fitness, and a National Advisory Board was established. William L. Hughes, of the national association, was appointed chairman. In 1942, a Division of Physical Fitness was established in the Office of Defense, Health, and Welfare Services. In 1943, John B. Kelly was appointed chairman of a Committee of Physical Fitness within the office of the Administrator, Federal Security Agency.

The war years had their impact on programs of physical education in schools and colleges of the nation. In many instances, elementary school physical education classes met daily and secondary and college classes also were increased in number. The program of activities took on a more formal nature with the purpose of physically conditioning the children and youth of America for the national emergency that existed. Such activities as running, jumping, throwing, climbing, and tumbling were stressed. Girls and women as well as boys and men were exposed to these programs.

Some significant happenings in this period were the following:

1. Broad physical training programs were established in the armed forces.

2. Physical reconditioning programs were provided for injured returnees.

3. Obstacle courses and other devices to condition youth were developed in schools.

4. Interest in physical education and health was stimulated as a result of Selective Service medical statistics.

5. Need for better interpretation of the meaning of physical education was stressed as sports leaders rather than professionals were selected to head physical training programs.

## Period VI: Cold War (1947–     )

After World War II the nation has been faced with a conflict of ideas and tensions as opposed to guns and bullets—the cold war. The democratic nations are aligned against the communistic nations. This cold war has brought about a national emergency and a need for a state of preparedness that warrants a physically fit populace at all times. The emphasis upon physical education is increasing. The need for health programs is recognized. The automation era has demonstrated the need for recreation on a wide scale.

Some significant milestones during this period are indicated here, in what we may term the *physical fitness story:*

1. Hans Kraus, M.D., and Ruth P. Hirschland published an article in December, 1953, in the *Journal of the American Association for Health, Physical Education, and Recreation,* entitled *Muscular Fitness and Health.* This article discussed the physical deficiencies of American children in contrast with European children.

2. John B. Kelly of Philadelphia and Senator James Duff of Pennsylvania called this article to the attention of the President of the United States.

3. At the request of President Eisenhower, Vice-President Nixon in July, 1955, convened a luncheon of prominent sports figures to explore the fitness problem.

4. President Eisenhower scheduled a Youth Fitness Conference in Denver for September, 1955 (postponed because of President's heart attack).

5. President's Conference on Fitness of American Youth was held June 18–19 at the Naval Academy in Annapolis. About 150 leaders in the field of sports education, youth programs,

recreation, health, and related areas met for two days and discussed the fitness problem in detail.

6. President Eisenhower issued an Executive Order establishing a President's Council on Youth Fitness.

7. Dr. Shane MacCarthy, in September, 1956, was appointed Executive Director of the President's Council on Youth Fitness.

8. President Eisenhower appointed a President's Citizens Advisory Committee on Fitness of American Youth. This committee of approximately 120 persons in the fields of physical education, business, and journalism has met periodically and made recommendations to the President of the United States.

9. American Association for Health, Physical Education, and Recreation held a fitness conference at the Woodner Hotel, Washington, D. C., September 12–15, 1956. Dr. Shane MacCarthy addressed conference.

10. In his first year in office Dr. Shane MacCarthy made speeches in twenty states and covered 50,000 miles.

11. Several states were active in the fitness movement. California, for example, developed an outstanding project where they called together members of many professional associations concerned with fitness and formed the California Committee on Fitness. This committee's work helped to promote the cause of physical education in the schools and the fitness of youth throughout this western state.

12. The state of Illinois developed a Governor's Conference on Youth Fitness which was held at Robert Allerton Park, Monticello, May 5–7, 1957. This conference had far-reaching effects throughout the state.

13. New York State developed a new Physical Fitness Test which is being used extensively throughout the public schools of New York.

14. Several cities such as Flint and Detroit, Michigan, and others developed special projects to promote the fitness of their youth.

15. The YMCA, Amateur Athletic Union, and other similar organizations undertook special projects to contribute to the fitness of their clientele.

16. Several business concerns responded to the call of fitness: General Mills established the Wheaties Sports Foundation and appointed Bob Richards of Olympic fame as its Director. Its program initially called for the expenditure of more than a million dollars to promote fitness through such products as Wheaties.

17. Sports Illustrated Magazine devoted regular features to fitness.

18. National Research Council of AAHPER appointed Dr. Paul Hunsiker of the University of Michigan in 1957 to test the American children in regard to their physical fitness.

19. June 1–7, 1958, was proclaimed by President Eisenhower as the first official National Fitness Week.

20. The College Physical Education Association published a special report entitled *Fit for College*.

21. *Operation Fitness U.S.A.* was undertaken by AAHPER.

22. AAHPER Physical Fitness Test was introduced.

23. John F. Kennedy became President of the United States and appointed Charles "Bud" Wilkinson of Oklahoma to head his Council on Youth Fitness.

24. The President's Council on Youth Fitness introduced its "Blue Book" with suggestions for a school-centered program. It stressed the physical fitness aspects of recreation, adult fitness, and health education.

25. The name of President Kennedy's Council was changed to The President's Council on Physical Fitness.

26. President Lyndon B. Johnson appointed Stan Musial to head his council on physical fitness.

27. President Johnson appointed Captain James A. Lovell, Jr., USN, to replace Stan Musial when he resigned this position.

In addition, such meetings and attitudes as are listed here might be considered *other milestones:*

1. National Facility Conferences
2. Professional Preparation Conferences held on health, physical education, and recreation
3. Conference on Social Changes and Implications for Girls' and Women's Sports Programs
4. Outdoor Education Project of AAHPER
5. Athletic controversy concerning sports for children below high school level
6. International relations in fields of health, physical education, and recreation stressed through conferences and other projects
7. Increased consciousness of importance of public relations through such media as publications, television, radio, newspapers, etc.
8. Increased interest in sports medicine
9. Conference on Education for Leisure
10. Conference on Recreation for Mentally Ill
11. National Conference on Social Changes and Implications for Physical Education Sports Programs for Women

12. National Conference on Outdoor Education
13. National Conference on Professional Preparation of Recreation Personnel
14. National Conference on Fitness for Secondary School Youth
15. National Conference on the Science Core in the Physical Education Professional Program
16. National Conference for Athletic Directors
17. National Conference on School Recreation
18. National Conference on Fitness for Elementary School Age Children
19. National Workshop on Equipment and Supplies for Athletics, Physical Education, and Recreation
20. International Relations Conference
21. Conference on Graduate Programs in Special Fields
22. National Facilities Conference

## Recent year-by-year milestones
### 1947

The Bureau of Health Education of the American Medical Association established the health and physical fitness project to help in the alleviation of health and fitness problems of school children of all levels (preschool through college), adults, and the industrial worker.

The war and postwar teacher shortage represented a critical problem for the nation. During the war 200,000 teachers left jobs and 100,000 emergency certificates were issued. Many of those who left did not return and the inadequately trained replacements were becoming permanent. The critical shortage forced administrators to discard their standards in selecting teachers. In the physical education field there was a need for reinterpreting the meaning and objectives of physical education and a rededication of teachers to the prewar ideals along with the desire of teachers to improve their professional status.

A grant from the Athletic Institute facilitated a National Facilities Conference at Jackson's Mill, West Virginia. Fifty-four outstanding education, park, and recreation leaders met with architects, engineers, and city planners to prepare a guide for planning facilities for health, physical education, and recreation programs.

St. Lawrence University held its first Winter Sports School. It was to be held annually and devoted to training school and community leadership for winter sports. The program was aimed at giving instruction in the organization and management of winter sports and teaching methods and techniques.

The Senate passed a bill authorizing the War Assets Administrator to transfer any surplus property that could be used for athletics to state, public, and nonprofit groups, without charge.

### 1948

Colgate University adopted a five-year program for teacher education in health, physical education, and recreation. The program led to the A.B. degree and certification by the state to teach one or more academic subjects in addition to physical education.

The National Conference on Professional Preparation in Health, Physical Education, and Recreation was held. The purposes of this conference were: (1) to upgrade the preparation of personnel in the three areas, (2) to define the nature of the professional preparatory program, and (3) to formulate national standards for certifying professional preparatory institutions.

An increased emphasis was discernible on the use of field trips in teaching. Recognizing the value and need for this type of learning experience, teacher training departments were introducing field or inspection trips as part of the curriculum. Schools and departments of physical education were beginning to follow the same plan. Such trips gave students an opportunity to "become aware of problems through observation of the conduct of programs in health and safety, physical education, recreation and coaching in public and private schools, and in municipal and institutional centers."

The International Congress for Physical Education, Recreation, and Rehabilitation was held in London. Under the auspices of England's Ministry of Education, its purpose was "to bring to the notice of the countries represented at the Olympic Games the steps being taken in Britain to develop physical education in schools and colleges, physical recreation in after-school life, and rehabilitation in the services and industry."

### 1949

An interest in Australian football developed in the United States. The game was inaugurated at Swarthmore College.

Extensive programs in convalescent reconditioning were evidenced in general hospitals.

Physical reconditioning programs were introduced into college physical education programs.

In Atlanta, Georgia, the Organization of the Southern Gymnastic League met. Its purpose was to "promote interscholastic and intercollegiate competitive gymnastics in Florida, Maryland, Virginia, North Carolina, South Carolina, Alabama, Mississippi, St. Louis, Tennessee, Kansas, and Georgia."

The First Congress on Physical Education for Girls and Women was held in Copenhagen. Twenty-five countries were represented.

## 1950

The National Education Association sponsored a National Conference on Standards for Teacher-Education Institutions. It was held at Indiana University.

The AAHPER met with the National Association of Secondary School Principals of the NEA and the Babe Ruth Foundation to establish the Babe Ruth Sportsmanship Program. The purpose of this program was to disseminate information on and enlist enthusiasm for good sportsmanship and fair play in the schools and for the general public.

A National Conference on Graduate Professional Preparation in health, physical education, and recreation was held at Pere Marquet State Park in Illinois.

## 1951

The Joint Committee on Educational Television began a study of educational television.

The Legislative Commission of the National Education Association approved the School Health Safety and Physical Education Instruction Act. It was introduced in the U. S. House of Representatives on October 20, 1951. The purpose of the act was "to authorize the appropriation of funds to assist the states and territories in extending and improving their programs of health instruction, safety instruction, and physical education, for all children of school age."

## 1952

The Research Council of the AAHPER was established as a section under the General Division. Its functions and purposes were "to promote research in the AAHPER through such activities as: initiating cooperative effort and a unified attack for research along strate-

gic lines, developing long-range plans, preparing and disseminating materials which will aid research workers in the field, synthesizing research materials in areas of scientific knowledge related to our professional fields, maintaining liaison with research workers and organizations in this and other countries."

## 1953

The American Football Coaches Association approved and adopted a code of principles and ethics. Its purpose was to protect and promote the best interest of the game of football and the coaching profession.

A national teacher supply and demand study was made and showed the approach of a critical shortage of physical education teachers.

A National Conference on Program Planning in Games and Sports for Boys and Girls of Elementary School Age was held in Washington, D. C. It was the first time "that professional education, medical and recreation leaders, representing almost all organizations that serve the child, met with leaders of organizations that promote highly competitive activities for children of elementary school age." Some recommendations of the conference were:

(1) "Programs of games and sports should be based on the developmental level of children." It was felt that there should be no contact sports for the age group of 6-12.
(2) "Competition is inherent in the growth and development of the child and depending upon a variety of factors will be harmful or beneficial to the individual."

The District of Columbia AHPER admitted Negro members.

## 1954

A new photometric photograph was developed that measures standing posture from four angles at once.

The First International Congress on Physical Education was held in the United States.

The National Council for Accreditation of Teacher Education took over the accreditation function of the AACTE (American Association of Colleges of Teacher Education).

The Council on Equipment and Supplies of the AAHPER was formed. Its purpose was to allow manufacturers, distributors, and buyers and consumers of materials used in the areas of health education, physical education, and recreation to work together on problems of mutual concern.

Coeducational physical education programs in high schools was found to be a growing practice.

A National Conference on Physical Education for College Men and Women was held in Washington, D. C.

## 1955

President Eisenhower established National Sports Festival Month for the purpose of calling attention to the values of sports and recreation in American life. During the festival period, individuals and organizations conducted sports programs according to the interests and resources of their respective communities.

The National Conference on Youth Fitness was called by President Eisenhower. The need for the conference was based on reports of the Kraus–Weber Tests and a comparison of the fitness of European and American youth. There was a need to increase personnel, facilities, and equipment, and to develop a broad program of activity for boys and girls.

Due to the ill health of the President, the October Conference on Youth Fitness was postponed.

The President's Conference on Youth Fitness was held in June. The total fitness of American youth, especially the age group 5–17, was discussed by 150 leaders in the field. At this time, The President's Council on Youth Fitness was formed. Shane MacCarthy was the first executive director. The President's Citizens Advisory Committee on the Fitness of American Youth was also formed at the conference.

## 1956

The National Conference on Intramural Sports for College Men and Women met in Washington, D. C. Its purpose was "to consider intramural programs for college men and women, to formulate principles, and to recommend administrative procedures relating to current and future programs and to provide greater opportunity for more young men and women to participate in healthful recreational activities."

Jay B. Nash was chosen the first Executive Secretary and Consultant of the New York State Association of Health, Physical Education and Recreation.

Shane MacCarthy addressed the 1956 AAHPER Conference on Fitness.

The Third Congress of the International Association of Physical Education and Sports for Girls and Women was held at Bedford College in London. Its purpose was "to provide a world wide exchange of ideas and information to contribute to the universal development of Physical Education and sports among girls and women."

## 1957

Vice-President Nixon presided over the first meeting of the Citizens' Advisory Council on Youth Fitness. The meeting was held at West Point.

G. Ott Romney was appointed Deputy Executive Director of the President's Council on Youth Fitness.

The AAHPER's Youth Fitness Project was begun with Paul A. Hunsicker as the Director. Its purpose was to test boys and girls in grades five through twelve for physical fitness and to establish national norms. Physical fitness was defined as follows: "Physical fitness is understood to include those qualities which permit an individual to perform life activities involving speed, strength, agility, power, and endurance, and to engage in the various kinds of physical activities required of modern day living, including sports and athletics, and to be able to maintain his optimum amount of fitness."

## 1958

The Second Annual Meeting of the President's Council on Youth Fitness was held with the President's Citizens' Advisory Committee, on the Fitness of American Youth.

The Annual Meeting of the World Confederation of Organizations of the Teaching Profession was held. The WCOTP appointed a committee to make plans for a World Federation of National and International Associations of Health Education, Physical Education and Recreation. The purpose was to provide a way in which to "unite representatives from all associations of health, physical education and recreation in one world wide organization for furthering and improving these fields."

## 1959

The AAHPER developed a physical fitness program known as "Operation Fitness–U.S.A." It was developed to promote fitness, leadership, public relations, and research. Part of the program was the National Fitness Test Project and the publication of the *Youth Fitness Test Manual*. The project established motivational devices such as certificates of recognition, achievement awards, and embroidered emblems for students at various levels of achievement.

The WCOTP established the International Council of Health, Physical Education and Recreation (ICHPER).

The AAHPER inaugurated its Scholarship Program. The program was developed to provide financial assistance for outstanding high school graduates who wish to continue professional preparation in physical education.

The President's Council on Youth Fitness sponsored National Youth Fitness Week.

## 1960

A nationwide track and field project was added to "Operation Fitness–U.S.A." Its main function was to stimulate the planning and operation of local track and field clinics for children and youth, and for teachers and leaders who wish to improve their skills and techniques.

Representatives of the AAHPER attended a working conference at the Army–Navy Club in Washington, D. C. It was designed to make plans to complement the work of the President's Council on Youth Fitness.

In an effort to improve professional preparation in the field, the AAHPER, at the 1960 Miami Beach Convention, set as a requirement for professional membership in the Association, the possession of a degree from a NCATE accredited institution. This requirement was to go into effect beginning in June, 1964.

President Kennedy released a statement on health and physical fitness in which he outlined the following four-step program:

1. Establish a White House Committee on Health and Fitness to formulate and carry out a program to improve the physical condition of the nation's populace.
2. Make physical fitness of our youth the direct responsibility of HEW (Health, Education, and Welfare).
3. Invite the governor of each state to attend an annual National Youth Fitness Congress.
4. Proclaim through all departments of the government that the promotion of sports participation and physical fitness is a basic and continuing policy of the United States.

*Sports Illustrated* published an article by President Kennedy entitled "The Soft American." The article emphasized the need for the physical fitness of American youth.

## 1961

The first official meeting of the Board of Trustees of "Operation Fitness–U.S.A." was held in Washington, D. C.

President Kennedy called a Conference on Physical Fitness of Youth to be held in Washington, D. C.

President Kennedy named "Bud" Wilkinson, athletic director and head football coach at the University of Oklahoma, as his special consultant on youth fitness.

The United States Olympic Development Committee, for the first time in its history, appointed a Women's Advisory Board.

President Kennedy issued a message to the schools on physical fitness. In it he urged the schools to accept the following three recommendations of the Council on Youth Fitness:

1. Identify the physically underdeveloped pupil and work with him to improve his physical capacity.
2. Provide a minimum of 15 minutes of vigorous activity every day for all pupils.
3. Use valid fitness tests to determine pupils' physical abilities and evaluate their progress.

## 1962

The Peace Corps indicated the need for experienced physical education teachers to help develop physical education programs in various nations around the world.

The Professional Preparation Conference was held in Washington, D. C., for improving professional preparation in the areas of health, physical education, and recreation, safety education, athletics, and outdoor education. The Conference was devoted to:

1. Developing suggested principles and standards . . . to serve as guides for institutions preparing personnel in these areas.
2. Defining the professional competencies in these areas.
3. Determining ways of improving the professional consciousness and professional stature of personnel in these areas.
4. Identifying the kinds of experiences through which prospective professional personnel can develop the necessary knowledge and skill to enable them to provide leadership in these areas.
5. Developing guidelines for the implementation of the Conference report.

The Division for Girls and Women's Sports and the Division of Men's Athletics of the AAHPER held their first joint conference so that the views of men and women in the profession could be expressed.

Senator Hubert H. Humphrey proposed a Five-Point Fitness Program.

The Joint Committee on Physical Education for College Men and Women met at the NEA Center in Washington, D. C., and worked on developing a series of questions that would serve as guidelines for program discussions by college faculties.

## 1963

The name of the President's Council on Youth Fitness was changed to the President's Council on Physical Fitness in an effort to more strongly emphasize the purposes of the Council.

A special committee met in Washington, D. C., to discuss the status of women in health, physical education, and recreation, and to formulate recruitment and selection standards for women entering professional preparation programs in these fields.

A new text, *The Education of American Teachers,* containing specific suggestions for the preparation of physical education teachers, was published under the authorship of James B. Conant.

A bill was passed by the State of California adding a physical performance test to its battery of required achievement tests in the state testing program.

A progress report issued by the President's Council on Physical Fitness showed that there was no physical fitness program being offered to at least 20% of the nation's youth in grades four through twelve. The report stated that only California had a daily physical education requirement for every school child.

A bill was approved by the House Committee on Interior and Insular Affairs authorizing the states to receive federal funds for the development, improvement, and acquisition of lands for outdoor recreation facilities.

The ICHPER delegate assembly, meeting in Rio de Janeiro, passed resolutions urging that all public schools have compulsory physical education classes at least three times a week, and that those conducting these classes meet standards of adequate preparation.

The AAHPER presented a special award to President John F. Kennedy in recognition of his interests, leadership, and support in the promotion of health and fitness.

## 1964

Approval was given to the AAHPER by its board of directors to enlist women as well as men physical educators for participation in the Peace Corps.

Two aid-to-education bills, totaling $2.7 billion, were passed by the U. S. Congress, and were directed toward higher education, vocational education, and the increasing of funds allotted to the National Defense Education Act.

The Professional Preparation Panel, formed to help raise the professional standards in health, physical education, and recreation, held its first meeting.

A four-point Code of Ethics for the education profession, delineating the responsibilities of the profession to the students, the community, the profession itself, and to professional employment practices, was adopted by the National Education Association.

The First National Institute on Girls' Sports was held for the purpose of promoting sports for girls and women.

A National Conference on Accident Prevention in Physical Education, Athletics, and Recreation met to discuss the problems, nature, and scope of accident prevention.

Fitness for Leadership, directed toward the upgrading of health and physical education programs in higher education, was issued by the President's Council on Physical Fitness.

Bill H.R. 3846 was signed to aid with the acquisition and development of outdoor lands for recreation.

## 1965

A study conference met to discuss and develop guidelines needed in the area of competition for girls and women.

The United States Track and Field Federation joined with the United States Junior Chamber of Commerce to form a national organization devoted to teaching the skills of track and field to youth, and to holding competition in this sport.

A proposal requiring a daily period of physical education for all elementary and secondary school pupils was put forth by the New York State Assembly's Joint Legislative Committee on Sports and Physical Fitness.

A United States commemorative stamp was issued honoring the Sokol Organization and the physical fitness movement.

The establishment of the Lifetime Sports Foundation was announced, with the purpose of promoting fitness and lifetime sports, and giving assistance to groups engaged in these areas.

The Swimming Hall of Fame was established in Fort Lauderdale, Florida. A museum and complete competitive facilities were announced as part of the complex.

The first general federal aid bill for elementary and secondary education was signed by President Lyndon B. Johnson.

The AAHPER Lifetime Sports Education Project, an adjunct of the Lifetime Sports Foundation, was approved by the Board of Directors of the AAHPER.

A grant from the Joseph P. Kennedy, Jr., Foundation enabled the AAHPER to establish the Project on Recreation and Fitness for the Mentally Retarded, for the purposes of research, program development, and leadership training.

A required, daily, half-hour period of physical education was adopted by the West Virginia elementary schools.

The Office of Physical Education at the United States Military Academy marked its 150th year.

A complete physical fitness test was described as part of the screening process for all Job Corpsmen processed at Camp Kilmer, New Jersey. The improvement and maintenance of physical fitness was a prime objective of the physical education program at Camp Kilmer.

The objectives of the Project on Recreation and Fitness for the Mentally Retarded were delineated by a special committee.

H.R. 9567, the Higher Education Act of 1965, was passed into law. Under Title VII of the act, matching funds were to be used for the construction of physical education instructional facilities.

## 1966

A study comparing the results of the AAHPER Fitness Test scores in 1958 and 1965 showed that children in grades one through twelve received higher scores in 1965 than did their counterparts in 1958.

H.R. 12928 was introduced to provide for health and physical education instruction under the National Defense Education Act.

Recreation and physical education programs accounted for almost 10% of the 500 projects financed under Title I of the Elementary and Secondary Education Act of 1965.

The effects of altitude on participation in sports was the topic of an international symposium held in Albuquerque, New Mexico.

A bill was signed in Massachusetts requiring a daily period of physical education in all elementary and secondary schools.

P.L. 83-531 was signed authorizing the AAHPER to receive funds for a national study of the physical education curriculum. Authorized under the Cooperative Research Act, it was to be the first such study in 40 years.

The National Foundation for Health, Physical Education, and Recreation was incorporated with the purpose of fostering an understanding of the contributions made by these fields.

Under Title I of the ESEA, $1 million for physical education was received by New Orleans, Louisiana.

A movement education project in the elementary schools of Plattsburgh, New York, was funded by Title III of the ESEA.

The Normal College of the American Gymnastic Union of Indiana University, Indianapolis, celebrated the 100th anniversary of its founding.

College and university administrators of health, physical education, and recreation held their first national conference.

Mary Wigman, the mother of modern dance, celebrated her eightieth birthday in West Germany.

## 1967

The National Conference on Graduate Education met to establish standards and policies related to all phases of graduate education in health, physical education, and recreation.

A study of certain lifetime sports included in secondary school physical education programs showed that while badminton received the greatest emphasis, very little golf, tennis, bowling, or badminton was actually taught.

The AAHPER enrolled its 49,000th member.

A National Conference on International Relations through Health, Physical Education, and Recreation met at the NEA Center in Washington, D. C.

The ICHPER Congress was held in Vancouver, British Columbia, Canada.

## CURRENT DEVELOPMENTS IN PHYSICAL EDUCATION

In looking at physical education since World War II, one can see many new developments. The tremendous expansion in general education has been accom-

**Table 12-2.** *Participation in leading sports activities, 1956–1966\**

| Sport | 1956 | 1961 | 1965 | 1966 |
|-------|------|------|------|------|
| Cycling | Unavailable | Unavailable | 57,000,000 | 59,000,000 |
| Boating | 28,000,000 | 36,000,000 | 39,300,000 | 40,370,000 |
| Volleyball | Unavailable | 20,000,000 | 40,000,000 | 40,000,000 |
| Bowling (tenpin) | 20,050,000 | 30,000,000 | 39,000,000 | 39,000,000 |
| Camping | Unavailable | 5,500,000 | 37,000,000 | 37,000,000 |
| Fishing | 25,000,000 | 30,300,000 | 35,400,000 | 36,200,000 |
| Ice skating | Unavailable | Unavailable | 20,000,000 | 30,000,000 |
| Softball (12-inch) | 6,675,000 | 14,500,000 | 22,500,000 | 25,800,000 |
| Roller skating | Unavailable | 15,000,000 | 25,000,000 | 25,000,000 |
| Billiards | Unavailable | Unavailable | 20,000,000 | 23,000,000 |
| Shooting sports | Unavailable | 18,000,000 | 20,000,000 | 20,000,000 |
| Table tennis | Unavailable | 20,000,000 | 20,000,000 | 20,000,000 |
| Golf | 5,100,000 | 6,000,000 | 7,750,000 | 10,025,000 |
| Shuffleboard | Unavailable | 5,000,000 | 10,000,000 | 10,000,000 |
| Water skiing | Unavailable | 6,000,000 | 8,750,000 | 9,100,000 |
| Tennis | 6,583,000 | 7,500,000 | 8,500,000 | 9,100,000 |
| Horseshoes | Unavailable | Unavailable | 9,000,000 | 9,005,000 |
| Archery (target) | 4,600,000 | 5,500,000 | 8,000,000 | 8,000,000 |
| Handball | Unavailable | 5,000,000 | 6,000,000 | 6,250,000 |
| Skiing | 2,180,000 | 3,450,000 | 4,000,000 | 4,625,000 |

\*From the Athletic Institute, Sportscope, Jan. 31, 1967.

panied by equal developments in physical education.

On the elementary level the self-contained classroom still continues to exist in many school systems. Under this type of organization, the classroom teacher handles all the special subjects, with specialists acting in a resource and consulting capacity. It is felt that for younger children this type of organization is best. All physical education personnel are not convinced, however, that this is the best type of organization.

The fields of health and recreation, in a move to find their place in the "sun," are pulling away from physical education. The recognition that specialists are needed in each of these areas, together with the fact that each is concerned with a distinct and separate body of knowledge, is resulting in a feeling that each should be a separate entity. There are some persons, however, who feel that because all these areas are so closely allied their objectives can be best achieved by working very closely together.

Coaches and athletic personnel have also shown some irritation at being closely associated with physical education personnel. This is especially true at the college and university level. Since athletics is the heart of the physical education program, many leaders in the field are doing everything possible to bring about a close working relationship between the two. The field of sports competition for youngsters has enjoyed a boom. Little Leagues and competition of a varsity pattern at the junior high school and elementary levels can be found in many communities from coast to coast. Although strongly in favor of sports for youth, educators are asking whether highly organized forms of sports are in the best interests of young people.

School camping and outdoor education are growing throughout the country. This movement is being endorsed by both physical education and recreation personnel. Both are also active in coordinating and participating in camp programs.\*

———
\*See Chapter 10.

School recreation programs are being initiated and encouraged by many administrators and lay people. Youth problems, with increasing talk of juvenile delinquency and more leisure, have led educators and others to stress the important role that the school has in motivating youth to participate in constructive rather than destructive play.

Professional-preparing programs are increasing in number. Some of the larger institutions have separate professional programs for health, physical education, and recreation personnel, whereas most of the smaller institutions have only physical education. There is a trend to have evaluative criteria developed so that the standards for such programs may be upgraded.

Many leaders in physical education are promoting a world physical education organization.* World seminars in physical education, such as that held at Helsinki in 1952, the first international congress in

*See Chapter 14 on International Physical Education.

physical education held in the United States in 1953, and the conference in Melbourne in 1956, are indications of this development. The first international congress on physical education to be held in the United States centered around topics of greatest interest to those represented. These included such subjects as recreation, sports, correctives, dance, and tests and measurements. Approximately 100 world leaders in physical education from over forty different countries attended these meetings. Another world conference on education was held in Washington, D. C., in the summer of 1959. This was the World Conference of Organizations of the Teaching Profession (WCOTP). This further accents the movement toward world interest in our professional fields.

ICHPER or International Council for Health, Physical Education, and Recreation has been active on the world scene and meets annually to consider problems of global interest. Pan-American institutes have been held, People-to-People Sports

Ninth Annual International Congress of the ICHPER at Seoul, Korea.

Committee has been active, and many other organizations have demonstrated their interest in world affairs.

Regardless of the many advances physical education has made over the years, it still has hardly scratched the surface in realizing its potentialities. Through well-qualified leadership, it can play a much greater part in building a healthy and physically, mentally, socially, and emotionally fit democratic society.

**Communist strongholds and physical education.** Russia is involved in a massive reorganization of Soviet sports aimed at enticing 50 million of its inhabitants into regular sports activities in the next few years. A special body called the Union of Sports Societies and Organizations of U.S.S.R. has been established to help promote this goal. The Russians have pointed out, "Physical training and sports must become part and parcel of the life of the Soviet people, particularly the youth." At the present time there are more than 200,000 sports organizations in factories, collective farms, institutions, and offices that include 50 million sportsmen in their ranks. In the area of sports, Soviet athletes have broken almost 4,000 Soviet records during the last ten years, 695 of which they claim to be world records. In the years to come they hope to add many laurels to this list.

Communist China has more than 1,800 outdoor stadiums, 271 swimming pools, and 57 indoor arenas at the present time. In one recent year 130 million persons took part in regular or spare-time sports activities, ten times the number that participated the previous year. One fifth of Communist China's population is engaged in athletic training and competition. Millions of persons have passed the "national sports prowess test" since the program was started in 1955.

**QUESTIONS AND EXERCISES**

1. Identify the following: Basedow, Guts Muths, Jahn, Spiess, Ling, Branting, Nachtegall, Nyblaeus, Bukh, Maclaren, Beecher, Delsarte, Homans, Sargent, Anderson, Hetherington, Wood, and Gulick.
2. In approximately 250 words describe the changing conceptions in regard to physical education that occurred during the modern European period.
3. Describe the growth of the Turnverein movement in Germany and in the United States. To what extent has it affected physical education in this country?
4. What were some of the principles of physical education as established by Adolph Spiess? Compare these with the principles of modern-day physical education.
5. What were some of the contributions to physical education made by Per Henrik Ling?
6. What has been the role of physical education in Denmark during the modern European period?
7. How has Great Britain influenced education in the United States?
8. Compare the attitude of most school administrators in colonial times in America with the attitude of most school administrators today.
9. Why were the Puritans opposed to play? What is the relationship between puritanism and asceticism?
10. Describe the growth of physical education in the United States during the national period.
11. What type of physical education has been evolving during the twentieth century?
12. To what extent do you feel that physical education has progressed from ancient times to the present? Document your answer.
13. Identify the following: Philanthropinum, Turnplatz, Royal Central Institute of Gymnastics, Primitive Gymnastics, American Turnerbund, Dio Lewis, Winship, American Association for Health, Physical Education, and Recreation, and National Gymnastics.

**SELECTED REFERENCES**

Ainsworth, Dorothy S.: The history of physical education in colleges for women, New York, 1930, A. S. Barnes & Co.

Bennett, Bruce L.: Improving courses in the history of physical education, Journal of Health, Physical Education, and Recreation 37:26, Feb., 1966.

Bucher, Charles A.: Little League baseball can hurt your boy, Look, Aug. 11, 1953.

Caillois, Roger: Man, play, and games, New York, 1961, The Free Press of Glencoe, Inc. (translated from the French).

Dulles, Foster Rhea: America learns to play, New York, 1966, Appleton-Century-Crofts.

Greenan, John T., and Gathany, J.: Units in world history, New York, 1934, McGraw-Hill Book Co.

Hackensmith, C. W.: History of physical education, New York, 1966, Harper & Row.

Heckel, Albert Kerr, and Sigman, James G.: On the road to civilization, Philadelphia, 1936, John Winston Co.

Leonard, Fred E., and Affleck, George G.: A guide to the history of physical education, Philadelphia, 1947, Lea & Febiger.

Lucas, John A.: Coubertin's philosophy of pedagogical sport, Journal of Health, Physical Education, and Recreation **35:**26, Sept., 1964.

McIntosh, Peter C.: Physical education in England since 1800, Toronto, 1952, Clarke, Irwin & Co.

Means, Richard K.: A history of health education in the United States, Philadelphia, 1962, Lea & Febiger.

Metzner, Henry: A brief history of the North American Gymnastic Union, Indianapolis, 1911, The National Executive Committee of the North American Gymnastic Union.

Randall, Martin W.: Modern ideas on physical education, London, 1952, G. Bell & Sons.

Rice, Emmett A., Hutchinson, John L., and Lee, Mabel: A brief history of physical education, New York, 1958, The Ronald Press.

Schwendener, Norma: A history of physical education in the United States, New York, 1942, A. S. Barnes & Co.

Seventy-fifth Anniversary of the AAHPER, Journal of Health, Physical Education, and Recreation, vol. 31, April, 1960.

Trever, Albert A.: History of ancient civilization, New York, 1936, Harcourt, Brace & Co., Inc.

Van Dalen, Deobold B., Mitchell, E. D., and Bennett, B. L.: A world history of physical education, New York, 1953, Prentice-Hall, Inc.

Weaver, Robert B.: Amusements and sports in American life, Chicago, 1939, The Chicago University Press.

Wells, H. G.: The outline of history, New York, 1931, Garden City Publishing Co., Inc.

West, Willis Mason, and West, Ruth: The story of man's early progress, New York, 1934, Allyn & Bacon.

Weston, Arthur: The making of American physical education, New York, 1962, Appleton-Century-Crofts.

Wilton, W. M.: What is the role of physical education? The Physical Educator **23:**150, Dec., 1966.

# Chapter 13

# Movement education–developing concept in physical education

The trend toward, and emphasis on, movement education is very probably the one outstandingly new concept in physical education in the United States today. Movement education as an initial phase of physical education is not new to Europe, however, for both Germany and England have long been involved in educating for movement.

Experimental programs in movement education are now being conducted in the United States, some of them government sponsored. Many books, articles, and pamphlets have been and are being written on movement education. The writers are a diverse group, including among others, kinesiologists, dance educators, researchers, and physical educators on all levels of instruction.

There is no one common definition of movement education, or movement exploration, as it is sometimes called. It seems to be both a philosophy of method in physical education as well as a teaching approach.

Is movement education a new concept, a fad, or simply a restatement of traditional concepts? In the hands of the experts, or those with special training in movement education, this is a decidedly new concept, a new approach, a new, exciting, and challenging kind of physical education. The implications of movement education are broad, for it seems that a sound, early experience in movement forms a sturdy foundation for the later learning of more sophisticated sports skills.

To understand the movement education trend better, it is wise to first explore the various concepts of movement education, in order to see it in its broad spectrum as a part of the whole that is physical education.

## The nature of movement education

Movement is integral to the human being. Everything that man does, whether he is reacting to his environment, or simply expressing himself, involves movement of some sort. Movement in itself is thus a tool of life, and the more efficiently man moves, the more meaningful his life is.

It is through movement that physical education proceeds. It is through movement education that physical educators seek to develop the fullest potential in their students.

Movement educators seek not only to

*Toledo Public Schools, Toledo, Ohio.*

Movement education strives to make the individual aware of his body.

have the individual understand and appreciate the movement of which he is capable, but also to appreciate the varieties of movement of which others are capable.

Programs of movement education are not conducted haphazardly. Rather, they are structured on a problem-solving basis, leaving the individual free to relate to force, time, and space through his particular use of balance, leverage, and technique. Movement educators hold that numerous activities have common elements, all of which are based on a comprehensive knowledge of movement fundamentals. The better the individual is able to perceive movement patterns, they feel, the more ease there will be in developing skills, for these skills will tend to develop as a concomitant of learning to move.

Movement education strives to make the individual aware of the movement of his entire body, and to become intellectually as well as physically involved. The challenge set by a problem in movement is first perceived by the intellect, and then solved by the body moving through space, reacting to any obstacles within that space, and to the limitations and existing restrictions. Learning accrues as the individual accepts and attempts to solve increasingly difficult problems. Inherent in this is the concept of individual differences. There may be numerous ways to solve a stated problem, and the individual chooses the method that best suits his abilities and capacities. Individual rather than group development is the basic premise of movement education.

Thus, movement education may be defined as individual exploration of the ability of the body to relate and react to the physical concepts of the environment, and to factors in the environment, be they material or human.

### The origins of movement education

The roots of movement education may be traced back to the theories of Rudolf Laban, a dancer, and to the effect his theories had on modern-day physical education in England. Laban fled Germany during World War II, and eventually settled in England, where he established the Laban Art of Movement Center, an institution that has trained many movement educators.

Laban stressed the fact that man's body is the instrument through and by which he moves, and that each individual is endowed with certain natural kinds of movement. Laban believed strongly in exploratory movement and in a spontaneous quality in movement. He was opposed to the rigidity of set series of exercises that left no room for creativity or self-expression. Laban was a movement analyst, and as such he believed that man could not

Seattle elementary schools utilizing Laban system of movement exploration.

only learn to move efficiently and effectively, but could also develop a strong kinesthetic awareness of movement.

During World War II, England revised her entire educational structure and restated her philosophy of education in all areas. Where physical education had once been little more than formal gymnastics, the freedom of bodily movement, creativity, and expression was stressed. Laban's principles were freely employed and over the course of the years have been expanded and broadened into the concept of movement education as it is carried on in England today.

Within the last ten years, a trend toward concentrated movement education has developed in the United States, based on the English programs. Unlike England, however, where movement education is concentrated in the early school years, in the United States movement education first received its impetus in the college and university physical education programs for women. Only recently have movement education programs been started in some elementary schools in the United States.

In England, the classroom teacher is in charge of physical education in the elementary schools, and both boys and girls,

beginning in the first grade, are educated in movement. In the secondary schools the movement education program is continued for girls under the guidance of a trained physical educator. The program is based on problem solving. The teacher sets the problem, then guides, assists, and suggests, but in no way dictates a solution. There is no teacher-demonstration, and thus no imitation, leaving the child free to establish his own patterns of movement, set his own tempo, and make wise use of space.

## Schools of thought

Despite varied viewpoints concerning movement education, it is generally agreed that movement education is activity-centered rather than verbal-centered, and thus the movement itself, the awareness of the body, and its range of abilities become all-important. Rather than a force to be overcome, the body becomes the prime tool through which all movement takes place.

Dance educators were perhaps the strongest early proponents of movement education. At present, kinesiologists have become extremely interested in this phase of the physical education program, adding yet another impetus.

The balance beam provides a medium for movement experiences.

Dance educators have long used the philosophy of educating for movement. As early as 1914, a dancer named Diana Watts published, in the United States, a book entitled *The Renaissance of the Greek Ideal.* This book was her philosophy of movement, drawn from her research into early Greek statues and paintings of athletes in motion.

Modern-day dance educators often describe dance as nonverbal communication. They feel that it is extremely difficult, if not impossible, to describe a dance in words, and that the movements of the body are the only way to convey the imagery of a dance. Dance is viewed as creative and expressive movement in time and space through the instrument of the body.

The kinesiologists are students of human movement, but in the realm of movement as an academic discipline. They view physical education as a process whereby human movement is studied and refined as an educational procedure. The kinesiologists contend that the student who has a good knowledge of how his body moves will not only learn skills more rapidly, but also perform more effectively and efficiently. They agree with the movement educators that movement education utilizes activity predominantly, and that activity is also the end result of the process of movement education.

Physical educators have used many of the concepts of movement education, often without cognition. In physical education, the student can be guided toward development only if the body is put to use, for movement of the body is the basic tool of physical education. However, in many physical education programs, intellectual awareness of the body is not developed, and there is thus no understanding of how the body moves through time and space. As physical educators are becoming more aware of the applications and implications of movement education, many are beginning to provide experiences in movement for their students, and are guiding their students into an understanding of, and an appreciation for, movement.

On the college level, particularly in programs for women, courses variously called, among other titles, Movement Education, Foundations of Movement, or Body Mechanics are now being offered. These courses allow for exploration of the capacities of the body, and for the discovery and increased understandings of the body's movement abilities.

Physical educators are becoming increasingly concerned with the development of the individual, and are making more allowances for individual differences in rate of skill learning. The intellect and body are increasingly viewed as interactive and interdependent. Those who have made a study of motor learning state that movement problems must be meaningful. That is, the student must understand the fundamentals of movement before he can successfully attempt the learning of a complex skill. It is up to the instructor to set the problem, ascertain whether the student understands it, and then observe and guide the learning in relation to the abilities, capacities, and needs of that student.

## The traditional approach vs. movement education

The traditional approach to physical education needs little explanation. Syllabi, or course outlines, specify several weeks of one activity followed by several weeks of another, often unrelated, activity throughout the school years. In the elementary schools in the United States, games of low organization, folk and square dance, tumbling and gymnastics, and lead-up games often comprise the bulk of the program. Later school years, for both boys and girls, are devoted to the learning of specific sport skills. Rhythmics, or fundamental movement, is sometimes included, but as a minor phase of the program serving as a transition period between activities or between indoor and outdoor seasons.

The movement education approach to physical education is founded on an entirely different premise. Movement education is not a gap-filler of several lessons, but an on-going method of teaching physical education beginning with the earliest school years. Movement education does not abandon or fully supplant the traditional approach as we know it. Rather, it forms a firmer foundation for more meaningful skill learning, for increased pleasure in the skillful use of the body, and for the development of life-long physical effectiveness and efficiency.

## The process of movement education

Movement education is based on problem solving, beginning with the simple. Learning accrues as the student solves a simple problem and accepts increasingly more complex ones. As a problem is solved, confidence develops, and higher proficiency is attained.

For example, a class of 30 first-grade children may be asked to walk around a room without colliding with each other or with walls or apparatus. This is the beginning of learning to use space wisely, and controlling the body within the confines of an area. Building upon this, the movement educator may then ask the children to run or hop or jump, again without colliding. By beginning with the

Movement education in New Zealand.

simple, natural skills of childhood, the movement educator is adhering closely to the known facts of child growth and development, that is, that it is the large muscles and gross motor skills that develop first. The movement educator seeks to enhance this development to pave the way for the later development of the finer motor skills and coordinations.

A child who is becoming educated in movement begins with the walking, running, twisting, and falling problems. As the child solves the initial problem of walking without colliding, he may then be asked to express a mood or feeling, to change direction at will, to change direction at a signal from the teacher, or to walk while using his hands and arms in different ways. Music may be added to lessons. As a specific lesson progresses, games may be played encompassing the problem that has been set. A lesson in hopping or leaping may include a game of modified tag. At the conclusion of a lesson, there may be a period of demonstration by the children so that the movements they have created may be evaluated and discussed by the entire class. In this way, a depth of understanding is reached concerning the movements.

As apparatus is added, the problem facing the child may be to move along a horizontal ladder in any way he wishes. As facility is gained, the problem may be made more complex by specifying that the child move along using his hands only, or using the outside rails only. With other equipment, the same procedure is used. Freedom of use and movement precedes problems of mounting, vaulting, and dismounting. This approach allows each child to succeed, since no patterns of movement are required or specified. As the child experiences success, he is motivated to improve on his performance. Demonstrations at the end of a lesson may show that one child vaults higher than another because he has learned that

the use of his arms will aid his jump. Discussion of this point by the class will give helpful information to those children who found their own vaults somewhat inadequate, but have as yet not been able to discover why.

The teacher of movement education must be imaginative and creative, since equipment that might best suit a particular class must often be improvised. It is the task of the teacher to guide, observe, and set the tone of each class. The teacher must first set the problem clearly and concisely, and in terms that are relevant to the particular needs of the class. The individuals within the group, rather than the group as an entity, must be the prime determining factor. The teacher must gauge the correct time needed for exploring a problem. A vigorous activity would not be explored for as long a time as a less arduous task. The teacher must guide the children toward success by helping them to evaluate and refine their own movements, and by providing encouragement to each child as he or she seeks to solve the problem. If a child is experiencing difficulty jumping onto a platform, the teacher might ask, "Can you use your arms in any way to help you jump higher?"

Class organization does not follow the formalized patterns of traditional physical education. Lines, circles, and set formations are avoided. For the sake of safety, penalties may be imposed for collisions or heedless use of space or equipment. Frequently, the individual may work with a partner or with a small group, depending on the nature of the problem. Individual achievement remains the keynote, however, and competition is avoided.

While much equipment is used, and different kinds of balls are thrown, caught, and bounced in many ways, there is still the eventual need to learn specific sport skills, such as the strokes of swimming, methods of pitching or batting a softball, the thrusts and parries of fencing, or the ways to trap and kick a soccer ball. The English have found that many of these specific skills must be taught by traditional methods, and they allot time in their physical education programs to this. However, they have found that prior experience in the solving of problems in movement gives the child a vast store of knowledge on which to build, so that specific skill learnings in the context of their application to a game are made easier. For example, a problem in using the feet or legs only to stop a rolling ball will teach the child the fundamentals of a soccer trap. A problem in propelling the body across a shallow pool will help the child discover how his body reacts in water, and give him confidence in keeping afloat through some self-chosen method of using his arms or legs or both.

The philosophy of movement education in the United States is not as far-reaching or refined at present as it is in England. Pilot programs have not been organized widely, and the outcomes of the programs that are being conducted are as of now largely a matter of speculation. Educating for physical fitness is the cornerstone of physical education in the United States today. Yet the implications of movement education for the field of physical education are broad. Well-organized and well-conducted programs of movement education started in the elementary schools might serve as a basis for developing individuals who understand and use their bodies wisely, who are creative and find joy in expressing themselves through movement, who have an increased awareness of ways of communicating through bodily movement, and who have developed sound recreational skills.

Before movement education comes to the fore in the United States, however, there must be more research into the nature of movement, the results of pilot programs must be evaluated and refined, and more educators must be trained in providing leadership in the area of movement education.

## QUESTIONS AND EXERCISES

1. What is meant by movement education?
2. Trace the history of movement education in Europe and the United States.
3. What are the various schools of thought regarding movement education?
4. How does movement education differ from the traditional approach in physical education?
5. What do we mean by movement as a process?
6. Read one reference on movement education and give a report to the class.

## SELECTED REFERENCES

Abernathy, Ruth: The search for significant persistent themes in physical education, JOHPER, March, 1965, p. 26.

Allenbaugh, Naomi: Learning about movement, NEA Journal, March, 1967, p. 48.

Alley, Louis E.: Utilization of mechanics in physical education and athletics, JOHPER, March, 1966, p. 67.

Barham, Jerry N.: Toward a science and discipline of human movement, JOHPER, Oct., 1966, p. 65.

Brown, Camille, and Cassidy, Rosalind: Theory in physical education, Philadelphia, 1963, Lea & Febiger.

Brown, Margaret C.: The English method of education in movement gymnastics, The Reporter of the NJAHPER, Jan., 1966, p. 9.

Godfrey, Barbara B.: Movement—the fundamental learning process, presented at the Physical Education Division Special Interest Meeting, AAHPER National Convention, Washington, D. C., 1964. Mimeographed.

Hackett, Layne C., and Jenson, Robert G.: A guide to movement exploration, Palo Alto, California, 1966, Peek Publication.

Henry, Franklin M.: Physical education an academic discpline, JOHPER, Sept., 1964, p. 32.

Howard, Shirley: The movement education approach to teaching in English elementary schools, JOHPER, Jan., 1967, p. 31.

Kleinman, Seymour: The significance of human movement: a phenomenological approach, NAPECW Report, 1962, p. 123.

Locke, Lawrence F.: Kinesiology and the profession, JOHPER, Sept., 1965, p. 69.

Locke, Lawrence F.: The movement movement, JOHPER, Jan., 1966, p. 26.

Lockhart, Aileene: Conditions of effective motor learning, JOHPER, Feb., 1967, p. 36.

Ludwig, Elizabeth A.: Basic movement education in England, JOHPER, Dec., 1961, p. 18.

NAPECW and NCPEAM: Quest, Monograph II, Tucson, Arizona, 1964.

Roane, Elma: Movement, Educational Quest, Spring, 1966, p. 6.

Tillotson, Joan: A brief theory of movement education. Mimeographed.

Ulrich, Celeste: No harbor, North Carolina AHPER Journal, Nov., 1966, p. 3.

# Chapter 14

# International physical education in our contemporary world

International education has become a major consideration in institutions of learning and among governmental and civic-minded officials and persons. It represents the key to a peaceful and prosperous future for all of mankind.

## WHAT IS INTERNATIONAL EDUCATION?

**International education is a term used to describe the many types of educational relations among countries of the world.** It applies to the ways various governments and people of the world communicate with each other through such means as individuals and materials. It is also the study that goes on in order to get a better understanding of the many peoples of the world. The aim of international education is to promote better cooperation and harmony among nations.

**International education is a term that contributes to the goal of man living peacefully with his counterparts in all sections of the world.** It involves knowledge and human behavior that transcends cultures, boundaries, and nationalism, and recognizes the dignity of man and his interdependent relationship with other men wherever he lives.

**International education is a term that recognizes the uniqueness of individuals and cultures.** International education recognizes that various peoples have customs, traditions, and beliefs that differ from other countries and cultures. These ways of thinking and behaving are a part of a way of life that should be recognized and accepted for their own worth without any attempt from the outside to change these ways of behaving. Each culture has a right to live according to its own belief and standard of values.

**International education tries to correct international misunderstanding and ill will.** International education is aimed at the study of nations, the forces that cause misunderstandings, and the control of these forces through peaceful educational means. It attempts to present true and accurate facts as a means of countering propaganda and information that distorts and erroneously describes a culture, country, or its people.

## SOME HISTORICAL MILESTONES IN INTERNATIONAL EDUCATION

1. In the seventeenth century, John Comenius, the Moravian bishop and educator, suggested an international Pansophic College as a means of advancing international understanding. He was called "the teacher of nations."

2. Marc-Antoine Jullien wrote his *Esquisse*

et *Vues Preliminaires d'un Ouvrage sur l'Education Comparée* in 1817 in which he proposed the development of an educational commission for the purpose of collecting information on education in Europe and disseminating it to interested parties.

3. Educators like Rousseau, Pestalozzi, Herbart, Froebel, Montaigne, and Kant envisioned international education as a means of accomplishing world peace.

4. The nineteenth century saw many plans for and creation of international educational organizations, international fairs, and student federations. Students started to study in foreign universities, and history textbooks critically evaluated the glorification of war.

5. The Council of the League of Nations in 1921 created a Committee on Intellectual Cooperation. In 1925, the Council established the International Institute of Intellectual Cooperation.

6. In 1925, the Bureau Internationale d'Education was founded in Geneva and published various comparative educational studies.

7. In 1938, H. G. Wells proposed a World Encyclopedia for the purpose of unifying knowledge toward international understanding.

8. In 1942, the Conference of Allied Ministers of Education, representing nine nations occupying Germany, met to plan and develop an educational and cultural program. The United States joined the conference in 1944 and submitted a draft of a constitution for the establishment of an Educational and Cultural Organization of the United Nations. This was later to become the Constitution for UNESCO. This famous paragraph was included in the constitution: "Since wars begin in the minds of men, it is in the minds of men that the defense of peace must be constructed."

9. In 1945, UNESCO, the United Nations Educational, Scientific, and Cultural Organization, was formed. It has concerned itself with such functions as textbook improvement, cultural interchange, mass communications, and international cooperation in the natural sciences.

10. In 1946, the Fulbright Act, named after its sponsor, Senator J. William Fulbright of Arkansas, started the first major international exchange program for students, teachers, and scholars. It was financed from foreign currency funds derived from the sale of surplus U.S. war materials overseas. The Smith-Mundt Act in 1948 and Fulbright-Hays Act of 1961 have helped to provide money for the program and consolidate the

program under the sponsorship of the State Department. In 1948, there were 22 nations and 84 grant recipients. Presently, the program involves approximately 136 nations and more than 5,100 grantees. Since its inception, the Fulbright Program has been responsible for more than 82,500 persons receiving exchange grants. Of this number, 29,000 Americans have studied abroad and about 53,000 foreign students and scholars have studied in this country.

11. Today, there are nearly 100,000 foreign students in the United States. More than 8,000 foreign interns and residents are employed in American hospitals.

12. The International Education Act of 1966, passed by the U.S. Congress, provides for the strengthening of American educational resources for international studies and research. In passing the Act, the Congress declared that a knowledge of other countries is of utmost importance in promoting mutual understanding and cooperation between nations, that American educational resources form the base for promoting understanding between the United States and other countries, and that opportunities would be made available for all U.S. citizens to learn more about other countries, peoples, and cultures. The Act provides for:

a. Graduate centers to be established as a setting for national and international research studies and training in international affairs.

b. Institutions of higher learning to be given grants to assist them in developing programs to improve undergraduate education in international studies. Grants could also be given for such projects as faculty planning, training of faculty members in foreign countries, expansion of foreign language courses, work in humanities related to international studies, student study and travel programs, and programs where foreign teachers and scholars could visit institutions of higher learning as visiting faculty or resource persons.

## EDUCATION—A FORCE FOR INTERNATIONAL RELATIONS*

On the main campus at the University of the Philippines in Quezon City is the

*Parts of this section have been adapted from Bucher, Charles A.: Health and physical education in other lands, Journal of Health, Physical Education, and Recreation 33:14, Dec., 1962.

"Oblation" statue. This majestic sculpture symbolizes the belief of Dr. Rizal, a former Filipino leader, when he proclaimed that youth is the hope of the motherland, and therefore young people must be provided with an excellent educational program. The world traveler soon realizes that what is true of the Philippines is true everywhere—all eyes are focused on youth and education.

Schools and colleges represent the road to success for the son of the owner of the rattan factory in Cebu City in the Philippines, they provide hope for a prosperous free China for the woman on her knees in the terraced rice fields of Taiwan, they symbolize the tools for effective self-government for the people in the struggling new countries of Africa, they signify honor for the family whose history has been closely linked to industry in Osaka, Japan, and they represent the path to leadership roles in many walks of life for aspiring young people in the countries of Europe. Although war clouds, great military machines, and spaceships to the moon are in the news, there is confidence among the peoples of the world that education will help human beings to better understand the importance and means of achieving true and lasting peace.

In contrast to America, many countries have national programs of education. The educational standards, courses of study, time allocations, attendance, and even facility requirements in some cases are outlined by a national ministry of education or other agency. Therefore in these countries there is great uniformity in the educational programs. It is sometimes difficult for the people in other countries to comprehend our system of individual state responsibility for education.

Americans should have a sense of pride and accomplishment in the manner in which their educational system has captured the imagination of the people of the world. Our educational system greatly impresses foreigners because America provides an education adapted to the needs of the poor man's son as well as the rich man's daughter, the student who wants to be a plumber as well as the one who wants to be a scientist, and the girl with the I.Q. of 90 as well as the one with an I.Q. of 140.

A comment made by a Chinese student still lingers clearly in my thoughts. After a lecture in southern Taiwan, the boy sadly commented, "What I wouldn't give to study in America." I have heard this remark repeated many times over by boys and girls throughout the world who look to America as a land of educational opportunity and the country that can provide the leadership for helping people to live a more peaceful, healthful, and prosperous existence. This remark undergirds a deep faith in America. In turn, it clearly shows the responsibility each American has to further educational excellence and to learn as much as possible about the cultures of the world.

## HEALTH AND PHYSICAL EDUCATION AROUND THE WORLD

Fitness and physical well-being are important objectives that concern all peoples. Individuals the world over are interested in sports, games, and other physical education activities. Physical education and the various gamut of activities that comprise the profession represent an interest common to people of all countries. A tennis match at Forest Hills or Wimbledon often includes players from Australia, Brazil, Spain, and France. The British Open Golf Tournament attracts enthusiasts from all over the world. Specialists in winter sports from many countries display their prowess at Saint Moritz. The Olympic festival is, of course, the greatest and most famous sports gathering, bringing together athletes from many

Boys and girls should have an understanding of the world.

nations. Through these international events, physical education has potentialities as one medium by which international understanding may be reached and by which people of various countries may be brought closer together.

Through such activities as Olympic festivals; competition in such sports as tennis, golf, crew, polo, soccer, and hockey; seminars on physical education and health; international conferences; and relations between educational institutions, other agencies, and individuals of various lands, goodwill can be promoted and the people of many cultures can come to better understand each other. The emphasis in all of these activities, however, must be on friendly competition, sociability, and the desire to meet the needs of people. The stress cannot be on athletic dominance, winning at any cost, and interest in selfish personal desires and ambitions.

## Leadership

The five most important things to the Chinese, in order of priority listing, are heaven, earth, government, family, and teacher. The teacher is very important to the Chinese way of life, and this is also true in many countries of the world.

There are many dedicated leaders in the professional fields of physical education, health, and recreation in other countries. These outstanding leaders, whether in Europe, Africa, Australia, Asia, or elsewhere, render a great service to students and citizens of their country and place their profession on a respected level in schools and colleges. Many of them feel their field of work is not regarded as important as some of the academic subjects such as science, mathematics, language, and history. But they are not discouraged and are working hard to gain status.

A foreigner in their midst is likely to be aware that in some Oriental countries, for example, there are many medical doctors on physical education staffs, few women teachers compared to the number in America, and a lower pay scale.

The students majoring in physical education, health, and recreation in professional-preparing institutions in many countries stimulate a traveler's interest. Their eagerness to know about world developments in their professional fields, the enthusiasm they display for the games and sports in which they engage, and the keen sense of humor they possess make it a joy to be with them. One realizes there is a rich reservoir of leadership in their respective nations for the years ahead. The professional-preparing programs vary in length and content from less than one year to four years and from one course in skills to much the same type of curriculum our students experience in this country.

**Facilities**

Few nations can compare their health and physical education facilities to those

*Courtesy Bunchana Atthakor;*
*TOT copyright.*

Sports in Thailand. **A** and **B**, Takraw is played with a ball of woven wicker. The object is to keep the ball in motion, hitting it with any part of the body—instep, heel, knee, shoulder, or forearm. It sounds simple, but actually the game calls for skill and stamina. **C**, Thai-style boxing. Thai boxing is completely different from boxing in other parts of the world. A player opens the bout, followed by a preliminary display of each boxer's skill and style; all this and the fight are accompanied by the music of two drums and a pipe. Although the bouts appear to be rough and tumble affairs, really they are exhibitions of scientific skill and split-second timing. **D**, Traditional Thai-style sabering. Each sword-fighter uses two Thai-style sabers, holding one in each hand. It is now an art as well as a sport, whereas in the old days it was also one of the actual combat weapons in warfare.

*Courtesy Department of Physical Education, Thailand.*

Thai athletes on parade.

*Courtesy Department of Physical Education, Thailand.*

Massed classical dancers perform.

The author in Bangkok with the head of physical education in Thailand.

in America. In some foreign schools and colleges, and in some sections of a country, province, or city, there are beautiful and modern facilities that compare favorably with or are better than ours. However, assessing facilities in the world as a whole, America is much more richly blessed with good facilities on a broad scale than are other nations. The eyes of many foreign health and physical education teachers would open wide if they could see some of our indoor swimming pools, spacious gymnasiums, health suites, and playground facilities. The Japanese teacher, for example, would notice the green grass on playfields compared to the dirt he has to contend with and the showers our athletes take after a workout compared with the cold sponge baths some of his sports participants must endure.

But with all our facilities, equipment, and supplies, the question arises as to whether they are used as advantageously in America as the foreigner uses his. To see the rooftop playgrounds and the corridors on the outside of school buildings jammed with physical activity in Hong Kong, to look into the judo halls and see the muscular action taking place on the tatami mats in Japan, and to observe

the games being played out of doors even during inclement weather in Formosa makes one wonder if, with all our facilities, a better job could be done.

## Activities

The activities that constitute the health and physical education programs in other countries are varied and interesting. In the Far East, for example, one is impressed to see more basketball being played in the Philippines than in America, the dexterity with which young and older persons alike kick the rattan ball in the game of sipa, and the beautiful folk dances which play such an important part in the Philippine culture.

The many sports and game activities in Hong Kong have a carry-over from England due to the British influence. More high school boys play field hockey than do girls. Cricket is engaged in by various clubs but not to any degree in the schools. Track and field events are very popular.

In Japan, judo, kindo (fencing), Japanese tennis, as well as many of the typical activities offered in American programs, are popular. But in traveling throughout Japan it is interesting to note the great amount of formal activity, such as calisthenics, apparatus, and stunts. Even in the elementary schools there is considerable use of apparatus activities.

The activities that young men engage in and the way these activities are taught are significant. American high school boys should see their counterparts in the Philippines doing folk dances and in Hong Kong playing field hockey. It is interesting to see these rugged, masculine boys engaging in what Americans view mainly as girls' activities. The use of textbooks and discussion groups in physical education in some schools also shows the importance placed on getting at the "why" of physical activity as well as the activity itself.

Athletic clubs in many different activities exist in some foreign schools, colleges, and communities. These clubs sponsor and provide for instruction and participation in many sports and other activities. Students and adults engage in apparatus, riding, dance, tennis, soccer, basketball, or other activity on a voluntary basis.

### Physical fitness

Physical fitness is a frequently discussed subject throughout the world. Of course, much of this interest has been sparked by the physical fitness movement in America and the comparative tests that have been administered in various parts of the globe. There is some concern in other countries as to whether the American children and youth are as inferior physically as the test results indicate. Many of the people abroad, especially those who have traveled throughout our country, question the results of these tests and doubt whether their boys and girls are in any better physical condition than ours.

### The future

A person who travels abroad, whether in Europe, Africa, South America, or in some country in the Far East or other part of the world, cannot but be impressed with the efforts being put forth by physical education, health, and recreation leaders to upgrade and improve their professional fields. They are dedicated people who in order to improve are forming professional associations within their countries. As one meets with these professional people, attends their meetings, and talks with students majoring in the field, he is firmly convinced that Americans should work closely with them. There is an urgent need for a strong professional association that binds together and helps each to progress a little more rapidly than he could alone.

I remember the night in Kanazawa, Japan, when a reception was being given for the United States Ambassador and his wife. When the Ambassador was called upon to speak, he pointed out that our two countries are linked together by strong economic and governmental ties. The future of the world, he stated, can be strongly influenced for the better through a close friendship and working together of the peoples of our two countries. What the Ambassador said has special meaning for leaders in health, physical education, and recreation. A close associated effort among leaders in these specialized fields around the world will have a salutary effect on the future of our individual countries and all the peoples on the face of the globe. A contribution can be made to a bright future for millions of human beings by helping to ensure health and well-being through our programs.

## GUIDELINES FOR INTERNATIONAL RELATIONS IN PHYSICAL EDUCATION

America is deeply involved in international affairs. If it is to occupy a position of leadership in the world, if it is to render a service to humanity over the face of the globe, and if it is to be a dynamic force for international peace, it must promote many facets of relationships to establish common bonds among peoples everywhere. One of these common

*University of the East, Manila, Philippines.*

Philippine folk dances.

bonds is physical education. Through sports and physical activities a medium is offered to further international relationships.

The work of the World Confederation of Organizations of the Teaching Profession; International Council on Health, Physical Education, and Recreation; International Association of Physical Education and Sports for Girls and Women; and the People-to-People Sports Committee will be discussed later in this chapter. These organizations and many others are making outstanding contributions. In

The author at a party in a school in the Philippines.

The author in the Philippines speaking to an audience of physical educators.

addition, the American Association for Health, Physical Education, and Recreation, through its International Relations Section, is also contributing. Some of these contributions include the following:

1. *Consultant services*—To domestic groups within the profession, professional groups in other countries, and in other ways

2. *Program services*—Developing and presenting programs at national and international meetings

3. *Newsletter*—Concerning international affairs and distributed to officers and interested persons

4. *Book project*—Books and professional publications collected within the United States and sent to other countries

5. *Hospitality*—Orienting, socializing with,

and in general making guests from other countries feel at home and benefiting from their visit to the United States.

The work of international cooperation, however, must not stop at the national level but must extend into the schools located in villages, towns, and cities from coast to coast. According to the Committee on International Relations, National Education Association, some ways by which the schools can meet the challenge are as follows*:

1. *Education for adaptability.* Education must seek to help people develop qualities of flexibility and adaptability to meet changing societal conditions. In physical education attempts should be made to help participants understand the role of sports and games in the various cultures of the world and the way such activities can help in promoting international understanding.

2. *Education for cultural empathy.* Education must seek to help people understand that cultures and countries are different. Folkways, mores, and ways of doing things vary as a person crosses borders. Physical education can help to show and educate people about the various games and sports of other nations, the uniforms they wear, their standards of sportsmanship, values, and other aspects that influence physical education around the world.

3. *Education for ideological clarity.* Education must make human beings aware of the principles democracy stands for and that are essential to the survival of our way of life. Since sports and games represent democracy in action, participants in sports can show respect for the other fellow, the necessity of playing by the rules, the best sports behavior in Olympic competition, and the ways physical education activities should be conducted in order to further the cause of humanity.

4. *Education for patience.* Education must teach people that deep differences do exist between the communist and democratic countries and that these differences will not be ironed out for many years to come. Therefore for those who believe in democracy there must be constant goals of fitness and preparedness so that this way of life may be preserved for generations to come.

5. *Education for knowledge of the world.* This is a "one world" era. Therefore, it is important to understand other peoples and other countries—the way they live, their customs, and their strong and weak points. Only as people know these facts will they understand why each person behaves as he does. Physical education can help to promote knowledge and understanding. Through an appreciation of the sports and games played by people in other countries, a better understanding of the culture develops.

6. *Education for responsibility.* Each persons must come to recognize that he or she has a stake in international relations. It is not limited to a few. As each person contributes to other people and countries, peace will have a much better chance of becoming a reality. Physical education should impress upon each student this responsibility.

## OPPORTUNITIES FOR SERVICE AT HOME

The physical educator does not need to travel to other countries in order to further good international relations. There is much work to be done in this country—at home. Some opportunities that are open to each physical educator on the home front are as follows:

1. *Teach national and cultural backgrounds of dances and games in physical education classes.* Sports, dances, and

*National Education Association, Committee on International Relations: Local association activities, Leaflet No. 12, Washington, D. C., July, 1962, The Association.

*Toledo Public Schools, Toledo, Ohio.*

The Toledo schools teach Philippine dances.

games should not be conducted in a vacuum. Boys and girls should understand their origin and the role they play in the various cultures of the world. Our physical education classes can play a dynamic part in furthering international understanding by orienting students about other countries through the medium of physical activities.

2. *Welcome foreigners.* Many physical educators, sports enthusiasts, and athletes visit and travel throughout the world. Each physical educator should be hospitable, make the person or persons welcome, and act as a guide to show and tell them about our programs. These courtesies will help to cultivate new friends for our profession and countries.

3. *Send books, CARE playground kits, and sports equipment to other countries.* People in other countries want information about our physical education programs. They welcome books, periodicals, and other literature that describe our programs, methods, and teaching techniques. An important service can be rendered by contributing literature to this worthy cause. Other countries are also interested in receiving sports equipment.

4. *Join international associations.* Physical educators should become involved in professional association work in international relations. The American Association for Health, Physical Education, and Recreation and many state associations have active sections or divisions in this area. In addition, such organizations as the International Association of Physical Education and Sports for Girls and Women are seeking members to help to carry out their objectives.

5. *Be knowledgeable about international affairs.* The physical educator should become acquainted with happenings on the international scene, world events that are taking place, and the work of such organizations as the United Nations. The physical educator should read and subscribe to some foreign publications.* As the physical educator becomes better informed about international happenings, he or she will be better qualified to pass along such information to students.

---

*One excellent resource of international information is *Other Lands and Other Peoples: a country-by-country fact book,* a publication of the Committee on International Relations of the National Education Association.

### International dates of special interest

Physical educators should be aware of international dates of special interest and the opportunities these days afford for planning special activities that can contribute to international understanding. A few dates are listed:

Columbus Day—October 12
United Nations Day—October 24
Thanksgiving—4th Thursday in November
Human Rights Day—December 10
Bill of Rights Day—December 15
Christmas—December 25
Brotherhood Week—February
Easter—March or April
World Health Day—April 7
Pan American Day—April 14
Flag Day—June 14

### Resources

The National Education Association also lists the following resources for those who wish to contribute to international education:

1. *Information about pen pals, classroom, and school affiliation may be obtained from:*
School and Classroom Department, People-to-People, Inc.
2401 Grand Avenue
Kansas City, Missouri 64141
2. *Materials on Asia may be obtained from:*
Asia Society
112 East 64th Street
New York, New York 10021
3. *Materials on Latin America may be obtained from:*
Department of Public Information
Pan American Union
Washington, D. C. 20006
4. *Periodicals*
INTERCOM—Foreign Policy Association
345 East 46th Street
New York, New York 10017
INTERCOM is an invaluable resource publication for teachers. Perhaps the most complete, reliable, and useful available.

### OPPORTUNITIES FOR SERVICE ABROAD

For the physical educator who is interested in serving abroad there are many opportunities to make this desire come true. A selected few are as follows:

1. *Student and teacher exchange programs.* Each year more than 7,000 persons representing over 100 countries are exchanged to teach, study, lecture, and engage in research or in other educational or cultural activities through programs sponsored by the Department of State. For more information write Teacher Exchange Section, Bureau of International Education, United States Office of Education, Washington, D. C.

2. *Peace Corps.* Physical educators are very much in demand for the Peace Corps. Jobs are open for men and women to organize and administer physical education programs, to coach school, community, and national teams, and to supervise community recreation programs. For detailed information write Peace Corps, Professional and Technical Division, Office of Public Affairs, Washington, D. C.

3. *Teach Corps.* The National Education Association has established a Teach Corps which utilizes the services of experienced American teachers in providing summer in-service training for teachers in foreign lands. For further information write Committee on International Relations, National Education Association, 1201 Sixteenth Street, N.W., Washington, D. C.

4. *United Nations Educational, Scientific, and Cultural Organization.* UNESCO seeks teachers to serve in developing countries around the world. It has an international fellowship and travel study program in war-devastated or underdeveloped countries. Write to UNESCO, Department of Exchange of Persons, 19 Avenue Kleber, Paris 16, France, or to Office of International Administration, United States Department of State, Washington, D. C.

5. *Armed forces.* Bases operated overseas by the armed forces have teaching positions available for elementary and secondary school teachers. For details write to branch of service, chief of per-

sonnel of the particular branch of service in which interested.

6. *World Health Organization.* For physical educators with competencies in the area of health, opportunities exist in various parts of the world. Write to Personnel Office, World Health Organization, 1501 New Hampshire Avenue, N.W., Washington, D. C.

7. *Fulbright grants.* An avenue for foreign service for those with advanced education and degrees may be available through the Fulbright program. This program has been in operation for several years and has been very popular for those interested in lecturing or teaching abroad for a year. If interested, write Conference Board of Associated Research Councils, Committee on International Exchange of Persons, 2101 Constitution Avenue, Washington, D. C.

8. *Private agencies and foundations.* There are many private agencies and foundations in the United States that are very much interested in international programs and frequently finance trips and make grants to carry on such programs. The Belgian-American Educational Foundation and the Institute of International Education are two such organizations. The interested physical educator should research the type of agency or foundation that might be interested in sponsoring a person with his or her qualifications.

9. *Other organizations.* See also Chapter 3, Settings for Physical Education Activities, for information on other opportunities through such organizations as: United States Agency for International Development (AID), The International Schools Service, Inter-American Schools Service, church-sponsored schools, and other teaching opportunities abroad.

## SELECTED INTERNATIONAL COMPETITIONS
### Olympic games

The First Olympiad was held in 776 B.C. at Olympia, Greece. It was originally a five-day event held every four years during the month of August. The earliest Olympics honored the Greek god Zeus. The facilities for these contests were open fields, and spectators lined the sides or sat on convenient slopes. An early Christian emperor named Theodosius termed the Olympics decadent, and abolished them in A.D. 394. In 1896, the Olympics were revived by the Baron Pierre de Coubertin, and were held in Athens. The United States participated that year, the Asian nations joined in 1932, and Russia entered for the first time in 1952. The first modern Olympics included competition in track and field, weight lifting, wrestling, swimming, cycling, tennis, gymnastics, fencing, and shooting. The scope of competition now includes, in addition to the above, boxing, rowing, yachting, water polo, canoeing, field hockey, basketball, the modern pentathlon, riding, soccer, handball, and judo. Tennis is no longer part of the Olympics.

The winter Olympic games were first initiated in 1924, and were held in Chamonix, France. They are now held in the same year as the summer Olympics, but need not be held in the same country. Events in the winter Olympics include the luge, ice hockey, speed and figure skating, skiing, and bobsledding.

The International Olympic Committee is responsible for the conduct of the games.

### The Olympics as an instrument for good international relations*

The Olympic ideal is dying. It will not permeate future games unless Americans and the rest of the world demand a change in emphasis. This great international festival is becoming cannon fodder in the cold war, with major stress being

---

*Parts of this discussion are adapted from an article by Bucher, Charles A.: Reader's Digest, Sept., 1955.

put on national pride, team victory, and beating Russia at all costs.

The drive to produce champions and to win is traditional in America and must be preserved. In the Olympic games, however, the emphasis is supposed to be on the individual athlete rather than the nation and on making friends rather than making points. As Eddie Eagen, a former officer of our National Olympic Committee said, "The Games' true purpose is to bring about world sportsmanship and good will. It is not an event to bring athletes together in competition to foster nationalism."

As now conducted, the Olympic games may be hampering international goodwill. The honor of the flag is not involved when a foreign contestant finishes a tenth of a second ahead of an American in the 100-meter dash. The honor of the flag is involved in the success or failure to promote the brotherhood of man.

Baron Pierre de Coubertin, the Frenchman responsible for the revival of the Olympic games in 1896, said: "The important thing is not winning, but taking part; the important thing in life is not conquering, but fighting well." All nations, large and small, are encouraged to participate, not for the purpose of gaining national honors, but in the spirit of friendly rivalry and respect for the ability of the individual athlete. Point scores were purposely disallowed to prevent the larger nations from monopolizing the games by sheer weight of numbers. It was felt that, regardless of how many points a large country might tally, a single victory by a representative of a smaller country should be considered of equal importance.

But sportswriters are bringing the cold war into sports and using point scores to attract readers. To read the American press, anyone would think that the Soviet Union and the United States were the only participants.

The Olympic games must also be kept out of politics. In the past, several congressmen have tried to introduce bills to pay the cost of sending our athletes to the Olympics and to subsidize their efforts in other ways. However, the Olympic ideal stresses that the money should come freely and spontaneously from the people. Furthermore, the armed services as a branch of the government must not be allowed to have preferential treatment which might jeopardize the men's amateur standing.

Although flag-waving politicians and journalists in many countries have become involved in the cold war of sports, the world can be thankful that the athletes on the field have not yet enlisted. Many times participants and spectators cannot understand the incompatibility of the battle raging in the press and the sportsmanship that is expressed throughout the games. Our athletes and the sports participants from the other countries of the world have expressed their good feeling for each other. There have been few unpleasant incidents, and most have been good sportsmen and made impressive showings both on and off the field.

To keep the Olympic ideal from dying, physical educators should strive to see that the following become "musts" in the organization and administration of the Olympic games within the United States and throughout the world:

1. Eliminate all point scoring systems
2. Keep games free of politics, government subsidy, and professionalism
3. Contestants become ambassadors of good will among nations
4. Award praise and publicity for excellence of individual performance, regardless of national origin

If the peoples of the world will put these principles into practice, the Olympic games will take on once again their historical significance and, in the words of Baron de Coubertin, "increase friendly understanding among nations for the good of humanity."

South Pacific Games.

## Asian Games

The Asian Games were first held in Manila in 1913. The participating countries of China, Japan, and the Philippines held what they called the First Oriental Olympic Games in that year. After 1921, the competition was renamed the Far Eastern Championships, and Ceylon, India, Indonesia, Malaya, and Thailand were invited to join, but were prevented from doing so by financial difficulties. A political dispute ended the competition between the three original nations in 1934. At that time, India invited Ceylon, Afghanistan, and Palestine to compete in the West Asiatic Games. War ended the competition after the first year. The First Asian Games were held in New Delhi, India, in 1951 under the sponsorship of the Asian Games Federation. Initially, competition was to be held every three years, but is presently held every four years. In 1954, eighteen countries participated, and nineteen competed in 1958. By 1962, twenty-two nations were involved. Objectives of the Asian Games include the setting of new Asian Game records, and the breaking of as many Olympic and world records as possible. Competition for men includes boxing, cycling, field hockey, soccer, basketball, riflery, water polo, weight lifting, and wrestling. Men and women compete in their own divisions in badminton, swimming and diving, table tennis, track and field, volleyball, and tennis.

## Pan-American Games

The Pan-American Games, initiated in 1951, are limited to nations of the Western hemisphere, including, among others, such nations as the United States, Canada, Argentina, Mexico, Bolivia, and Brazil. Presently, about twenty-four nations compete in these games, which are held every four years, between Olympics. The Pan-American Sports Organization administers the games under the same guidelines set down for Olympic competition.

Men compete in many of the same activities that are included in the Olympics, with the addition of tennis and baseball. Women compete in Olympic events, and also include basketball, tennis, and synchronized swimming in their schedule of events.

## British Empire and Commonwealth Games

This competition is limited to member nations of the British Empire. The games began in 1930 and are held every four years in a non-Olympic year. The British Empire and Commonwealth Games Federation administers the competition in which approximately forty nations join. The events are of an individual rather than a team nature, and include badminton, boxing, cycling, fencing, shooting, swimming and diving, track and field, weight lifting, and wrestling.

## World Maccabiah Games

These games were initiated in 1931, and are held in Israel every four years. They are limited to Jewish athletes. The International Maccabiah Games Committee administers the games on the Olympic pattern. Presently, about twenty-five nations participate. Men compete in many of the Olympic events plus golf, bowls, and table tennis. Women also compete in Olympic-type events and add golf and table tennis to their list of activities.

## World University Games

The International Federation of University Sports has conducted this competition since 1947. It is held every two years during an odd-numbered year. Approximately thirty-five countries send university students to participate in the games. Events included are track and field,

The Maccabiah Games.

basketball, soccer, gymnastics, tennis, fencing, and swimming and diving.

## SELECTED MAJOR INTERNATIONAL COMPETITIONS IN SELECTED AMATEUR SPORTS

*Badminton.* The International Badminton Federation sponsors international competition in this sport. The Thomas Cup for men was initiated in 1940, and the Uber Cup for women in 1956. Competition is held every three years.

*Chess.* The first World Chess Championships were held in 1851, under the sponsorship of the International Chess Federation. This organization continues to host this competition on a yearly basis.

*Cycling.* The Tour de France, sponsored by the International Cycling Union, is a yearly event.

*Golf.* The Americas Cup Golf Match, between the United States, Mexico, and Canada, has been held every two years since 1952. The Walker Cup Match, first held in 1922, matches the United States against Great Britain every two years.

*Ice skating.* The World Figure Skating Championships have been held yearly since the late 1870's. The World Speed Skating Championships have been a yearly event since 1893. Both are under the sponsorship of the International Skating Union.

*Riding.* The International Horse Show is held on a yearly basis.

*Rowing.* The Royal Yacht Club has sponsored the Henley-on-Thames Royal Regatta yearly since 1839.

*Shooting.* The National Rifle Association each year sponsors several international postal matches under the rules set down by the International Shooting Union: the International Free-Pistol Postal Match, the Mayleigh Cup International Smallbore Rifle Postal Match for Women, and the International Smallbore Rifle Three-Position Postal Match. International outdoor postal matches are held

**Table 14-1.** *Spectator sports and popular dances of other countries*\*

| Country | Sport | Dance |
|---|---|---|
| Australia | Soccer, cricket, boxing, swimming, tennis | Modern, ballet |
| Belgium | Soccer, cycling, tennis | Ballet, folk |
| Canada | Hockey, football, baseball, basketball, skiing | Modern, ballet |
| Denmark | Soccer, gymnastics, handball, swimming, track and field | Modern, ballet |
| Dominican Republic | Baseball, tennis | Folk |
| England | Football (soccer), boxing, cricket, tennis | Modern, ballet |
| France | Soccer, tennis, cycling, boxing | Ballet |
| India | Soccer, cricket, field hockey, tennis, badminton | Folk |
| Mexico | Bullfighting, soccer, baseball, jai alai | Modern, folk |
| Norway | Skiing, soccer, skating, track and field, swimming | Modern, folk |
| Peru | Soccer, bullfighting, boxing, track and field | Folk |
| Russia | Soccer, track and field, gymnastics, hockey | Ballet |

\*From Wessel, Janet: Movement fundamentals, Englewood Cliffs, N. J., 1961, Prentice-Hall, Inc., p. 271.

for Smallbore Rifle Prone and Three-Position, Free-Rifle Three-Position, Free-Pistol, and Center-Fire Rifle.

*Skiing.* The Federation Internationale de Ski sponsors the World Ski Championships every three years.

*Soccer.* Every four years, the International Federation of Soccer sponsors the World Cup Matches.

*Swimming.* The International Amateur Swimming Federation sponsors the World Swimming Championships every year.

*Tennis.* The United States Outdoor Tennis Championships have been sponsored yearly since 1881 by the United States Lawn Tennis Association. Under the guidance of the International Lawn Tennis Association, committees of the nations involved have sponsored the Wimbledon Championships since 1877; the Davis Cup for men since 1900; and the Wightman Cup for women of the United States and England since 1923.

*Yachting.* About every three years since 1851, the New York Yacht Club has sponsored the America's Cup in cooperation with the yachting body of the challenging nation.

## SELECTED INTERNATIONAL ORGANIZATIONS

There are many organizations that are concerned with physical education in international affairs. These organizations render an invaluable service to humanity. In a "one world" era it is not only important for the physical educator to be acquainted with professional organizations that are active on the domestic scene but also those that play active roles on the international scene. A few of the outstanding international professional organizations with which the physical educator should be familiar are as follows:

### World Confederation of Organizations of the Teaching Profession

The World Confederation of Organizations of the Teaching Profession (WCOTP) was founded at Copenhagen, Den-

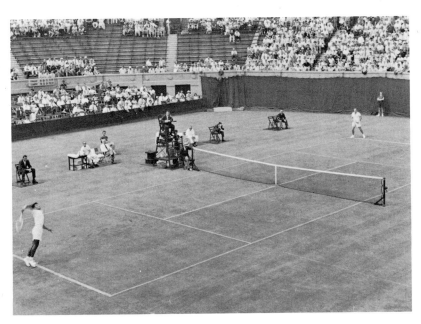

Davis Cup match in tennis.

mark, in 1952. It is composed of 132 national members; in addition, many associate members represent millions of teachers in 81 countries around the world.

The purposes of the WCOTP include providing an organization in which professional teachers at all educational levels can utilize education for furthering international understanding and world peace, teachers can unite their efforts to upgrade their educational policies and practices throughout the world, and international educational policies can be molded by the associated effort of teachers from all the countries represented in the organization.

Although membership in WCOTP consists largely of associations and institutions, interested persons may subscribe for and receive its publications. Membership consists of national members (educational or teachers' associations), associate members (regional, provincial, state, and local teachers' associations and institutions), and international members (international educational organizations).

The WCOTP is governed by an assembly of delegates, the highest governing body; an executive committee, which carries out the work of the confederation for the assembly of delegates; and a secretary general, who executes the decisions of the assembly and executive committee.

WCOTP has three international members concerned with specialized phases of education: the International Council on Health, Physical Education, and Recreation (ICHPER), the International Council on Education for Teaching (ICET), and the International Reading Association (IRA).

WCOTP conducts conferences and seminars throughout the world for leaders of teacher organizations and other educators on various educational problems. Conferences and seminars have been held in such places as Ceylon, United States, Costa Rica, Viet Nam, Nigeria, and Peru. The WCOTP also works closely with the United Nations, especially with such organizations as the World Health Organization, Economic and Social Council, and the Food and Agriculture Organization.

WCOTP publishes an annual report and, in addition, such periodicals as *Panorama: Teaching Throughout the World* and *Echo*. These publications appear in many different languages.

## International Council on Health, Physical Education, and Recreation

At the annual meeting of the WCOTP in Rome in 1958, a special committee discussed and formulated a statement of the purposes and functions of organizations of health, physical education, and recreation. The committee drafted a constitution and presented it to the WCOTP assembly of delegates for approval. Then, in 1959, at the annual meeting of the WCOTP in Washington, D. C., an official decision was made to form an International Council on Health, Physical Education, and Recreation (ICHPER). WCOTP approved this organization in August, 1959.

The purposes of ICHPER include helping WCOTP to accomplish its objectives; encouraging, developing, and upgrading programs of health, physical education, and recreation throughout the world; working closely with other international organizations concerned with these special fields; improving the professional status of teachers; supporting, encouraging, and sponsoring the exchange of research findings and information for the profession; and promoting the exchange of teachers and students among the countries of the world.

The groups throughout the world who are eligible to join ICHPER are international organizations in health, physical education, and recreation, national organizations, and regional or geographical area organizations. The aim of the Council is to bring representatives from countries into this one organization so that it can be the official world spokesman for the professions. Through such representation it hopes to promote better school programs in health, physical education, and recreation. More specifically, it will do this by attempting to improve teaching methods, training teachers, providing materials for teaching, and doing research. It is anticipated that ICHPER will plan and conduct conferences, seminars, courses, world congresses, lectures, demonstrations, exhibits, and many other experiences to carry out its objectives.

The administration of the Council rests with an assembly of delegates appointed by member organizations or the executive committee and an executive committee composed of officers of the Council and members elected by the assembly of dele-

gates. The officers of the Council include the president, the vice-president, and the secretary-general. The president and vice-president are elected for three-year terms, and the secretary-general is appointed by the executive committee. ICHPER met in Washington in 1959, Amsterdam in 1960, New Delhi in 1961, Stockholm in 1962, Rio de Janeiro in 1963, Paris in 1964, Addis Ababa in 1965, Seoul in 1966, Vancouver in 1967, and Dublin in 1968.

Materials and information on ICHPER can be secured by writing to this organization at 1201 Sixteenth Street, N.W., Washington, D. C.

There are six types of membership, with annual fees as follows: individual, $10; institutional, $10; contributing, $25 or

ICHPER conference in Seoul, Korea. Members of the Kyung-Hee University gymnastic team performing before the delegates of the congress.

High school girls performing a Korean folk dance at Chang-Chung gymnasium for delegates of the WCOTP delegate assembly and the ICHPER congress.

Students in colorful native costumes from the Hansung girls middle and high school, Seoul, Korea, perform mass demonstration.

The secretary-general of ICHPER addressing the delegate assembly.

more; international, $10; national, $10; and regional, $5. Membership each year provides four issues of *ICHPER Bulletin,* a four-page newsletter reporting significant professional developments and activities, four issues of *Gymnasion,* Proceedings of the International Congress of ICHPER, and research reports.

In the years ahead it is expected that ICHPER will be very active on the international scene, making recommendations to governments, advising on equipment and facility needs, exchanging personnel, assisting member organizations, supporting recreational activities, and providing leadership in many ways for the fields of health, physical education, and recreation.

## International Association of Physical Education and Sports for Girls and Women

Women in physical education, feeling the need to know about and participate in sports in other countries, and to solve common problems, prompted the foundation of the International Association of Physical Education and Sports for Girls and Women. Membership is open to women who engage in physical education work at any of the educational levels, elementary through college, as well as leaders in adult programs. Members can participate in the congresses that are held, usually every fourth or fifth year, in one of the fifty-one countries that participate in the Association. Meetings have been held in 1949, in Stockholm; 1953, in Paris; 1957, in London; 1961, in Washington; and 1965, in Cologne. The 1969 meeting will be in Tokyo. The Cologne meeting saw 673 delegates from forty nations. Members also receive publications of the Association. Dues are $3. Aims of the Association are as follows:

1. To promote closer working relationships among women physical educators in various countries of the world
2. To work closely with various organizations that render services to women
3. To afford opportunities through congresses and meetings to discuss and help in the solving of mutual problems
4. To encourage research and exchange of

*Courtesy Dr. Gunsun Hoh,*
*Republic of China.*

Physical education programs in the Republic of China.

The author lecturing at Cheng Kung University, Taiwan.

persons and ideas and to promote other activities related to physical education and sports for women

## The International Federation of Physical Education

The International Federation of Physical Education (FIEP) was founded in 1923 in Brussels. The home office is now located in Lisbon, Portugal. The aims of this organization are to promote health, wholesome recreation , and the social adaptation of the individual. Its bulletin is printed quarterly in five languages and carries articles related to research in the areas of science and exercise, book reviews, and international views of physical education. Its publications are the *FIEP Bulletin*, the *International Chronicle,* and a bibliographic bulletin called *Books and Magazines.*

## The International Council of Sport and Physical Education

The International Council of Sport and Physical Education (ICSPE) was founded in 1958 in Paris, and the first general assembly was held in Rome in 1960. The aims of this organization are to be a clearinghouse for international cooperation in sports and physical education, to promote the social good of sports and physical education, and to promote research and the exchange of ideas and assistance between countries. The ICSPE cooperates closely with the United Nations Educational, Scientific and Cultural Organization, the World Health Organization, ICHPER, and other related organizations such as the International Olympic Committee. The ICSPE publishes the *ICSPE News-Letter*.

## International Recreation Association

The International Recreation Association (IRA) was founded in 1956 in Philadelphia. This organization seeks to advance recreation on an international basis by aiding various countries in need of assistance, by answering inquiries and placing qualified teachers and leaders in youth agencies, and by distributing information. The IRA publishes the *IRA Bulletin* and distributes a hospital recreation guide, *On The Mend.*

## International Bureau of Education

The International Bureau of Education (BIE) was founded in 1925 in Geneva and serves as an international educational information center for all countries. This organization publishes research studies on educational organizations and an international bulletin printed in English and French. The Ministries of Education in member countries send an educational progress report each year that is incorporated into an educational yearbook. An Intergovernmental Conference on Public Education is sponsored each year. The Bureau also maintains an extensive library of education textbooks, journals, and legislative documents pertaining to education.

## Federation Internationale de Medicine Sportive

Membership includes persons who are interested in research, teaching, coaching, and medical aspects of sports. They concern themselves with the physiologic aspects of sports and also the science of better performance in sports, as well as the prevention and care of injuries incurred in sports.

## People-to-People Sports Committee

The People-to-People Sports Committee is one of the forty-one people-to-people programs established in 1956. It has as its main purpose the involvement of Americans in the conduct of international affairs through sports. Its headquarters is at 20 Exchange Place, New York, New York, It is a private group that has engaged in such projects as tours of the United States by basketball teams from other countries and the sending of a boys' baseball team from California to Japan and Korea. Its key to success has been its ability and willingness to get individual and business help in defraying expenses for foreign visitors and in helping American athletes go overseas. The key persons responsible for the committee's work are a director, a secretary, and a chairman. They work closely with the United States Information Agency and the United States Department of State in carrying out their work.

A project that has been very successful with the Committee has been the distribution of six sports kits—baseball, basketball, boxing, soccer, softball, and volleyball. Besides balls and other equipment, rule books are also included. Civic organizations such as Lions and Kiwanis clubs are asked to buy sports kits. It is possible for them to specify where the kit is to be sent, by city, country, or a group of individuals in another country. Through these sports kits the Committee feels that the government can establish good relations with youth and sports organizations abroad and Americans can show their feelings toward other peoples.

## PHYSICAL EDUCATION IN SELECTED COUNTRIES AROUND THE WORLD
### Australia

The island continent of Australia, composed of six states, is approximately the same size as the mainland United States. The Pacific ocean on the east and the Indian ocean on the west are the boundaries of the flattest of the world's continents, the only continent that is occupied by a single nation. The climate of Australia varies with a tropical climate in the north and east, to a more moderate temperature range further inland.

The population of Australia is almost totally made up of people of British descent, although many European immigrants have recently settled there. Manufacturing, commerce, building, construction, and farming are the major sources of income.

*Educational structure.* Education is compulsory between the ages of 6 and 15, except in Tasmania, where the upper age is 16. The six state governments are responsible for the progress of education in their own states. A director of education heads the state education department in each capital city, and under him are the directors of the specific educational areas. Each state has a state director of physical education.

*Philosophy of education.* The Australian educational system seeks to accomplish such goals as preparing its students to be well-rounded individuals, satisfying the needs and abilities of each individual, and vocational preparation.

*Philosophy of physical education.* Physical education is required in all elementary and secondary schools and in all teacher-training curriculums in colleges and universities. It seeks to develop physical fitness in students by promoting proper growth and by building adequate amounts of strength, endurance, and coordination. Social and emotional development and the learning of recreational skills are also primary aims.

*Physical education in infant's schools.* These schools are attached to the primary schools, and children may enter when they are 5. Physical education is the responsibility of the classroom teacher and is a phase of the total program. The emphasis is on creativity, self-expression, and the acquiring of skills needed in later school years. Dancing and rhythmics make up the bulk of the physical education activities.

*Physical education in elementary schools.* This educational level accepts children from the age of 8 until they have completed the work of the seventh grade at age 12 or 13. Physical education is the responsibility of the classroom teacher, who may call upon physical education resource people attached to the state education department. In grades one through four, approximately one hour a week is devoted to physical education, while grades five through seven have approximately two hours of physical education a week. The activities included in the program are games, marching, stunts and tumbling, gymnastics, track and field, and lead-up games for such sports as tennis, softball, and basketball. Where a pool is available, swimming is taught.

*Physical education in secondary schools.* Australia has four kinds of secondary schools: five- or six-year college-preparatory high schools; three- to four-year junior high schools for those students entering vocations; two- to five-year home science schools for girls planning to become teachers or nurses, or who will enter other service occupations; and three-year agricultural schools. All secondary schools have physical education specialists, although two schools may share the services of a single specialist. Up to three hours a week, including participation in the intramural program, are devoted to physical education. Dancing, rhythmics, the skills of various sports, gymnastics, games, track and field, and swimming are all parts of the program.

*Physical education in higher education.* Physical education is required only for those planning to enter the teaching profession.

*Physical education facilities.* Indoor facilities, especially gymnasiums, are generally poor, but many indoor facilities are currently under construction. Equipment is generally inadequate. Outdoor facilities are more than ample.

*Teacher training.* Professional programs in physical education are offered at the state universities in three states, and through the state education department in conjunction with the universities in the remaining three states. A diploma course lasts for two to three years, and a degree course from four to five years, depending on the amount of part-time study the prospective teacher engages in. Skills courses are given in activities including cricket, softball, tennis, basketball, and swimming. Theory courses include, among others, biology, chemistry, anatomy, physiology, physiology of exercise, nutrition, hygiene and first aid, tests and measurements, methods of physical education, history of physical education, coaching, and practice teaching. There is a shortage of physical education teachers at the present time.

## Canada

Canada is the second largest nation in square miles in the world. Only the Soviet Union has more land area. Canada has great reaches of timber as well as much farm land. The climate is bitterly cold in winter in some areas, and intensely hot during the summer in others. Some areas receive no snow at all, while others have an almost year-round snow cover.

Both the French and English languages are spoken in Canada. Agriculture is a leading industry, but mining, forestry, and fishing are leading occupations.

*Educational structure.* Each of the ten Canadian provinces controls and administers its own schools. Thus, although the compulsory entry age for school is 6 years nationwide, the age that youth may leave the schools may be from 14 to 16, depending on the particular province. Likewise, some elementary schools include only the first six grades, while in other provinces the first seven or eight grades are part of the elementary school. Canada has many church-supported schools that set individual policies free of any provincial controls.

*Philosophy of education.* General education in Canada has been strongly influenced by the philosophies of the United

States, Great Britain, and Europe. The provision of an adequate education for all and preparation for a vocation are primary educational concerns.

*Philosophy of physical education.* The attainment of physical fitness, basic skills needed for life and leisure, and social and emotional fitness are major objectives. The development of recreational skills has always been of major importance. Canada also places great emphasis on educating for movement, and is considered to be a leader in the area of movement education.

*Physical education in elementary schools.* A general shortage of trained elementary school physical educators has placed the classroom teacher in the role of responsibility for physical education on this level. In general, three 15-minute periods of physical education a week are given. The activities included are movement skills, sport skills, and activities designed to increase physical fitness.

*Physical education in secondary schools.* In general, two 35-minute periods a week are conducted by a trained physical educator. The activities of the elementary school are continued, and dance, gymnastics, tumbling, basketball, volleyball, and other team and individual sports are added. Where a pool is available, swimming instruction is included in the program. In some schools, the program is much like that found in high schools in the United States, but sports particularly enjoyed by Canadians, such as rugby, curling, and ice hockey are parts of the program.

*Physical education in higher education.* Physical education on the college and university levels is limited. Where programs and requirements are in effect, football, hockey, basketball, swimming, tennis, and badminton are among the activities offered.

*Physical education facilities.* Although most elementary schools have playrooms rather than gymnasiums, facilities in general are good and improving. There is much continuing construction of gymnasiums. Qualified staff for all school programs is a goal of professional associations in Canada.

*Teacher training.* The length of the program, the specific courses offered, the degree conferred, as well as the standards that must be met for certification, vary from province to province. Common courses required of all teachers are methods, history, and philosophy of physical education, educational psychology, and student teaching. Because of particular provincial standards, a teacher certified in one province may not be eligible for certification in another.

## East Pakistan

East and West Pakistan are more than a thousand miles apart. Most of the population of this divided nation lives in the more educationally and economically advanced, but smaller, East Pakistan. The Himalayan mountains are on the north, the Bay of Bengal to the south, and Burma and India to the east and west. The climate is hot and humid.

Most of the people are rural dwellers and farmers. They speak English and Bengali. The British, to whom Pakistan once belonged, left many of their influences on its education and culture.

*Educational structure.* East Pakistan has a director of public instruction who is responsible for the schools. Subordinate to him is a director of physical education, who is responsible for this area of instruction, including all syllabuses.

*Philosophy of education.* The schools of East Pakistan seek to accomplish such goals as raising the literacy level of the country and imparting the cultural heritage of the land.

*Philosophy of physical education.* The aims of physical education include an attempt to give an understanding of the cultural heritage through native games, to increase physical fitness, and to improve the health of the people.

*Physical education in elementary schools.* In grades one through five, the classroom teacher, sometimes aided by a district physical education instructor, is responsible for all instruction. Fitness activities, drills, rhythms, lead-up games, aquatics, and games native to the country are taught.

*Physical education in secondary schools.* In grades six through ten, physical education is not compulsory, and is often entirely omitted from the school curriculum. Where physical education is a part of the program, trained instructors do the teaching, including in the program such activities as gymnastics, game skills, drills, and a limited number of team and individual sports.

*Physical education in higher education.* As a general rule, physical education is not offered in the colleges and universities.

*Physical education facilities.* The indoor facilities are generally poor according to American standards. Classes are conducted almost entirely out-of-doors.

*Teacher training.* Only the College of Physical Education at Dacca presently trains physical educators. Two years of college followed by a three-month physical education course is required for teaching in the public schools. For district and administrative posts, or for college teaching, a four-year general college course plus an additional year of training in physical education is mandatory. Courses offered include methods and materials in physical education, administration of physical education, and student teaching. Much of the activity work is devoted to drills in the physical training connotation. Physical educators do not enjoy the same prestige as teachers of academic subjects and are not as well paid.

## England

England is smaller than a combination of several of the states in the United States, and no part of the country is more than 75 miles from the sea, resulting in a nation that enjoys water sports, particularly sailing. England has rolling chalk cliffs on the south, mountains to the west and north and vast flat plains on the east. Especially during the winter, fog and rain are common, but in general the climate is mild.

The people of England are urbanized and engage mainly in the manufacture of steel and other commodities. Shipping and boatbuilding are large industries. The rural areas are dotted with small farms, but these do not produce enough of the marketable items needed.

*Educational structure.* England has a dualistic educational structure, made up of state-supported schools and independent schools. Although there is a ministry of education, all state schools are autonomous. They form their own educational syllabuses and establish their own curriculums.

*Philosophy of education.* English schools attempt to accomplish such goals as helping their students become individuals who are capable of thinking and acting independently. An environment is provided in which the child can develop socially and individually, grow mentally and physically, learn to live a good and useful life, and learn to become a worthy citizen.

*Philosophy of physical education.* Although there is no common syllabus for physical education, both the state and the independent schools attempt to help the child gain a joy and appreciation of bodily movement, to develop and maintain fitness, and to gain the skills, attitudes, and appreciations he needs to enjoy his leisure and work productively.

*Physical education in elementary schools.* Education in England is compulsory from the age of 5. At that time, the child begins an almost daily program of physical education under the guidance of his classroom teacher. Four times a week, for about 40 minutes each time, the child

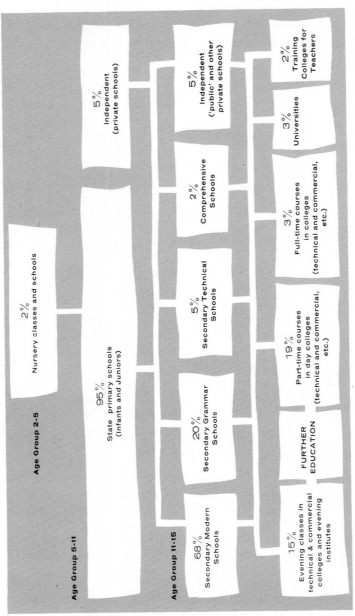

The structure of education in Britain.

*From At School in Britain, distributed by British Information Services,
45 Rockefeller Plaza, New York, N. Y.*

engages in vigorous outdoor sports and games. He runs, climbs, jumps, throws, and explores all the varieties of movement. As he progresses through elementary school, he begins to learn some of the skills of gymnastics, apparatus, and dance, the fundamentals of such dual sports as boxing and tennis, and engages in track and field events. He is introduced to basketball, soccer, rugby, cricket, lacrosse, and hockey.

*Physical education in secondary schools.*

The secondary schools have a specialist in physical education on the staff, although the classroom teacher may often supplement and help the work of the specialist. The program for boys and girls is separate and is heavily weighted with gymnastics. The skills of the elementary grades are improved on, and swimming is often added to the curriculum. Physical education is offered four periods a week. Two periods are instructional, and the other is a double period once a week

Physical education in India.

where a single game or sport is played, often competitively.

*Physical education in higher education.* There is no required program in physical education except for those preparing to teach in the elementary schools. Facilities, equipment, and personnel are available if the student wishes to participate in physical activities.

*Physical education facilities.* The quality and quantity of facilities vary widely. Playing fields are abundant at all schools, but few elementary schools have gymnasiums. School camp facilities are often provided, and athletic clubs often make their facilities available to the schools.

*Teacher training.* There are no specialists in physical education in the elementary schools. Elementary classroom teachers must take courses in physical education and handle this part of the program. Teacher training for grades above the elementary level is accomplished through programs ranging from one to three years in length. College graduates who wish to teach physical education must take a one-year specialized course. There are seven colleges for women and two for men that offer a three-year program in physical education exclusively. England at present is experiencing a shortage of well-qualified physical educators.

### India

In the north, where the land is fertile, India's mountain states of Nepal, Sikkim, and Bhutan share the Himalayan mountains with Red China. The Indian ocean is the southern frontier, and the south has a very damp climate. India is densely populated, and the population continues to grow faster than India can produce food for her people. The large cities of Calcutta, Madras, and Bombay are overpopulated. India's climate is hot and there is a long rainy season.

Many Indians are engaged in farming but cannot grow much more than what they personally need. The chemical, steel, and engineering industries employ most of the urban population.

*Educational structure.* The state controls education through its ministry of education, with an elected education minister. The ministry is departmentalized, and includes a department of physical education. Each state has its own director of physical education who serves in an administrative and supervisory capacity. Education is compulsory from the age of 6 through 14.

*Philosophy of education.* The aim of education in India is to provide an opportunity for the individual to reach his full potential, culturally, vocationally, and personally.

*Philosophy of physical education.* Physical education in India seeks to help the individual develop physically, mentally, and socially; to learn skills that have a recreational value; and to reach his full potential as a person.

*Physical education in elementary schools.* In grades one through five, physical education is the responsibility of the classroom teacher. Physical education is offered each day in most schools, for a total of two hours each week. Calisthenics, games, and stunts make up a major part of the program.

*Physical education in intermediate schools.* In grades six through eight, physical education is taught by a specialist. Four classes are held each week, each class being about 30 minutes in length. Activities offered are calisthenics, rhythmics, games, gymnastics, track and field, and marching.

*Physical education in secondary schools.* This is a three-year school, and essentially the same activities are offered as are given in the intermediate school, but in greater depth. Depending on the school, there may be from one to four physical education periods a week.

**Table 14-2.** *Education in Britain**

| | 1954–1955 | | | | 1964–1965 | | | |
|---|---|---|---|---|---|---|---|---|
| | England and Wales | Scotland | Northern Ireland | United Kingdom | England and Wales | Scotland | Northern Ireland | United Kingdom |
| Total school population[a] | 7,199,492 | 863,900 | 252,400[f] | 8,315,792 | 7,764,825 | 917,400 | 300,200 | 8,982,425 |
| Total number of students in further education[b] | 1,814,200 | 199,800 | 32,300 | 2,046,300 | 2,747,700 | 327,500 | 51,300 | 3,126,500 |
| Total number of students in teacher training[c] | 27,261 | 3,500 | 1,600 | 32,361 | 65,851 | 7,800 | 2,100 | 75,751 |
| Total number of university students: full time / part time | 81,705 / 16,146 | 14,100 / 5,200 | 2,198 / 511 | 98,103 / 21,857 | 138,711 / 18,077 | 25,300 / 3,600 | 4,618 / 753 | 168,629 / 22,430 |
| Full-time teachers in maintained and aided schools[d] | 242,557 | 34,800 | 9,000[g] | 286,357 | 287,693 | 38,100 | 12,600[g] | 338,393 |
| Number of school places completed since 1945 | 1,362,880 | 169,900 | 33,110 | 1,565,880 | 3,771,100 | 617,200 | 154,940 | 4,543,240 |
| Expenditure on education from public funds[e] | £484,100,000 | £59,000,000 | £13,020,000 | £556,120,000 | £1,360,200,000 | £160,200,000 | £39,376,000 | £1,559,776,000 |

*From British Information Services: *Education in Britain*, 1966.
[a]Includes independent schools both recognized and unrecognized.
[b]Grant-aided establishments.
[c]Includes university departments of education and art-training centers.
[d]Primary and secondary schools, including nursery schools.
[e]Including university expenditure.
[f]Excludes independent schools.
[g]Includes teachers in institutions of further education.

*Physical education in higher education.* Although many colleges and universities have a two-year requirement, the lack of facilities and personnel often makes the program difficult to carry out. When the program is operable, two hours a week of physical education are offered. The activities included in the programs vary widely from gymnastics and team and individual sports to combative activities, and the student is largely allowed to elect his activities.

*Physical education facilities.* Although most schools have outdoor play areas, the lack of gymnasiums and playgrounds severely hampers the program, particularly in the lower grades.

*Teacher training.* There are fifty schools that train physical education instructors exclusively. India also has more than 2,000 teachers' colleges, and two universities that train physical educators. There is a one-year program that leads to a certificate, a two-year program that leads to a diploma, and a three-year pro-

gram that leads to a bachelor's degree. Theory courses offered include principles, history, methods, organization, and administration of physical education, anatomy, physiology, and psychology. Practical courses include camping, cricket, volleyball, apparatus, and story plays.

### Israel

Israel is a Middle Eastern country lying between Europe and Africa, and on the western edge of Asia. It is bounded on the west by the Mediterranean sea, on the east by Jordan, and the northeast by Syria. Lebanon is to the north and Egypt to the southwest. The climate is mild in the winter and sunny and warm in the summer.

Hebrew is the official language of the country, but English is frequently spoken. Only about a third of the population is native born. Immigrants from Asia, Africa, and Europe make up most of the population. The people engage in farming, shipping, industry, and science and

Main building at Wingate Institute for Physical Education, Israel.

Students engaging in physical education activity at Wingate Institute for Physical Education, Israel.

Mass gymnastics at the Gadna demonstration, Ramat Gan Stadium, Israel.

technology. Military training is compulsory for all men and women for two years beginning at the age of nineteen.

*Educational structure.* Education is free and compulsory between the ages of 5 and 14. Beyond the age of 14, tuition is charged in the public schools. The Ministry of Education and Culture is responsible for all phases of primary and secondary education.

*Philosophy of education.* Education is geared toward developing a citizenry who can contribute to the advancement of the country. Toward this end, school programs are heavily weighted with courses in Hebrew culture and literature. The schools also strive to help their students develop as individuals and seek to give them practical training for vocations.

*Philosophy of physical education.* Physical education is conducted under the guidance of an Authority for Sports and Physical Education, a state arm that is responsible for the coordination of all physical education. Physical education is devoted primarily to increasing and maintaining physical fitness and to providing instruction in leisure-time pursuits.

*Physical education in kindergartens.* Although school need not be started by children until the age of 5, these schools are provided for students from the ages of 3 through 5. Physical education is required for a period of two hours each week. The program includes dances, rhythmics, games, and native activities.

*Physical education in elementary schools.* This school terminates with the eighth grade. Physical education is required two hours each week, and the program of the kindergarten is continued through grade three. Beginning with the fourth grade, the skills of such sports as soccer and basketball are added, and specialists are in charge of the program.

*Physical education in secondary schools.* In addition to the two-hour physical education requirement, there is a two-hour

premilitary training period weekly, based on physical education activities. The programs, taught by specialists, include rhythmics, wrestling, handball, table tennis, swimming, track, soccer, gymnastics, apparatus, volleyball, and basketball.

*Physical education in higher education.* Except in programs of teacher training, physical education is not offered or required.

*Physical education facilities.* Facilities are extremely poor according to American standards, both indoors and out-of-doors. In many areas, the school building itself is inadequate even for the process of general education.

*Teacher training.* The Physical Education Teachers College at Wingate Institute and the related Institute of Education for Movement at present offer a two-year professional program in physical education. Theory courses include anatomy, first aid, health, physiology, biology, remedial exercise, history and administration of physical education, psychology, theory of movement, methods of physical education, and practice teaching. Skill courses include folk dance, rhythmics, swimming, games, and remedial exercises. Gymnastics, apparatus, basketball, volleyball, soccer, track and field, and boxing and wrestling are among the team and individual sports that are offered.

There is an acute shortage of well-trained physical education teachers, especially women, but the training program is now being enlarged and improved.

## Italy

Italy is a peninsula bounded by the Alps on the north and by the Mediterranean sea on the other sides. No point in Italy is more than 80 miles from the sea. The Appennine mountains extend from the Alps down the middle of Italy to the sea, forming a country of valleys. The climate is usually warm and sunny.

The people of Italy are striving toward

a more industrialized and modern economy. The vast majority of the people are employed in industry: automobiles, business machine manufacture, steel, oil, wine production, and handicrafts. Those persons who are in agriculture are mostly grape growers, but their number is decreasing.

*Educational structure.* A national minister of education is responsible for control of the various school curriculums, and for the supervision, organization, administration, and coordination of all education. A higher council of public education serves as a central advisory committee on the national level. Each provincial government has advisory committees on education that include primary and secondary education sections as well as a director of physical education. On the local level, there are inspectors and supervisors of education, as well as school boards. These boards are staffed by teachers, and are advisory rather than policy-making bodies.

*Philosophy of education.* Education in Italy is compulsory from the age of 6 through 14. The aim of education is to produce a worthy, law-abiding citizen, who is prepared to labor for the good of society, his country, and himself.

*Philosophy of physical education.* The militaristic prewar aims of physical education have given way to the objectives of helping each individual reach his potential physically, morally, and mentally.

*Physical education in elementary schools.* The elementary schools encompass grades one through five. Physical education is taught by the classroom teacher during four 35-minute periods each week. Activities included are those that help to increase balance and coordination, fundamentals of movement, lead-up games, and rhythmics.

*Physical education in intermediate schools.* In grades six through nine, physical education is taught by a specialist for two one-hour periods each week. Rhythmics, apparatus and tumbling, calisthenics, winter sports, water sports, fencing, track and field, and soccer make up the program.

*Physical education in high schools.* Depending on choice of career, an Italian child may select a four- or five-year high school. Physical education follows the same content as that of the intermediate school.

*Physical education in higher education.* Physical education is not offered or required in the colleges and universities of Italy.

*Physical education facilities.* Italy has, in general, excellent facilities for physical education, particularly for outdoor activities. At present, many facilities are in the planning stage or are nearing completion.

*Teacher training.* Only the University of Rome presently offers a teacher training program in physical education. This is a three-year course heavily weighted in the sciences and the development of skill proficiency. Before being licensed, a prospective teacher must meet high standards of physical fitness, pass a practical test of skill proficiency, and take a written cultural examination.

Teachers of physical education are in very short supply and do not enjoy the status or prestige of other educators.

## Japan

Japan is an island nation made up of four large and many small islands. The northeast division of the island chain is mountainous and cold. The middle section ranges from vast flat plains to mountains, and has a mild climate. The southwest is flat and enjoys a warm climate. The southwest is the most densely populated section, and boasts manufacturing, mining, and fishing among its industries. The rainfall in all regions is heavy.

Japan has a large population and

*Courtesy S. Ebashi, University of Tokyo, Tokyo, Japan.*

Japanese physical education programs.

The author meets with Japanese students. Professor Ebashi, of the University of Tokyo, is the interpreter.

shows one of the highest rates of population increase in the world. Many of Japan's workers are engaged in agricultural trades, but a recent and continuing employment trend is toward industry.

*Educational structure.* The ministry of education and local school boards help to advance the progress of Japanese education. The ministry of education, however, is a liaison agency rather than a controlling one. Its functions are to give guidance to educational and research institutions, aid with procurement and disbursing of educational funds and materials, and to coordinate many of the educational services. The school boards serve the same function as do those in the United States.

*Philosophy of education.* The aim of Japanese general education is to develop a well-rounded individual who will be patriotic, responsible, and a moral citizen.

*Philosophy of physical education.* Physical education is compulsory from elementary school through college. The aim is to develop sound and fit minds and

bodies, to imbue a spirit of democracy in sports and life, and to develop a healthy and health-knowledgeable individual.

*Physical education in elementary schools.* The ministry of education publishes a course of study that is followed in the elementary schools. All of the children have three 45-minute periods of physical education each week, and in addition may participate in intramurals. The activities covered are rhythmics, apparatus, gymnastics, calisthenics, track and field, and various ball games. The skills of swimming, skiing, and skating are often included, and physical performance tests are administered periodically.

*Physical education in upper elementary schools.* This level covers grades seven through nine. In the seventh grade, physical education classes are held three times each week. In grades eight and nine, one period of health and two of physical education are offered. The activities of the lower elementary school are continued, but the boys also receive instruction in judo, kindo, and sumo, while the girls have additional instruction in dance and rhythmic exercise. Performance tests are also given at this school level.

*Physical education in secondary schools.* The basic elementary program is continued for all students, with the addition of such team sports as basketball, softball, and volleyball. Individual and dual activities include tennis, badminton, and advanced instruction in swimming and diving.

*Physical education in higher education.* The activity program of the secondary schools is carried over to the colleges and universities. All students are required to take two university credits in activity courses and two additional credits in physical education theory courses. Electives among the latter include kinesiology, physiology, the history of physical education, and the administration of physical education.

*Physical education facilities.* Japan has inadequate facilities in many of its elementary schools and few parks for recreation. It lacks research facilities and adequate laboratories for major students in colleges and universities. Some public schools do have adequate gymnasiums, and many have substantial outdoor play areas.

*Teacher training.* There are three private schools, fifty-four state colleges and universities, one private university, and five junior colleges that offer courses in teacher preparation. The private schools and universities prepare teachers for the secondary schools in a four-year program. The junior colleges offer a two-year program geared toward those students who are preparing to teach in the elementary schools. Besides a varied and intense grounding in activities, prospective physical educators must also take courses in organization and administration, methods and materials, practice teaching, principles, physiology of exercise, kinesiology, and history, sociology, and psychology of physical education. All teachers must take

an examination before they can be licensed to teach.

The teacher in Japan is a revered person. He is held in high esteem and enjoys much status and prestige.

## New Zealand

The North Island and the South Island, separated by Cook Strait, make up New Zealand. Most New Zealanders live on North Island. In general, the climate is temperate. The Maori's, a Polynesian people, make up a very small segment of the population. Most New Zealanders are of British birth or descent. The nation is irregular and mountainous to the extent that many children cannot travel to school, and must study at home by radio or through correspondence courses.

*Educational structure.* Education is compulsory from the age of 7 through 15. The state education department controls all education, including syllabuses, but delegates much of its authority to local education boards. The secondary schools are run by boards of governors. Parent committees help to run the primary schools. The education department has a division of physical education.

*Philosophy of education.* Education is provided free for everyone up to the age of nineteen. Individualism is stressed, as is mental, social, and physical development.

*Philosophy of physical education.* The schools of New Zealand believe strongly in physical fitness and its maintenance, in the development of lifetime sports skills, and in striving to help the individual become a thinking, mature, and responsible adult.

*Physical education in elementary schools.* In grades one through six, the classroom teacher, at times aided by a physical education specialist, is responsible for instruction. Three 30-minute instructional periods a week are supplemented

New Zealand physical education.

by a single 30-minute game period each week. This latter period is highly organized. Basic movement skills, dances, games, and the sport skills of volleyball, cricket, gymnastics, apparatus, and swimming are included in the program.

*Physical education in secondary schools.* A physical education specialist is available in the secondary schools, but the classroom teacher continues to give instruction in physical education. Two 40-minute instructional periods and a 30-minute game period are standard in most schools. The elementary school skills are continued, and winter and summer sports, leisure-time activities, and track and field are added to the program. Physical education is not compulsory after the tenth grade.

*Physical education in higher education.* Physical education is not offered or required in the colleges and universities of New Zealand.

*Physical education facilities.* The elementary schools have good outdoor facilities, but have limited or no indoor facilities. However, swimming pools are available on a wide scale. The secondary schools often have an indoor gymnasium-type room available and adequate equipment for the program.

*Teacher training.* The School of Physical Education of the University of Otago is the only school that trains physical educators exclusively. Nine teachers colleges and five universities also train physical educators. The courses vary in length from two to three years, depending on whether the preparation is for the elementary or secondary school level. To teach on the secondary level, the teacher is required to have a two-year university course, two years of successful teaching, and a postgraduate year of study in physical education. This leads to an Endorsed Teacher's Certificate. Academic courses required include anatomy, physiology, kinesiology, chemistry, physics, and general education. Activity courses cover a wide range including camping, rugby, mountaineering, and dancing.

In the colleges and universities, the status of physical education instructors is sometimes viewed as not being on the same level as other staff members. In the public schools, equal status with academic teachers is enjoyed.

**Peru**

Peru is largely an agricultural country. It has flat plains that have a warm and rainy climate. The mountainous regions have a variable temperature and light rainfall, while the coastal areas are dry and have a generally moderate temperature.

Most of the Peruvians are engaged in sheep and cattle ranching, and other forms of agriculture. The small percentage of urban dwellers work in the cotton, mining, and fishing industries.

*Educational structure.* The state controls all phases of public education through its minister of education. There is a director of physical education, and there are local ministries of education. Many of Peru's schools are operated by the Catholic church. The state schools require attendance from the age of 7 through 14.

*Philosophy of education.* Peru strives to develop, through its schools, a citizenry that is patriotic, has good moral principles and habits, and is intellectually curious.

*Philosophy of physical education.* Physical education is not as important to the Peruvian as are the goals of intellectual development of general education. The building of physical fitness to enhance mental development is at present the major goal.

*Physical education in elementary schools.* The elementary school includes grades one through six. Physical education is taught twice a week for a total of 80 minutes. Many outdoor games are played, and dance and gymnastics are also taught.

*Physical education in secondary schools.* Secondary education includes grades seven through eleven. The secondary schools give instruction in physical education twice a week for a total of 90 minutes. The activities of the elementary school are continued, and soccer and basketball are added to the curriculum.

*Physical education facilities.* Gymnasiums exist in some secondary schools, but in general facilities are so inadequate that all classes must be held out-of-doors, and not at all if the weather interferes.

*Teacher training.* The National Institute of Physical Education is the only school that trains teachers of physical education exclusively. Twenty-six teachers colleges and seven universities also offer training. A four-year course is standard, and the normal theory courses are given, plus such other academic subjects as nutrition, music, and languages. Activity courses include camping, apparatus, basketball, track and field, and volleyball.

Teachers of physical education enjoy the same status as other teachers, but they are in extremely short supply, and many of those who are currently teaching are not well trained.

## Sweden

The climate in Sweden ranges from Arctic cold in the north, to a temperate climate in the central section, to a mild southern climate. The north has glaciers and high mountains, and long, severe winters. The south has open land and many sandy beaches, a short winter, and a long summer. The whole country is heavily forested.

The people of Sweden populate most heavily the large cities and towns of the south. They engage in such occupations as steel production, shipbuilding, farming, mining, fishing, and forestry.

*Educational structure.* The Royal Board of Education oversees and administers the schools of Sweden, but delegates much of its authority to the provincial school boards. Education is compulsory through the ninth grade.

*Philosophy of education.* The aim of Swedish education is primarily to help individuals realize their full potential as independent and reliable adults, who are sound in both mind and body.

*Philosophy of physical education.* Physical education in Sweden has as its major objective the all-around development of each individual, both physiologically and psychologically.

*Physical education in elementary schools.* In grades one through five, boys and girls are taught together by the classroom teacher. They have two or three physical education classes a week for a total of 1½ hours. Folk dance, rhythmics, games, and winter sports make up the program.

*Physical education in intermediate schools.* The intermediate school encompasses grades four through six. The physical education classes are still taught by the classroom teacher and the program is the same as that of the elementary school.

*Physical education in senior schools.* In grades seven through nine, physical education is taught by a specialist. The program includes folk dance, gymnastics, games, track and field, swimming, winter sports, and orienteering. The classes are held three times a week for a total of about an hour, and are conducted out-of-doors whenever possible.

*Physical education in secondary schools.* The secondary school is a three-year school designed for the college or university-bound student. Physical education is conducted from one to four hours a week, depending on the individual school. The program parallels that of the senior school.

*Physical education in higher education.* Physical education is not required in the

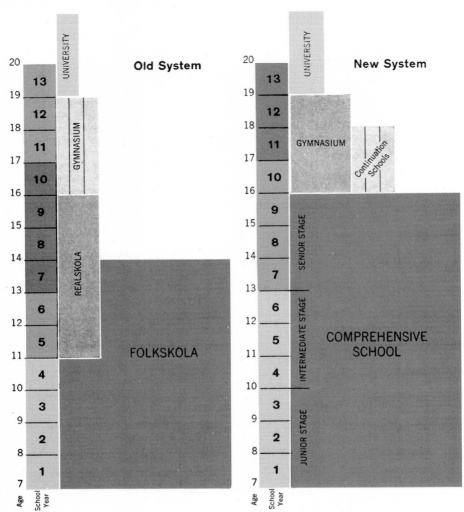

*Saturday Review, July 16, 1966. Adapted from Studio Focus, Sweden,*
*The intellectual face of Sweden, Ergo International.*

Structure of education in Sweden under new system as compared to old system.

colleges and universities of Sweden, but ample facilities and equipment are available for those who wish to participate in activity.

*Physical education facilities.* All Swedish schools have a gymnasium, a playroom, and an outdoor play area. There are also many parks, swimming pools, and private and public athletic clubs with ample facilities.

*Teacher training.* The Royal Central

Gymnastic Institute and twenty teacher-training schools offer two-year teacher preparation courses. Besides a broad range of activities including gymnastics, dance, and mountaineering, prospective teachers also must take such science courses as anatomy and physiology, first aid, history of physical education, courses in methods and materials, and student teaching.

In general, physical education teachers in Sweden do not always enjoy the same

*Courtesy Swedish Information Service.*

Swedish housewives' gymnastics.

*Courtesy Swedish Information Service.*

Idla-Flickor.

*Courtesy Swedish Information Service.*

Swedish physical education class in one of the Swedish schools.

status as academic teachers, and many times are lower salaried.

## Union of South Africa

The Union of South Africa is made up of four provinces: Natal, the Orange Free State, Transvaal, and Cape Province. South Africa enjoys a temperate climate. South Africa is bowl shaped and is ringed by mountains. The Atlantic and Indian oceans are its seacoasts.

South Africa is a multiracial country that operates on the principle of apartheid, or the separation of races. There are two official languages, English and Afrikaans. Ranching, mining of gold and diamonds, and the growing of wheat and tobacco occupy most of South Africa's working population.

*Educational structure.* The Union Department of Education supervises, coordinates, and administers the universities, special and technical high schools, and universities for white residents. In each province, a department of education administers its own public schools and teacher-training colleges. Each of these major departments also has a division of physical education. The Department of Bantu Education administers the schools for the nonwhite population.

*Philosophy of education.* The schools of South Africa seek to develop a sound and responsible citizenry, whether black or white.

*Philosophy of physical education.* Physical education is compulsory throughout the public school system. It seeks to develop individuals who are mentally and physically fit, have good health habits and knowledge, have good social behavior, and have developed an interest in recreational pursuits.

*Physical education in elementary schools.* A trained physical educator, often aided by the classroom teacher, gives each child a half-hour period of physical educa-

tion three times a week. Movement skills, rhythmic activities, folk dancing, games, calisthenics, and apparatus are all part of the program.

*Physical education in secondary schools.* In the secondary schools, physical education classes are conducted once or twice a week for 30 minutes each time. These classes are taught by a physical education teacher and include the activities of the elementary school plus track and field, gymnastics, volleyball, and swimming, if a pool is available.

*Physical education in higher education.* Physical education is not required or offered in the colleges and universities of South Africa.

*Physical education facilities.* Facilities are generally poor according to American standards. Gymnasiums are lacking, although construction is continuously going on. The schools do have outdoor fields and, in some cases, all-weather outdoor facilities.

*Teacher training.* Five universities and fourteen teachers colleges offer preparation in physical education. In general, the universities require three years of general university work, plus a year of specialization in physical education to teach on the secondary level. A two-year general education course, plus a year of specialization in physical education, satisfies the elementary level teaching requirement. The teachers colleges offer two-year courses. Theory classes include principles, philosophy, and foundations of physical education, physiology and anatomy, kinesiology, physiology of exercise, organization and administration, tests and measurements, statistics, and student teaching. Required activities include rugby, cricket, mountaineering, and camping.

The status of physical education teachers is considered to be lower than that of academic teachers, and such teachers are in short supply.

## The Union of Soviet Socialist Republics

The Soviet Union is an anomaly of many climates and cultures. The land mass crosses the continents of Europe and Asia and experiences nine different climates ranging from Arctic cold to desert heat. The largest climatic zone has long, cold winters, and short, warm summers. Characteristically, this region has a moderate rainfall, relatively low humidity, and many clear, dry days.

Much of the population of Russia is urban. The Russian people come from more than 200 ethnic groups that speak at least 150 languages. The Russian-speaking people make up half the population. This diversity of culture and language affects the schools: over the country as a whole, forty languages are used in the instructional programs, with the Russian language itself a common elective subject.

*Educational structure.* The process and progress of education in Russia are directly controlled by the state through its ministry of higher education, and the ministry of culture, a subordinate body. Within each of the fifteen Soviet republics, there is also a ministry of education that is responsible to the state.

Physical education in Russia is also under state control. Subordinate to the Presidium of the Central Committee is the Republic Sports Committee, and under it, the fifteen regional sports committees. Most aspects of physical education, from teacher placement to sports clubs, to curriculum and the publishing of journals, are controlled, organized, and scrutinized by the Central Committee.

*Philosophy of education.* The purpose of Soviet education is to prepare the student, both physically and mentally, to serve the state. The goals of the state take precedence over any personal goals the dent may have. The student is expected to become a selfless, willing, and highly productive worker; to consider the needs of society above his own personal needs; and to devote his life to the improvement of society.

*Philosophy of physical education.* The purpose of physical education in the Soviet Union is to build a nation of superbly physically fit individuals. The Soviets regard physical fitness as the key to the survival and progress of their nation. Physical education is compulsory for all students until the completion of their second year in a university, vocational, or technical school. Great emphasis is placed on physical activity as a recreational pursuit for all citizens, and there are many mass activities provided for everyone, regardless of age. The spectator is not regarded as a productive citizen.

*Physical education in preschools.* The ministries of health and education provide and supervise preschool institutions. A child may be accepted into one of these schools beginning at two months of age. For those old enough to participate, the physical education program is essentially one of basic movement. Children are taught and encouraged to run, climb, jump, throw, and play games of low organization.

*Physical education in elementary schools.* At the age of 7, Soviet children begin their years of compulsory schooling. In the first and second grades, the emphasis in physical education is on rhythmic activities, gymnastics, and active games. At the third-grade level, skiing and track and field are added to the program. Through the fourth grade, the child is taught by his classroom teacher. Throughout his elementary school years, the child receives 45 minutes of physical education instruction at least twice a week, along with supplementary activity periods at the discretion of the teacher.

*Physical education in secondary schools.* Secondary education includes grades five through eleven, and physical education is taught by a specialist. Although the major emphasis is still on gymnastics, such activities as basketball, soccer, volleyball, and water sports are also stressed. The skills of skiing and track and field continue as part of the program. Unless the weather interferes, the program is an outdoor one, and coeducational. The classroom teacher continues to provide periods of vigorous activity over and above the biweekly 45-minute instructional periods. It is at this level that the life-long concept of intense competition is introduced.

*Physical education in higher education.* Physical education is required in the first two years of university-level education. Students are given a variety of activities to choose from, but all must learn to swim and all are required to pass physical fitness tests.

*Physical education facilities.* The facilities provided for physical education are excellent. There are parks set aside specifically for recreational and cultural pursuits. There are many camps, sports clubs, and youth groups, all with their own facilities. Beyond this, there are special sports schools devoted to giving intensive instruction to children. Between the ages of 12 and 18, a child with a high degree of facility in a sport is recommended for acceptance at one of these schools. Here, outside of school hours, he receives concentrated coaching twice a week for two hours each time. This system has helped to develop many of the Russian champion athletes.

*Teacher training.* The Soviet Union prepares its physical educators to be either teachers or coaches. The coaches concentrate on one particular sport, and work in the sports clubs. The teachers who go into the schools are trained intensively in gymnastics. They also concentrate, although less than the coaches, on a particular game or sport.

Graduates of eleven-year secondary schools may enter one of the sixteen training institutions for physical educators, or go to one of the fifty colleges or universities, or one of the more than twenty other specialized schools of physical education. Prospective teachers and coaches must be highly proficient in the skills of physical education and have taken specific background courses in sciences and Russian studies. If accepted, they enter a four-year program that, in the academic areas, closely parallels the programs in the United States.

The graduate teacher or coach in Russia is an important person. He is highly respected and has much power and authority.

## West Germany

In the north, where Germany is bounded by the Baltic and North seas, the land is relatively flat. The hills and mountains become increasingly higher through the midsection until the supreme height of the Alps is reached in the south. Germany has a moderate climate, with warm summers.

The population of the German Federal Republic, which is almost entirely urban, includes many refugees from East Germany. These people are mainly white-collar workers or skilled artisans. The small segment of rural dwellers is engaged in the raising of stock, while the urban workers are employed in the iron, coal, steel, auto, and optical industries.

*Educational structure.* Each of the ten states of West Germany has its own ministry of education, which is directed by a minister of education. The ministries are responsible for the administration of the public schools in each state, and for introducing new legislation pertaining to the schools.

*Philosophy of education.* Following the division of Germany after World War II, the German schools were reorganized to eliminate the militaristic aspects. West Germany, the United States, England, and France cooperated to achieve the reorganization. Thus, in philosophy, the schools of West Germany became much like those of the Allied countries. At the present time, general education is compulsory from the age of 6 through 14. The aim of general education is to produce a well-rounded, moral, and responsible individual. German schools are structured to suit individual needs. Thus, those students who complete the four-year elementary school may go on to the terminal intermediate school or to a secondary school. The intermediate school is designed for those who will enter an occupation or go on to technical training following the completion of grade ten. The secondary school is designed for the college- or university-bound student, and

German physical education.

German physical education.

terminates with grade thirteen, the equivalent of the first year of college.

*Philosophy of physical education.* The aim of the program is to contribute to the total development of the individual through activity and participation. Sought-after goals are the development of physical fitness, a love of movement, creativity, and a sense of fair play.

*Physical education in elementary schools.* During the first four years of schooling, classes in physical education are held two or three times a week for a total of one hour. Activities included are basic movement skills, such as running, jumping, throwing and climbing; gymnastics; tumbling and apparatus; games of low organization; and swimming.

*Physical education in intermediate schools.* This school includes grades five through ten. Physical education is offered two or three times a week for a total of about one hour. The program of the elementary school is continued in the intermediate school with the addition of track and field, soccer, volleyball, and basketball.

*Physical education in secondary schools.* This school division encompasses grades five through thirteen. Physical education is taught three times a week for a total of one hour. The program is essentially the same as that of the intermediate school, but in some schools rowing, skiing, ice skating, and hiking are added to the curriculum.

*Physical education in higher education.* West German universities have departments of physical education, and some training is compulsory for all students. However, the program is limited at the university level both by equipment and facilities and the lack of sufficient status of these departments in the educational structure.

*Physical education facilities.* West Germany has a severe shortage of facilities and well-qualified teachers of physical education.

*Teacher training.* West Germany has two schools solely devoted to training teachers of physical education. These schools have a three-year course which students may enter after spending one year in another teacher training institution. These schools also train teachers for all three levels of public instruction. Germany has three teacher-training colleges and twenty-six universities that offer degree courses in physical education. Students electing a three-year course teach on the elementary level. To teach on the intermediate or secondary level, a four-year course is mandatory. These schools offer a broad range of activity courses, similar to those in American universities, and in addition require theory courses such as anatomy, physiology, psychology, health, and student teaching.

On the public educational level, physical education teachers are regarded in the same light as teachers of academic subjects.

### QUESTIONS AND EXERCISES

1. Do a comparative study of physical education in one country in each of five continents.
2. What role does education play in the lives of other countries in the world?
3. Trace the history of ten sports, showing the country that was responsible for its origin.
4. Do a research paper on the Peace Corps and how physical education is helping to promote international goodwill through this organization.
5. What are three outstanding international organizations in health, physical education, and recreation, and what are the objectives of each?
6. Write an essay of approximately 500 words on the history of the Olympic games.
7. Prepare a plan for students majoring in physical education to follow in promoting good international relations within their college.
8. Invite a foreign person to your class to

discuss the role of sports and physical education in his country.

## SELECTED REFERENCES

American Council on Education: Universities of the world outside the U.S.A., 1875 Massachusetts Avenue, N.W., Washington, D. C.

Basic facts about the United Nations, New York, 1962, United Nations Office of Public Information.

British Information Services: Education in Britain, 1964, Harrow, Her Majesty's Stationery Office.

Committee on International Relations, National Education Association: Other lands, other peoples: a country-by-country fact book, Washington, D. C., 1961, The Association.

Committee on International Relations, National Education Association: Resources for teaching about the United Nations: with annotated bibliography, Washington, D. C., 1962, The Association.

Institute of International Education: Handbook on international study, 1 East 67th Street, New York, New York.

International Council of Health, Physical Education and Recreation (assorted publications), 1201 Sixteenth Street, N.W., Washington, D. C.

Johnson, William, editor: Physical education around the world, Indianapolis, 1966, Phi Epsilon Kappa Fraternity.

Publications of the World Confederation of Organizations of the Teaching Profession: *Panorama: teaching throughout the world* and *Echo*. (Also assorted publications, 1201 Sixteenth Street, N.W., Washington, D. C.)

Van Dalen, Deobold, Mitchell, Elmer, and Bennett, Bruce: A world history of physical education, Englewood Cliffs, N. J., 1961, Prentice-Hall, Inc.

The javelin cast

*Works of R. Tait McKenzie.*
*Courtesy Joseph Brown, School of*
*Architecture, Princeton University.*

**PART FIVE**

# Scientific foundations of physical education

# Chapter 15

# The biological makeup of man

*Quest magazine, Monograph III, Dec., 1964.

*To A Physiology Professor**

*Wise is the one*

> *who can dissect*
> *with uncommitted facts*
> *pounding heart longings*
> *sucking lung desires*

> *who can analyze*
> *with principled laws*
> *muscle-sculptured action*
> *gravity-bound patterns*

> *who can understand*
> *with humbled reason*
> *thinking eye thoughts*
> *feeling brain sight*

> *who can communicate*
> *with child-like rapture*
> *passion-filled flesh pittings*
> *undaunted human aspiration*

*He combines seeing with the seen.*
—Betty Willis Brooks

*Better to hunt in fields, for health*
*Unbought, than fee the doctor for a*
*Nauseous draught. The wise, for cure,*
*On exercise depend; God never made*
*His work for man to mend.*
—John Dryden

Today, physical education is based on scientific facts and principles. As such, its program is developed as a result of systematized knowledge based on verifiable general laws. This knowledge covers many areas of learning. The physical education program is established with respect to the biological, psychological, and sociological aspects of growth and development. It aims to develop youth into citizens who have the capacity to enjoy a happy, vigorous, and interesting life. To accomplish this task, it is necessary to know the individual, how his physical body functions, how he learns, why he acts as he does, and his relation to the group, society, and world of which he is a part. Furthermore, the human being represents a unified whole, each part being necessary to the successful functioning of every other part. The individual reacts as a "whole" organism and not just in parts. Therefore education should be concerned with whether or not activities benefit the "whole" individual and not just one part. When a child swims, there should be concern not only for the physical development which ensues from this experience but for the social, mental, and emotional aspects as well.

In Chapters 15 through 18 an attempt is made to point out some of the scientific knowledge that has a bearing on physical education and the "whole" individual from the standpoint of biology, psychology, and sociology. Such knowledge will help to clarify the role of physical education in our society.

## MAN'S BIOLOGICAL HISTORY

This chapter will be devoted to the fundamental scientific interpretations of

physical education which are biological in nature.

## Man's potential— and his performance

Dr. Joseph W. Still spent many years studying human physical and intellectual behavior. The illustration shown below depicts his research into the physical

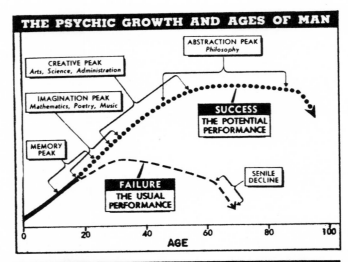

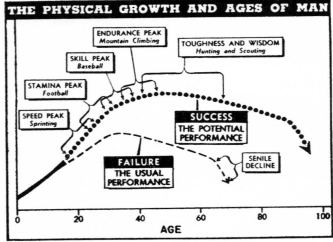

*Still, Joseph W.:*
*The New York Times Magazine,*
*Nov. 24, 1957.*

The physical and psychic growths and ages of man—possibility and performance. The upper lines indicate the physical and psychological potentials of normal people, with peak periods for various activities. The lower lines indicate how most people fail to measure up.

growth and ages and the psychic growth and ages of man.

A study of these charts will show that not more than 5% of the population follow the upper success curves (dotted line). The failure curve in regard to physical growth shows the physical development of people today to be lacking. They are exposed to very little physical exercise; they eat, drink, and smoke too much; and they decline rapidly after 30 years of age. It will also be noted that four sections are identified where peak performance in various sports occurs. The psychological growth chart also shows an emphasis on the failure type of performance. Mental traits excel at different stages of development. Memorizing ability is great in youth, creative imagination reaches its height in the twenties and thirties, skill in analysis and synthesis of subject matter reigns in the middle years, and the age of philosophy characterizes the later years. Dr. Still raises the question, "How can we prevent these failures?" He goes on to point out, "As a starter, everyone should say: If I want respect as a human being I have the obligation to respect and care for and develop my body and mind."* I am sure we would all agree that this is a good philosophy for successful living.

Biologically man is designed to be an active creature. Although changes in civilization have resulted in his decreasing the amount of activity needed in accomplishing the basic tasks associated with living, man's body has not changed. Therefore man must become well informed as to the health requirements that his biological base demands and recognize the importance of vigorous physical activity in his life. If he does not, his health, productivity, and effectiveness in life will suffer. Being physically educated is essen-

tial to proper functioning in life. Furthermore, it is closely tied in with man's mental powers, as well as with his emotional, social, and spiritual powers.

If man is to survive as a productive creature living a vigorous and interesting life, there must be a recognition of the biological requirements placed upon him. Physical education is essential to the life he lives. Physical activities can contribute much to his effectiveness. Skills, health knowledge, and protective services are necessities.

**Evolution**

A study of the evolution of man points to the necessity for physical activity. Evolution refers to the development of a race or of a species, during which period of development a series of changes take place and morphological and physiological characteristics are acquired that distinguish a particular species or group.

The evolution of man shows that he has made great progress in developing himself from a lower form of life. If a person studies the history of mankind, it will be discovered that man has gradually evolved. Evidence shows that there have been many eras of growth. During the first era there existed only one-celled plants and animals. Next came the era of the invertebrates, when forms of life such as sponges and starfish existed without a spinal column. Then followed the age of fishes, amphibians, reptiles, dinosaurs, mammals, birds, *Homo sapiens,* and, finally, historic man. Thus man has evolved.

Physical education must help to develop a higher and better plane of living as its part in this "evolving" process if it is to justify its worth. A study of evolution shows that man should not follow a sedentary existence but, instead, should be active, should exercise the various parts of his body, and should spend more time in the out-of-doors. Therefore phys-

---

*Still, Joseph W.: New York Times Magazine, Nov. 24, 1957.

ical education has many potentialities. To train youth successfully nature's methods should be followed. This holds true also in regard to the activities in which man engages. Primitive man obtained his food, provided shelter, and protected himself against a hostile environment through activities that involved walking, running, hopping, climbing, throwing, carrying, leaping, and hanging. These are consistent with the evolutionary process. These activities have formed the basic movements for man throughout his long history. They are a part of his inheritance. The games, dances, and other physical education activities that are utilized today have as a basis these racially old activities. For example, basketball is running and throwing, and dancing is walking, leaping, stretching, and hopping. It seems that man, in his attempt to evolve into a higher and higher plane of living, should follow a physical education program based on these fundamental activities rather than one that does not conform to such standards. These activities will best serve the purposes of developing a body with a strong framework and adequate motor mechanism. They will aid in enabling man to move with freedom, with rhythm and grace, and with less utilization of energy.

## Biological defects of man in the light of his structure

Biologically, the "evolving" process in man has resulted in many advantages and also many disadvantages. Today man has a high standard of living. He has automobiles, trains, and jet planes to take him wherever he wants to go, television and radio sets to see and hear world events, highly mechanized machinery to manufacture goods for every need and desire, beautiful houses and buildings in which to live and congregate, and other conveniences and luxuries to please and entertain him. However, there is another

side to the picture. Are all of these devices, inventions, and luxuries that are characteristic of his mode of life helping him biologically? Hickman, an expert on physiology, points out some interesting facts in respect to the highly specialized and artificial life that man leads. These are summarized in the following paragraphs.

*In this "evolving" process man has changed his means of locomotion from a quadruped to a biped position.* This has had implications for his health. It is believed man originally walked on all fours.* An upright position has influenced adversely man's digestive and circulatory systems. It has compressed his large intestine with resulting conditions of constipation and colitis. This position has caused an irregular distribution of blood as a result of the heart's being below several parts of the body. It is a contributing cause of fainting. Hemorrhoids and varicose veins are caused to some degree by the increased blood pressure in lower regions of the body. An upright posture has increased the difficulty of balance, and consequently many postural problems have developed. In a report to the National Academy of Sciences, S. W. Briton, University of Virginia scientist, pointed out that the upright position was due to the development of a superior brain in man, but that at the same time such a position resulted in fallen arches, varicose veins, and possibly sinus and heart trouble. He also reported that such a position resulted in major adjustments on the part of the circulatory and nervous systems.

The problem that arises as a result of man being placed in a biped position can be alleviated through physical education

---

*According to the April 3, 1950, issue of Life Magazine, there is now evidence to show that primitive prehumans stood erect. Raymond Dart, famed anthropologist from South Africa, discovered the pelvis of an early ape man which indicated an erect posture.

activities that stress standing, walking, jumping, leaping, and other fundamental movements. It is important to compensate for this position by developing in each child a strong trunk musculature to house the vital organs and nerve centers. It is important to strengthen the abdominal muscles so that the viscera is in proper position. Furthermore, the elements of body mechanics must be recognized so there is proper body balance as man carries himself on his legs.

Man has a very complex nervous system which has difficulty adapting to present-day living. Evidence of this is the high rate of insanity and mental disorders that prevail. The type of competition wherein man is continually striving to get ahead of his fellowmen has resulted in several nervous maladjustments. These maladjustments have their effect on the entire human mechanism. Diseases such as angina pectoris may be to a great degree the result of conditions that involve worry and sorrow. Seven hundred thousand people die each year of heart disease, which many individuals feel is related to the nervous tension involved in modern-day living.

As a result of the fast pace man follows, he is placing more and more reliance on drugs and narcotics as a means of enjoyment, stimulation, and escape. Tobacco, coffee, tea, and alcohol are good examples. Many other drugs and narcotics are used as sedatives and to eliminate pain. The result of all this indulgence and self-medication has meant mental and physical deterioration to many users. Instead of aiding and helping to cure man's maladjustments, they have frequently tended to aggravate the situation.

Tobacco, drugs, colds, and respiratory diseases are blunting man's sense of taste and smell to the point where they are now greatly inferior to those of other animals. Close work, sewing, writing, and the like have been detrimental to man's

eyesight. The noise from jet planes, the screeching of subway trains, and the blare of automobile horns have helped to deaden man's hearing. Man is losing some of the senses which have been of great assistance over the years in interpreting his environment.

It has been stated that individuals in the United States are the best fed of those anywhere in the world but at the same time are the most undernourished. This is very true for a broad segment of the population. Today it is common practice to prepare foods that tickle the palate. Steaks, chops, and other choice cuts of meat taste good but are lower in nutritional content than many of the lower-priced cuts, such as liver and kidneys. Many people also eat an overabundance of rich sweets and pastries, to the neglect of selecting their diet from the four basic groups of food. Such practices have led to dental caries and possibly to disorders of the stomach, such as ulcers, tumors, and cancer. Furthermore, a great amount of the food lacks bulk, and consequently the alimentary tract does not function satisfactorily.

Man has evolved into a hairless animal, which necessitates the wearing of clothing and provision for shelter. These artificial devices for protection against the elements have resulted in irregular body surface temperatures, with greater susceptibility to cold. Furthermore, clothing prevents the body from absorbing the healthy rays of the sun. This is conducive to rickets, tuberculosis, and other maladies.

Originally the purpose of the sex drive was to procreate the race. When not used for this purpose the sex drive was latent in man and did not cause many of the social problems that exist today. Society has evolved to a point where the sex instinct has to be curbed through will power or other outlets found for it. In weaker members of the population, outlets are sought in the form of perversion and other means considered anti-social. This has resulted in crime, mental disorders, and venereal disease. Unhappiness, pain, and shame have been visited upon many families as the result of promiscuity in sex relations.

Man spends more and more of his time indoors. His work, recreation, and living are mainly confined to offices, buildings, houses, and modes of transportation that are overheated, lack fresh air, and are not conducive to good health. In following the line of least resistance, man finds

it much easier to settle back in a chair where it is warm and comfortable than to face the elements where he might have to exercise a bit to get the blood circulating.

Along with less outdoor life, man is congregating in cities where hundreds of people live in one block and breathe germs into each other's faces. Man's early existence was in the wide open spaces where he developed a strong and sturdy body and a nervous system that was adapted to his needs. The changeover to

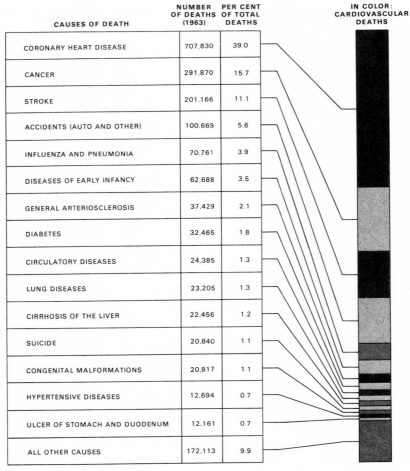

| CAUSES OF DEATH | NUMBER OF DEATHS (1963) | PER CENT OF TOTAL DEATHS |
|---|---|---|
| CORONARY HEART DISEASE | 707,830 | 39.0 |
| CANCER | 291,870 | 15.7 |
| STROKE | 201,166 | 11.1 |
| ACCIDENTS (AUTO AND OTHER) | 100,669 | 5.6 |
| INFLUENZA AND PNEUMONIA | 70,761 | 3.9 |
| DISEASES OF EARLY INFANCY | 62,688 | 3.5 |
| GENERAL ARTERIOSCLEROSIS | 37,429 | 2.1 |
| DIABETES | 32,465 | 1.8 |
| CIRCULATORY DISEASES | 24,385 | 1.3 |
| LUNG DISEASES | 23,205 | 1.3 |
| CIRRHOSIS OF THE LIVER | 22,456 | 1.2 |
| SUICIDE | 20,840 | 1.1 |
| CONGENITAL MALFORMATIONS | 20,817 | 1.1 |
| HYPERTENSIVE DISEASES | 12,694 | 0.7 |
| ULCER OF STOMACH AND DUODENUM | 12,161 | 0.7 |
| ALL OTHER CAUSES | 172,113 | 9.9 |

*Time-Life Books Special Report:*
*The healthy life, New York, 1966, Time, Inc.*

Major causes of death in the United States.

an urban, indoor existence has been so rapid in his history that adaptation is far from being realized at the present time.

The maxim "survival of the fittest" has become a thing of the past. Present-day humanitarian values decree that the unfit should be protected and allowed to endure, as well as the fit. Therefore the unfit, as well as the fit, are allowed to procreate the race. This results in many undesirable strains being continued from generation to generation. The humanitarian outlook on such a practice is understandable. However, in viewing this condition from a purely biological viewpoint it can be seen that the race is weakened thereby, not only from the standpoint of resistance to disease but also in regard to perpetuating many factors that will make disease more imminent.

A perusal of the facts just mentioned would tend to encourage one to believe that man is living a decrepit, weak, and unhealthy existence and is degenerating to the point where he may become extinct. The facts do set one's mind to thinking in this direction. Whether or not man can adapt himself to a highly industrialized, urban, inactive existence remains to be seen. At the present time, the facts in regard to his mental and physical deterioration sound a warning. The great advances made by the medical profession in combating infectious diseases have been outstanding. These diseases are rapidly being brought under control. But what about such maladies as nervous disorders, heart disease, and cancer? What are the solutions to these scourges of mankind? Is man attempting to change too rapidly from an existence characterized by out-of-door living, simple diet, active pursuits, and quiet living to one characterized by an indoor existence, choice food, fast living, and inaction? Is man's nervous system adequate to meet such a rapid change? The answers lie in the future.

## HEALTH OF THE NATION

The United States ranks very high in regard to the health of its people when compared with the other nations of the world. However, in analyzing the health statistics of this country, it can readily be seen that disease and ill health are prevalent in great numbers in the population

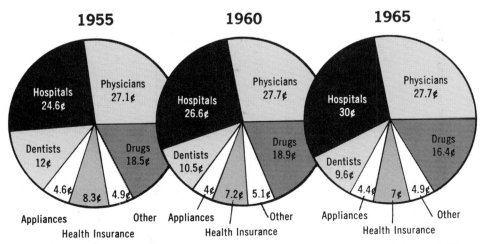

*AMA Health Education Service for Schools and Colleges, Vol. 7, Chicago, April, 1967, American Medical Association.*

Distribution of the health care dollar for years 1955, 1960, and 1965.

and that much of this disease and ill health are preventable. Although we have the best facilities and personnel in the world for combating disease, there is still room for improvement. One of the important government agencies working toward improved health conditions is the United States Public Health Service.

Some health statistics that show where improvements can be made in the health of the nation are as follows:

1. One out of ten college students will have emotional conflicts of sufficient severity to warrant professional help.

2. The number of suicides is going up and three times as many suicide attempts are made by females as by males. The most common age for both sexes is 19 years.

3. There are approximately 10 million overweight teen-age boys and girls in the United States, and from 15 to 20% of all adolescents are overweight to the point where it is a medical problem.

4. An estimated one billion unfilled dental cavities exist in men, women, and children throughout the United States.

5. Venereal disease rates are going up with more than 600,000 cases a year among young people ages 15 to 24.

6. More than $8 billion is spent each year on tobacco.

7. More than 107 million Americans breathe polluted air, detrimental to their health.

8. An estimated one out of four hospital beds throughout the world is occupied by a person suffering from disease caused by polluted water.

9. The American public is defrauded of over $100 million a year through the mails, much of which is concerned with health matters.

10. Estimated costs of sick-leave payments in industry exceed $2 billion annually.

11. Of the draftees not qualified for military service, about one half are turned down for medical reasons.

12. Six out of every ten Americans use laxatives frequently.

13. There are more than 5 million men and women alcoholics in the United States.

14. A majority of drug addicts are between 18 and 20 years of age.

15. At least 5,000 lives could be saved annually if occupants were not thrown from vehicles in accidents. If used, seat belts would cut down on these fatalities.

16. Each year over 325,000 people die whose deaths should have been prevented.

17. Nearly 5 million man-years of work are lost each year as a result of bad health.

18. Thirty to 60% of all patients seeking

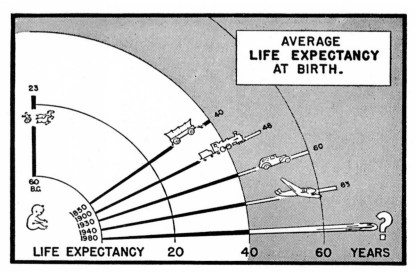

*Adult Hygiene and Geriatrics,*
*Indiana State Board of Health.*

doctors' advice today have emotional disorders.

19. Approximately 250,000 to 400,000 children under 18 years of age appear in juvenile courts each year.

In respect to young people, health statistics show that, as a result of better nutrition, boys and girls in the United States are taller and heavier than their parents. They enjoy an unprecedented freedom from infectious diseases because of antibiotics. They learn more at an earlier age than did their parents because of new educational techniques. Although the draft statistics have shown that overall rejection rates from the armed services have climbed from 22.7% in World War II to 23.6% during the Korean War to an estimated 35.2% in 1964, military statisticians note that part of this increase is because mental testing has been more discriminating. On the positive side it has been noted by the Army Surgeon General's Office that the recruit of today is 1.2 inches taller and 18 pounds heavier than the recruit of World War I, and ½ inch taller and 7 pounds heavier than the recruit of World War II. College statistics of young people tell a similar story. The average Yale freshman was 5 feet 7½ inches tall and weighed 136 pounds in 1885, and only about 5% of the class stood more than 6 feet tall. Today the average freshman is more than 3 inches taller and 20 pounds heavier, and better than 30% of the class is over 6 feet tall. Young women at Vassar and Smith colleges are about 2 inches taller and 10 pounds heavier than were comparable girls at the turn of the century. Girls are also maturing earlier as indicated by the onset of menstruation which has dropped from the age of 14 in 1900 to 12.8 years of age today. However, an estimated 10 to 15% of American teen-agers are too fat and have poor eating habits. Many of them are physically inactive. The statistics indicate, however, that the stamina

and skill of teen-agers in the United States is improving.

Modern-day man is a victim of many preventable defects and diseases. Industrial life, with its concentration of people in urban areas, its sedentary aspects, routine work, unemployment, and other evils, may be listed as contributing factors. The tension associated with modern-day living and the fear, hate, and worry that contribute to many mental disorders are other factors. Man was not intended to live an existence characterized by fear of atom and hydrogen bombs; hate for people of other races, creeds, and nationalities; and worry over his security. There is a need for a greater number of doctors, nurses, and psychiatrists and for more facilities to aid in the prevention and cure of disease. Furthermore, there should be more measures established to cross the chasm between medical services and low incomes.

Physical education cannot prevent or treat many of the defects and diseases found in human beings today. However, it can contribute to a healthy populace in many ways. It can provide a source of pleasure and a substitute for worry, hate, and fear among many persons suffering with mental disorders. Our modern industrial age has contributed markedly to weak physiques and to insufficient strength. Physical education can help in developing strength, stamina, endurance, and a state of physical fitness in the individuals who are lacking in these important characteristics. It can also help by providing a means of relaxation after long hours of work. Physical education can develop in the children of today the skills, interests, and attitudes that will ensure them many enjoyable moments during their leisure time. Physical education can also help in developing the "whole" individual so that a healthier, more stable, and more peaceful world can be built.

*New York University Camp,*
*Lake Sebago, N. Y.*

Physical education can provide a source of pleasure.

## MAN'S ORGANIC FOUNDATIONS
### Biological basis of life

The cell of the human body is the biological basis of life. The human body starts from one cell and, as a result of many divisions and redivisions, many thousands of cells are formed. Many of the cells are formed into units that function as the organic systems of the body. Every part of the body has cells—the brain, liver, stomach, and arms and legs included. One estimate has been made that there are 400 billion cells in the body and that there are approximately 5 million cells in a small drop of blood.

The cells of the body are alive. They take in food and oxygen and give off waste material. In order to keep alive, the organism must have this food and oxygen and must eliminate wastes. The cells perform this function. They are bathed in a liquid called lymph which carries food and oxygen to the cells and takes away wastes.

The muscles of the body are made up of cells. In the evolutionary process these muscle cells developed from rather simple to complex structures. The muscular system developed before many of the other systems of the body. As the muscle cells became more specialized, other units of cells were needed to carry food and oxygen to the various parts of the body and to carry away wastes. Thus began the excretory, digestive, respiratory, and circulatory systems. These systems developed in response to a need that was stimulated and initiated by the muscular system. They develop in a human body and grow strong in response to the work placed upon them by the muscular system. Therefore, muscular work increases the capacity for the individual for performance.

**Makeup of the human body**

The human body is a very intricate mechanism, the makeup of which should be familiar to every physical educator. As the Old Testament states about the human body, "I am fearfully and wonderfully made." The student of physical education will study the human body in detail during his training. The following discussion will be concerned with only a brief review of some of the aspects of the human mechanism which have special implications for the biological interpretations of physical education.

**The skeleton.** The skeleton of the human body can in many ways be compared to the framework of a building under construction. The framework represents the foundation or outline on which the building will be constructed. It represents the size, shape, and contour of the building. The skeleton also performs this function for the human body. It is a framework that protects the various bodily systems.

The bones that make up the skeleton in older persons have less animal matter than do the bones of children. Therefore an elderly individual's bones are brittle, break easily, and heal slowly. In children small amounts of mineral matter make bones more flexible, and consequently they can be bent in various shapes. This has implications for a child's posture. The child's skeleton is very flexible; therefore, such practices as habitual standing and sitting in a stooped position for long periods of time may result in abnormal posture.

The body has joints that make movement possible. Basically, there are two kinds of joints with which physical educators should be especially concerned, the ball and socket and the hinge. Examples of a ball and socket joint are the shoulder and the hip, and examples of the hinge joint are the elbow, knee, or fingers. The joints of the body are essential to movement. The physical educator should be well informed as to the action of the joints in various activities and the care and training that are needed to develop and strengthen these areas.

**Musculature.** The musculature of the human body is an essential to movement; consequently, the physical educator should be familiar with its composition and action. In studying anatomy and kinesiology he will discover in detail the various muscles and how they function in body movement. He will discover how important muscles are to the human body, how they provide for locomotion, give form to the body, produce body heat, and make breathing, circulation, and other vital movements possible.

This discussion of musculature is confined to a discussion of two principles with which every physical educator should be familiar. These principles are *muscle tonus* and *reciprocal innervation*. *Muscle tonus* means the constant, partial contraction of the muscles of the body. This is essential to good posture as well as to the efficient functioning of some of the organic systems. This slight contraction on the part of muscles makes it possible for them to react to stimuli within the space of a very short time. Such a phenomenon makes muscle contraction possible with a minimum expenditure of energy. A state of muscle tonus is essential to good body health. *Reciprocal innervation* refers to the part that antagonistic muscles play in performing coordinated movements. This principle works on the theory that whenever a group of muscles contracts to perform a movement, the antagonistic muscles relax, so that a coordinated, smooth, rhythmical movement results. A good example of this principle is the movement of flexing the arm. The biceps contracts and the antagonistic muscle, or triceps, relaxes, resulting in free and easy action. When a person is a novice in a game, he quite often performs in an awkward and uncoordinated manner because his antagonistic muscles do not relax and allow for free and easy movement. The proper coordinations between the muscle groups have not been established.

**Circulatory system.** The circulatory system of the body carries food and oxygen to and brings wastes from the multitude of cells that make up the organism. These elements are transported by means of blood through a system of tubes called blood vessels. The blood is kept flowing as a result of heart action.

There are two sets of blood vessels— *the arteries that carry the blood from the heart and veins that carry the blood to the heart.* Arteries divide into smaller and smaller branches called capillaries which connect with the cells. The capillaries unite with veins and then the veins, with various small tributaries, unite into larger veins going to the heart.

The heart has four chambers, the two upper chambers being the auricles and the two lower chambers the ventricles. The veins send blood to the auricles, the walls of the auricles contract, and the blood then goes to the ventricles. The ventricles contract, sending blood to the various parts of the body. After forcing the blood into the arteries, the heart relaxes for a moment and rests. Then the process is repeated. There are two valves

between the auricles and the ventricles and two at the mouths of the arteries. The valves prevent the blood from flowing backward.

The blood follows a definite route through the heart. The right side of the heart sends blood to the lungs where the blood picks up oxygen and then goes back to the left side of the heart. On the left side of the heart, the blood is forced into the arteries and to the entire body. After nourishing the cells and picking up the wastes, it goes back to the right side of the heart. The entire process consumes less than one minute.

The composition of the blood is interesting to examine. The liquid part is known as plasma. Within the plasma float millions of little red and white corpuscles. The red corpuscles carry oxygen from the lungs to the various cells throughout the body, and the white corpuscles kill disease germs that enter the body. About nine tenths of the blood is plasma and the rest is dissolved food and other materials such as wastes. The capillary walls are very thin, and as the blood goes through them, the plasma escapes and becomes lymph surrounding the cells. Oxygen breaks loose from the red corpuscles and passes into the lymph and to the cells. Waste materials pass through the lymph into the blood. The lymph acts as a middleman between the cells and the blood as it passes oxygen and food to the cells and wastes to the blood. In addition to the blood capillaries, there are also lymphatic capillaries that take the impure lymph from among the cells and carry it to the blood.

The machine that is the center of the circulating system is the heart. Its action results in nourishment being sent to the millions of cells throughout the body. It beats continuously day and night. It is essential to life. Nothing should be done to harm this delicate piece of machinery. The body should be protected against dis-

The La Sierra, California, high school physical fitness program.

ease germs which might impair its use. Exercise should be adapted to an individual's needs, so as not to place too much of a strain on the heart. This is especially true of adults who have passed middle life. However, it should be remembered that the heart is a muscle, and like all muscles, it becomes stronger with use. This has implications for the physical educator in providing activities for children of school age. If a child's heart is normal and healthy, it cannot be injured through exercise. There is considerable evidence to support this tenet. This should not preclude, however, that physical educators should determine through an examination of health records and consultations with physicians whether a child has a rheumatic fever history or some other cardiac disturbance that might make strenuous exercise questionable. Furthermore, the physical educator should be cognizant of the fact that even though the normal heart tissue of children cannot be damaged by exercise, very strenuous exercise can do damage to other parts of the body besides the heart. For example, overfatigue has implications for a child's emotional health.

**Respiratory system.** The respiratory system consists of air tubes leading into billions of microscopic permeable air sacs in the lungs. It has two main functions— taking oxygen into the body and giving off carbon dioxide.

In respect to oxygen, the body leads a hand-to-mouth existence. Oxygen cannot be stored; it must be taken in as needed. The body takes in oxygen every minute of the day and night. If the organism stops breathing, it will die within the space of a very short time. Carbon dioxide is given off through the respiratory system. It is formed in the cells and carried by the blood to the lungs and then escapes into the air.

The chest cavity, where the lungs and also the heart are located, is protected by the sternum or breast bone and the ribs. In breathing, the ribs lift upward and outward, and the diaphragm is pulled downward. The air passes to the lungs through the trachea which is kept open by rings of cartilage. The trachea divides, with a branch going to each lung. Within the lungs these branches divide again and again and end in little air sacs. The branches of the trachea are called bronchial tubes. The walls of the air sacs are very thin, and the blood flows in them through capillaries. Oxygen passes into the blood through the walls of the air sacs. Carbon dioxide passes into the sacs and out of the lungs. The air in the lungs gives off oxygen and takes on carbon dioxide.

One important point should be clear to the physical educator in interpreting the respiratory system for his work. So-called "breathing exercises" are not beneficial to the human mechanism. They should be discounted because it is a physiological fact that oxygen cannot be stored up for future use but is taken in as needed. The respiratory system supplies enough oxygen in normal activity for body needs. The amount of oxygen used by the cells is determined by the needs of the tissues and not by the oxygen that is available. Except for corrective therapy, breathing exercises have no value for the human body.

**Nervous system.** The nervous system is the "boss" of the human body. It issues the orders and controls and regulates everything the organism does. It controls the organs and other parts of the body; acts as an organ of the mind; regulates body heat, secretion of digestive juices, and excretion of wastes; and controls every movement that is made. The nervous system is composed mainly of the brain, spinal cord, nerves which go out from the brain and spinal cord to various parts of the body, and ganglia or masses of gray tissue found in inner organs of the body.

The fundamental unit of the nervous system, the nerve cell or neuron, is found in all the various parts of the nervous system and especially in the brain and spinal cord. It is of gray color. It is through the neuron that messages are carried between the receptors or cells that receive the impulses to the effectors or cells that react to the impulses, such as found in a muscle or gland. The nerve fibers that connect nerve cells with various parts of the body are white in color, gray in the center, and the machinery that carry the messages or impulses. The gray core of the fiber is a branch of a nerve cell.

Three kinds of neurons are found in the nervous system: first, the *sensory* neuron, second, the *motor* neuron, and third, the *intermediate* neuron.

The sensory or afferent neuron carries impulses into the central nervous system. These impulses may be carried from the skin, eye, ear, and various other parts of the body to the brain. These impulses are responsible for feeling, seeing, hearing, and for understanding the condition of the body at all times. The motor or efferent neuron sends messages from the spinal cord to the muscles and results in muscular action. The intermediate neuron lies entirely within the central nervous system itself and has no contact with the outside.

The brain, a vital part of the nervous system, is located within the cranial cavity and weighs approximately fifty ounces. It has three principal divisions. The first division is the *cerebrum* or major part of the brain. The gray outer layer of the cerebrum or the *cortex* is the seat of intelligence. It thinks and feels, decides what individuals will do, and governs the whole body. The second section, the *cerebellum*, is located under the back lobes of the cerebrum. It assists in controlling muscles of locomotion, balance, and equilibrium. The third division, the *medulla oblongata*, is the enlarged upper end of the spinal cord and is composed in large part of fibers that connect various parts of the body and brain, some of which are sensory and some motor fibers. The medulla also has centers that control the heart and lungs. When the medulla is injured, death results. The heart stops beating and breathing stops.

The nervous system controls the body to a great degree unconsciously or involuntarily. This is called *reflex action*. An example of this can be seen after striking an individual just below the knee-cap. Involuntarily the leg will move upward. Practically all control of the internal organs is carried on by reflexes. These are natural reflexes and the organism is born with them.

Another set of reflexes, different from the natural ones, consists of those that can be developed through practice. A swimmer does not think of how he is going to swim—how he is going to move his arms or his legs in the crawl stroke. Instead, it becomes automatic with him as a result of practice. An important part of education is concerned with developing the right kind of these reflexes. In physical education such social reflexes as fair play, respect for the individual, courtesy, and the like are important. As a result of practice, these attributes become a reality without thought to one's actions. In a sense these habits can be viewed as reflexes that are formed by repetition of acts. Physical educators should remember that this type of reaction is most readily formed in youth and that many situations exist in the playground, gymnasium, and swimming pool where they can be most readily practiced.

The nervous system needs good care if it is to serve the individual. Adequate sleep is an essential for a well-ordered nervous system. Continual loss of sleep will make one irritable, cross, and upset. Fresh air and exercise are an antidote for people who find themselves getting a "case of nerves." Finally, a peaceful mind free from worry, fear, and hate is conducive to an existence that is free from emotional strife and an upset nervous system.

**Excretory system.** Wastes produced by the cells and picked up by the bloodstream must be eliminated from the body. This is accomplished by four widely separated organs. The *lungs* eliminate the carbon dioxide as previously explained. Water, salts, and small amounts of other wastes are eliminated by the *perspiration glands* in the skin. The *kidneys* extract water, salts, and urea, which is the waste produced from the use of certain foods by the cells. The *liver* helps in the process of removing wastes from the bloodstream.

The large intestine is often classified as an organ of excretion although it has little to do with getting rid of the wastes produced by the body cells. The large intestine eliminates undigested food.

**Endocrine system.** There are two general classes of glands in the body which manufacture substances or secretions to be used by the body. The glands with ducts or passageways pour their secretions into another organ like the salivary glands and the liver. There is a second type of gland called an *endocrine* or *ductless gland* which produces substances that are absorbed directly into the bloodstream and carried throughout the entire body. These substances contain important chemicals known as hormones, which have far-reaching effects on body growth, development, and function.

Examples of endocrine glands are the *thyroid,* which produces a hormone that regulates the rate of metabolism or the chemical changes that take place in cells to produce energy; the *pituitary,* the so-called "master gland," that manufactures several hormones of great importance in physical growth and development; and the *gonads,* which are responsible for the bodily changes in boys and girls at adolescence.

The work of the endocrine glands is so interrelated that it is hard to assign a specific function to a specific gland. The hormones work together to stimulate and regulate many body characteristics such as size, shape, and appearance, and many body functions such as metabolic rate.

**Integumentary system.** The skin and membranes of the body are grouped together to form the integumentary system. Their major task is protection of underlying tissues.

The skin covers the surface of the body and provides a tough layer of protection from bacteria, dirt, mechanical injury, and temperature. It also contains glands that produce oil to keep the skin pliable, and perspiration which is of importance in regulating body temperature.

The internal organs of the body are lined with membranes that also serve as protection to underlying tissues. Many of these membranes secrete lubricating substances, such as mucus, which among other things keeps tissues moist.

**Reproductive system.** The continuation of the race is accomplished through the reproductive systems of men and women. The sex organs of male and female unite to produce a new human being. The reproductive glands are known as *gonads*. In the male they are called testes, and produce sperm. In the female they are called ovaries, and produce eggs, or ova. In addition to the ovaries the reproductive system of the female includes the uterus and a passageway from the uterus to the outside of the body. In the male there are tubes leading from the testes to the outside of the body.

## The impact of heredity

The difference in growth rates as well as the differences in the physical makeup of human beings is the result of heredity. Heredity is the process by which certain physical and mental characteristics are transmitted from parents to their children. Not all personal characteristics are inherited. Other factors, such as education and environment, influence one's characteristics. Heredity does give a person the color of his eyes, the color and texture of his hair, the size and shape of his facial features, the color of his skin, and his basic body build.

Some physical defects may be inherited from parents. These include such things as color blindness, deafness, and extra fingers and toes. Scientists are still uncertain about the role heredity plays in intelligence, but reliable evidence suggests that both high and low levels of intelligence run in families.

A person is the result of a complex biological process in which each of his parents contributed certain characteristics to his makeup, as they in turn, and all others in their family back through time, were produced by the same random selection of characteristics from their parents. Each person as he produces children will similarly hand on certain characteristics, but neither he nor his parents nor their parents before them had any control over the characteristics transmitted to the next generation. So it is that the body build, hair color, skin color, and so on that make up a person are individual in nature. Unless he is an identical twin, he will find that the other members of his family may differ markedly from him in size and appearance.

**Chromosomes and genes.** As you already know, your existence as a human being is the result of the union of a male germ cell (sperm) with a female germ cell (ovum) to form a single cell or fertilized egg. Over approximately a nine-month period, the fertilized egg divides and subdivides and grows in size until a human being is formed.

Within each of the male and female germ cells are tiny structures called *chromosomes*. There are forty-eight such chromosomes in the nucleus of each human cell. Each of these chromosomes, in turn, carries thousands of additional structures called *genes* which determine the characteristics that are inherited by human beings.

Genes are arranged in rows of fine

fibers within the chromosome, looking much like a string of beads when examined under a microscope. (Genes, by the way, are so small—some scientists believe them to be the size of viruses—that until the development of the electron microscope in recent years, study of them was very difficult.) Genes exist in pairs within the cells of each human being. During the union of the male germ cell with the female germ cell, each germ cell contributes one of the pair of genes to the other, thus forming one new pair of genes. The separation occurs by chance. That is, if your father is brown eyed, he may carry a pair of genes for brown eyes or he may have a pair of mixed genes, one-half of the pair producing brown eyes (which, for him, are dominant) and one-half of the pair capable of producing blue eyes. Your mother, on the other hand, may have blue eyes, in which case she carries only blue-eyed genes. Now in the union of germ cells that produced you, if the male cell carried your father's gene for brown eyes to your mother's gene for blue eyes, you will have brown eyes. But you will be a mixed brown, having a pair of genes, one of which produces brown eyes, the other of which produces blue. Thus, when you produce children, you might produce a blue-eyed baby.

If, on the other hand, your father were mixed brown and passed the blue-eyed gene to your mother, you would be blue-eyed, meaning that the pair of genes you possess for eye color carry only blue-eyedness. If you, in turn, married a blue-eyed person, your children would probably have blue eyes. If you married a person with brown eyes, you might have either blue-eyed or brown-eyed children.

The chance nature of genetic selection is best seen perhaps in the determination of sex. Each human being possesses what is called the *sex chromosome*. The female produces only Y chromosomes (two in number) but the male produces both an X chromosome and a Y chromosome. The male germ cell, then, carries either an X or a Y chromosome, but not both, when it unites with the female germ cell. If the male X is carried to the female Y, a male child (XY) results. If the male germ cell carries a Y chromosome to the female, a female child (YY) is formed. Since thousands of male germ cells are present each time the sex act is performed, but only one female egg (and then only at certain times), the random or chance nature of fertilization and heredity is obvious, for only one of the germ cells from the male can unite with the germ cell of the female. Remember, too, that each germ cell (whether male or female) carries one-half of a pair of characteristics which unite to form one complete pair of characteristics in the new cell.

## Physical and motor growth and development

Physical educators should be familiar with the various physical characteristics, in addition to those already presented, that are present in human beings from infancy to adulthood. A thorough knowledge of these factors will enable a physical educator to plan a program of activity that will meet the needs and interests of each individual with whom he works. Such a knowledge would include the following:

1. Various ages by which individuals are classified
2. Various aspects of physical and motor growth during infancy, preschool years, the elementary school period, and adolescence
3. Physiological differences between males and females
4. General rules that should be followed in respect to physical and motor growth and development

**Ages of development.** Individuals are classified in various ways according to age. The most common are estimations of chronological, anatomical, physiological, and mental age. These may all be helpful to the teacher of physical education.

*Chronological* age represents the age of an individual in calendar years and months. *Anatomical* age is usually related to the ossification of bones. Quite frequently the small bones in the wrist are used for this purpose. An x-ray examination is needed to determine anatomical age. Sometimes the stage of dentition is also used to determine this type of age. *Physiological* age is related to puberty. It may be determined by the quality and texture of the pubic hair in boys and by menstruation in girls. The last classification is *mental* age, which is arrived at by determining, through tests, the degree to which an individual has adjusted to his environment and is able to solve certain problems.

Although the physical educator will be interested in all the age classifications of the individuals with whom he works, he should have special interest in the physiological age. It seems that this, more than any other age classification, is a determining factor in arranging a program of activities adapted to the needs and interests of any one person.

**Physical and motor growth at various levels.** The characteristics of physical and motor growth in the child during infancy, the preschool years, elementary school, and adolescence are very interesting for the physical educator. From a study of these characteristics, one can see that the child, a dynamic individual, craves activity. The type of program provided should depend to a great degree upon child growth and development characteristics, such as the maturation level of the child.

*Infancy.* During prenatal life the fetus grows very rapidly. For example, there is an increase in height to an average of 20½ inches. After birth, growth continues to be rapid for a period of two years and then begins to slow down. At birth and for about eighteen months thereafter, the head is big in proportion to the rest of the body.

Development occurs from the head downward or in the *cephalocaudal* direction. The fact that the arms develop faster than the legs is an indication of this. During prenatal life the arm buds develop before the leg buds. Development also is from the axes of the body to the extremities or in the *proximodistal* direction. For example, the ability to use the hand develops in the palm of the hand before the fingers. This may be seen by watching a baby manipulate a block. He pushes it around with the palm of his hand for some time before he is able to pick it up with his fingers.

In discussing the cephalocaudal and proximodistal directions of development, it seems wise to bring out information as to whether educational programs for young children should be concerned mainly with big-muscle activity or with the fine-muscle activity that is associated with the use of the fingers, eyes, and the like. Many educators claim that the child's main concern during the growing years should be big-muscle activity. This is based on the premise that fine-muscle coordinations develop after the large-muscle coordinations in the child. Many times such fine-muscle skills as reading, writing, and the like are utilized in the educational process too early in life and thus prevent the child from engaging in activities that more rightfully belong on the earlier levels. Jersild, on the other hand, points out that there is some basis for this argument but that it is not entirely true. He points out that a child can pick up objects with his thumb and forefinger and perform many manual manipulations, thus utilizing the fine muscles, before he is able to walk and run, activities that utilize the large muscles. According to Jersild the choice of play materials should not be based only on whether they involve large-muscle or small-muscle activity but should provide for both types of activity. On the basis of physiological facts it would seem that big-muscle activity plays an important part in normal growth and development and that during the growing years the child should have ample opportunity for such activity in order to become a well-developed, healthy human being.

Other implications for physical educators include a knowledge of the infant's skeleton. The skeleton is largely made up of cartilage and fibrous tissues, and as a result the bones are soft. Proper care must be given to avoid deformities and postural difficulties. The spine of a child is very flexible, and for proper development it should receive proper physical activity. This will minimize the possibility of increased lumbar curve.

*Preschool years.* During the preschool years the child develops many physical skills. He develops skills in running, climbing, and skipping. These not only aid in his physical development but also provide a basis for social relationship. He associates with other children and finds out how they react to their environment. During this period the child gains great pleasure from his physical activity. This affects his emotional life. As he gains ability in certain physical acts, he gains self-confidence. He has better use of his arms and legs and utilizes more and more skills. This motor development makes possible more avenues of learning as he begins to explore his environment.

Certain maturation levels should be recognized in children. If allowed to develop independently, to a certain point, a child will do things as a part of the natural course of growth. Jersild lists several examples of this. He explains how 2-year-old children were prompted to button their own clothes. However, at the end of several weeks of practice they did not do any better than another group of children of the same age who had not practiced. He shows how this also applies in the learning of such skills as skipping and tricycling. The motor skills that are provided for children should definitely be related to their readiness to utilize and perform them. Jersild points out that we need more research into the skills that children should have at various ages. More should be known about skills that are of value in themselves, as distinguished from skills that develop a child socially and intellectually and skills useful for a limited period of time, as contrasted with skills that are developed for future use.

Motor learning has been recognized as an essential for all children and important to the social and emotional life of a child. It helps him to become independent. It plays a part in his intellectual development. Through motor skills the child acquires concepts as to size and

Preschool years.

weight and finds out about such things as gravity and balance. Emotionally they help him to solve problems that would otherwise enrage and stump him. Newell Kephart, head of the Achievement Center at Purdue University, has conducted much research that supports the relation of motor skills to the mental as well as physical development of the child.

*Elementary school child.* During his elementary school years the child acquires fundamental skills that affect his present existence and that he will use throughout life. According to a study of men 20 years old and older, it was found that many of their hobbies and adult leisure-time interests were based on their childhood experiences. The physical educator should recognize this as having implication for his work. If adults are to have physical skill in various activities, their foundation

should be laid during the early years of life.

During the elementary school years the child develops socially. He makes contacts through motor activities. He is accepted by the group if he can participate with some degree of skill. He gains independence by learning to do things by himself. He increases his knowledge in respect to his environment. In all this development, motor skills play an important part. Through them he develops his "whole" organism.

Physical educators need to know what skills children possess at certain age levels, those skills possessed by most children and those possessed by just a few, the importance of skills in the lives of children, and the environmental factors contributing to or thwarting skill development. These are essential facts if physical education is to

Elementary school years. New Zealand physical education program.

contribute further in the development of the child.

*Adolescence.* During adolescent years the body reaches maximum powers in the use of its musculature. This also applies to its capacity to learn motor skills.

During the elementary years boys are superior to girls in many activities, such as running, jumping, and throwing. This is even more pronounced in adolescent years. This can be explained by the fact that boys have more opportunities than girls to participate in these activities and also because of certain anatomical differences. A girl has a wider pelvis, and the angle of attachment of the femur to the thigh is different in girls than in boys. Boys are also stronger than girls. After the age of 14 or 15 years, boys and girls probably should not participate together in the more strenuous types of physical activities.

In the middle and later adolescent years activity decreases in most individuals. In a large part, this decrease results from interest in an occupation, decrease in the number of different activities in which one can engage, and social and other interests which appear to be stronger. Available evidence shows that there are more excuses from physical education classes in high school than elementary and junior high school. This falling off of activity continues into adult life and produces one of the problems with which physical educators should be concerned. The public should be better informed as to the value of adapted activity throughout life.

*Postadolescent years.* At this age physiological maturity has been reached. Boys are still developing muscularly. Improved motor coordination becomes evident in those youths who are active in many dif-

*Central High School, Evansville, Ind.*

During adolescent years the body reaches maximum powers in the use of its musculature.

ferent types of physical activity. These are years when endurance increases, emotional balance is better, there is an interest in physical attractiveness, and recreational activities become popular. It is also a time when strong convictions and ideals are being developed, prejudices and antagonisms become intensified, there is a desire for deeper friendships, and much thought is given to the future. There is a need during these postadolescent years for periodic health examinations, for opportunities to participate in coeducational and recreational activities, for experiences in helping others in the development of skills and playing of games, for practice in planning for many social activities, for opportunities to gain increased skill and competence in activity areas of their choice, and for practice in critical thinking and problem solving.

**Differences in boys and girls.** The physical educator should be cognizant of certain differences in the physical makeup of boys and girls. The pelvic girdle of the female is much broader than that of the male and does not completely develop until in the twenties. This means that activities that would result in any pull on this region should be guarded against. Boys are stronger than girls, especially in the shoulder girdle region. The thigh bones of girls join the pelvis at a more oblique angle than that of boys. The center of gravity is lower in girls. In respect to body weight the muscular strength of girls is lower than in boys. Other differences include a more stable knee joint in the girl than in the boy, greater length of bones in boys than girls, and boys are taller and heavier on the average than are girls.

Activities that are provided for girls and women should be selected in light of psychological as well as physiological considerations. Those that emphasize feminine qualities such as grace and rhythm and involve a minimum of body contact

should receive priority. Furthermore, regularity in engaging in physical activity should be stressed, even during the menstrual period, if there are no harmful results.

## Implications of growth and development characteristics for athletics for junior high school boys

One of the most controversial areas in athletic programs is the one concerned with junior high school boys.

Biologically, children in grades seven to nine are composed of preadolescents and young adolescents. In grade seven, among 11-, 12-, and 13-year-old children, preadolescents predominate—approximately two-thirds are boys and one-third girls. In grade 8, among 12-, 13-, and 14-year-olds, young adolescents increase in number. In grade 9, among 13-, 14-, and 15-year-olds, young adolescents predominate with older children in the minority.

Preadolescents are children who belong to later childhood. They have not yet experienced the growth spurt. Instead, growth is usually slow. Young adolescents are characterized by fast-growing arms and legs, changing facial features, broadening hips and shoulders, and changing voices. They resemble men and women more than they do children.

The growth spurt, experienced by junior high school students, is a very rapid and spectacular one both from its outward expression in the form of height, weight, and size, and also in respect to sensitive biochemical activity resulting in internal physical changes.

Girls normally have their growth spurt between the ages of 8½ and 11½ years, reaching a peak at about 12½ years and leveling off at 15 to 16 years of age. Boys begin later than girls, with their growth spurt normally occurring between the ages of 10½ and 14½ and with the peak being reached at about 14½. Following this there is a gradual decline, the rate of growth usually being complete between the ages of 17 and 20.

Biologically, an adapted program of activities is needed to meet the changing physical makeup of the junior high school student. The period of growth and development through which the student is passing requires a program adapted to his needs. There is a special need for team-type activities that will satisfy the "gang" urge. There is a need for competition. There is a need for a wide variety of activities that will help in the development of body control, enable each student to experience success, provide consideration for energy output and fatigue, and protect the sensitive individual. There is a need for activities that will offer a channel of release for tensions rather than increase the amount of tension. Furthermore, in selecting activities, the danger of injury to the skeletal framework, as well as dangers in regard to students over-

The normal child needs from two to six hours of activity a day.

extending themselves to the point of exhaustion through competitive activity, must be kept in mind. There is a need for keeping accurate records of growth and achievement, for a program of health supervision and medical services, and to make provision for work in body mechanics.

Because of the uneven way in which growth takes place, it is difficult to know how old a child is during the early adolescent period. "Old" in this frame of reference does not refer to years but to other kinds of age—age of his skeleton, mental age, physiological maturity, and emotional maturity. This raises the question as to how students can be properly grouped for forms of athletic activity which in many instances should rightfully be limited to the "older" youngsters.

## Implications of growth and development characteristics for girls' and women's athletics

The question of athletics for girls is a highly controversial matter. The questions of how much, how little, and what is a happy medium are frequently raised with enthusiastic supporters on all sides of the issue. There seems to be a general consensus that athletics can render a valuable service to girls. The question arises as to what type of program can best render this service. Girls can develop a better state of total fitness, skills for worthy use of leisure time, and other desirable qualities and attributes, just as boys and men can. However, it must be recognized that girls and women are not boys and men. There are many biological, sociological, and other differences that must be taken into consideration. It is impossible to take the boys' program and duplicate it for the girls without any changes.

The girls' program should be concerned especially with the individual sports and activities, as well as the team games. The women in charge and those doing the officiating should be qualified. Official girls' rules should be followed. The girls' games should be separated from the boys', except in coeducational activity, which should occupy a prominent place in the program. The social aspects should be stressed, and body contact should be eliminated altogether. Health safeguards should be observed, and limited seasons and restrictions on the amount of competition of any one girl should be enforced. Publicity and commercial aspects should be controlled so that the girls are not exploited.

The Division of Girls and Womens Sports of the AAHPER has established guidelines for athletics. These should be reviewed and followed wherever such programs exist.

## General rules pertinent to physical and motor growth and development

Certain general principles may be stated in respect to physical and motor growth and development. The physical educator should continually be conscious of these principles in planning and directing a physical education program for children:

1. The normal child needs from two to six hours of activity a day. In that all of this activity cannot take place during school hours, the time spent in activity in school should be devoted to providing instruction that may be utilized in after-school hours.

2. Aside from heredity and the nutritive environment, the organic systems of the body can be developed only through muscular activity.

3. Because of the softness of a young child's bones particular attention should be given to the prevention of posture abnormalities.

4. A child's physiological age is an important consideration in determining the type of physical education program best fitted to his growth and development.

5. Large-muscle activity is an essential for the proper growth and development of normal children.

6. The various parts of a child's body grow at different rates of speed.

7. A child's intellectual, social, and emotional growth and development are greatly increased through motor activity.

8. A "skills" program should take into consideration the maturation levels of children.

9. Disease, malnutrition, and insufficient exercise are causes of growth disturbances in children.

Physical education at the junior high school level, Seattle Public Schools.

10. Skills utilized in adult leisure hours are acquired most readily during childhood.

11. The acquisition of skills aids the awkward, adolescent child to obtain satisfaction and enjoyment through participation.

12. Adolescent boys and girls should participate in physical education programs that are adapted to their needs and physiological make-up.

13. The values of physical activity to everyone, regardless of age and regardless of sex, should be brought to the attention of all.

## Body types

Psychologists often classify individuals on the basis of "body types" or physique. This is based on the body structure of an individual. Through such a classification, it has been thought possible to distinguish certain physiological and personality traits that might be associated with each type.

One method of classification is that promulgated by Kretschmer, who classified the human body into four groupings based upon physical features. Types distinguished are the *asthenic,* a word which has a Greek derivation and means "without strength," referring to those individuals who are lean, slim, shallow chested, and tall in proportion to their weight; the *athletic,* from Greek meaning "a contender for a prize"—the muscular individual, the fellow with broad shoulders and well-developed chest, robust and strong; the *pyknic,* from the Greek meaning "thick" and referring to the individual who has a broad, rounded figure, large head, heavy neck, and ruddy face; and the *dysplastic,* in the Greek meaning "badly formed" and designating individuals who have abnormal bodies and have builds that are abnormal and not found in the asthenic, athletic, and pyknic types.

Within certain limits body types may be used as an indication of athletic ability. For example, the pyknic type usually will be interested in a sport such as football, soccer, or hockey, whereas the asthenic type will choose running or tennis. Classifications based on body types, however, are not always reliable, and physical educators should be careful as to how much they rely on them as a basis for classifying groups for physical education activities. Age, physiological maturity, interests, skill, size, strength, physical fitness, and other similar criteria should be used with the various body-type classification in making such judgments.

Another classification that has been used divides body types into *endomorph,* which is similar to Kretschmer's "pyknic" type; *mesomorph,* similar to the "athletic" type, and *ectomorph,* similar to the "asthenic" type. Sheldon uses these classifications and has developed a system of somatotyping whereby an individual's body classification can be more accurately analyzed by giving it a number classification showing relationship to endomorph, mesomorph, or ectomorph. This is based on the premise that there are no clear-cut or absolute "endomorphs," "mesomorphs," or "ectomorphs." Instead, body build represents a variation of all three. Sheldon then goes on to give a detailed description of the various somatotypes that he has found in his research.

Willgoose relates body types and physical fitness. Table 15-1 shows that within certain groups of somatotypes there are different interests and abilities in athletics. Willgoose points out there is some overlapping in this structure but that it might be useful in considering athletic performance.

## Body mechanics

The attitudes about good posture have changed from that of a rigid, static, upright, unnatural position to one of efficient, graceful, yet somewhat relaxed body movement. Physical educators are concerned with dynamic posture in sitting, standing, walking, running, and other body positions. The aim is to have each individual develop a body carriage

**Table 15-1.** *Body types and physical fitness\**

| Mesomorphic endomorphs | Endomorphic mesomorphs | Extreme mesomorphs | Ectomorphic mesomorphs | Mesomorphic ectomorphs |
|---|---|---|---|---|
| *(S-types: 631, 532, 541, 542, 543)†* | *(S-types: 452, 361, 462, 451, 453)* | *(S-types: 171, 162, 262, 172, 252)* | *(S-types: 253, 254, 163, 164, 265)* | *(S-types: 235, 126, 136, 145, 146)* |
| Table tennis | Baseball | Sprints | Lightweight | Bicycling |
| Floating | Football (lineman) | Basketball | wrestling | Cross-country |
| (swimming) | Heavyweight | Middleweight | Long-distance | Table tennis |
| Croquet | boxing | boxing | running | Basketball center |
| Fly and bait | Heavyweight | Middleweight | Tennis | (short periods) |
| casting | wrestling | wrestling | Gymnastics | Archery |
| Bowling | Swimming | Quarterbacks | Weight lifting | (Also many |
| | Soccer (backs) | Football (backs) | Javelin | athletic games, |
| | Ice-hockey (backs) | Divers | Pole vault | except those re- |
| | Weight tossing | Tumbling | High jump | quiring weight |
| | | Lacrosse | Fencing | and sheer |
| | | Soccer (forwards) | Badminton | strength) |
| | | Ice hockey | Skiing | |
| | | (forwards) | Jockey | |
| | | Handball | | |

\*Willgoose, Carl E.: Journal of Health, Physical Education, and Recreation 27:26, Sept., 1956.
†S-types in the table refer to those body types given in Sheldon, William H.: Atlas of men, New York, 1954, Harper & Bros.

suited to his own body build. The best posture will be characterized by balance and proper alignment of body segments to give one maximum support and movement with the least strain.

Good posture is valuable for appearance since it influences the concept others have of the individual. One's posture may even influence self-concepts and attitude of mind. Good posture makes for efficiency of movement since poor posture causes additional muscular effort, fatigue, and undue strain. In some cases the strain may be enough to alter structure, resulting in limited use of body parts. In extreme cases chronic strain may lead to arthritic conditions.

Poor posture may be the result of several causes including weak musculature, faulty diet, fatigue, disease, arthritis, vision and hearing defects, overweight and obesity, skeletal defects, faulty postural habits, and injuries such as back strain. Even negative attitudes toward exercise and desirable posture can be basic causes of poor body carriage.

**QUESTIONS AND EXERCISES**

1. Why is it necessary for the physical educator to be able to interpret physical education from the biological point of view?

2. What is the status of America's health? What are the implications for physical education?

3. What is the extent of preventable health defects and diseases in the United States?

4. Trace the role of physical education in the evolution of man.

5. What are the biological defects of man in light of his structure? What are the implications for physical education?

6. Why is it essential for physical educators to understand the makeup of each of the following parts of the human body: skeleton, musculature, circulatory system, respiratory system, nervous system, excretory system, endocrine system, integumentary system, and reproductive system?

7. Select one of your classes and categorize members into endomorphs, mesomorphs, or ectomorphs.

8. Identify each of the following: chronological age, anatomical age, physiological age, mental age, asthenic body build, Sheldon, maturation, cephalocaudal development, proximodistal development, and Jersild.

9. Describe what you would believe to be an ideal education for a child from birth until 10 years of age.
10. Construct a chart depicting the physical and motor growth of a child during infancy, the preschool years, elementary school, adolescence, and postadolescence.
11. Develop an outline of a physical education program for each of the following age ranges based on information provided in this chapter concerned with child growth and development, characteristics, and needs: 1 to 5 years, 5 to 7 years, 8 to 10 years, 11 to 13 years, and 14 to 16 years of age.
12. What part does heredity play in physical differentiation?
13. Discuss several additional factors that affect man's growth, and relate these factors to their implications for physical education.

**SELECTED REFERENCES**

American Association for Health, Physical Education, and Recreation: Children and fitness, 1960; Exercise and fitness, 1964; The growing years—adolescence, 1962; Washington, D. C.

American Association for Health, Physical Education, and Recreation: This is physical education, Washington, D. C., 1965, The Association.

Bartley, F. H., and Chute, E.: Fatigue and impairment in man, New York, 1947, McGraw-Hill Book Co.

Britton, S. W.: New theory held in development of human brain, New Haven Register, April 25, 1950.

Bucher, Charles A.: Interscholastic athletics at the junior high school level, Albany, N. Y., 1965, The University of the State of New York.

Bucher, Charles A., and Reade, Evelyn M.: Physical education in the modern elementary school, New York, 1964, The Macmillan Co.

Bucher, Charles A., Olsen, Einar A., and Willgoose, Carl E.: The foundations of health, New York, 1967, Appleton-Century-Crofts.

California Association for Health, Physical Education, and Recreation: Values inherent in the daily program of physical education, Journal of CAHPER, special issue, March, 1965.

Clarke, H. Harrison: Evaluation: isometric vs. isotonic exercises, Physical Fitness Newsletter 11:19, May, 1965.

Department of Classroom Teachers, American Educational Research Association of the National Education Association: What research says to the teacher, in Hunsicker, Paul: Physical fitness, 1963, The National Education Association.

Hickman, Cleveland Pendleton: Physiological hygiene, New York, 1950, Prentice-Hall, Inc.

Jennings, Herbert: The biological basis of human nature, New York, 1930, W. W. Norton & Co., Inc.

Johnson, Warren R., editor: Science and medicine of exercise and sports, 1960, New York, Harper & Bros.

Johnson, Perry B., and others: Physical education—a problem-solving approach to health and fitness, New York, 1966, Holt, Rinehart and Winston.

Kretschmer, E.: Physique and character (Translated by W. J. H. Sprott), London, 1925, Kegan Paul, Trench, Trubner.

Layman, Emma McCloy: Mental health through health, physical education and recreation, Minneapolis, 1955, Burgess Publishing Co.

Mitchem, John: Isometric exercise—an evaluation, The Physical Educator 20:28, Oct., 1963.

National Association for Physical Education of College Women and National College Physical Education Association for Men: Science and physical education, Quest, Winter Issue, Monograph III, Dec., 1964.

Riedman, Sarah R.: The physiology of work and play, New York, 1950, The Dryden Press.

Ryan, Allan J.: Medical care of the athlete, New York, 1962, McGraw-Hill Book Co.

Schneider, Edward C., and Karpovich, Peter V.: Physiology of muscular activity, Philadelphia, 1949, W. B. Saunders Co.

Selye, Hans: The stress of life, New York, 1956, McGraw-Hill Book Co.

Sheldon, W. H.: The varieties of human physique, New York, 1940, Harper & Bros.

Steinhaus, Arthur H.: How to keep fit and like it, Chicago, 1957, The Dartnell Corp.

Still, Joseph W.: Man's potential—and his performance, New York, Times Magazine, Nov. 24, 1957.

The Athletic Institute in cooperation with The American College of Sports Medicine: Health and fitness in the modern world, a collection of papers presented at the Institute of Normal Human Anatomy, Viala Regina Elena, 289, and the Ministry of Foreign Affairs, Rome, Italy, The Athletic Institute, 1961.

Time, Inc.: The healthy life, Time-Life Books Special Report, New York, 1966, Time, Inc.

# Chapter 16

# Biological fitness

> *The health of the people is the foundation upon which all their happiness and all their powers as a state depend.*
>
> —Disraeli
>
> *. . . And so, my fellow Americans, ask not what your country can do for you— ask what you can do for your country.*
>
> —President Kennedy

## EDUCATION FOR FITNESS

During the trying political, economic, and social times through which the world is passing and with youth and adults who, to a large extent, do not fully understand and appreciate the importance of health and fitness, a heavy responsibility rests upon the shoulders of educators. If a nation is to remain strong physically, mentally, spiritually, and socially, there must be *education* for *fitness*. Furthermore, this education must take place largely through the formal processes of physical education, health education, and recreation programs in our schools and colleges. Knowledge about the human body must be imparted, desirable health attitudes inculcated, and proper health practices instilled. The responsibility for accomplishing this herculean task must be assumed mainly by physical educators, health educators, and recreation educators. They must continually strive for sound school and community programs in their special fields. They must interpret articulately the need for educational institutions to educate, not only in science and mathematics but also in those essentials that comprise other aspects of total fitness. This is a major challenge that faces society in the days and years ahead. If educators can accomplish this job, they will not only render a valuable contribution to their country but to the health and happiness of millions of human beings as well.

## WHAT DOES "PHYSICAL FITNESS" MEAN TO YOUNG PEOPLE?

In order to discover what the term "physical fitness" means to elementary, high school, and college students, 10,000 children and young people were surveyed throughout the United States. The answers given were then analyzed to determine the most common concepts held by students in regard to their understanding of the term "physical fitness."

The survey showed that a uniform meaning of the term "physical fitness" has not been communicated to students in our schools and colleges. The variations in the answers that were obtained in the survey may mean that there is a lack of uniformity in the understanding of the term by teachers in the field, that there is very little, if any, teaching being done as to the meaning of this term, that students are formulating their own definitions, and that the home and community are influencing the student's understanding of this term.

### Elementary school

At the elementary school level the most prevalent answer given by all students, and also by the majority of the girls surveyed at this level, was that "physical fitness" means "to be healthy." Among the boys, the most prevalent answer given was that it means "to keep the body in shape." The other most frequently mentioned answers by both boys and girls were that it means "exercise," "to be good in sports," and, "to have good body coordination."

Boys and girls in elementary school are passing through a very formative period. It would seem important that meaningful basic concepts regarding the meaning of physical fitness be communicated to them at their level of understanding. Since the home has a great influence on the child's thinking, it also implies that parents should be informed in regard to the meaning of physical fitness and its place in a physical education program.

### Junior high school

Among the girls at the junior high school level, the term "physical fitness" takes on a different meaning from the girls' elementary school interpretation. "Exercise" has now become the number one answer to express the meaning of the term, while the concept "to be healthy" has moved to second place. This may indicate that girls are now being introduced to formal exercise in physical education classes, and that teachers are stressing the importance of exercise as a means of becoming physically fit.

The second most prevalent answer among the girls was "to be healthy." This answer may possibly indicate that the home and community continue to influence the student's thinking. Health is frequently stressed in the home and among neighbors and other members of the community.

Junior high school boys gave the same answer as to the primary meaning of the term "physical fitness" as did the elementary school boys. They both placed the greatest emphasis on "keeping the body in shape." The survey seemed to indicate that from the elementary school to the junior high school level there is no significant change in the meaning of the term "physical fitness" among the boys. The fact that this answer has been constant may indicate that teachers and parents have accepted this interpretation of physical fitness and are continuing to emphasize this point of view. The general thinking of a significant segment of our society stresses the importance and desirability of boys "keeping their bodies in shape."

"To be healthy" was the third most prevalent answer among the junior high school boys, the second most common answer offered by junior high school girls, and was first on the list for elementary school girls, as expressing their understanding of the term "physical fitness." The second most prevalent answer among the junior high school boys was that physical fitness and "exercise" are synonymous. This was the third most prevalent answer offered by the elementary school boys. As with the girls, this may indicate that boys are also being influenced by the introduction of formal exercise into their physical education classes. The emphasis given by boys to the definition "to keep their bodies in shape," may also be a reflection of the feeling in our society that this is what the term "physical fitness" means.

At the junior high school level we find the introduction of two new terms used by the students to define physical fitness. One of the new answers was that physical fitness means "conditioning your body." Possibly the students who gave this answer were merely using a more sophisticated terminology for "keeping the body in shape." The introduction of this new statement may have no significance except to show that students at this age level are able to express themselves in a more articulate manner. The other new term that was introduced was that physical fitness means "good body coordination." This answer may be a reflection of the teachings taking place in physical education classes. It may also imply that teachers are attempting to give these students a more meaningful understanding of the term.

### High school

The most prevalent answer given by boys on the high school level in regard to the meaning of "physical fitness" was that it means "to keep the body in shape." The second most common answer offered by the high school boys was one that was rarely mentioned at the lower educational levels, that is, that physical fitness means "to be good in sports." Since boys are exposed to a greater emphasis on sports in high school, and engage in both team and individual sports, this may provide the answer as to why this point is stressed by the high school boys.

The data for the high school level also show, for the first time in the survey, that the answer "endurance" is given. This may indicate that in some schools physical educators are attempting to increase the scope of the concept that they are teaching. It may also be an indication of the influence of factors outside the school such as television, magazines, and general public opinion.

The second most frequent answer given by junior high school girls in regard to the meaning of the term "physical fitness" was that it means "to be healthy." High school girls placed this answer first. This may indicate that students are receiving more health instruction at the high school level, and that there is more emphasis being placed on the relation of health and physical fitness.

The next answer in order of frequency given by high school girls was that physical fitness means "to keep the body in shape." This is an age when girls are maturing physically, interested in boys, and conscious of good health practices. Consequently, girls are interested in doing all those things that will help them to be most attractive to the boys.

High school girls are less apt to define the term "physical fitness" as meaning "sports" or "exercise" than are junior high school girls.

### College

When asked to define the term "physical fitness," most college boys felt it meant "to be strong and healthy." The concept of strength, along with health, was introduced at the college level. College men students also introduced a new dimension in regard to physical fitness: "coordination of mind and body." Evidently some students had grasped the concept of the "unity of man."

The largest percentage of college women still interpreted physical fitness as meaning "to be healthy." A concept of physical fitness also given by college girls involved a consideration of physical fitness as meaning the "ability to do everyday tasks." It was the first time that this answer appeared, and might indicate a better understanding of the functional aspects of physical fitness in day-to-day living.

### Some implications that might be drawn from the survey

The implications of this survey as to what children and young people regard as the meaning of the term "physical fitness" include the following:

Weight-training class with boys working at exercise stations.

1. As an objective of physical education, students do not clearly understand the meaning of physical fitness and its place in educational programs.

2. There is a need for communicating the meaning of the term "physical fitness" to students at all educational levels and to the public in general.

3. Physical educators should assume the responsibility for communicating key concepts to students in regard to terms such as "physical fitness." This responsibility should be part of the subject matter and the theory underlying their field of endeavor.

4. There should be better communication between professional leaders in physical education and those practitioners functioning in schools, colleges, and various agencies at the "grass roots" level.

5. Physical education cannot be limited to activity alone. There must also be provision for getting at basic concepts underlying the field of physical education and making sure these basic concepts are understood by all persons concerned.

## FITNESS AND HEALTH*

According to the Greek poet Homer, one setting for the adventurous wanderings of Odysseus was on the island of the Phaeacians. There, King Alcinous arranged to have the best of his athletes perform for his guest. After a superb and spectacular display of sports feats, Odysseus was asked if he too wished to demonstrate his skill. Seizing a discus larger than had been used by any of his counterparts and dashing on the field with a heavy cloak restricting his movements, he opened wide the eyes of his competitors by showing his superior strength and fitness in hurling the missile farther than all the rest.

History is replete with illustrations of

*Parts of this discussion have been adapted from Bucher, Charles A.: Health and fitness, Educational Leadership **20:**356, March, 1963.

*American Association for Health,*
*Physical Education, and Recreation.*

peoples throughout the world who considered physical prowess and strong, healthy bodies the vital ingredients for survival and power. The desire for physical excellence and well-being has its roots deeply embedded in historical tradition. For early man the ability to survive was dependent to a large degree upon his accuracy with the bow and arrow, swiftness of foot, strength of muscle, and ability to withstand trying physical ordeals. Nature literally kicked him into activity, as one historian relates.

As man became more and more civilized, the concept of "survival of the fittest" was augmented by other catalytic agents that propelled him into action. Statements from two of the world's great thinkers illustrate these motivating factors. Aristotle said, "The body is the temple of the soul and to reach harmony of body, mind and spirit, the body must be physically fit." John Locke wrote, "A

sound mind in a sound body is a short but full description of a happy state in this world; he that has these two has little more to wish for."

As motives for well-being have changed, so have the preventive and medical procedures for achieving and maintaining fitness and health. Herb medicines, witch doctors, healing chants, and bloodletting remedies have given way to wonder drugs, immunizations, and vitamins. Today there is much scientific knowledge to direct human beings assuredly along the path to good health. And according to the health experts, the way each human being lives will be a major determining factor for the health and fitness of that individual. Although heredity plays a part, to a large degree health and fitness are acquired characteristics. The food that is eaten, amount of rest obtained, physical activity engaged in, and other health practices that are followed play important roles in determining human welfare. In other words, it is important to follow a good health regimen if one is to be healthy and fit. This is especially important today in an automated society where advertising lures, medical quackery, fake shortcuts to health, and other temptations embrace human beings on all sides.

In order to help people follow a healthful regimen, *education* is essential. It is important to educate students about English so that they can communicate articulately with their fellow human beings, about mathematics so that they can add their grocery bills accurately, and about the fine arts so that they can appreciate and enjoy Picasso and Beethoven. It is also important to educate people about their physical selves so that they can function most efficiently as human beings and accomplish all they are capable of achieving. And to attain this objective they need to know scientific facts essential to good health, possess desirable health attitudes, develop skills to make activity exciting and enjoyable, and be physically active. The end result will be productive, vigorous, and rewarding lives. And as Will Durant advises, health is mostly within each person's will. "In many cases, sickness is a crime," this philosopher states. "We have done something physiologically foolish, and nature is being hard put to it to repair our mistakes. The pain we endure is the tuition we pay for our instruction in living."

Much of this education should take place early in life when the organic foundations are being laid, skills are more easily learned, and attitudes are formed. Unfortunately, too many people do not recognize the need for this education until cholesterol deposits have closed their arteries, ulcers have penetrated their duodenum, or cancer has started its insidious attack upon their lungs. As one wise man has said, "We never appreciate health so much as when we lose it." Although it may be difficult to change the health habits of adults, schools and colleges *can* and *should* educate young people about their health and fitness. This is not only essential from the individual's point of view but also in view of this country's national posture. President Kennedy stated, "The strength of our democracy is no greater than the collective well-being of our people. The vigor of our country is no stronger than the vitality and will of our countrymen. The level of physical, mental, moral, and spiritual fitness of every American citizen must be our constant concern. "

The fact that 10 million out of 40 million schoolchildren could not pass a screening test of minimum physical fitness and that many more had undesirable health practices offers some evidence that our educational programs have been inadequate in this regard.

Sound school physical education and health programs are needed. In order to have outstanding programs, educators must have a clear understanding of the philosophy of physical education and health and their worth in education. The following definition of terms and concepts will be of help in setting the stage for education for fitness of young and old people alike.

1. *Fitness implies more than physical fitness.* Fitness is the ability of a person to live a full and balanced existence. The totally fit person possesses physical well-being but also such qualities as good human relations, maturity, and high ethical standards. He also satisfies such basic needs as love, affection, security, and self-respect. School health and physical education programs are vitally concerned with physical fitness but also strive to contribute to total health and fitness.

2. *Physical fitness includes more than muscular strength.* The term *physical fit-*

*La Sierra High School, La Sierra, Calif.*

The milking machine.

*ness* implies soundness of such body organs as the heart and lungs, a human mechanism that performs efficiently under exercise or work conditions (such as having sufficient stamina and strength to engage in vigorous physical activity), and a reasonable measure of skill in the performance of selected physical activities. Physical fitness is related to the tasks the person must perform, his potential for physical effort, and the relationship of his physical fitness to his total self. The same degree of physical fitness is not necessary for everyone. It should be sufficient to meet the requirements of the job plus a little extra as a reserve for emergencies. The student who plays football needs a different type of physical fitness from the student who plays in the school orchestra. The question "fitness for what?" must always be asked. Furthermore, determining the physical fitness of a person must be done in relationship to his own human resources and not those of others. It depends on his potentialities in the light of his own physical makeup. Finally, physical fitness cannot be considered by itself but, instead, as it is affected by mental, emotional, and social factors as well. Human beings function as a whole and not as segmented parts.

3. *Physical education is not the same as health education.* Although closely allied, health and physical education are separate fields of specialization. Whereas physical education is concerned primarily with ed-

American Association
for Health, Physical
Education, and Recreation.

ucation of and through the physical, the school health program is concerned with teaching for health (for example, imparting facts about good nutrition), living healthfully at school (for example, providing healthful physical and emotional environment), and providing services for health improvement (for example, instituting measures for communicable disease control).

4. *Both health and physical education contribute to physical fitness.* The student needs to engage in regular physical activity, but in addition, needs to under-

stand the impact this activity has on his organism. The student needs to have activities fitted to his individual requirements but also to have these activities conducted in a safe and healthful environment. The student should develop skill in various sports but also should develop skill in first aid and home nursing. These are only a few examples of how the health and physical education programs complement and supplement each other in the achievement of the objective of physical fitness.

5. *Health education and physical edu-*

*cation must be integral parts of the educational program in order to most effectively achieve the goal of physical fitness.* These subjects are not frills or appendages of the school's curriculum, nor are they a means for entertaining students. They should be vital parts of every educational program in this country. Only as they are so recognized will it be possible to achieve the goal of fitness and health for all young people. Furthermore, such recognition cannot be merely in the form of lip service but must be repeatedly injected into programming, scheduling, and other practices that reflect the true educational philosophy of each school.

6. *Good leadership—the key to good health and physical education.* The good health or physical education teacher is not someone who merely looks healthy, can produce a string of sports victories, or give a good speech before the Rotary Club. Leadership is basic to the health and physical education professions, and this means men and women who know their subject, the boys and girls they are teaching, and the best methods and techniques for teaching.

7. *Physical fitness is not synonymous with physical education.* Physical fitness is *one* objective of physical education. It is important to have physically fit boys and girls. However, as long as the word *education* is a part of the term *physical education*, there are more extensive responsibilities. Developing physical skills, imparting knowledge about the human organism, and using the body as a vehicle for achieving desirable social traits also represent desirable goals. Any program or curriculum aimed merely at building strength and muscle is failing in its educational mission.

8. *Interschool athletics represent only one part of the total physical education program that contributes to physical fitness.* The school physical education pro-

gram includes the class program for all students, the adapted program which fits the activities to handicapped or atypical individuals, the intramural and extramural program which provides a laboratory experience for the skills and knowledge imparted in the class program, and the interscholastic athletic program for those students with exceptional physical skill. All four of these aspects of the physical education program must function in a manner that affords balance and harmony, and allows for the achievement of physical fitness and other objectives for ALL students.

9. *The development of physical skills— a major contribution to long-term physical fitness of students.* Obstacle courses and calisthenics represent forms of "canned" activities that yield organic benefits to the student, but a major contribution of any physical education program is to teach boys and girls a wide variety of physical skills. Skills are the motivating agents that will accelerate a boy and girl to engage in activities and promote physical fitness, not only in the present but throughout a lifetime as well.

10. *Administrative support and understanding are needed to achieve physical fitness.* The quality of school health and physical education programs will be largely determined by the administrative leadership of the school and community. Boards of education, superintendents of schools, principals, and other administrative officials will decide the prestige these programs have in the eyes of the students, whether credit is given to the subjects when calculating the requirements for graduation, how much money is provided in the budget for their development, the attention given to girls as well as to boys, the degree of emphasis on physically underdeveloped students as compared to gifted athletes, and the answers to other administrative matters that affect the physical fitness of students.

*La Sierra High School, La Sierra, Calif.*

The Blue Team doing extension press-ups.

## PATHS TO PHYSICAL FITNESS

### Physical fitness?*

You know the model of your car,
You know just what its powers are,
You treat it with a deal of care,
Nor tax it more than it will bear.

But as to Self—that's different;
Your mechanism may be bent,
Your carburetor gone to grass,
Your engine just a rusty mass.

Your wheels may wobble and your cogs
Be handed over to the dogs
And then you skip and skid and slide
Without a thought of things inside.

What fools, indeed, we mortals are,
To lavish care upon a car,
And ne'er a bit of time to see
About our own machinery.

—John Kendrick Hangs

*Quoted in Sportscope, Oct. 15, 1962, Chicago, The Athletic Institute, Inc.

The American Medical Association has outlined seven paths that lead to physical fitness. The physical educator should recognize the many-faceted approach to physical fitness and thereby understand that this quality cannot be achieved solely through physical activity.

1. *Proper medical care*—To be physically fit requires regular medical examinations, immunizations against communicable diseases, emergency care, and prompt treatment by qualified medical personnel when such care is warranted.

2. *Nutrition*—"You are what you eat" has much meaning in regard to physical fitness. The right kind of food should be eaten in the right amounts.

3. *Dental services*—Good oral hygiene is essential to physical fitness. This means regular visits to the dentist, treatment of dental caries, and proper mastication.

4. *Exercise*—Exercise is important, but to have a salutary effect there must be a proper selection of activities adapted to the age, condition, and other needs of the individual, together with proper exposure to these activities in terms of time and intensity of workout.

5. *Satisfying work*—Work that is adapted to one's interests and abilities and performed in a satisfying working climate is essential to physical fitness. There should be good mental attitude, recognition, and a sense of achievement and belonging.

6. *Healthy play and recreation*—To achieve physical fitness requires play and recreation in an atmosphere that has as its by-products fun, enjoyable companionship, and happy thoughts.

7. *Rest and relaxation*—Adequate sleep, rest, and relaxation are essential to good health and physical fitness.

## COMPONENTS OF PHYSICAL FITNESS

Larson and Yocom* have surveyed physiological research and listed the following ten factors as the components of physical fitness. These have implications for the physical education profession. They are presented here in adapted form.

1. *Resistance to disease.* Heredity and environment both help to determine the ability of the individual to resist disease. Among the important environmental factors are diet, exercise and recreation, rest habits, and proper personal hygiene.

2. *Muscular strength and muscular endurance.* A person who has sufficient strength and endurance can sustain vigorous activity and perform strenuous work over an extended period. For an individual to be physically fit, he must have strong and efficient muscles. He must have a balanced proportion of good muscle fibers, the ability to bring the needed number of muscle fibers into play when there is work to be done by the muscles, efficient body levers, a working rhythm, and good coordination.

3. *Cardiovascular – respiratory endurance.* When a person contracts a series of muscle groups over a period of time long enough to put a strain on his circulatory and respiratory systems, but without causing a stoppage of the work, that individual has cardiovascular–respiratory endurance. These two systems are important to fitness because they work together to supply the muscles with fuel and oxygen, both of which are needed for muscular con-

tractions. The more efficient the cardiovascular and respiratory systems of the individual, the longer he will be able to sustain work, since his muscles will be well supplied with their fuel and oxygen. The individual who has a high degree of this kind of endurance has improved his physical fitness, since his muscles receive large supplies of fuel and oxygen; he has a slower pulse rate and lower blood pressure; his lungs have a larger surface area, allowing for the absorption of more oxygen by his blood; he has a larger supply of red corpuscles, which also aid in increasing the oxygen supply; and he is less prone to fatigue.

4. *Muscular power.* Muscular power is explosive power such as that needed for putting the shot, high jumping, and sprinting. A person who has muscular power also has two of the components of muscular power: strength and speed. The powerful individual is able to use his speed and strength in an efficient, coordinated, and skillful manner.

5. *Flexibility.* Total body flexibility depends on the flexibility of the individual body joints and their supporting structures. Flexibility infers that the body is capable of making a wide range of movements, such as those needed for swimming, diving, and tumbling. The more flexible a person is, the less energy he spends in accomplishing a skill.

6. *Speed.* A person who possesses speed is able to make a series of similar movements in a short span of time. Speed in swimming relates to the number of arm and leg strokes a swimmer takes in a given period of time. Muscular strength and the aspect of speed are highly related.

7. *Agility.* The agile individual can change the position of his body in space efficiently and easily. Agility, strength, and endurance are important factors in agility. Agility is particularly important to the hurdler in track, lacrosse player, and diver.

8. *Coordination.* The coordinated individual is able to put together a series of movements into a flowing and rhythmical pattern. Different kinds of activities and bodily movements require different kinds of coordination. Agility, balance, and speed are important components of coordination.

9. *Balance.* Balance is the maintenance of equilibrium through neuromuscular control. Many of the skills of physical education, such as tumbling, trampolining, and skiing require good balance. Coordination is a factor in balance, and for some skills, agility also plays a part.

*Larson, Leonard A., and Yocom, Rachael Dunaven: Measurement and evaluation in physical health, recreation, and education, St. Louis, 1951, The C. V. Mosby Co., pp. 158-162.

*La Sierra High School, La Sierra, Calif.*

The Blue Team doing hanging sit-up test.

10. *Accuracy.* The accurate individual can control the movement of one object toward another, such as pitching in baseball, throwing for a goal in lacrosse, or casting a fishing fly. Although there is some relationship between accuracy and balance, they are not related closely enough to have a strong dependency on each other.

## EXERCISE AND PHYSICAL FITNESS*

Scientists attending a 1967 session of the Federation of American Societies for Experimental Biology heard about an experiment at Howard University where three dozen roosters ran a mile a day on a treadmill five times a week for a period of almost six months. The birds were fed on a diet high in cholesterol, a fatty substance that clings to the insides of the arteries—often closing them as rust clogs a pipe. When the arteries of the roosters were examined after the six

months of exercise, little if any deposits of cholesterol were found. However, in sedentary birds that were also used in the experiment, fat stuck to the arteries. The fats even invaded the coronary arteries, the small blood vessels that feed blood to the heart muscle itself, and that if clogged bring on a coronary heart attack by starving the heart of oxygen.

This is not an isolated piece of evidence. Dr. Menard Gertler, of New York University, has demonstrated that the physical activity of the U. S. Marines' basic training keeps the fat content of the blood down, even though the men were eating large amounts of calories each day consisting of animal fats—just the type that is supposed to increase fat and cholesterol in the blood.

A Harvard group of researchers investigated the farmers of a two-mile-high Swiss village in the Alps. Each day the men climbed 3,000 feet to farm a plateau. Although they ate a high-animal-fat diet, the blood cholesterol levels were down.

*Parts of this discussion have been quoted and parts adapted from Bucher, Charles A.: Today's Health (published by the American Medical Association) 34:24, Dec., 1956.

Other experiments have shown that exercise decreases the tendency of the blood to clot and increases the capacity of the blood to dissolve clots already formed.

In general, exercise lowers blood pressure and slows heart rate, two important considerations in heart conditions.

Being active is not a sometimes thing but a continuing must for good health. Exercise is needed all year long. The benefits of physical activity cannot be "canned up" when the temperature is hovering in the eighty's and "dished out"

*Phil Hutchison, The Daily Times,
Davenport, Iowa.*

Muscular strength is a component of physical fitness. Davenport Public Schools, Davenport, Iowa.

as it drops into the twenty's any more than the body can be put in cold storage on Labor Day and thawed on the Fourth of July. For proper functioning, the human organism needs this essential ingredient on a regular basis, just as it demands nutritious food every day.

Many busy men and women limit their sports and activity to the summer months. There are others who even deplore the thought of getting into action at any time of the year. Those who hate exercise love to soothe their guilty consciences and flabby muscles by talking about the animal kingdom. The lazy tortoise avoids exercise and lives 200 years or more. The clumsy elephant saves his strength and reaches the ripe old age of 100 years. Flies that buzz around the fastest die the soonest. Businessmen sag lower into their living room chairs and mothers playing bridge settle deeper into their corsets, saying "Why exercise?"

Dr. Edward C. Schneider, a famous physiologist, after a lifetime study of the effects of exercise, came to the conclusion that "Frequently repeated exercise, extending over months and years . . . is necessary for healthy existence; it is a physiologic need of a primitive kind which cannot safely be eliminated by civilization. It is difficult to find men who have been injured by muscular exercise but easy to find many who have failed of normal development and been ruined by the lack of it."

The "don'ts" of exercise are well known. Don't exercise after 40 years of age. Don't exercise when you're tired, when it's cold, or after eating. Don't exercise—it will injure your heart and you will die sooner. More should be said about the "do's." You do need exercise to get the most out of life. You do need exercise to keep in the best of health. Exercise is good for the normal heart. Exercise contributes to good mental health.

Dr. George W. Calver, former physician

for the Supreme Court and Congress, outlined ten commandments for keeping these men fit. Two of these were "exercise rationally" and "play enthusiastically." As Dr. Calver counseled, "Give 5% of your time to keeping well and you won't have to give 100% getting over being sick."

The worth of exercise rests upon a basic principle, the law of use. Hippocrates called attention to this many hundreds of years ago, when he said, "That which is used develops and that which is not used wastes away." Modern medical practice recognizes the law of use.

Although there are many claims for exercise that are not true, many accusations against it are also false. Two of these are that exercise will shorten life and that it is bad on the heart. Sir Alan Rook, Senior Health Officer of Cambridge University, compared the longevity of 834 sportsmen from his university with a group of "intellectuals" and men chosen at random. Sir Alan concluded: "No evidence could be adduced from the information available that cardiovascular causes of death were more prominent in the sportsmen or occurred at an earlier age." Other research studies have come to the same conclusion.

Medical authorities state that proper exercise cannot harm the heart. Dr. E. Cowles Andrus, former president of the American Heart Association, advises, ". . . it is clear that strenuous exercise, properly supervised, does not cause disease in the normal heart." Dr. Paul Dudley White, world-renowned authority on heart disease, reasons this way: Men who slow down at 40 years of age may have a heart attack sooner. For some reason that cannot be explained at the present time, such a slowdown seems to increase the possibility of hardening of the arteries. He capped his reasoning with this remark, "The general warning to stop vigorous exercise at 40 seems to me ridiculous." Dr. White cites five benefits from exercise:

1. Maintains muscle tone
2. Relieves nervous tensions and provides relaxation
3. Aids digestion
4. Helps to control obesity
5. Improves functioning of the lungs by deepening of respiration

In addition to Dr. White's benefits, other advantages of exercise cited by experts include:

1. Added strength and endurance help in performing daily tasks with less fatigue
2. Better movement accrues for the human body
3. Exercise helps to maintain health of the heart and blood vessels
4. Exercise helps in the building of a desirable self-concept
5. Exercise helps in the prevention of accidents

Other fitness myths that have been cited include: middle age begins at 40 years of age—chronologically it starts at about 26 years of age; hardening of the arteries is a natural part of getting old—not necessarily, blood vessels are dependent partially on regular exercise to keep in shape; rest or sleep is the best way to eliminate fatigue—not always, physical activity can act as an antidote to some kinds of fatigue; youngsters will be harmed through sustained exercise—it depends, if they are fit, their physical endurance is tremendous and the exercise will be conducive to good health; and there are shortcuts to fitness—no, the truth rests in a continuing program of activity, good nutrition, rest, sleep, relaxation, and adequate health care.

The values of exercise are not limited to the body; they also contribute to sound mental health. Exercise makes a person feel better. I spoke with at least 1,000 people on this subject. In addition, my students have surveyed at least 10,000 more. Comments follow a pattern, "I feel more alive when I exercise"; "I have more energy"; "I don't feel as tired in the evening"; "I can do a lot more work." Those

| EIGHTEEN TESTS OF FITNESS | | | NORMAL MEN (% PASSED) | NORMAL WOMEN (% PASSED) | YOU |
|---|---|---|---|---|---|
| **1** | | Assume a diver's stance, arms outstretched, standing on your toes with your eyes closed. Hold this stance—and your balance—for 20 seconds. | 95% | 56% | |
| **2** | | Squat with your palms on the floor. Tip forward, resting your legs on your elbows, toes off the ground in a squat handstand, and hold for 10 seconds. | 25% | 14% | |
| **3** | | With your finger touching the floor, walk in a circle around it 10 times in 30 seconds. Then walk a straight 10-foot line within five seconds. | 1% | 36% | |
| **4** | | Keeping your legs together and knees straight, bend at the waist and touch the floor with your finger tips. Women should touch palms of their hands. | 75% | 86% | |
| **5** | | Slowly bend from a sitting position, knees flat, until your forehead is eight inches, or two fists, one atop the other, from the floor. | 67% | 73% | |
| **6** | | Lying on your stomach with your feet pinned to the floor and your fingers laced behind your neck, raise your chin until it is 18 inches from the floor. | 35% | 25% | |
| **7** | | Kneel with your insteps flat on the floor. Using just your back and arms, spring erect, both feet together, and hold your balance for three seconds. | 65% | 25% | |
| **8** | | From a standing position, jack-spring from the floor, touching your toes at waist height without bending your legs. Repeat five times quickly. | 38% | 13% | |
| **9** | | Repeat six times: (1) squat; (2) kick legs backward; (3) kick legs forward between arms; (4) turn over; (5) squat; (6) stand. | 10% | 14% | |
| **10** | | With a partner who is lying down (and who is within 10 pounds of your weight), lift and carry him fireman-style—all in 10 seconds from floor to carry. | 94% | 54% | |
| **11** | | With your hands on your hips and the back of your head on a partner's knee or the edge of a chair or sofa, hold your body rigid for 30 seconds. | 78% | 66% | |
| **12** | | Lying prone, with arms outstretched, lift your midsection four inches in an extended press-up using just hands and toes. Women may use forearms. | 1% | 60% | |
| **13** | | Do a standing broad jump the length of your height. If you are under 25, the distance should be the same as your height plus one foot. | 71% | 8% | |
| **14** | | Do 15 full-length push-ups with your hands positioned beneath your shoulders. Women should do 30 push-ups, keeping their knees on the floor. | 65% | 34% | |
| **15** | | Chin yourself, or, on your back, straddled by a partner, grasp his hands and pull up until your chest strikes his legs. Men repeat 20 times, women 10. | 79% | 73% | |
| **16** | | Sit on the floor with your knees stiff. With hands on hips, lean back so your legs come off the floor in a V-sit, and hold 60 seconds. | 68% | 40% | |
| **17** | | Run in place for two minutes at double time, or 180 steps per minute. Then take three breaths and hold your breath for 30 seconds. | 15% | 12% | |
| **18** | | Do 200 two-foot hops, 200 straddle hops, 200 scissor, or alternate stride, hops, 50 hops on each foot and 50 squat jumps. | 9% | 6% | |
| | | TOTAL PASSING SCORES | 10 | 7 | |

Categories (left margin, top to bottom): BALANCE (1–3), AGILITY (4–6), POWER (7–9), FLEXIBILITY (10–12), STRENGTH (13–15), ENDURANCE (16–18)

A stiff but reliable test of fitness.

*Reproduced by permission of Time-Life Books, The healthy life,* © 1966, Time Inc.

who exercise regularly never fail to mention that exercise makes them feel better. If a person feels better, his attitude toward others will probably be friendlier. He is happier, makes wiser decisions, and his world in general looks better.

The benefits to sound mental health are especially great when a person engages in games and sports. He finds release from tensions, relaxes, forgets his troubles, and loses himself in the game. Dr. William

Menninger, the famous psychiatrist, points out that physical activity provides an outlet for instinctive aggressive drives by enabling an individual to "blow off steam," provides relaxation, and is a supplement for daily work. He stresses the fact that "recreation, which is literally re-creating relaxation from regular activity, is a morale builder. It is not a luxury, a waste of time or a sin."

Socialization is also provided in many

**Table 16-1.** *Physical fitness ratings of popular sports in the United States\**

| | | | Strength | | | |
|---|---|---|---|---|---|---|
| *Sport* | *Endurance* | *Agility* | *Leg* | *Abdomen* | *Arm and shoulders* | *Age range recommended* |
| Archery | L | L | L | M | H | All ages |
| Badminton | H-M | H | H | M | M | Singles to 50 |
| Basketball | H | H | H | L | L | Under 30 |
| Baseball | M | H | H | M | M | Under 45 |
| Bicycling | M | L | H | L | L | All ages |
| Bowling | L | L | M | L | M | All ages |
| Boating | M | L | M | M | H | All ages |
| Field hockey | H | H | H | M | M | Under 30 |
| Football | H | H | H | H | H | Under 30 |
| Golf | L | L | M | L | L | All ages |
| Handball | H-M | H | H | M | H | Singles to 45 |
| Heavy apparatus | | | | | | |
| Tumbling | L | H | H-M | H | H | Under 45 |
| Hiking | M | L | H | L | L | All ages |
| Horseshoes | L | L | L | L | M | All ages |
| Judo | H | H | H | H | H | Under 30 |
| Lifesaving | H | M | H | H | H | Under 45 |
| Skating | | | | | | |
| Speed | H | M | H | M | L | Under 45 |
| Figure | M | H | H | L | L | All ages |
| Skiing | H | H | H | M | M | Under 45 |
| Soccer | H | H | H | M | L | Under 45 |
| Swimming | | | | | | |
| Recreational | M | L | M | L | M | All ages |
| Competitive | H | M | H | M | H | Under 30 |
| Table tennis | L | M | M | L | L | All ages |
| Tennis | H-M | H | H | M | M | Singles to 45 |
| Track | | | | | | |
| Distance | H | L | H | M | M | Under 45 |
| Sprints | M | M | H | M | M | Under 45 |
| Volleyball | L | M | M | L | M | All ages |
| Wrestling | H | H | H | H | H | Under 30 |

*Key to abbreviations:* H, high; M, medium; L, low (fitness values).
\*Steinhaus, Arthur H.: How to keep fit and like it, Chicago, 1957, The Dartnell Corp., p. 70; copyrighted by George Williams College.

| TYPE OF FOOD | NUMBER OF CALORIES PER SERVING | SLEEPING | READING | TYPING |
|---|---|---|---|---|
| RAW CARROT | 42 | 36 | 23 | 18 |
| BOILED EGG | 77 | 66 | 43 | 33 |
| BREAD AND BUTTER | 78 | 67 | 43 | 34 |
| TWO STRIPS OF BACON | 96 | 82 | 53 | 41 |
| LARGE APPLE | 101 | 87 | 56 | 44 |
| FRIED EGG | 110 | 94 | 61 | 47 |
| ONE GLASS OF BEER | 114 | 98 | 63 | 49 |
| GELATIN WITH CREAM | 117 | 100 | 65 | 50 |
| ONE GLASS OF ORANGE JUICE | 120 | 103 | 67 | 52 |
| PANCAKE WITH SYRUP | 124 | 106 | 69 | 53 |
| ONE GLASS OF MILK | 166 | 142 | 92 | 71 |
| CHEESE PIZZA | 180 | 154 | 100 | 77 |
| DRY CEREAL WITH MILK AND SUGAR | 200 | 171 | 111 | 86 |
| HALF A BREAST OF FRIED CHICKEN | 232 | 199 | 129 | 100 |
| T-BONE STEAK | 235 | 201 | 131 | 101 |
| ICE-CREAM SODA | 255 | 219 | 142 | 110 |
| TUNA-FISH SALAD SANDWICH | 278 | 238 | 154 | 119 |
| HAMBURGER | 350 | 300 | 194 | 150 |
| ONE-SIXTH APPLE PIE | 377 | 323 | 209 | 162 |
| SPAGHETTI | 396 | 339 | 220 | 170 |
| STRAWBERRY SHORTCAKE | 400 | 343 | 222 | 172 |

*Numbers in activity columns are minutes.*

Balancing calorie intake and outgo.

| BOWLING | GOLF | ROWING | WALKING | TENNIS | BICYCLING | STAIR-CLIMBING | SWIMMING | RUNNING |
|---|---|---|---|---|---|---|---|---|
| 10 | 8 | 8 | 8 | 6 | 5 | 4 | 4 | 2 |
| 17 | 15 | 15 | 15 | 11 | 9 | 8 | 7 | 4 |
| 18 | 16 | 16 | 15 | 11 | 10 | 8 | 7 | 4 |
| 22 | 19 | 19 | 18 | 14 | 12 | 10 | 9 | 5 |
| 23 | 20 | 20 | 19 | 14 | 12 | 10 | 9 | 5 |
| 25 | 22 | 22 | 21 | 15 | 13 | 11 | 10 | 6 |
| 26 | 23 | 23 | 22 | 16 | 14 | 12 | 10 | 6 |
| 27 | 23 | 23 | 23 | 16 | 14 | 12 | 10 | 6 |
| 27 | 24 | 24 | 23 | 17 | 15 | 12 | 11 | 6 |
| 28 | 25 | 25 | 24 | 17 | 15 | 13 | 11 | 6 |
| 38 | 33 | 33 | 32 | 23 | 20 | 17 | 15 | 9 |
| 41 | 36 | 36 | 35 | 25 | 22 | 18 | 16 | 9 |
| 45 | 40 | 40 | 38 | 28 | 24 | 20 | 18 | 10 |
| 53 | 46 | 46 | 45 | 33 | 28 | 24 | 21 | 12 |
| 53 | 47 | 47 | 45 | 33 | 29 | 24 | 21 | 12 |
| 58 | 51 | 51 | 49 | 36 | 31 | 26 | 23 | 13 |
| 63 | 56 | 56 | 53 | 39 | 34 | 28 | 25 | 14 |
| 80 | 70 | 70 | 67 | 49 | 43 | 36 | 31 | 18 |
| 86 | 75 | 75 | 73 | 53 | 46 | 38 | 34 | 19 |
| 90 | 79 | 79 | 76 | 56 | 48 | 40 | 35 | 20 |
| 91 | 80 | 80 | 77 | 56 | 49 | 41 | 36 | 21 |

games and sports. Psychologists say every human being has the desire to belong to a club, gang, or association. This is an essential human need. Games and sports offer opportunity for recognition and a feeling that one belongs to a group. Like the ex-con said who was recently caught in an Eastern city, "I'm glad to go back to jail. Here I'm nothing, but up there I'm first baseman on the baseball team."

Although exercise has many physical, mental, and social benefits, this does not mean a person should rush out and buy himself a tennis racket and schedule three sets of tennis for Saturday afternoon. In order to secure these benefits, exercise must be used with discretion. Following are some suggestions that reflect the opinion of medical experts and provide good advice for physical educators:

1. Encourage a thorough medical examination at regular intervals to determine the type of exercise most beneficial to the individual.

2. Encourage people to select, if possible, a sport or an activity around the house, such as gardening, in preference to calisthenics. The mental and social values are greater.

3. After 40 years of age, encourage people to cut down on the "explosive" sports requiring fast starts, quick stops, and prolonged ac-

tivity without rest. Examples are badminton, tennis, handball singles, and basketball.

4. If a person is out of training in a sport, advise him to return to action gradually. A little today and a little more tomorrow is a good prescription.

5. Encourage persons to exercise out-of-doors if possible.

6. Encourage persons to select activities that are adapted to them.

7. Encourage people to give their full attention to the activity and leave their worries at the office.

8. Encourage individuals engaging in sports that involve body contact or other hazards to use essential protective equipment, especially for head, neck, eyes, and teeth.

9. Encourage individuals to play in areas where safety precautions have been taken to avoid the danger of injuries.

10. Encourage individuals to participate with others of the approximate same degree of skill, training, and size when these factors are pertinent to the competition.

11. The way a person recuperates after exercise should be a guide in its wise use. Breathing and heart rate should not be excessively fast ten minutes after stopping exercise. Extreme fatigue should not persist two hours after stopping. The activity should not cause broken sleep at night or a tired feeling the next day. If any of these symptoms occur, the activity should be cut down. If they continue, the person should see his or her doctor. Ex-

Volleyball is a sport for all ages.

ercise is good, but it must be adapted to the individual's needs.

## Exercise and general health

Exercise and training have important implications for the general health of a person. Studies of 5,000 patients at the Columbia Presbyterian Medical Center in New York City and the Institute of Physical Medicine and Rehabilitation, New York University, indicated that approximately 80% of the patients with low back pain experienced this difficulty because of muscle weakness or stiffness. Follow-up studies showed that pain symptoms decreased as muscle strength and flexibility increased. If exercise was stopped, the ailments came back again. Other studies in recent years have added to a gradually accumulating volume of evidence that exercise has a salutary impact on degenerative diseases, on slowing the aging process, on the ability of an individual to meet emergencies, and on the prevention of vascular degeneration.

Steinhaus has taken twenty-five popular sports and rated each in respect to various components of physical fitness. The participant can use Table 16-1 as a checklist to determine what activities will best meet his fitness needs.

## Isotonic and isometric exercises*

Muscles function by contracting in such a manner that the muscle shortens and the ends are brought together (concentric), or the muscle lengthens and the ends go away from the center as in the beginning of a pull-up when one lowers himself into a hanging position (eccentric) (isotonic). Or, a muscle contracts when the muscle builds up tension and holds without any shortening or lengthening (static or isometric is derived

---

*This discussion is based on Bucher, Charles A., and Nagel, John: Isometrics: new method for new muscles, unpublished.

from the words *iso,* meaning same and *metric,* meaning length).

Isometric exercises have taken the country by storm. Athletes are using them to become better baseball, football, and basketball players. Some patients convalescing in hospitals are finding them helpful in restoring the strength lost while being sick. Handicapped individuals offer testimonials that they have therapeutic value. Polio victims repeatedly acclaim their worth. And, of course, the weak, physically underdeveloped person is amazed at their results.

The worth of isometric exercises to the athletic world has been expounded through the sports news channels. Several years ago Marty Broussard, chief trainer of the champion Louisiana State University Tiger football team and the 1960 Olympic team at Rome, used isometrics to win fame for the athletes under his care. Frank Budd, world record holder from Villanova in the 100-yard dash, adopted them to improve his performance. Bob Pettit, former professional basketball player with the St. Louis Hawks, said they improved his basketball ability tremendously. Athletes at Istrouma High School in Louisiana were helped by isometric exercises to run roughshod over opponents. Weight lifter Lou Riecke and high jumper Bob Avant, as well as many players from the San Francisco 49'ers, Pittsburgh Pirates, and a host of other notables and teams, are converts to this new muscular religion. Current champions in many athletic events use isometric exercise in their training programs.

If these claims for isometrics are true, the value of this system of physical activity is not limited in use to star high school, college, and professional athletes. It can be used by anyone who has the desire to improve his strength. If a person is a little on the weak side, isometrics may be better suited to him than to the super-healthy, physically fit fellow because his improvement will be more rapid and pronounced. This fact was demonstrated as far back as 1958 when isometrics proved their value to some average high school boys. In a study conducted by Rarick and Larsen, the students performed a daily, single, six-second workout. After only six weeks the boys, regardless of whether they were tall, short, or skinny, improved their strength. This experiment, together with other studies, sold many professional physical educators on the worth of isometrics for students, and in turn, the pupils who have tried them are also singing their praises.

### What is isometric exercise as compared to isotonic exercise?

Since physical educators are interested in building strength, a first concern is to know what strength is. A professor at the University of California defines it as the ability to work against resistance. In everyday terms it is known as possessing that physical quality that enables a person to lift a fifty-pound bag of cement, climb a rope in the gymnasium, or lift a girl in his arms.

Strength, when combined with other physical elements, yields additional qualities important to any person who wants to get the most out of his body. For example, strength combined with speed gives power. Power is that quality that permits Oscar Robertson to jump high and snare rebounds off the board, Willie Mays to throw a baseball with rifle-shot precision to home plate from center field, and Jim Ryun to sprint like a deer down the cinder path.

The traditional way of building strength is to get muscles into action by increasing the resistance offered them. Terms commonly used for this form of exercise are *isotonic* and *dynamic*. The classical story is of the man who started lifting a small animal weighing about 25 pounds and continued to lift the animal each day un-

til it became full grown, weighing over 200 pounds. The man's muscles gained strength as the workload was progressively increased from day to day. The people who lift weights in the school gymnasium or YMCA are trying to do the same thing —build strength by following what is called the principle of overload. They gradually increase the amount of weight they lift.

In isotonic or dynamic contraction, the muscle shortens and the resistance, such as that offered when a stack of books is lifted from a school desk, is overcome. Physical work is accomplished by utilizing movement and resistance in the exercise. Isometric contractions, on the other hand, are static types of contractions since there is no joint or muscle movement. Instead, the muscle is put in a state of tension. All the energy that is expended in contracting the muscle isometrically is converted into heat. The resistance, whether it be a radiator, desk, office file, wall, or anything immovable, cannot be overcome. In other words, a force is exerted against an immovable object in which neither muscle nor object moves but in which the pressure or exertion is applied to create a tension within the contracting muscle.

Here is a simple example. Place yourself between two walls. Put your back against one wall and your hands against the other wall. Now push with all your strength against the wall. Even though you grunt and groan and give it all you have as you contract your muscles maximally, it is impossible to move the resistance, in this case the wall. This is the way strength is developed in isometric exercise. As you can see, it is a very simple procedure. There are still several points that need to be known before starting to exercise, such as how much force to apply and how long to apply it, as well as what to do after a desirable level of strength has been achieved.

## Where did it all start?

When did isometric exercise start? What is its history? Briefly, the principles underlying isometric contractions have been public domain for years. One physiologist relates how scientists shortly after World War I used frogs in their experiments. When they tied down one of the frog's legs but not the other, they were surprised to find that the leg that could not move still gained considerable strength. The muscles in the immobilized leg were in a state of static tension and thus strength was developed. These researchers had the basic knowledge about isometrics but for some reason dropped their laboratory work and did not apply the idea to building strength in human beings. Some thirty-five years ago research in this field was conducted at a college famous for training physical educators, Springfield College in Massachusetts. However, the results were not conclusive and the experiments were discontinued. Not much was heard about isometrics for the next twenty years. Then, in 1953 two German physiologists, Dr. T. Hettinger and Dr. E. A. Muller, did considerable research and published their findings in a German magazine. This article attracted considerable attention and created anew throughout the world an interest in isometric exercises. In America such men as Steinhaus, Karpovich, Drury, McCloy, Rasch, Morehouse, and Bender, realizing the significance of the Germans' study, started conducting their own experiments. Many of their findings confirmed the work done in Europe—isometric exercises are of real value in building strength in human beings.

In the last ten years an increased interest in applying this method of exercise to patients and in the treatment of injuries was developed. It was not until recently, however, that isometrics has truly come into its own. Articles appearing in such widely read magazines as *The Read-er's Digest, Sports Illustrated, Scholastic Coach,* and *Amateur Athlete;* discussions at physical education and athletic conventions; and even hi-fidelity records have provided the forward push. Probably the greatest boost was given when it was found that isometric contractions had value for athletic performance. When the coaches, trainers, and owners of professional teams heard the news they were very much interested. Today, although some physiologists have reservations about all the claims made for isometrics, there is general agreement that they can play an important role in developing body strength.

## What results can be expected?

How much strength can one expect to develop in his or her body through this form of exercise? How long will it take to do the job? Muller and Hettinger found that one short isometric contraction of a muscle involving less than maximum force (they suggest two-thirds effort) and performed daily for six seconds over a period of five or six weeks would increase strength at the rate of 5% a week. This estimate is believed to be too generous by most American researchers, who believe 2% a week is a better estimate. Simple arithmetic will show that less than one minute would be required to exercise a muscle group per week. An entire exercise program involving the major muscle groups, such as those of the arms, abdomen, shoulders, and back, will take about 5 minutes per day, including rest periods. On the other hand, if a person is lifting a barbell, he might have used up this much time in merely chalking his hands, to say nothing of the 1 to 2 hours a day, three times a week, required to do lifts. One estimate has been made that ten seconds of isometric contractions can be equal to 100 or more isotonic contractions. If this is true, it would be possible to elicit many more strength gains in ten minutes of isometric work than in one hour of isotonic exercise.

Isometric contractions get results. Mc-Cloy, one of America's pioneers in this area, concluded as a result of his experiments that when these exercises are engaged in regularly for a period of one year a normal person's muscles can be strengthened as much as 100% and those of a physically underdeveloped individual as much as 150%.

After a person has gained the necessary strength he must still continue to exercise. The benefits cannot be "canned up" and

A series of exercises recommended by the American Medical Association.

**1. THE STRETCHER** (Minimum 4; Maximum 10)
(1) Stand erect; (2) Spread feet apart, reach high with hands, rise on toes; (3) Return to starting position.

**2. THE TWISTER** (Minimum 6; Maximum 15)
(1) Sit erect with legs straight, feet apart, hands out wide; (2) Touch right hand to left toe, keeping left arm back and horizontal; (3) Return and exercise opposites.

**3. THE SIDE BENDER** (Minimum 6; Maximum 15)
(1) Stand erect, feet apart, hands out wide; (2) Raise left arm straight over head, slide right arm down leg; (3) Return and exercise opposites.

**4. THE STRIDE SQUAT** (Minimum 6; Maximum 15)
(1) Stand erect, hands behind head; (2) Stride forward deeply with right leg, keep left toe in place, keep bent left knee off floor; (3) Return and exercise opposites.

**5. THE CURL** (Minimum 6; Maximum 15)
(1) Lie on back, knees bent, hands behind head; (2) Tuck chin, "curl" as far forward as possible, aiming right elbow to left knee; (3) Return and exercise opposites.

**6. THE PUSH-UP** (Minimum 6; Maximum 15)
(1) For men: On hands and toes; For women: On hands and lower legs; For both: Keep trunk and neck straight, fingers forward; (2) Lower trunk to two inches from floor; (3) Return.

**7. THE COMPRESSOR** (Minimum 6; Maximum 15)
(1) Lie on back, hands out wide, feet apart; (2) Roll onto left hip, keep legs straight and right arm on floor, touch right toe to left hand; (3) Return and exercise opposites.

**8. THE HIGH-STEPPER** (Minimum 10 Steps; Maximum 20 Steps)
(1) Stand erect, elbows bent, fists clenched;(2) Run in place, pump knees and arms vigorously.

**ISOMETRIC EXERCISES** — which involve muscular contractions without movement — follow. Hold each contraction forcefully for six seconds. Repeating is not necessary.

**9. THE ORGAN GRINDER** Push hand against hand, then pull hand against hand.

**10. THE THINKER** Push forehead against palm; then push back of head against palm(s).

**11. THE BIRD** Push back of hand against door jambs; then push palms in same manner.

**12. THE SAMSON** Push palms against door jambs; then straighten arms high against jambs and push again.

**13. THE SIESTA** Sitting with back against one door jamb, push foot against other side; then push other foot in same manner.

*From Physical Fitness, Chicago, 1964, American Medical Association.*

forgotten. But one encouraging note, a person does not need to spend as much time to maintain the desired strength level. Muller felt that one isometric contraction per day at one-fifth maximal effort was sufficient. McCloy suggested that for the first year strength can be maintained by a workout once a week and after twelve months by a session once every thirty days. Other researchers are more conservative in their estimates.

A person should not abandon all the dynamic exercise done in weight training. Isometrics are not the complete answer to strength and fitness. Probably the biggest drawback is their inability to develop stamina and endurance, those qualities that permit a person to engage in vigorous activity for extended periods of time without becoming exhausted. But as part of a total fitness program they should help because strength is essential to good physical performance, whether it is pole vaulting, lifting a ladder to paint the house, or hiking through the woods. Isometric exercise will help to build this needed strength. And in order to make up for some of those qualities that cannot be developed, a person might engage in some running, swimming, or similar type of activity. Or else isometric contractions can be supplementary to regular workouts in sports. Of course, if a person is not following any exercise program at the present time, isometrics should prove helpful.

## Some research findings on isometric and isotonic exercises

Selected research studies* indicate the following:

1. Both forms of exercise, isotonic and isometric, build muscular strength. However, the evidence to date shows little if any difference

---

*Clarke, H. Harrison: Physical fitness newsletter, Research Review, No. 3, May, 1965. For other references, see end of chapter.

in the effectiveness of the two forms of achieving strength increase—results of over a dozen studies indicated this conclusion.

2. Isometrics can be carried on in many different locations including one's office or while waiting for a train.

3. The motivation factor is usually not as great in the case of isometrics as with isotonics.

4. Studies have not shown a strength gain of 5% per week (claimed by some persons) for ten weeks (50% for the entire period) when a single six-second contraction was used against resistance equal to two-thirds of the muscle's strength. Most studies support a strength gain, but it has not been as great. Many of them show only 2% or 3% a week.

5. Rarick and Larsen found that strength that was retained after the exercise programs were followed over a period of time was greater in the case of isotonic than isometric exercises.

6. Bender, Kaplan, and Johnson found that isometric contractions were often harmful when exercises of a gross nature, such as pressing the whole body upward against a bar, were used. Many times the wrong muscles are developed.

7. Bender and Kaplan found that isometric contractions must be executed at various angles throughout the range of motion if benefits are to accrue, rather than at one point in the range of motion of a joint.

8. Royce found there is a greater interference in circulation to an exercising muscle in isometric than in isotonic contractions.

9. Clarke found that oxygen debt is 40% greater in isometric exercises.

10. Thompson found that the effects of isometric and isotonic work have different effects on blood pressure.

11. Berger found that isotonic exercises will improve jumping ability better than will isometrics.

12. The evidence from existing research seems to favor isotonic exercise rather than isometric exercise as a means of conditioning a muscle.

## Exercise and the daily program of physical education in the schools

Recently the daily period of physical education was challenged by some California legislators. In order to show the need for the daily program, the CAHPER published a special issue of its journal* which contained a wealth of statements and research findings supporting the daily period of physical education. Statements and scientific evidence were listed from cardiologists, American Medical Association, California Heart Association, physiologists and psychologists, nutritionists, educators, school administrators' associations, defense authorities, Parent-Teacher Associations, students, and the President's Council on Physical Fitness. Some of the arguments set forth for a daily program were: (1) it is essential to the physical fitness of the students, (2) it provides a badly needed break from intellectual demands, (3) it is needed for the optimal functioning of the brain, (4) it is a preventive measure against heart disease, (5) it helps to prevent obesity, (6) it develops necessary strength and endurance, (7) it enables individuals to meet emergencies more effectively, (8) it is conducive to good mental health, (9) it reduces tension, (10) it develops muscle tone, (11) it contributes to emotional fitness, (12) it helps to ensure a healthy populace, and (13) it contributes to scholastic achievement.

## EFFECTS OF TRAINING

The results derived from regular periods of muscular work or exercise are many and varied. The individual who participates regularly in exercise adapted to his needs and thereby attains a state of physical fitness may be called "trained." The individual who allows his muscles to get soft and flabby and is in a poor physical condition may be referred to as "untrained."

Space does not permit listing all the advantages of the "trained" state. Therefore, certain advantages that seem to

*California Association for Health, Physical Education, and Recreation, Journal of the CAHPER, Values inherent in the daily program of physical education, March, 1965, Special Issue.

stand out as being important to the vital organs of one's body will be mentioned here.

**Effects of training on general health of heart muscle.** There is evidence available to show that the heart muscle increases in size through use. With greater demands placed upon the heart through physical activity, a hypertrophic condition exists. This is a healthy condition. The term "athletic heart" has often been used to connote a heart that has pathological or diseased indications because of participation in physical activity. Physiologists maintain this is incorrect. Instead, they indicate that an "athletic heart" is a normal condition that follows the law of use. The law of use may be stated in these terms: "that which is used develops and that which is not used atrophies." This applies to all of the muscles of the body. Since the heart is a muscle, this condition indicates a stronger and better developed heart.

There is considerable controversy over whether a heart may be impaired through extreme muscular effort. There is general agreement that a child with a normal heart cannot damage this vital organ through exercise. The controversy concerns individuals 35 or 40 years of age. The proponents of the theory that a sound and normal heart cannot be impaired through activity are many. Others feel that sudden, explosive exertions may cause heart strain. A report published by the American Association for Health, Physical Education, and Recreation, prepared after considerable research by eminent medical doctors, physiologists, and health and physical educators, points out that the normal heart and circulatory system become stronger through use. However, the report continues, strenuous competitive physical activity should not be engaged in by older persons *unless* they have done this regularly and have kept themselves physically fit.

**Effects of training on stroke volume of**

heart. As a result of research on such men as DeMar, the great marathon runner, Olympic athletes, and others, it is generally agreed that there is a greater volume of blood per heartbeat pumped through the body of the trained person than the untrained person. The research on De-Mar showed that his heart pumped 22 liters of blood as contrasted with 10.2 liters in an untrained individual.

**Effects of training on pulse rate.** As a result of evidence gathered from tests performed on Olympic athletes and others, there appears to be evidence that the trained individual has a lower pulse rate than the untrained person. One estimate has been made that the heart of a person beats from six to eight beats slower when he is in training as compared to when he is out of training. In many athletes, pulse rates are ten, twenty, and as much as thirty beats lower than in those individuals who follow sedentary pursuits.

Before exercise the trained individual's heart has a lower rate than an untrained person's heart, but under exercise both increase about the same proportionately.

Individuals convalescing from an illness show by their pulse rates the effects of training. As their condition improves and they become more physically fit, their pulse rate decreases. If the pulse rate does not go down, it is interpreted as a lack of improvement in their physical fitness.

The pulse rate of the trained individual returns to normal much more quickly after exercise than does the pulse rate of the untrained individual. Many cardiovascular tests have been patterned on this premise.

**Effects of training on blood.** The rate of lactic acid formation is lower in the trained individual, resulting in a lower blood lactate concentration. This allows for greater work output on the part of the trained individual. Lactic acid is the substance that is transferred from glucose when a muscle contracts. The more lactic acid, the more fatigued an individual will

become. Lactic acid begins to appear in the blood when the oxygen supply gets low and is inadequate. It escapes from the muscles and goes into the blood. Some of it is buffered. The liver transforms some of it into glycogen, and then it is sent back to the muscles as needed in the form of blood sugar. Some is eliminated through the kidneys.

In addition to the lower rate of lactic acid formation, another effect of training on the blood is the reduction in the osmotic resistance of red corpuscles. It is thought that this may be due to the rise in body temperature during muscular work.

**Effects of training on arterial blood pressures.** Schneider and Karpovich point out that experiments on DeMar showed that the increase in blood pressure is less in the trained individual than in the untrained individual. They further point out that under exercise DeMar's systolic blood pressure increase was 50 mm. Hg, whereas the increase in an untrained man, who was used as a means of comparison, was 125 mm. Hg.

Karpovich, in a later work, refers to additional studies in which this condition has also held true.

The relation of blood pressure to muscular work depends on duration of the exercise, intensity, and on the rate of performance.

**Effects of training on red corpuscles.** There is considerable disagreement as to the effect of training on the red corpuscle count. However, there appears to be agreement that, as a result of training, the bone marrow becomes redder, indicating an increased rate of blood manufacture. As a result of this agreement, it seems reasonable to conclude that there is an increase in the number of red corpuscles in the trained individual.

The person who follows a sedentary or inactive existence, and then pursues strenuous work, destroys a considerable number of red corpuscles, which it takes several days to restore. A period of anemia results, and the individual is not fit to follow strenuous muscular effort for a period of several days. However, the trained individual has developed the red marrow in his bones. Any ordinary destruction of red corpuscles, for any given time, does not affect the individual because the loss is quickly made up. In the trained individual there is a better balance between the destruction and manufacture of red corpuscles.

**Effects of training on white blood cells.** More knowledge is needed concerning the effects of training on the white blood cells. However, it seems clear that the white blood cells or leukocytes increase in number in the blood after a period of muscular work, whether it be mild or severe. The increase in the white blood cells seems to vary in proportion to the degree of intensity of muscular work. It is thought by many that the increase can be credited to a redistribution of the cells in the vascular system.

**Effects of training on respiration.** Evidence is available to show that there are several effects of training on the respiratory system. Some of these are as follows:

1. There is greater expansion of the chest. This is true during the early years but will not affect it to any degree during adulthood.
2. There is a slower rate of breathing. Some evidence shows that the trained person takes as little as six to eight breaths a minute, as compared to eighteen to twenty by the untrained person.
3. The depth of the chest is increased.
4. The blood is exposed to oxygen over a greater area. This is not true of sedentary or inactive individuals because a greater portion of their lungs becomes closed off to air that is inhaled.
5. There is deep diaphragmatic breathing. In the trained person, the diaphragm moves very little.
6. In performing similar work, a trained individual takes in smaller amounts of air and absorbs oxygen from the air in greater amounts than does an individual not in training. It is

believed that the increased number of capillaries in the lungs caused by greater amounts of blood being exposed to the air at any given time is responsible for this economy in respiration.

**Effects of training on the muscular system.** Evidence is available to show that there are several beneficial effects of training on the muscular system. Some of these are as follows:

1. The sarcolemma of the muscle fibers (the part that surrounds each fiber by a connective tissue sheath) becomes thicker and stronger.
2. The amount of connective tissue within the muscle thickens.
3. The size of the muscle increases. It is believed that muscle fibers increase in size but do not increase in number.
4. The muscle has greater strength. It is necessary to exercise a muscle in order to increase its strength. It is reputed that Milo of Crotona, a 17-year-old boy weighing 149 pounds, lifted a bull daily, which weighed 75 pounds to start, until it weighed 290 pounds. The boy's muscles increased in strength through use as the bull increased in size.
5. The muscle gains in endurance. An experiment is reported on an ergograph being attached to the flexor muscles of a finger and the number of contractions recorded. The increase was from 273 contractions to 918.
6. There is a chemical change in the muscle. There is an increase in phosphocreatine content, glycogen, nonnitrogenous substances, and hemoglobin. All of these aid the muscles in working more efficiently.
7. The nerve impulse travels more readily across the motor end plate in the muscle fiber.
8. There is a greater number of capillaries. This results in better circulation of blood to muscles.

**Effects of training on the digestive and excretory systems.** Exercise helps to keep the digestive and excretory organs in good condition. The nerves and muscles of the stomach and intestines become well toned and better able to function in an efficient manner. Also, exercise usually makes a person hungry, and, in general, hunger can improve digestion.

**Effects of training on the nervous system.** The nerves and muscle work together because the muscles are controlled by the nerves. Messages are relayed by the nerves to the muscles which react in the way the individual wishes, whether by running, playing a musical instrument, or hitting a tennis ball. Consequently, any kind of muscular exercise enhances nerve–muscle coordination. Furthermore, nervous fatigue may be lessened by pleasant physical activity because the nervous fatigue that has accumulated through anxiety or mental work is offset through muscular activity.

**Differences between trained and untrained individuals.** A trained individual is in a better state of physical fitness than the individual who follows a sedentary, inactive life. When two individuals, one trained and one untrained, of approximately the same build are performing the same amount of moderate muscular work, there is evidence to indicate that the trained individual has a lower oxygen consumption, lower pulse rate, larger stroke volume per heartbeat, less rise in blood pressure, greater red and white corpuscle counts, slower rate of breathing, lower rate of lactic acid formation, and a faster return to normal of blood pressure and heart rate. The heart becomes more efficient and is able to circulate more blood while beating less frequently. Furthermore, in work of a very strenuous nature that cannot be performed for any great period of time, the trained individual has greater endurance, a capacity for higher oxygen consumption, and a faster return to normal of heart rate and blood pressure. Training results in a more efficient organism. As a greater efficiency of heart action enables a larger flow of blood to reach the muscles and thus ensure an increased supply of fuel and oxygen more work is performed at less cost; improvements are brought about in respect to strength, power, neuromuscular coordination, and endurance; there is a better coordination and timing of move-

ments; and an improved state of physical fitness results.

## PRINCIPLES OF TRAINING

Some principles of training have been compiled by Forbes Carlile.* These will be helpful to the reader who is interested in helping his students achieve peak performance in sports or other forms of physical activity. They are presented in adapted form.

1. The training load should follow the principles of frequency and intensity. The load must be severe and frequently applied so that the body can adapt maximally to a particular activity.

2. Training is an individual problem. As such, factors like age, work and study load, physical makeup, time available for sleep and rest, and training facilities available are important considerations in arranging a training schedule for any person.

3. Physical and emotional stresses, in addition to the training exercise routine, must be taken into consideration for each individual. For example, such conditions as manual labor performed, daily traveling, and emotional pressures from home, school, and other sources are important considerations.

4. Excessive stress on the individual will lower the performance level and therefore attention should be constantly given for manifestations of stress.

5. Periods of rest and physical and mental relaxation must be interwoven with doses of exercise in order to get the best results. This is true during a single training session as well as week by week.

6. Training for a particular sport and many times for different events within a sport (such as sprinters and distance runners in track) is specific and geared to the particular sport or event. Therefore, training procedures for one sport or activity are not necessarily helpful for other sports or activities.

7. Flexibility and strength are two components that are essential to free-flowing movements and efficiency in sports performance. There should be provision for exercises that develop these qualities especially during the off-season. Such exercises should be carefully designed and directed at specific groups of

---

*Carlile, Forbes: Ten principles of training, Track Techniques 1:23, Sept., 1960.

# A.M.A. resolutions on health and physical education*

## School and college physical education

*Whereas,* the medical profession has helped to pioneer physical education in our schools and colleges and thereafter has encouraged and supported sound programs in this field; and

*Whereas,* there is increasing evidence that proper exercise is a significant factor in the maintenance of health and the prevention of degenerative disease; and

*Whereas,* advancing automation has reduced the amount of physical activity in daily living, although the need for exercise to foster proper development of our young people remains constant; and

*Whereas,* there is a growing need for the development of physical skills that can be applied throughout life in the constructive and wholesome use of leisure time; and

*Whereas,* in an age of mounting tensions, enjoyable physical activity can be helpful in the relief of stress and strain, and consequently in preserving mental health; therefore be it

*Resolved,* that the American Medical Association through its various divisions and departments and its constituent and component medical societies do everything feasible to encourage effective instruction in physical education for all students in our schools and colleges.

---

*Two resolutions of special interest to those in the fields of health and physical education were passed by the House of Delegates of the American Medical Association in June, 1960. Both resolutions are reprinted here in their entirety.

## School and college health education

*Whereas,* the rapid advances in medicine can be fully utilized only when the people are properly informed about them, motivated to use them wisely, and willing to accept personal responsibility for health; and

*Whereas,* health instruction programs in schools and colleges offer a unique opportunity for the teaching of the necessary health concepts and principles to all of our people during their formative years; and

*Whereas,* the American Medical Association through its Joint Committee on Health Problems in Education with the National Education Association, its Department of Health Education and other departments and councils has stimulated and supported such teaching; and

*Whereas,* good health significantly assists the individual to achieve his optimum personal potential and to make his optimum contribution to community and national welfare; and

*Whereas,* in the current re-evaluation of school and college programs, it is important to give careful consideration to instruction in the science of healthful living in the curriculum; therefore be it

*Resolved,* that the American Medical Association reaffirm its longstanding and fundamental belief that health education should be an integral and basic part of school and college curriculums and that state and local medical societies be encouraged to work with the appropriate health and education officials and agencies in their communities to achieve this end.

muscles and joints. Scientifically designed weight-training exercises plus stretching exercises are especially good.

8. Interval training has been found to be one of the best procedures for a modern training schedule. This consists of rhythmically carrying out an activity from 30 seconds to 1 minute at fairly intense effort (but not all out). Each period of exercise is followed by 10 seconds to 2 minutes of slow recuperative activity.

9. Nutrition is an important consideration in any training schedule. Therefore, the person in training should adhere to a good diet that contains the essential food groups.

10. Three popular conditioning and training techniques today are as follows:

A. *Circuit training*—this represents a series of exercises, usually ten, that are performed in a circuit and in a progressive manner, doing a prescribed allocation of work at each station, and then checking the progress against the clock. As the performer becomes stronger, the number of repetitions and the quality of the exercise are increased. Activities should be selected with care.

B. *Fartlek* (Swedish for speed play)—this is free-relaxed running. The course usually consists of a soft surface and considerable uphill and downhill running. The following schedule is recommended: (a) easy running for 5 to 10 minutes, (b) steady, fast running, (c) easy running with wind sprints for 50 to 60 yards, (d) rapid walking for 5 minutes, (e) uphill running, and (f) maintain a fast pace for about one minute.

C. *Interval training*—this has been briefly mentioned above. Four factors that are important in using this technique are: (a) distance (to build endurance)—should be long enough to create a stress in the performer, (b) speed—runner increases speed over a designated distance that is possible to repeat allowing rest between each run, (c) number of repetitions—depends upon its value or purpose, and (d) rest or recovery period—the recovery interval is gradually reduced as training progresses.

11. The most important fact in a program of training is to achieve the goals of physical readiness and psychological readiness when your schedule indicates it is important.

## TOBACCO AND FITNESS

Smoking speeds up the pulse rate, raises the blood pressure, constricts the blood vessels, and may cause other physical damage. Smoking has also been linked to many diseases. For example, the correlation between cancer and smoking has been established. There is considerable evidence to indicate that smoking is detrimental to the maintenance of physical fitness. There is no evidence to indicate that it contributes to a higher level of physical performance.

Studies have been conducted in respect to smoking and physical performance. One study of 2,000 runners was conducted over several track seasons. It showed that the nonsmokers took more first places in competition than did those runners who smoked. Another study showed that students who do not smoke grow more in height, weight, and lung capacity than do those who smoke. The increase in the chest development among the nonsmokers was also greater. Tests of physical steadiness have shown that nonsmokers are far steadier than smokers.

Coaches and physical educators are almost unanimous in feeling that athletic performance and muscular power are lessened through smoking. They feel that fatigue begins earlier among the smokers. Very few coaches of high school and college teams knowingly permit their athletes to smoke. Knute Rockne, a former famous coach at Notre Dame, said: "Tobacco slows the reflexes and any advertising that says it helps an athlete is falsehood and fraud."

## ALCOHOL AND FITNESS

Alcohol depresses the central nervous system. It acts on the higher brain centers that affect decisions, judgment, and memory. The control of the lower brain centers are lost, reaction time is slowed, and physical and emotional pain are reacted to more slowly.

Coaches, almost universally, will not permit their athletes to drink during the seasons of play, or at any time during the school year. As in smoking, although there is considerable evidence to show that alcohol hinders physical performance, there is no evidence to show that it improves performance in any way. A great number of automobile accidents can be attributed to loss of control through drinking.

Although drinking has become a popular social custom in our society, the young man or woman who is striving to achieve or maintain a high level of fitness should objectively examine the evidence that shows the result of such a habit.

### DRUGS AND FITNESS

Marijuana, heroin, LSD (lysergic diethylamide acid), and similar drugs detach a person from reality. They make him oblivious to danger. They induce a sense of well-being by postponing feelings of fatigue. And they start a habit of use that is very difficult to stop.

The use of such drugs as amphetamine (found in pep pills), marijuana, cocaine, heroin, and LSD has become popular among a few of this nation's young people. Some drugs have also been used in sports where a high level of energy is required, as in long-distance cycling races. Such a practice is denounced by physical educators, coaches, and sports medicine associations.

The use of drugs is against the law. The continued use of drugs brings about a permanent physical deterioration.

### WEIGHT CONTROL

There is no easy path to weight reduction. There are no reliable gimmicks or shortcuts. And too many persons are overweight. Weight control involves watching one's diet and following a healthful regime, including regular amounts of physical activity. If a person is careful about his or her caloric intake and engages regularly in physical activity, there will be a gradual weight reduction. However, in some cases, persons step up their exercise and similarly step up their

appetite, resulting in an excessive food intake.

Some research has indicated that exercise does not necessarily increase appetite and thereby make it more difficult to lose weight. The research by Mayer* and his colleagues has shown that, contrary to popular belief, exercise does not necessarily result in greater food intake. An important factor is whether the individual was active to start with. If sedentary in his pursuits there can be a step-up of activity without increase in appetite. Conversely, if activity is decreased below a certain point, depending upon the individual, appetite does not decrease correspondingly. In some cases it may, in fact, increase.

In a few cases obesity may be the result of disease. If a person suspects some disturbance, the first step should be to go to a physician for advice. There is great danger in following any highly commercialized solution involving gadgets and appetite depressant pills. To follow the advice of any person other than a qualified physician is risky and may not only result in a loss of hundreds of dollars but be harmful to one's health.

As far as "spot reducing" goes, medical opinion says "No."† This is an erroneous belief. Weight reduction in such special areas of the body as the hips, thighs, and buttocks is not possible. There is no physiological basis for such claims. Only through a general weight reduction program can a person hope to affect the areas mentioned.

Claims made for massage and shaking devices are also ineffective, according to

---

*Mayer, J.: Exercise and weight control, in Exercise and fitness, Atlantic Institute, 1960.

Mayer, J.: Exercise and weight control. In Johnson, Warren, editor: Science and medicine of exercise and sport, New York, 1960, Harper & Bros., chap. 16.

†Journal of the American Medical Association, May 14, 1955.

authoritative opinion. Dr. Peter V. Karpovich, a respected expert in the field of physiology and associated with Springfield College in Massachusetts, says that the claims of self-massage and shaking devices for loss or redistribution of fat deposits are based on misrepresentation of facts. They are useless as a means of weight loss.

## STRESS

Stress, according to Dr. Hans Selye,* is essentially the rate of all the wear and tear caused by life. Each person experiences some degree of stress during each moment of existence. Stress can be caused by an injury, but it can also be caused by a happy occasion. Stress can be good, and it can also be bad for a person.

The important thing is that the body must be prepared to meet stress. The formula for enjoying life is learning how to make adjustments in a world that is constantly changing and in which events do not always run smoothly. These adjustments can be more readily made by the person who understands his or her body and the ways and means of meeting stress. It is felt that to some extent disorders involving such things as nervous disturbances, high blood pressure, and ulcers are caused by lack of understanding in knowing how to adapt.

Selye points out that stress has three phases. The first is the alarm that is sounded by the endocrine, circulatory, or nervous systems. If the stressor persists, the body offers a resistance in an attempt to combat the stressor agents. Finally, if the battle is not waged successfully, the body enters a stage of exhaustion that can have very severe consequences.

The important thing for the physical educator to recognize is that physical activity, it is believed, can help to break the

*Selye, Hans: The stress of life, New York, 1956, McGraw-Hill Book Co.

chain of harmful stress and thus have a beneficial impact upon the body. Therefore, in order to maintain a proper body balance, activity is essential and should be encouraged as an antidote to those harmful stressful experiences that appear in every person's life.

## FATIGUE

Fatigue is a phenomenon that all individuals experience. It is a temporary inability of the muscular system to perform efficiently. It is felt at the end of a hard day's work, after strong muscular effort, when one has time on his hands with nothing to do, after one has passed through an exciting experience, and after periods of intense emotional strain. It results in a decrease in the ability to do work and a feeling of uneasiness. It is a phenomenon that may be aided by sleep, recreation, and physical activity.

There are different types of fatigue. First, there is a *physical* fatigue which a person experiences after a hard day's work, after extreme muscular work, after playing tennis all day, or after pitching hay for 8 hours. The cure for physical fatigue is a good sleep. Second, there is *mental* fatigue. This is the type of fatigue a person experiences after cramming 5 hours for an examination, after working on his income tax a whole evening, or after finishing the monthly report to the boss. Mental fatigue may also be the result of nothing to do or boredom. When a person sits around without anything to occupy the mind, yawns start to appear and a state of mental fatigue ensues. Finally, mental fatigue may be the result of a trying emotional experience, such as attending the funeral of a close friend, getting angry at your next-door neighbor, or worrying about where the next meal is coming from. In many cases the cure for mental fatigue is participation in some form of recreational activity. When a person is engaged in painting a beautiful picture, weaving a rug, trying to catch a bass, or getting par on the golf course, he forgets about his mental problems, boredom, and emotional upsets and enjoys living. Fatigue disappears and the individual is ready to conquer new worlds.

Karpovich lists six places where fatigue may be located. There are three possible seats of fatigue apart from the central nervous system. These are in the fiber of the muscle, at the points of union between the muscle fiber and its nerve or motor end plate, and in the motor nerve fiber. The other three possible seats of fatigue are located within the central nervous system. These are at the synapse, where impulses pass from one neuron to another and where fatigue causes the transmitting of impulses to be slowed, in the nerve cell body, and in the secondary end organs.

### Teacher fatigue*

Fatigue, as related to our energy and performance, can be both harmful and beneficial. Constructively, it can induce us to refreshing sleep or sound the warning signal that exhaustion is not far off. Destructively, it can destroy initiative or transform us from exuberant, active human beings into tired, lifeless creatures oblivious of our responsibilities.

Teaching is one of the most fatiguing of all the professions. Students sap the teacher's energy; papers to be graded or extracurricular activities drain vitality; evening meetings or other after-school responsibilities interrupt rest.

Teacher fatigue can be alleviated by action proceeding from an analysis of the factors causing it and an understanding of how they can be minimized.

Environmental factors may contribute to fatigue. A teacher's bank account of energy may be depleted in schools that

are located next door to noisy factories or that have poor systems of ventilation, dim lighting, or overheated classrooms.

Type of work can also affect the degree of fatigue. Too much work or work that is unsatisfying or monotonous can result in mental fatigue. Too much physical labor can cause muscular weariness.

The attitude of a teacher toward his or her work may be a source of trouble. Whether he or she regards the position as challenging or boring makes a big difference. The poor physical condition of the instructor or a lack of cultural, recreational, or community interests may be the culprit. Emotions such as hate, frustration, and anxiety are notable troublemakers. The teacher's daily habits with regard to diet, exercise, relaxation, rest, and play can also contribute to or help alleviate fatigue.

Cutting down on fatigue requires the help of the teacher and the school. Some things the teacher can do to deal with the problem are as follows:

1. Be inwardly motivated and propelled toward accomplishing school tasks. If a teacher does not recognize the importance of teaching and does not derive satisfaction from his or her job, the fatigue is probably from boredom.
2. Try to cut down on emotional turmoil by planning, by facing problems realistically, and by setting attainable standards. Work to develop self-control and try not to become involved in feelings of anger, fear, hate, and frustration.
3. Eliminate monotony by varying tasks. Throw out the class plan that has been used over and over again. Vary the daily schedule. Get a "new look."
4. Live a balanced life that involves participating in some vigorous activity, following a nutritious diet, getting ample rest and relaxation, and spending a few moments each day in self-evaluation. All work and no play also makes dull teachers.
5. Try to cut down on routine chores.
6. Practice some technique for relaxation. Gardening is better than TV, and making a set of bookends is often more refreshing than stretching out on the sofa.

---

*This discussion is based on an article by Bucher, Charles A.: National Education Association Journal, Dec., 1959.

7. Remember fatigue is cumulative; rest before it builds up.

## RELAXATION AND RECREATION

Relaxation contributes to one's health and may actually be in the form of physical activity. Relaxation is essentially a mental phenomenon concerned with the reduction of tensions that could originate from muscular activity but that are more likely to result from pressures of contemporary living. Today's way of life has created high-tension living. Mounting pressures have resulted in an increase of certain mental and physical ailments. Ulcers, heart attacks, and nervous and psychiatric disorders may be related to states of tension.

A technique for achieving relaxation or nervous reeducation has been developed by Jacobson.* It has two basic steps.

In the first step the individual learns to recognize muscle tension in subtle as well as in gross forms. Gross tension is easily identified. With fists tightly clenched, he holds his arms outstretched to the side at shoulder height for 1 minute. He observes the feeling of exertion and discomfort in the forearms and shoulders. The arms are dropped to the side and the muscles of the arms and hands relaxed completely. The effortless relaxation which Dr. Jacobson calls the "negative of exertion" can be noted. Subtle tension, involving less muscle effort than that just illustrated, is sometimes difficult to detect. It takes concentration and practice to learn to recognize minor tension in the trunk, neck, face, throat, and other body parts.

In the second step the individual learns to relax completely. First, the large muscle groups—arms, legs, trunk, and neck—are relaxed. Then the forehead, eyes, face, and even the throat have tension eased

*Jacobson, Edmund: Anxiety and tension control, a physiological approach, Philadelphia, 1964, J. B. Lippincott Co.

through a program of passive relaxation. Carried out in the proper fashion, the program teaches the subject to relax his whole body to the point of negative exertion. The result is a release of tension, an antidote to fatigue, and also an inducement to sleep.

Leisure-time activities such as games and sports, hobbies and avocations, and intellectual and artistic endeavors like painting and sculpturing are considered to be excellent means for eliminating boredom and tension. These recreational activities provide a means of relaxation. Long abused as simply childish diversion or amusement, recreation is being suggested as an antidote for some of the tensions each person experiences in his daily life.

## FITNESS STATE OF THE UNION— A PROFESSIONAL CHALLENGE

A positive or a negative picture can be painted for the state of the Union's fitness. On the positive side it can be shown that there are fewer deaths today per thousand population than existed five decades ago and that the average life expectancy has increased since 1900.

*Deaths per 1,000 population for the 1-year to 24-year age group:*
  1910—5.6 deaths
  1960—0.8 death
*Deaths per 1,000 population for the 25-year to 44-year age group:*
  1910—7.6 deaths
  1960—2.3 deaths
*Average length of life:*
  The average length of life for babies born in 1959 is 69.7 years as compared with 47.3 years for babies born in 1900.
*Persons who were 45 years of age in 1959:*
  These persons could on the average expect to live another 29.3 years as compared to 24.8 years for those persons who reached 45 years of age in 1900.

These health statistics are encouraging and to a large degree are a tribute to better hospital and medical care in the

United States. But it is not sufficient to make a judgment on the nation's fitness by looking only at this bright side of the coin. The other side must also be considered—the negative side. The fitness state of the Union cannot be judged solely by deaths per thousand persons or length of life. It is important also to be cognizant of such factors as the vigor, strength, emo-

tional stability, and the muscular state of the Union—factors basic to the full development and use of each person's inherent capacities. Educators must be concerned not only with whether people are alive or dead but also with such factors as how vigorous a life they are living, how healthy they are, how emotionally fit they are, and how well they have developed

Fitness is developed in the physical education programs at the elementary and secondary school levels.

all the facets of their total makeup. When educators take a look in this direction, the outlook is not as favorable and there is still much work to be done.

1. On validated physical fitness tests American youths lag far behind their counterparts in England, Austria, Italy, Switzerland, Denmark, Japan, and other countries around the world.
2. During recent years approximately 40% of Americans called up for the armed services were turned down for moral or physical deficiencies.
3. Approximately one half of all hospital beds are occupied by patients suffering from some form of mental illness.
4. The rate of failure has risen steadily on the fitness examinations of college freshmen in some institutions of higher learning.
5. An estimated 60% of the nation's school-children do not participate in a daily program of vigorous physical activity.
6. In a recent year schools in five states, working in cooperation with the President's Council on Physical Fitness, gave standardized physical tests to more than 200,000 students. Nearly one half of the youngsters failed to meet minimum standards of strength, agility, and flexibility. Fewer than one in ten passed more comprehensive tests of physical achievement.
7. Only an estimated 28% of the schools in this country have adequate health and physical education programs.

## PRESIDENT'S COUNCIL ON PHYSICAL FITNESS

As a result of the Kraus-Weber studies of the physical fitness status of American and European youth, President Eisenhower created the President's Council on Youth Fitness, the name being changed to the President's Council on Physical Fitness by President Kennedy. Under Eisenhower's administration a nationwide program was established that emphasized cooperation with state, city, and town officials to raise the nation's fitness level. When President Kennedy came into office, he appointed Charles B. Wilkinson, football coach of the University of Okla-

*Courtesy Dr. Gunsun Hoh, Republic of China.*

Physical fitness testing in a high school in Tainan, Taiwan. This was part of the test program carried out in Southeast Asia to compare results to those of the performance of American children.

homa, his special presidential consultant and placed the Council under his direction. The Council developed and organized, with the cooperation and help of nineteen leading school and medical organizations (the American Association for Health, Physical Education, and Recreation played a most active role), a suggested program of physical fitness for the nation's schools. The President's Council on Physical Fitness has devoted much time to promoting a school-centered program for physical fitness. In addition, it has accomplished special working relationships with institutions of higher learning, community groups, voluntary agencies, and other key organizations. It

has mobilized mass media to communicate to the general public the need to be fit. It has utilized television, movies, radio, and articles in national magazines very effectively in this promotional campaign.

The President's Council on Physical Fitness in recent years has been responsible for the conduct of various regional physical fitness clinics that have featured some of the nation's physical fitness leaders and also the Council staff. Statewide councils or commissions have been established in more than thirty states by either the governor of the state or other agency or organization. State superintendents of education have indicated their active support of the physical fitness movement

Pamphlet containing some of the suggested elements of the President's physical fitness program for the schools.

in approximately one half of the states. Statewide conferences on fitness have been held in a majority of the states in the country. The record, *Chicken Fat,* written for the Council, has sold nearly 300,000 copies. Several fitness films have been produced. Publications have been printed for all segments of the population, including boys, girls, and adults. Materials have been prepared for release to TV stations, radio stations, and other communication media. Millions of dollars worth of free advertising has been made available to the Council. Presidential Fit-

ness Awards have been established and demonstration centers have been developed.

The demonstration centers merit further discussion. For example, in California, twenty-one schools have been selected as state and national physical education demonstration centers. The purpose of these centers is to focus attention upon outstanding school programs of health and physical education that contribute to the development of a physically fit youth. The President's Council on Physical Fitness extended the invitation to the Cali-

THE WHITE HOUSE
WASHINGTON

January 4, 1967

For fifty years the schools of California have conducted daily physical education classes for all pupils, from kindergarten through high school.

The beneficiaries -- the youth of the state -- have offered the most convincing proof that schools can provide for physical fitness without sacrificing academic achievement. Planned, supervised and properly equipped programs of physical training are essential to the development of sturdy young Americans.

I congratulate the State of California on a half-century of leadership in this field and on its support of the recommendations of The President's Council on Physical Fitness. Its record is its tribute.

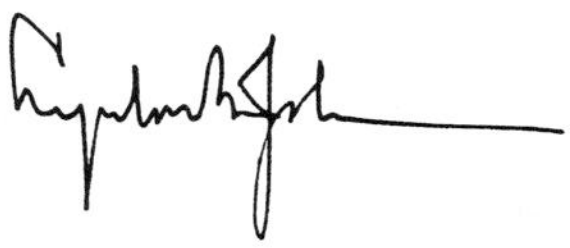

A letter from President Johnson about physical education in California.

Representatives of the President's Council on Physical Fitness participating in demonstrations for the Council.

Representative of the President's Council on Physical Fitness participating in a demonstration for the Council.

fornia State Department of Education who accepted and turned the project over to the California Committee on Fitness, composed of fourteen professional and allied associations and state agencies. These centers in California have attracted much attention with school administrators and other interested persons visiting these centers. In order to be selected as one of the demonstration centers, a school had to meet twenty-two criteria that spelled out the standards for well-rounded school health and physical education programs. A total of 113 school districts were considered for the coveted honor and after considerable study, eleven senior high schools and eleven junior high schools were selected as California State and National Physical Education Demonstration Centers. These centers may be visited by interested teachers, administrators, school board members, and others.*

---

*Information concerning the listed schools and their programs may be secured by contacting the Bureau of Health, Physical Education, and Recreation, Department of Education, Sacramento, California.

The President's Council on Physical Fitness believes the following elements are basic to instruction in physical education and health:

1. Full recognition by physical educators, health educators, parents, citizens, and school administrators that the attainment and maintenance of physical fitness is a basic responsibility of physical education and health education.
2. A daily class period allotted to physical education, grades K through twelve.
3. During this period, every girl and boy participates in sufficient vigorous activity to insure the benefits which result from exercise. This is the unique function of physical education.
4. Every physical education class should be conducted to provide proper warm-up, sequence of activities, progressive development of strength, endurance, and other physical attributes.
5. Teachers must, themselves, project the image of fitness. They always should endeavor to be examples through personal appearance, enthusiasm, and participation.
6. In addition to the period allotted for physical education, sufficient curriculum time should be provided to adequately teach healthful and safe living, which includes an under-

standing of the effects of inactivity and the role of exercise in the development and maintenance of good health.

In order of priority, the Council's objectives include:

1. To encourage all elementary and secondary schools to provide a physical éducation program which includes the four basic concepts . . . :

    (a) Every child should have a medical examination, with proper follow-through, upon entrance to school, and periodically thereafter at least three additional times in his school career.

    (b) Use of a screening test to identify the physically underdeveloped child, and provision of a developmental program to meet individual needs.

    (c) A daily physical education period which conforms to items 2 and 3 above.

    (d) Use of a comprehensive testing program to evaluate pupil progress and to motivate improvement.

2. To encourage elementary and secondary schools to work toward quality programs, encompassing the administrative standards set forth in the "Blue Book."

3. To develop basic recommendations for health education . . . and to work for the implementation of the recommendations.

4. To establish suggested guide lines for health education and physical education at various grade levels to encourage progressively developmental programs in school systems throughout the country. (Because of the increasing mobility and urbanization of the American population, such guide lines are recommended to encourage equalized opportunities for all our children and youth.)

5. To develop basic recommendations to insure the physical fitness of college students.*

The United States Office of Education surveyed the nation's schools to find the impact on physical education of the President's Council and found that 56% of the 108,000 public schools improved their programs during one school year. Improvement meant they added a screening test to identify physically underdeveloped pupils, and/or a comprehensive test of physical

---

*President's Council on Physical Fitness: Policy statement on school health and physical education (mimeographed).

achievement, and/or more vigorous physical activity during the class period.

John F. Sweeney, Director of Guidance and Counseling for the Springfield, Missouri, public schools, conducted a special study for the President's Council which attempted to determine some relationships between academic performance and physical fitness. Sweeney was interested in finding out how students who maintain a high level of physical fitness performed in their academic work and also what their attitude was toward school and their studies. The research rated students in four areas: (1) grade average, (2) attendance, (3) participation in extracurricular activities, and (4) attitude. There were two student groups, one a very select group of 442 freshmen and juniors who had passed a comprehensive test of physical achievement and ranked in the upper 40% of their classes on the basis of physical performance. The other group was composed of 200 juniors and freshmen whose records were taken at random from the school files. Equal numbers of boys and girls were in both groups. The select group's collective grade average was better, they participated in 50% more extracurricular activities, missed fewer days of school, and had a more enthusiastic attitude toward their schoolwork. The accompanying charts illustrate the results graphically.

## PROGRESS BEING MADE TO IMPROVE PHYSICAL FITNESS OF NATION'S CHILDREN AND YOUTH

Data indicate that progress is being made in improving the physical fitness of American youth. According to information released by the President's Council on Physical Fitness, the 1960's have witnessed improvement in physical achievement standards among the nation's youth. For example, 9.2 million children are participating in school physical education programs; four out of every five pupils now successfully pass standardized physi-

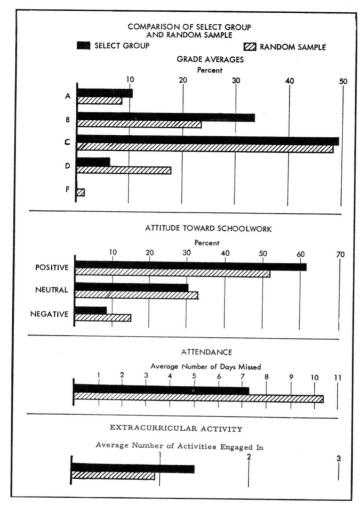

Wilkinson, C. B.: *Report to the
President, Dec. 10, 1962.*

Relationship of academic performance to physical fitness.

cal fitness tests (only two out of three passed in 1961) ; 68% of all schools have strengthened their physical activity programs; the number of parochial schools providing physical education instruction has doubled; seventeen states have raised their school physical education requirements; and teaching positions for health and physical education have increased by 27%—school enrollments have increased 11%. Supervisory positions in physical education have also increased at both local and state levels. Twenty-seven states have indicated an increase in more than 300 such positions. Rhode Island and West Virginia have established state supervisory positions in health, physical education, and recreation.

A survey conducted by Hunsicker and Reiff* and supported by the Cooperative

*Hunsicker, Paul A., and Reiff, Guy G.: A survey and comparison of youth fitness, 1958–1965, Ann Arbor, 1965, University of Michigan Press.

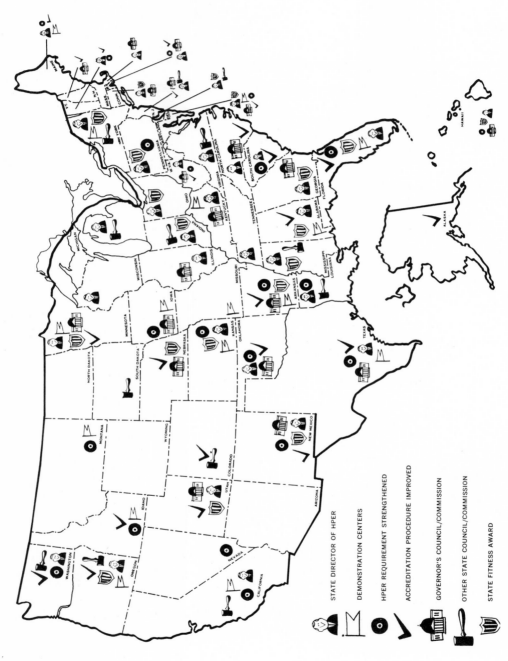

*From A report to the President, 1967, the President's Council on Physical Fitness.*

STATE DIRECTOR OF HPER

DEMONSTRATION CENTERS

HPER REQUIREMENT STRENGTHENED

ACCREDITATION PROCEDURE IMPROVED

GOVERNOR'S COUNCIL/COMMISSION

OTHER STATE COUNCIL/COMMISSION

STATE FITNESS AWARD

State support for physical fitness programs.

LEGEND

1958    1965

STANDING BROAD JUMP
(10-year-old boys)
4'6"
5'0"

SITUPS
(16-year-old girls)
20    28

600-YARD RUN
(14-year-old boys)
2 MINS., 30 SECS.    2 MINS., 6 SECS.

50-YARD DASH
(11-year-old girls)
8.9 SECS.    8.4 SECS.

SOFTBALL THROW
(16-year-old boys)
164'
181'

SHUTTLE RUN
(14-year-old girls)
11.5 SECS.    12.2 SECS.

*From A report to the President, 1967,*
*the President's Council on Physical Fitness.*

Comparison of test results.

Research Program of the U. S. Office of Education shows the progress made in grades five through twelve when the AAHPER Youth Fitness Test was used as the instrument of measurement. There was an increase in the physical fitness level of public school children during the period 1958–65. In 1958–59 the test was given to approximately 8,000 pupils in order to develop national norms for the seven-item test. In 1964–65, a similar group of pupils were given the same test and fared much better than their counterparts did several years earlier. A comparison on two items of the text, for example, shows that in 1958, a 15-year-old boy ran 600 yards in 2 minutes, 19 seconds and did 45 situps, while a 15-year-old girl ran 600 yards in 3 minutes, 19 seconds and did 18 situps. In 1964–65, on the other hand, the 15-year-old boy ran 600 yards in 2 minutes and did 73 situps, while the 15-year-old girl ran 600 yards in 2 minutes and did 28 situps.

A survey conducted by the Division of Health, Physical Education, and Recreation in New York State in 1963 and again in 1965 shows the improvement in the physical fitness of students in one of the nation's most populous states.* In 1963, 25% of those students in grades four to twelve were physically underdeveloped as indicated by the New York State Physical Fitness Screening Test, whereas in 1965 only 12% were classified as underdeveloped. The lowest physical fitness levels were found at the elementary school level and the highest at the high school level. Throughout the school years boys were slightly above the girls in their physical fitness achievement levels. At all grade levels public school pupils were significantly higher in their physical achievement levels than private school pupils.

---

*Straub, William: State survey shows 130,040 pupils physically unfit, New York State Journal of Health, Physical Education, and Recreation **19**:22 (Fall Issue), 1967.

Reasons given for the progress made by New York State students in achieving higher physical fitness levels in recent years include the increased national, state, and local emphasis upon physical fitness, the recognition by pupils of the importance of physical fitness in their own lives, and the increased skill development by pupils in the "lifetime" sports.

### Still room for improvement

There is still much progress to be made in improving the nation's level of physical fitness. For example, 14% of the children in school today do not participate in any physical activity program, and an additional 27% participate only one or two days per week; only four schools in ten provide physical education programs five days per week; and 23% of the schools have administered the American Association for Health, Physical Education, and Recreation seven-item physical achievement test, but on this test, only 57% of the boys and 51% of the girls were reported to have scored "satisfactory" on all items.

Tests also show that American boys and girls in their physical development are weak in such areas as the shoulder girdle. They are also lacking in endurance and flexibility. Statistics show that approximately one half of the draftees being disqualified from the armed services are failing because of physical reasons. Furthermore, records show that one out of every four Americans is overweight.

### PROGRESS BEING MADE IN ADULT FITNESS

The children and youth of America are not the only members of the nation's population becoming physical fitness minded. Adults are conscious of the state of their physical fitness. The President's Council on Physical Fitness has contributed much to this movement by publishing a pamphlet entitled *Adult Physical*

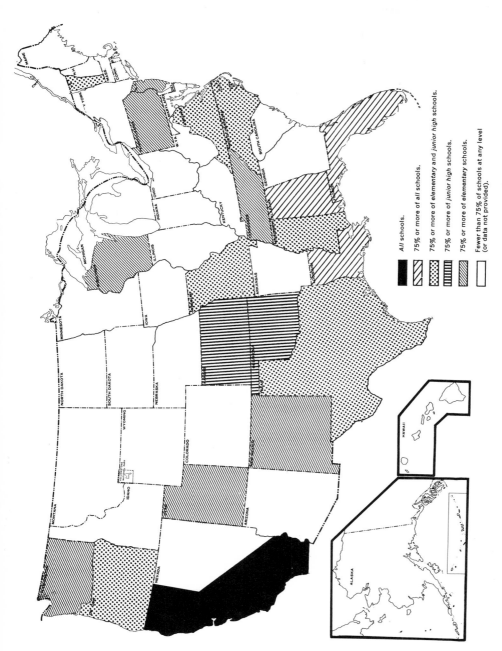

All schools.

75% or more of all schools.

75% or more of elementary and junior high schools.

75% or more of junior high schools.

75% or more of elementary schools.

Fewer than 75% of schools at any level (or data not provided).

*From A report to the President, 1967, the President's Council on Physical Fitness.*

Daily physical education programs in the schools.

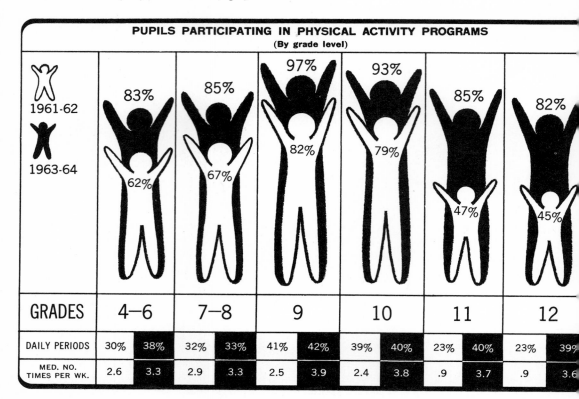

### PUPILS PARTICIPATING IN PHYSICAL ACTIVITY PROGRAMS
#### (By grade level)

| GRADES | 4–6 | | 7–8 | | 9 | | 10 | | 11 | | 12 | |
|---|---|---|---|---|---|---|---|---|---|---|---|---|
| 1961-62 | 83% | | 85% | | 97% | | 93% | | 85% | | 82% | |
| 1963-64 | 62% | | 67% | | 82% | | 79% | | 47% | | 45% | |
| DAILY PERIODS | 30% | 38% | 32% | 33% | 41% | 42% | 39% | 40% | 23% | 40% | 23% | 39% |
| MED. NO. TIMES PER WK. | 2.6 | 3.3 | 2.9 | 3.3 | 2.5 | 3.9 | 2.4 | 3.8 | .9 | 3.7 | .9 | 3.6 |

*From A report to the President, 19*
*the President's Council on Physical Fitne*

*Fitness,* which provides a home exercise program for men and women, and also distributing information on exercise, aging, and other pertinent subjects. The Young Men's Christian Association has provided special clinics, programs, and pilot studies on physical fitness for adults, including business executives. Industrial concerns have developed fitness and recreation programs for their personnel on a large scale throughout the country. The armed forces have shown increased interest in how they can better physically train the men in uniform. Also, such organizations as the American Medical Association, parent-teacher associations, adult education organizations, athletic clubs, and gymnastic organizations have given emphasis to the adult fitness movement.

The need for adult physical fitness is a result of several conditions. Some of the more pertinent factors are the increased leisure, the changing nature of man's work involving less and less activity, the pressures and speed of modern existence, the prevalence of heart disease and other ailments where exercise is thought to be a preventive factor, and the desire for greater productivity.

Industrial organizations have expanded their fitness programs in recent years. Physical activities are very popular, including such sports as softball, bowling, basketball, golf, tennis, volleyball, judo, aquatics, badminton, and handball. These activities are offered under conditions where individuals, couples, and families can participate and where industrial leagues provide activity for the more competitively minded persons. In addition to a broad program of activities for the rank and file of the working population, executives are also being provided programs. Exercise routines, massage, weight-control programs, sports competition, and many other activities are being offered. Industrial concerns feel that the large investment they have in their key men must be protected and so physical fitness programs are coming into vogue to help increase the productivity of the executive class and also increase their service in number of years to the company.

Recently, the Central Atlantic Area Council of YMCA's Physical Education Committee conducted a five-day business–industry physical fitness course for executives. The purpose of this conference was to help these key persons achieve a better understanding and practice of total fitness. The program included lectures and discussions on such topics as "Aging, Stress, and Productivity and the Need for Regular Exercise," "Principles and Effects of Physical Training," "Motor Fitness, Fatigue and Low Back Problems," "Nutrition, Weight Control, and Heart Disease," and "Finding the Time to Exercise." Exercise routines and cardiovascular testing were also included as part of the program.

## FITNESS SUCCESS FORMULA

Newspaper and magazine articles and television and radio commercials are sounding the need for a tougher, stronger, and more physically fit youth. Schools and communities are building spacious gymnasiums, playgrounds, and athletic facilities. Taxpayers are pumping thousands of hard-earned dollars into exercise and sports programs.

But is the answer to physical fitness as simple as this? Will providing the facilities, the leagues, the equipment, and the opportunities for youth to be participants be enough to yield the desired results?

The answer is NO. A physically fit population cannot be achieved solely through exercise programs for a captive youth in

the schools and dazzling athletic programs in the communities of the nation. There are many physically fit adults who never exercised in a school gymnasium or played in an organized community recreation program, but they had something that many young people do not have—respect for their bodies and a determination to stay in "top" shape. They wanted to be physically fit because they knew it was good for them, and so they provided time and their own means to achieve this goal.

Today's American boys and girls have better food, medical care, and housing than any generation preceding them. They weigh more, are taller, have less disease, and possess firmer foundations for a strong, healthy body than most youngsters around the world. It is paradoxical, therefore, to find that tests of physical fitness picture them as soft, flabby, and weak. These muscular yardsticks show America's young people cannot run without puffing, perform sit-ups without groaning, or lift without grunting. And when they were compared with their counterparts abroad, they came out second best. Why?

The explanation being clarioned to the local communities is that our youngsters do not exercise enough. To correct this situation these remedies are cited: "Get them into sports." "Build more gymnasiums and swimming pools." "Put them on bicycles." "Make them walk to school." "Turn off the TV set." "Give them calisthenics."

Educators and public-spirited citizens listen to this advice and conclude that the answer to physically inept young people is to provide a daily program of exercise in the schools and a wide variety of sports programs in the community. Simply by providing opportunities for physical activity, they feel our youth will become strong and tough. BUT WILL THEY?

What school personnel and the public in general must recognize is that to get the desired results, boys and girls must also be inwardly motivated to want to be physically fit. The reason children and youth are soft is not only that they do not have the opportunity to achieve physical fitness but also that they do not fully appreciate and know why physical fitness is important to themselves and to their country. They do not see the relationship between their fitness and their personal success, health, and productivity. They do not know simple physiological facts that would help them to understand what happens to their bodies when they exercise regularly. They do not possess skill to motivate them into activity. There is nothing inside that propels them into action.

Also, young people do not seem to fully appreciate the stake they have in the future of this country and how they can most contribute. They do not seem to understand that to be physically fit is fundamental to the preservation of the democratic way of life and the accomplishment of national purposes. Democracy is not a spectator sport. It is a game where all Americans are participants, and today's life-and-death struggle demands all-out effort on the part of each person. This requires total fitness, including intellectual, physical, and emotional fitness.

I invited five teen-agers with high I.Q.'s into a graduate-school education class at New York University. These boys and girls represented outstanding high schools in New York, Pennsylvania, and New Jersey. Each of these schools had broad physical education and athletic programs. In a frank exchange of opinion, these youngsters showed they were devoid of information as to what physical fitness is and the physiological benefits accruing from exercise. They possessed few physical skills and felt the main purpose of the physical education and athletic program is to have some fun and improve school morale.

The author spent his sabbatical traveling 6,500 miles and visiting many high schools and colleges throughout the United States. It was very disturbing to find that many young people think it is smart to cheat on their health. They feel it is high fashion, sophisticated, or romantic to smoke two packs of cigarettes a day, drink a coke and eat a candy bar for lunch, and go to bed at 2 A.M. They think they will get by without any bad effects.

I traveled around the world observing education programs in many parts of the globe. One thing that impressed me in Japan, where comparative tests have shown their young people to be much more physically fit than in the United States, is that textbooks, lectures, and discussions are a part of many physical education programs. The schools and colleges attempt to get at the "why" of the activity as well as the activity itself. Many higher education institutions, for example, follow this type of program.

*The United States has a very intelligent crop of young people and they are not going to sweat or puff unless given a good reason. And if they are to be physically fit, they are going to have to understand and know that the time spent in the pursuit of this goal has its rewards.*

The importance of educating young people in health matters is shown by a study conducted by the American Cancer Society among 22,000 high school students in Portland, Oregon. The research team set out to determine what type of approach was best in influencing smoking among students. Of the five different approaches that were used, the most effective was that of providing the facts about smoking and then allowing the student to decide whether or not to smoke on the basis of this knowledge. Previous to the study, each successive school grade had a higher percentage of smokers than the preceding grade. For example, 14.5% of the freshmen boys smoked, whereas 35.4%

of the senior boys smoked. But after a year's study of basic facts, the student body as a whole showed that the number of new students who took up smoking dropped from 13 to 7.7% among the boys and 6.4 to 2.1% among the girls. The researchers projecting these figures over a four-year period estimated that about 20% of the high school students who would ordinarily be smoking regularly by graduation time would not do so.

When young people become educated about desirable health practices, it helps to ensure an intelligent choice because they KNOW it is the wise thing to do. Boys and girls need to be *physically educated* to understand why they should have such essentials as regular physical activity, good nutrition, and proper rest and sleep. This approach will get results.

What are the essential ingredients for a physically educated youth? The answer is written into this formula:

**Knowledge + Attitude + Skill + Activity =
Physical fitness**

## Knowledge

Today's boys and girls need to know the facts about physical fitness. First of all, young people should recognize that physical fitness is the basis for excellent performance whether as a student, scientist, teacher, mechanic, or as a leisure-time sports enthusiast. As President Kennedy pointed out, "The foundation of intellectual fitness is physical fitness." Well-being is a means to an end, the end being a more productive, vigorous, interesting, and rewarding life.

Boys and girls need to know that physical fitness is more than just having enough strength to chin themselves and carry out their daily duties. It also means having a sound, healthy heart, lungs, and musculature and other aspects of medical fitness; and the best time to get good organic development is before 20 years of age. It means having the necessary stamina,

speed, agility, endurance, and coordination to use bodily equipment in an efficient manner; and it means possessing physical skills that will enable a person to engage in sports successfully.

Young people need simple physiological knowledge, such as this: Exercise makes the blood circulate faster to meet the need for more oxygen and food; as a result the cells of the body benefit; the blood manufactures more red cells and hemoglobin; and the cells are better nourished and grow larger so that the muscles gain in strength and flexibility.

Boys and girls should know that the values of exercise rest upon the application of three scientifically based principles.

1. *Frequency.* The benefits cannot be stored; they are only gained through regular participation.

2. *Duration.* A sufficient length of time is needed to give the body a good workout.

3. *Intensity.* The activity must be vigorous enough to place a load on the circulatory and respiratory systems.

Young people need to know that, although the path to physical fitness is the result of heredity and the absence of strains and drains on the human system, the most important consideration for them is *the way they live*—kind of food they eat, exercise they get, hours they sleep, and other health habits they follow.

Fallacies need to be exploded, such as the one that exercise is the best means of weight reduction. Although it plays a part, the best means of weight reduction is through caloric reduction. To burn up one pound of fat, one scientist has estimated that a 155-pound man must walk 144 miles at the rate of two miles an hour or do 5,714 push-ups.

## Attitude

Facts and knowledge are not enough to ensure physical fitness, however. Examples of men, women, and young people who possess the knowledge but do not act accordingly are replete in every community. The woman who knows that a lump in her breast requires medical attention but fails to see her physician, the man who knows the value of seat belts in his car but does not take the time to have them installed, and the boy who knows milk is good for him but reaches for soda pop are illustrative evidence to support this premise.

Attitude is important to physical fitness. The interest in and desire for well-being is the catalyst that sparks the boy and girl to want to apply the knowledge they know to be true. Mothers and fathers play an important role in the development of proper attitudes among youth. If a father remarks that he had rather have a soggy body than a soggy mind (as though it were an "either-or" proposition), his children are likely to react the same way and try to avoid physical activity. The development of an interest in health and being healthy, a determination to be physically active, and desire to develop all of one's potentials, are important attitudes to develop.

## Skill

The need for motor skills is also an important part of becoming physically educated. As a boy develops skill in skating, his interest in the activity increases and he spends much of his leisure time in perfecting this skill. The girl who develops skill in swimming does the same thing. In addition to physical fitness, skill kindles within a person the desire for action and competition. Skill provides such essential human needs as recognition, belonging, and the joy of accomplishment. Many tired businessmen get up at 7 A.M. on Saturday and Sunday mornings because they have developed the skill of hitting a small, white ball 250 yards down the fair-

way, and they are more physically fit for doing so.

One of the main contributions a school or community can make to their boys and girls is to develop a wide variety of physical activity skills for each season of the year: archery, handball, squash, volleyball, skiing, field hockey, dance, and many more activities. These skills will contribute to year-round and life-long physical fitness, since the youngster will not only enjoy participating during school hours but also will be active on his own after school, on holidays, during vacation periods, and throughout life. One criterion of a good education program is what the boy and girl do when they are away from the teacher and the school, and skills will help to ensure that such time is spent in a constructive manner.

The ability of youth to develop skills accents the need for more instruction during this golden age of skill learning in activities than can be engaged in throughout a lifetime. Only about 1 out of 1,000 students will probably engage in baseball when they leave school, but the number increases sharply in tennis, golf, and badminton.

Each boy and girl should develop skills in such fundamental movements as running, throwing, and jumping and in such basic activities as swimming, as well as in various sports for each season of the year.

## Activity

With scientifically based knowledge, wholesome health attitudes, and a wide variety of physical skills, activity becomes meaningful. Young people will engage in healthful physical exercise regularly because they know it is just as essential to their body as good food and because they want to be fit so that they can become all they are capable of becoming. Furthermore, with this knowledge, attitude, and skill, activity will be a part of their personal regimen throughout life.

Long-term physical fitness is not going to be accomplished by calisthenics and sports programs carried on in a vacuum. Long-term physical fitness for each of our young people will only become a reality when every boy and girl clearly understands the need for such activity, has the desire to be physically fit, and possesses the skills to make activity exciting and enjoyable. When children and young people have acquired these essentials, they can be called *physically educated,* recognizing that this is what will make coming generations healthy and the nation physically strong. The development of physically educated youth requires opportunities for participation in healthful physical activity. But even more important is the need for teachers and youth leaders who are dedicated to the task of helping all boys and girls and who recognize the importance of exercising the brain as well as the muscle cells in developing physically fit youth.

## ROLE OF SCHOOL AND COMMUNITY IN FITNESS

One of the chief avenues for reaching the youth of America is the schools. Here are a few reasons why the schools are an important part of the fitness picture:

1. They are the only agency through which nearly 60 million children and youth can be reached directly.
2. They have teachers trained for instilling youngsters with the desire to be fit and for carrying out conditioning programs.
3. It has been estimated that 80% of all the physical activity skills acquired during a lifetime are learned by children between the ages of 7 and 17 years.

Education in its broadest sense means preparation for life. It should help each individual to become all he is capable of being. Therefore it is inexorably tied in with fitness. Education must be concerned

with developing in each individual optimum organic health, vitality, emotional stability, social consciousness, knowledge, wholesome attitudes, and spiritual and moral qualities. Only as it accomplishes this task will it achieve its destiny in the American way of life.

Schools have the responsibility for providing many opportunities for understanding and developing fitness. The schools should be "fitness conscious." Programs must be constituted so that experiences and services contribute to fitness. This means that health knowledge, attitudes, and practices are stressed; protective health services are provided; physical activities are available to and engaged in by all—not just the few who are skilled; necessary facilities are provided; the environment is conducive to proper growth and development; experiences in every area stress proper social and ethical behavior.

Leadership exemplifies fitness, and fitness is the responsibility of all disciplines in the school and all teachers and staff. It should permeate the entire program and all persons connected with it. It is not the responsibility of only one area and just a few people.

Schools should provide community leadership in this area. The schools, however, represent only one force for developing a fit populace. The home, the church, recreational agencies, volunteer groups, and other organizations also have major contributions to make. Schools should work closely with and play a leading role in mobilizing the entire resources of each community to do the job.

Children and youth should want to be fit. Unless this desire is resident in each child, the way of life that results in fitness will not be achieved. By the time children leave school behind and enter into adult life, the importance of fitness in achieving personal ambitions and desires, in feeling well and happy, in living most and serving best, and in contributing to a strong nation must be inculcated in every boy and girl.

This is a responsible role for our professions to pursue and a very necessary one. It is a challenge we must meet if we are not to become "a nation of softies." Physical education can make a significant contribution to fitness for living. If it achieves its four main objectives of organic development, skill development, mental development, and social development it will contribute not only to the physical but also to the total fitness of the individual.

The President's Council on Physical Fitness raises questions that should be asked in respect to each person's school, child, community, and personal fitness program. They are presented here in adapted form*:

**Your school's physical education and health program**

Does it emphasize vigorous activity?
Is each boy and girl involved?
Does it have evaluation procedures to identify physically underdeveloped pupils?
Is there outstanding professional leadership?
Are the physical education facilities adequate?
Is provision made for health instruction and services?

**Your child**

Is he overweight?
Is he underdeveloped?
Has he developed skill in several sports and games?
Have health defects been corrected?
Does he have proper health care?
How does he spend his free time?
How are his energy and stamina?

**Your community**

Does it provide a recreation program for all persons?

---

*President's Council on Physical Fitness, Physical fitness facts, Washington, D. C., 1964.

Have fitness centers and clubs been established?
Is instruction provided?
Are the facilities adequate and used year-round?
Has a community recreation committee representative of the entire community been established?

**You**

When was your last medical checkup?
Do you engage in some form of vigorous physical activity each day?
Are you providing for your health needs?

## QUESTIONS AND EXERCISES

1. Trace the history of the current fitness movement and discuss its implications for the professions of physical education, health, and recreation.
2. Why is it important that boys and girls fully understand the meaning of the term "physical fitness"? How can physical fitness educators help to educate for fitness?
3. What is the relationship of exercise to physical fitness?
4. Formulate a physical fitness program for an average school system. Justify your program completely.
5. To what degree should physical education confine itself solely to the development of physical fitness?
6. Discuss and compare the value of isometric and isotonic exercises.
7. How does the "trained" person differ from the "untrained" person?
8. Who are five leaders in the profession who have played important roles in bringing the importance of physical education to the public?
9. What relationship is there between physical education and a Vic Tanny gymnasium?
10. What are some of the characteristics of the physically fit individual?

## SELECTED REFERENCES

American Association for Health, Physical Education, and Recreation: Fitness for youth, Statement approved at Fitness Conference, Dec., 1956, The Association.
American Association for Health, Physical Education, and Recreation: Fit to teach, Third AAHPER Yearbook, Washington, D. C., 1957, The Association.
American Association for Health, Physical Education, and Recreation: Journal of Health,

Physical Education, and Recreation **29:** Sept., 1958.

Bender, Jay A., and Kaplan, Harold M.: The multiple angle testing method for the evaluation of muscle strength, Journal of Bone and Joint Surgery **45A:**135, 1963.

Bender, Jay A., Kaplan, Harold M., and Johnson, Alex J.: Isometrics: a critique of faddism versus facts, Journal of Health, Physical Education, and Recreation **34:**22, May, 1963.

Berger, Richard A.: Effects of dynamic and static training on vertical jump ability, Research Quarterly, AAHPER **34:**419, Dec., 1963.

Bucher, Charles A.: Administration of school health and physical education programs, St. Louis, 1967, The C. V. Mosby Co.

Bucher, Charles A.: Fitness and health (editorial), Educational Leadership **20:**356, March, 1963.

Bucher, Charles A., Koening, Constance, and Barnhard, Milton: Methods and materials for secondary school physical education, St. Louis, 1965, The C. V. Mosby Co.

Bucher, Charles A., Olsen, Einar A., and Willgoose, Carl E.: The foundations of health, New York, 1967, Appleton-Century-Crofts.

Bucher, Charles A., and Reade, Evelyn M.: Physical education in the modern elementary school, New York, 1964, The Macmillan Co.

Clarke, David H.: The energy cost of isometric exercise, Research Quarterly, AAHPER **31:** 3, March, 1960.

College Physical Education Association: Fit for college, Washington, D. C., 1959, American Association for Health, Physical Education, and Recreation.

Gallagher, J. R., and Brouha, L.: Physical fitness, Journal of the American Medical Association **125:**834, 1944.

Hunsicker, Paul: What research says to the teacher, Physical Fitness, Washington, D. C.,

1963, The National Education Association.

Hunsicker, Paul A., and Reiff, Guy G.: A survey and comparison of youth fitness 1958–1965, Journal of Health, Physical Education, and Recreation **37:**23, Jan., 1966.

Johnson, Perry B., and others: Physical education—a problem-solving approach to health and fitness, New York, 1966, Rinehart & Winston.

Presidential physical fitness award, Journal of Health, Physical Education, and Recreation **37:**23, Feb., 1966.

Rarick, Lawrence G., and Larsen, Gene L.: Observations on frequency and intensity of isometric muscular effort in developing static strength in pre-pubescent males, Research Quarterly, AAHPER **29:**476, Dec., 1954.

Royce, Joseph: Isometric fatigue curves in human muscle with normal and occluded circulation, Research Quarterly, AAHPER **29:** 333, Oct., 1958.

Selye, Hans: The stress of life, New York, 1956, McGraw-Hill Book Co.

The Journal of Sports Medicine and Physical Fitness, official journal of the Federation Internationale de Medicine Sportive, published by Edizioni Minerva Medica (Torino, Italy). See all issues.

Thompson, Clem W.: Some physiological effects of isometric and isotonic work in man, Research Quarterly, AAHPER **25:**476, Dec., 1954.

YMCA, Journal of Physical Education, Vol. 64, Nov.–Dec., 1966, Special Fitness Issue.

Your child's health and fitness: Insert in National Education Association Journal **51:**33, Feb., 1962.

Additional materials on the subject of fitness may be secured from the President's Council on Physical Fitness, Washington 25, D. C., and the American Association for Health, Physical Education, and Recreation, 1201 Sixteenth Street, N. W., Washington, D. C.

# Chapter 17

# Psychological interpretations of physical education

Psychology is a science that studies the individual and his activities from the time he is conceived until the time he dies. It studies his behavior, his ways of reacting, and how he learns. It is concerned with the many traits, feelings, and actions that make up the mind. It compares the normal to the abnormal person and the criminal to the law-abiding citizen.

The word "psychology" comes from the Greek words *psyche,* meaning mind or soul, and *logos,* meaning science. Therefore from these Greek words it can be seen that psychology is the science of the mind and the soul. The psychologist studies human nature scientifically and, rather than formulate conclusions from casual observations, he sorts out and checks and rechecks human characteristics under reliable conditions. In this manner and through the use of acceptable scientific evaluation, it is possible for him to determine the condition under which certain human characteristics will operate. The data derived through the psychologist's work are impersonal and free from prejudice, bias, and emotion and focus attention on an impartial and realistic examination of all the evidence.

## WHAT IS LEARNING?

Learning implies a change in a person —a change in his method of performing a skill, practicing a habit, gaining ability in performance, or changing an attitude toward a particular thing. Learning implies a progressive change of behavior in an individual. It implies a change that occurs as a result of experience or practice. It results in the modification of behavior as a result of training or environment. It involves such aspects as obtaining knowledge, improving one's skill in an activity, solving a problem, or making an adjustment to a new situation. It implies that knowledge or skill has been acquired through instruction received in school or some other setting or through a person's own initiative in personal study. Learning goes on all through life. It starts as a result of a felt need. When old forms of behavior are no longer capable of meeting new situations, a felt need results. When a person finds that his present equipment or methods of response are inadequate to solve a need, he learns new responses to meet the situation. For example, when a skill is not performed proficiently enough to receive commendation

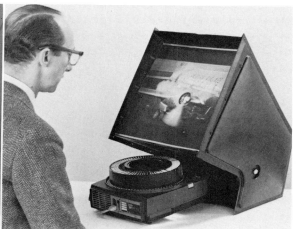

*Courtesy Hudson Photographic Industries, Inc.,*
*Irvington-On-Hudson, N. Y.*

New techniques for teaching.

and approval from others, there is a felt need to improve this skill.

To have a learning situation there is a need for certain elements such as a motivated human being; a felt need that will provide the incentive for learning; the absence of a skill, knowledge, or other ingredient that has not as yet been learned but which is desired by the hu-

man being; and finally, an effort on the part of the human being to achieve this particular goal.

Motivation is a basic factor to all effective learning. The desire within a human being prompts him to seek a solution to his recognized need through an appropriate line of action. This line of action may require practice, effort, mastery

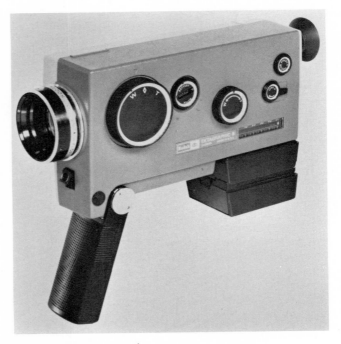

Four-speed movie camera with auxiliary battery case.

Projector with remote control receptacle, automatic timer, selector switch, and dissolve control receptacle.

Lightweight projector.

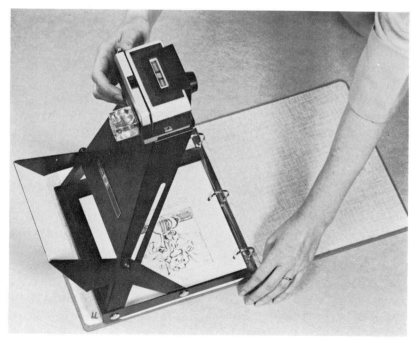

*Courtesy Eastman Kodak Company,*
*Rochester, N. Y.*

Slide production kit.

of knowledge or other behavior in order to be successful in achieving the goal. The speed with which the goal is achieved will depend upon the degree to which the individual is motivated, his capacity, and the nature of the task to be performed.

## THEORIES OF LEARNING

Psychologists have attempted to explain the phenomenon of learning and answer such questions as how it best takes place and what are the laws under which it operates. The basic theories of learning, for purposes of discussion, may be said to be divided into two broad categories. The first category may be called the connectionist theories. These theories state that learning consists of a bond or connection between a stimulus and a response or responses. The second category may be called cognitive theories. Those psychologists that support these theories feel that the various perceptions, beliefs, or attitudes (cognitions or mental images) that a human being has concerning his environment determine what type of behavior the human being will have. The manner in which these "cognitions" are modified by the experience that the human being has indicates the learning that takes place. The basic principles underlying the cognitive theories were developed by the gestalt psychologists.

### Thorndike's laws of learning

E. L. Thorndike, a psychologist whose theories of learning have had a great impact on educators and education, believed in a stimulus–response theory, or S–R bond theory. His laws of readiness, exercise, and effect have influenced educational programs.

Thorndike developed these laws that set forth the conditions under which learning best takes place. Because psychology is a rather new science and because there are many contradictory views as to various psychological principles, laws of learning should not be regarded as the final word. However, they are working principles and, as such, deserve the attention of all physical educators who desire to seek the most efficient and effective ways of teaching.

### Law of readiness

The law of readiness means that an individual will learn much more effectively and rapidly if he is "ready"—if he has matured to that point and if there is a felt need. Learning will be satisfying if materials are presented when an individual meets these standards. This law also works in reverse. It will be annoying and dissatisfying to do something when the individual is not ready. The closer an individual is to reaching the point of readiness, the more satisfying the act.

In physical education activities the teacher should determine whether the child is ready in respect to various sensory and kinesthetic mechanisms and in respect to strength in some cases. The teacher should ask such questions as: Does the child have the capacity, at this time, for certain skills? Does he have the proper background of experience? Is the material that is being presented timely? Should it be postponed until some future time, or is now the time to present it? Most physical educators agree, for example, that competition on an interscholastic basis should not be part of the program for elementary school children. The child is not mentally, emotionally, and physically ready for such an experience. There is also considerable agreement that fine-muscle activity should not play too pronounced a part in the program for young children. Instead, their program should largely consist of activities which involve the large muscles.

The law of readiness also has implications for the learning of skills. An adult has difficulty hitting a baseball, riding a bicycle, throwing a football, and performing other physical activities if he has not developed some skill in these activities during his youth. During youth, on the other hand, individuals can achieve performance in these skills without too much difficulty. They are at the proper maturation level for the learning of such skills, and their neuromuscular equipment has developed to a point where skills are learned more economically and effectively. They do not mind passing through an awkward trial-and-error period. Physical educators should bear this in mind and set as their goal the development in youth of many skills that are interesting and varied. In this way they will have the foundational equipment when they reach adulthood to engage in a variety of physical education activities that will provide many enjoyable hours of wholesome recreation.

## Law of exercise

The law of exercise, in respect to the development of skills in physical education, means that practice makes for better coordination, more rhythmical movement, less expenditure of energy, more skill, and better performance. As a result of practice, the pathway between situation and response becomes more pronounced and permanent.

In many ways this law of learning is similar to the law of use and disuse. As a result of continual practice, strength is gained, but as a result of disuse, weakness ensues.

Learning in education is acquired by doing. In order to master the skill of bowling, swimming, or handball a person must practice. However, it should be restated that practice does not necessarily ensure perfection of the skill. Mere repetition does not mean greater skill. Practice must be meaningful, with proper attention being given to all phases of the situation. The learner, through repetition and a clear conception of what is to be done,

steadily makes progress toward the goal he is attempting to attain.

## Law of effect

The law of effect maintains that an individual will be more likely to repeat experiences that are a joy and are satisfying to him than those experiences that are annoying. If experiences are annoying, the learner will shift to other responses that are satisfying.

This law of learning, as applied to physical education, means that every attempt should be made to provide situations in which individuals experience success and have a satisfying and enjoyable experience. Leadership is an important factor. Under certain types of leadership undesirable experiences would be satisfying. One coach might approve of hitting an opponent and make this an enjoyable experience. Under other coaches such an act would be an annoying experience because it would be condemned and would not be tolerated. Leadership is the key to good teaching.

## Neural path of learning

The complicated mechanism of the nervous system controls and regulates an individual's behavior and is the key to the development of neuromuscular skill. The process by which this is performed is very interesting.

Neuromuscular skill is developed as a result of an impulse traveling through a reflex arc. The reflex arc is the path from a sense organ through a nerve center to a muscle. It is composed of three neurons, a neuron being a nerve cell including all of its various branches. The impulse enters through a nerve fiber, commonly known as the receptor or sensory nerve, goes through a connector, and passes on to the effector or motor nerve.

The receptor or sensory nerve reacts to certain stimuli in the environment. These nerves may be found in such parts of the human body as the eyes, ears, tongue, nose, skin, muscles, and joints. These specialized sensory nerves, however, react to only certain types of stimuli. For example, the ears will not react to smell or the eyes to sound. They are the media through which the individual responds to the various conditions of his environment. The connector nerve is that part of the reflex arc that connects the receptor or sensory nerve with the effector or motor nerve. The spinal cord is a connecting center in the simplest type of reflex arc, whereas the brain, as well as the spinal cord, is used in complex reflex arcs. The effector or motor nerves are the response mechanisms. As a result of impulses traveling through the reflex arc, muscular contraction and glandular activity take place. The sensory nerves carry impulses to the nerve center; the connectors relay them to the response organs; and the motor nerves carry impulses away from the nerve center to the muscles. In many ways this resembles a telephone exchange; there are many wires carrying messages to and from the central office. The receptor or sensory cells, the connector cells, and the effector or motor cells are very numerous. For example, it is estimated that there are millions in the receptor organs of the eyes alone.

To have neuromuscular activity, there must be a path or connection between the effectors and the receptors. The lines that carry the messages or impulses from the receptors to the effectors are the nerves. There are nerves throughout the body. The nerves in the muscles lead to and from the brain and the spinal column.

*Youth Services Branch, Los Angeles City Schools, Los Angeles, Calif.*

Physical education skills should be taught in the most effective way possible. Tennis instruction using stroke developer.

The message comes in on a sensory nerve to the spinal cord or the brain. There it is transmitted to a motor neuron, which in turn carries it to a group of muscle fibers and makes them contract. Many authorities believe the nerve impulse to be an electrochemical wave that is transmitted over nerve fibers. As one practices an activity and as learning takes place, it is believed there is a neural growth —dendrites and axons at the synapses develop and grow. The "all-or-none" principle applies to nerves and muscles. A nerve fiber or a muscle fiber discharges all of its available energy when it is stimulated. Neuromuscular skill is developed when a pattern is laid between the sense organs and the muscles. Continuous practice in the performance of physical acts conditions the nervous and muscular systems to a point where habits and skills are performed with increasing degrees of coordination in activity.

## Three theories of learning affecting physical education

Several theories of learning have been presented during the course of educational history. Many contradict each other, with the result that physical educators are frequently confused as to what is the best way to teach activities.

Three of the theories of learning that affect physical education may, for convenience's sake, be called the trial-and-error theory, the conditioning theory, and the whole method theory.

The *trial-and-error* theory, in reference to learning, means that skills are mastered only after a period of practice, during which time a path is made in the nervous system. This results in proper muscle stimulation and action. When a novice first attempts to learn a skill, he has uncoordinated awkward movements. Later, if he practices conscientiously, he performs the skill with a much higher degree of smoothness and with rhythmic movement and little expenditure of energy. Greater satisfaction and enjoyment also result from gaining proficiency in the performance of a skill. Thus the acquisition of a skill is a matter of trial and error. Through practice a person gradually cuts down on the errors, and this results in better performance.

The *conditioning* theory maintains that learning is a result of conditioning, not of developing a path in the nervous system. A person reacts in a certain way because of the influence of certain types of stimuli. When certain stimuli are exerted on the organism, the reaction that has been associated with such stimuli occurs. Various reactions are established through experience or through a conditioning process to certain situations or stimuli that present themselves.

The other psychological theory that has implications for the teaching of physical education activities is the *whole method* theory. This theory is based on the premise that a person reacts as a whole to any situation. The whole individual attempts to achieve a goal. Furthermore, the greater the insight or understanding an individual has concerning the goal he wishes to attain, such as paddling a canoe or guiding a bowling ball to a strike, the greater will be his degree of skill in that activity. An individual reacts differently each time he performs a physical act. Therefore it is not just a question of practice, as it would be if he performed it the same way each time. Instead, the more insight he has of the complete act, the greater his skill. The individual performs the whole act and does it until he gains an insight into the situation or until he gets the "feel" or the "hang" of it.

At first it would seem that these theories are completely contradictory. One claims that you learn through a trial-and-error process. Another maintains that it is a process of conditioning. The third states that it is by insight into the total act to be performed. The physical educator might well wonder which is the best procedure and how he should teach. After analyzing the various theories, however, he recognizes certain points that he can utilize. It can be seen from a study of all three theories that a person must practice to learn a skill. Whether this practice be utilized to make a path in the nervous system or whether it be utilized to gain insight into the situation can be left to the psychologists to debate. In the meantime, the physical educator can have his students practice in as meaningful a way as possible. The teacher of physical education, however, must realize that practice in itself is not sufficient but that through meaningful practice the participant gets a better idea as to the ultimate goal or performance he wishes to attain. During the class period the teacher should be continually vigilant for opportunities to help the student gain a better understanding of all phases of the activity or skill to be mastered.

### Additional principles of learning having implications for physical education

Some general principles of learning that are generally recognized as having value in the learning process include the following: Motivation generated within the person himself is one of the most important factors in any learning situation. Rewards are more important than punishment. Goals must be realistic and capable of being accomplished by the learner. More intelligent persons are capable of learning certain types of material and skills better than those persons who are lower on the intelligence scale. Active participation on the part of the learner will aid learning and continued practice in-

*Lawrence Central High School, Indianapolis, Ind.*

Teaching golf skills correctly represents a challenge for the physical educator.

creases learning. Frequent recall helps in the retention of material. The better the learner understands the job to be accomplished and is aware of his mistakes, the more the learning situation will be improved. Failure is tolerated best when there have been a series of successes. When the learner gains insights that permit him to see relationships that will help in the solving of new tasks, the greater the learning.

The paragraphs that immediately follow discuss some of the principles of learning in more detail.

## FACTORS AND CONDITIONS THAT PROMOTE LEARNING

Learning will best take place when certain factors exist and under certain conditions. Physical educators should continually review their teaching situation to determine whether they have the right type of teaching environment, the right materials, and the right teaching method for an optimum teaching situation. A few of the essential principles for effective learning that psychologists have expounded as a result of much experimentation and research are as follows:

1. *The student should know the goals toward which he is working.* Learning progresses much faster when goals are clear. Mental practice or thinking through the movement desired should be utilized more extensively in skill learning than it is. The student should have a clear picture of what constitutes a successful performance. For example, if high jumping is being taught, the proper form and technique should be clearly demonstrated and discussed. This can be done by the instructor discussing, demonstrating, and/or utilizing the many filmstrips and other visual aids that are available to show what is involved in the execution of the skill. In this way, after practicing for a

*Glencoe Public Schools, Glencoe, Ill.*

Practice must be meaningful.

time, the student can compare his performance with the successful performance and can change his responses accordingly. As he approaches the standard that has been set, the goal toward which he is working becomes increasingly clear. A knowledge of the goal enables the individual to see the problem as a whole and so see it in a coherent pattern.

It should also be recognized that pupils are more likely to be enthusiastic about a project if they have participated in the planning.

2. *Effective motor learning is based on certain prerequisite factors.* According to McCloy,* there are prerequisites to effective motor learning. These are muscular strength, dynamic energy, ability to change direction, flexibility, agility, peripheral vision, visual acuity, concentration, an understanding of the mechanics of the activity, and an absence of inhibitory factors.

3. *The length and distribution of practice periods are important considerations for effective learning.* There is some agreement that practice periods are most profitable when they are short and are spaced over a period of time. The number of repetitions, such as shots at the basket or serves in tennis, should be considered as the unit of practice rather than the total number of minutes spent in the practice session. Forgetting proceeds rapidly at first and then more and more slowly in the learning situation. Furthermore, fatigue works adversely on the rate of learning and also on the accuracy of learning. According to some psychologists, when subject matter is very interesting and meaningful to the learner, practice periods may be made longer. Therefore, it seems the length and spacing of periods should be adjusted to the class and material being learned. For example,

---

*McCloy, Charles H.: Research Quarterly, AAHPER **17:**28, May, 1946.

if the physical educator has a class in volleyball that is very much interested and enthusiastic about this activity, the length of the instruction period could be longer, and the time between practice periods could be less than when he is working with a class that is indifferent, uninterested, and cannot see the need for developing skill in such an activity. This appears to be a sound approach to the teaching of physical education activities.

4. *The physical educator should be familiar with the learning curve as it applies to individuals.* Learning curves are not always constant, and they are different for each individual. The learning curve depends on the person, the material being learned, and the conditions surrounding the learning. Learning may start out with an initial spurt and then be followed by a period in which progress is not so rapid, or there may be no progress at all.

The initial spurt in learning may have been caused as a result of such factors as the enthusiasm for a new activity, mastering the easier parts of the task first, or the utilization of old habits in the first stages of practicing the new activity. All of these factors may be present from time to time in the teaching of soccer, badminton, handball, and other physical education activities.

Many learning curves also show that progress slows down as practice continues. This would seem to be true of many physical education activities wherein the easier acts are acquired first, and as the activity becomes increasingly difficult, the learning rate is not so rapid as during the early stages. The physical education instructor should take such conditions into consideration instead of immediately coming to the conclusion that perhaps this instruction is inadequate or that the individuals in his class are not quick to learn.

A period in which there is a leveling off of learning is known as a plateau. It may be due to a variety of reasons, such as loss of interest, failure to grasp a clear concept of the goal to be attained, preparation for a shift from a lower to a higher level in the learning process, or poor learning conditions. Physical educators should be cognizant of plateaus and the conditions causing little or no apparent progress in the activity. They should be especially careful not to introduce certain concepts or skills too rapidly, without allowing sufficient time for their mastery. They should also be on the lookout for certain physical handicaps to learning progress, such as fatigue, eye trouble, or lack of strength. Certain individuals cannot go beyond a given point because of physiological limits in respect to such things as speed, endurance, or some other physical characteristic. Physiological limits are absolute and cannot be surmounted and should be so recognized by physical education instructors. However, problems due to the physiological limits are rare, and in most cases it is the psychological limit that has to be overcome. By utilizing techniques to motivate the interest and enthusiasm of the learner, this goal can be accomplished.

5. *As a general rule, learning is more effective when skills are taught as whole skills and not in parts.* In physical education it seems that the whole method should be followed when the material to be taught is a functional and integrated whole. This would mean that in swimming, which is a functional whole, the total act of swimming would be taught. You learn to swim by using your arms and legs, and this can be taught as a whole. In a sport such as football, however, the game consists of blocking, broken-field running, tackling, passing, punting, and the like. Each of these skills represents a functional and integrated whole by itself and, as such, should be taught separately. The important point for the physical education instructor to remember is that

the material to be learned should determine the procedure to be followed. "Whole" learning is recommended for those activities or phases of activities that represent an integrated, functional unit. The physical educator should analyze each of the activities in his program to determine the functional whole.

6. *Education is a doing phenomenon— thus a person learns by doing.* A person learns through his own responses, meaning practice or a repetition of the act. During this repetition or practice, errors should be avoided as much as possible, and the ones that are made should be corrected. By continually practicing a tennis serve, a person learns to be accurate and effective with such a service. By continually shooting basketballs at a basket, a person becomes skilled in putting the ball through the hoop at all angles. Precision performance comes only after considerable practice. At the same time, it must be recognized that practice must be purposeful if progress is to be achieved.

7. *The leadership provided determines to a great degree how much learning will take place.* As far as a child is concerned, a leader does not usually have to motivate the desire to engage in physical activity. It is a part of the child's makeup. However, the leader should set up certain situations to achieve other values. The physical educator should make sure that the student has a clear picture of the goal to be accomplished. The ability to demonstrate helps in showing the student the proper technique in performing some particular physical skill. Verbal guidance also helps the learner to get a clearer picture of what he is to do. The instructor should be continually alert to detect correct and incorrect responses in the activities that comprise the physical education program. He should make clear to the student what he is doing wrong. He should encourage correct performance. This is a stimulus to more success. The

*Courtesy NBC Television.*

As a general rule, learning is more effective when skills are taught as whole skills and not in parts.

physical educator should be able to present material on the pupil's level of understanding, should recognize individual differences, and utilize his personality to further the teaching situation.

8. *The learner should know the progress he is making.* Knowledge that one is progressing toward a set goal is encouraging and will promote a better learning situation. Research shows that when students are aware of the progress they are making (through charts or other media), the learning process is stepped up and the learner enjoys his work to a much greater degree. The physical education instructor should use charts and graphs and have periodical consultations with students in order to utilize effectively this psychological principle.

9. *The material that is presented in the learning situation should be appropriate to the proper maturation level of the student.* Maturation is growth that takes place without any special training, stimulus, or practice—it just happens. It is closely associated with the physiological development of all individuals. Therefore, the material must be adapted to individ-

ual maturation levels. Tennis should not be part of the primary grade physical education curriculum because the student is not ready for the activity at this time. Muscular development, strength, endurance, emotional stability, and other factors are criteria that should be taken into consideration in determining the maturation levels for various physical education activities.

10. *Each individual is different from every other individual.* There are differences that are innate and differences that exist as a result of one's environment. There are differences in regard to intelligence, which have implications for the way the mental processes function. There are emotional differences that have to do with drives, attitudes, and ideals. There are physiological differences in respect to sense organs, glandular functioning, and physical capacity. These are only a few of the ways in which individuals differ.

Individual differences must be taken into consideration by the physical educator. Human potentialities and limitations in respect to such things as mental capacities, character traits, personality

*Richwoods Community High School,*
*Peoria Heights, Ill.*

The leadership provided determines to a great degree how much learning takes place.

traits, physical traits, and knowledge and habits must be thought through when planning physical education programs if these programs are to realize their potentialities. Programs should be prescribed for the individual rather than the group. This principle should be aggressively brought to the attention of school boards and administrators. This principle implies the need for more teachers of physical education and more classes. It is impossible to prescribe individual programs to any degree with seventy-five pupils per class, per teacher. The administration must recognize its responsibility in respect to individuals. Physical educators must also be prepared to assume their responsibility by being able to determine the ways individuals differ and by being able to prescribe the physical activities for each member of the class.

The greatest effort will usually be put forth by pupils when the range of the challenge, such as a skill to be learned, is not too easy or not too hard but when success seems possible.

11. *Learning takes place most efficiently when the student has a motive for wanting to learn.* Motivation is an inducement to action. Usually, the greater the motivation, the more rapid is the learning. Motives should be of the intrinsic rather than the extraneous type. Rewards, awards, and marks should not be a means of motivating activity. The worth of the activity in itself should be the motive. In physical education activities, such motives as the desire to develop one's body, the desire to develop skill in an activity so that leisure hours may be spent in an enjoyable manner, the desire to become a member of a group, and the desire to maintain one's health are worthwhile motives. When these are present, learning takes place. Homeostasis, or the tendency of the body to take compensatory action in order to maintain a physiological balance, is related by some psychologists to

motivation. It not only applies to biological conditions, but to psychological conditions as well. The desire of the human being to maintain the steady state results in motivation to achieve basic human needs.

12. *Progress will be much more rapid when the learner gains satisfaction from the learning situation.* Satisfaction is associated with success. As the learner is successful in mastering a particular physical skill, his desire to learn increases so that he can experience additional success. On the contrary, if he does not experience satisfaction, the situation often becomes distasteful, and the learner turns to areas in which he may experience this satisfaction. Many individuals become dissatisfied with physical education because they do not have a satisfactory experience. The physical education instructor may give his attention to the individuals who are most skillful and overlook the "dub" and the less skilled member of the class. This should never be the case. The instructor should attempt to make sure that all members of a physical education class gain satisfaction from the activities in which they engage. Praise or other forms of rewards, to be most effective, should follow as soon as possible after the desired behavior is attained, and the best type of reward is that which gives a person a sense of achievement.

13. *Learning takes place much more effectively when the student intends to learn.* If the student has made up his mind that he intends to learn a certain skill, if he has arrived at the point where he sees a need for the skill, the learning situation is much more wholesome. The physical education instructor should attempt to clarify in the student's mind the need of physical activity for enriched living. As the need is recognized, the intent to learn becomes increasingly greater; consequently, learning takes place more effectively.

14. *A learning situation is greatly improved if the student diagnoses his own movements and arrives at definite conclusions as to what errors he is committing.* Self-criticism is much more conducive to good learning than teacher-criticism. If the student discovers his own mistakes, they are corrected much more readily than if discovered by someone else. A masterful teacher will develop teaching situations in which the student is led to self-criticism. This is a sign of good teaching. In physical education activities the student should be encouraged to analyze his own performance so that he may determine for himself where improvement can be made. This, in turn, will result in a more meaningful experience.

15. *The learning situation should be such that optimum conditions are present for efficient learning.* This means that distracting elements have been eliminated from the setting, the proper mental set has been established in the mind of the student, the proper equipment and facilities are available, the learner has the proper background to understand and appreciate the material that is to be presented, and the conditions are such that a challenging teaching situation is present.

16. *Audiovisual aids will aid considerably in helping to present a more favorable learning situation.* In physical education, movies, slides, filmstrips, pictures, tape recorders, posters, and other audiovisual aids may be used to help give the student a clearer concept of what he is striving to attain.

17. *The time that a skill will remain in the possession of the learner will depend on the extent to which it has been overlearned.* If a skill has been mastered and there has been continual practice of the accomplishment, a considerable time will elapse before such a skill is lost to the owner. A good example of this is the ability to swim. Once the skill has been mastered and overlearned, an individual can

still swim even after long lapses without practice in this activity. The better a skill is overlearned, the longer the period before it will be lost. This applies to many other physical education activities. If a student wants to remember a skill, he should overlearn it through continued practice.

18. *Errors should be eliminated early in the learning period.* As one of our popular magazines states, "It's easier to start a habit than to stop one." When instructing in such skills as field hockey and softball, the physical education teacher should attempt to eliminate incorrect performance as early as possible so that errors do not become a fixed part of the participant's performance. Inefficient methods once learned are difficult to correct.

19. *The student should become less and less dependent upon the physical education instructor for help and guidance.* During the early periods of instruction when the basic techniques of the skill are being learned, instruction and help are needed frequently. However, as the basic fundamentals are mastered, the student should rely less upon the teacher's help and more upon his own resources. Excessive direction by the teacher may result in apathy, defiance, escape, or scapegoating.

20. *Mental practice enhances the learning of motor skills.* Mental practice has been shown to be a valuable procedure when combined with overt practice in the motor activity. Some experience with the motor task to be achieved, when used as a prerequisite to mental practice, appears to enhance the learning situation in that the novice does not appear to benefit as much from the mental practice as does the partially skilled person.

21. *Implementation of the principle of reinforcement will enhance learning.* One of the most fundamental laws of learning is reinforcement. In essence it means that the behavior most likely to emerge in any given situation is one that is reinforced

or found successful in a previous similar situation. Therefore, the best-planned learning situation will provide for an accumulation of successes. The reinforcement (reward) should follow the desired behavior almost immediately and should be associated with the behavior in order to be most effective. Repetition without reinforcement does not provide an optimum learning situation. The sense of satisfaction resulting from achievement is an excellent form of intrinsic reward (reinforcement).

## CONCOMITANT LEARNING

When an individual is engaged in a skill or activity, he learns more than just the details of that one skill or activity. In tennis, for example, he learns such skills as serving and volleying. At the same time, however, he learns about tennis racquets and how they are constructed. He learns about tennis shoes, about the various types of composition for surfaces of tennis courts, and about the construction of tennis balls. He also learns about the other participants with whom he is associating, about his instructor, about rules of sportsmanship, about tolerance, about respect for the individual, about competition, and about respect for opponents. The concomitants in a learning situation should be recognized as being just as important as the technical aspects of the skill that the teacher is attempting to present. One of the principal differences between an excellent and a mediocre teacher is that the mediocre teacher is concerned only with the teaching of the mechanical aspects of a certain skill to the students, whereas the excellent teacher is concerned with the entire learning situation and how the learner reacts to the "whole" situation. A physical educator should not only be concerned with the neuromuscular or physical development of the individual, but he should also be concerned with the mental, emotional, and social development.

## THEORY OF FORMAL DISCIPLINE

In the eighteenth and nineteenth centuries the theory of formal discipline prevailed. This theory promulgated the idea that the mind was divided into thirty or more faculties, such as memory, reason, will, judgment, imagination, and attention. Furthermore, it was thought that through certain exercises these faculties might be developed. For example, it was believed that a study of geometry would develop one's reasoning powers and a study of Latin would result in mental discipline which was applicable to all subjects in the curriculum. In the field of physical education, it was thought that neuromuscular skill could be developed through certain exercises.

Modern psychologists do not believe in this theory. Instead, they maintain that the mental processes in man function as a unity. Furthermore, the total organism functions in an intellectual act.

## TRANSFER OF TRAINING

The theory of transfer of training is based on the premise that a thing learned in one situation can be used in other situations. For example, if one learns courtesy in a game situation on the gymnasium floor, this amenity would be transferred to dealings with other persons whom he meets on the street, at home, or at church. Many present-day psychologists do not adhere to this theory as such, however. They believe that transfer of learning takes place only if two situations are alike and recognized as being alike by the person affected. For example, strength in lifting weights should be useful in lifting and storing boxes in a warehouse. Transfer, however, is not automatic. The more meaningful and purposeful an experience, the more likelihood of transfer. As a result of research, it has been pointed out that transfer of training occurs best in bright pupils, in situations that are similar, in situations where there is an attitude and an effort on the part of the learner to effect transfer, where there is an understanding of the principles or procedures that are foundational to the initial task, and in situations where one teaches for transfer. The more lifelike the problems and activities, the greater the possibility of transfer to life situations.

At first glance it would appear rather difficult for physical educators to realize that desirable social traits are developed in the activities that go on in the gymnasium, playground, or swimming pool. However, there is evidence available to show that social traits can be developed through experiences that give satisfaction to the learner. If an individual learns that he can win approval from a group in a physical education class more effectively by being courteous, practicing fair play, and respecting the rights of others, it seems quite probable that such an individual will transfer these traits to his relations with other people. Through experiences in playing basketball, soccer, or baseball he has learned that he can have a much more satisfying social experience if he follows certain modes of behavior. It is the nature of the human being to want satisfying experiences. Physical education, through its very nature, has the opportunity to provide experiences in which these desirable modes of behavior may be developed, and it is believed by many that such experiences mold the individual into ways of acceptable social conduct which will apply to day-to-day living.

## OTHER PSYCHOLOGICAL BASES FOR PHYSICAL EDUCATION

In addition to helping physical educators teach their subject matter in a more meaningful manner, psychology is related in other ways to their field of endeavor.

### Physical education and psychological development

Psychology is concerned with human behavior and physical activity can affect

behavior in many ways. Scott lists seven ways in which physical activity contributes to psychological development.*

1. *Attitudes are changed.* Physical education can contribute to the development of wholesome attitudes toward such factors as exercise, learning of motor skills, fitness, and use of leisure hours. The desire for and interest in physical activity will play a very important role in determining the support the profession of physical education obtains in trying to achieve its goals of a fit population.

2. *Social efficiency is improved.* Physical education has the potential, it is believed, to contribute to proper group adjustments, to the development of such desirable social traits as honesty, sportsmanship, and reliability, and to the development of a socially desirable personality. Social efficiency is discussed in Chapter 18.

3. *Improved sensory perception and responses accrue.* Although the research is inconclusive, there is some feeling that physical education can help to make a person more sensitive and responsive to his environment through the development of such characteristics as speed, visual perception, reaction time, depth perception, and kinesthetic awareness.

4. *Improved sense of well-being exists.* Physical education, it is believed, contributes to good mental health. Through play and various forms of physical activity, an opportunity is afforded for emotional release and having fun, and it provides a supplement for daily work. Being physically active contributes to the development of a healthy personality. As William Menninger, a famous psychiatrist, stated in a speech, "Good mental health is directly related to the capacity and willingness of an individual to play. Regardless of his objections, resistances, or past practice, any individual will make

---

*Scott, M. Gladys: Research Quarterly **31:** 307, May, 1960.

a wise investment for himself if he does plan time for his play and takes it seriously."

5. *Better relaxation is promoted.* Physical education has some support that shows it can help to release muscular tension, together with affording an efficient motor response. Through selected forms of physical activity, there seems to be evidence that some forms of stress can be alleviated and thereby relaxation promoted in the individual.

6. *Relief is provided on psychosomatic problems.* More research should be conducted to determine the contributions to certain physical states such as chronic fatigue, dysmenorrhea, and phobias. Scott points out there is more objective evidence on the effects of exercise on dysmenorrhea than on the other aspects.

7. *Skills are acquired.* One of physical

education's greatest contributions is through the development of physical skills in its programs. Physical educators should attempt to understand as much as possible how learning takes place and the various factors that influence learning. For this reason, a major portion of this chapter is devoted to a discussion of this subject.

The science of psychology plays an important part in the teaching of physical education activities. Members of the physical education profession are interested in learning the best ways to teach skills. Skills should be taught in the most efficient and economical way possible. Therefore, they should be taught according to the principles of psychology, which point out such things as the laws of learning, the factors and conditions that promote learning and the transfer of training. Only if physical education activities are taught

*Youth Services Branch, Los Angeles City Schools, Los Angeles, Calif.*

Cartridge loop projector used in high school golf instruction program.

scientifically will the participant realize the most benefit. Therefore, the purpose of this chapter is to give the student a brief introduction to psychology as a foundation for the learning process in physical education.

In addition to the factors Scott identifies, Cratty* lists some reasons why physical educators should be interested in psychological relationships:

1. The social psychologist is interested in determining the attitude of young people and adults toward physical activity.

2. The physiological psychologist is interested in the relationship of such things as stress and tension to vigorous physical activity.

3. The clinical psychologist and psychiatrist are interested in such things as body image and self-concepts in the formation of a healthy personality. Some of them have also advanced the thesis that to improve such things as cognition, visual perception, speech and hearing, perceptual-motor characteristics must be taken into consideration.

4. Many psychological variables relate to physical activity that relate directly to the teaching–learning situation, the way human beings behave, and the impact of practice in behavioral change.

5. Many psychological parameters relate to sports that concern themselves with such factors as mental preparation of the athlete, problems of motivation, nature of movement perception, personality development of athletes, and the therapeutic values of competition.

6. Professional preparing institutions have introduced courses in recent years concerned with motor learning and psychology of motor activity.

7. Many questions need to be answered by our profession such as: "What is the nature of kinesthesis?" "How often should physical education be taught each week?" "What are the causes of muscular tension?" "What are the conditions for the retention of a skill?" The answers to these and other questions involving psychological factors will result in a superior program of physical education.

## Body image

The concept of body image is another aspect of concern to the physical educa-

*Cratty, Bryant J.: Psychological bases of physical activity, Journal of Health, Physical Education, and Recreation 36:71, Sept., 1965.

tor since it involves a psychological experience. The attitudes and feelings of a person toward his body affects his personality development. Whether he views his body as something ugly, with lack of confidence in its performance, or as something that is well developed and can meet the challenge of any physical situation will affect his relations with other people and also his role in a physical education experience. This is particularly pronounced during the adolescent period. For example, some research has shown that when a boy's physique is small, not well developed, and weak over an extended period of time, his behavior is affected. He will become overly shy or assertive and will reflect internal discord. The person who matures late may find his relations with classmates affected when he is kept out of games because his classmates desire to be successful in their game experience. He may consequently develop an unfavorable attitude toward physical activity. On the other hand, the person who matures early may find that, although he was always the star during the early game experiences in adolescence, as other persons matured he lost this status and the adjustment presented some difficulties. Other personality problems have been found in such individuals as boys with feminine characteristics, students with narcissistic characteristics, and boys and girls who possessed certain types of body mechanics and posture.

As physical educators understand the role of body image, they will be better able to understand why various students have certain attitudes and feelings toward physical activity and the contributions that physical education can make to these persons.

## Athletics

There are many psychological implications for athletics. Such questions as the role of athletic competition in personality development, in developing character, and in contributing to academic achievement still largely remain unanswered and need to be explored further. It has been argued that athletics help to develop greater interest in subject matter and develop better students. However, this cannot be adequately supported at this time. The need for more research is obvious.

It has been demonstrated in some cases that competitive athletics have the potential for satisfying such basic needs as recognition, belonging, self-respect, and feelings of achievement, as well as to provide a wholesome outlet for the physical activity drive and creative expression. These are desirable psychological effects. At the same time, however, in some cases it has been demonstrated that competitive athletics can produce harmful effects if they are conducted in light of adult interests, community pressures, and as an end in themselves, rather than as means of fuller psychological development of the student.

It would appear that a vital factor in having athletics contribute to the psychological development of the individual rests upon the leadership that is provided. Leadership must provide for individual differences, the right activities, and an environment free from adult and community pressures. The focus of attention must always be on the participant rather than the spectator.

## PHYSICAL EDUCATION AND ACADEMIC ACHIEVEMENT*

Although 9-year-old Susan has normal intelligence, she could not master the fundamentals of arithmetic, social studies, English, and writing, regardless of how hard she tried. Her academic difficulties were compounded by a partial paralysis of the right side of her body. After her

---

*This section is adapted from an article by the author which appeared in NEA Journal 54:38-40, May, 1965.

parents and teachers had tried unsuccessfully everything they could think of to help her, she was referred to the Achievement Center for Children at Purdue University, where much research has been done on children with academic difficulties.

At the Center, Susan spent 2½ years in a specially designed program of motor activity under skilled leadership. As a result, her academic and physical improvement was termed "miraculous" by her mother, the principal, and her classroom teacher. Her report card jumped two letter grades in every school subject, and for the first time she was able to participate in a full schedule of classroom activities.

Susan is just one of numerous boys and girls, most of whom do not have a physical handicap like hers, who have been helped to improve academically at the Center by taking part in a program of motor activities used as an integral part of a perceptual-motor training program.

More research is needed to establish and define the exact relationship of physical activity, motor skills, and health to academic achievement, but the evidence to date firmly establishes the fact that a close affinity exists. Indeed, the kind of physical education program which leads to improved physical and social fitness and health are vital to the education and academic achievement of every boy and girl.

This fact has been recognized throughout history by some of the world's most profound thinkers. For example, Socrates stressed that poor health can contribute to grave mistakes in thinking. Comenius noted, "Intellectual progress is conditioned at every step by bodily vigor. To attain the best results, physical exercise must accompany and condition mental training." Rousseau observed that "an enfeebled body enervated the mind" and included a rich program of physical activities for *Emile*.

More recently, such authorities as Arnold Gesell, Arthur T. Jersild, and the Swiss psychologist Jean Piaget found that a child's earliest learnings are motor (involving neuromuscular systems, and resulting in movement such as running, jumping, reaching, etc.) in nature and form the foundation for subsequent learnings.

As D. H. Radler and Newell C. Kephart wrote in their authoritative book *Success Through Play,* "Motor activity of some kind underlies all behavior including higher thought processes. In fact behavior . . . can function no better than do the basic motor abilities upon which it is based."

Academic achievement refers to the progress a child makes in school as measured by his scores on achievement tests, his grade-point averages, his promotion from grade to grade, and the development of proper attitudes. As any experienced teacher knows, academic achievement requires more than intellectual capacity. Nonintellectual factors, such as the will to achieve, health, and self-concept, are almost certain to play an important part in a student's ability to achieve academically.

Physical education is related to academic achievement in at least four ways: (1) through emphasis on the development of motor skills, (2) by promoting physical fitness, (3) by imparting knowledge and modifying behavior in regard to good health practices, and (4) by aiding in the process of social and emotional development which leads to a more positive self-concept.

Typical of the research studies confirming the relationship between motor skills and academic achievement is that of G. L. Rarick and Robert McKee who studied 20 third graders grouped according to their motor proficiency. The study showed that the group with high motor proficiency had a greater number who achieved "excellent" or "good" ratings in reading, writing, and comprehension than the group with low motor efficiency.

In another study, Jack Keogh and David Benson experimented with the motor characteristics of forty-three underachieving boys, ages 10 to 14, enrolled in the Psychology Clinic School at UCLA. They found that, as individuals, half of the boys from 10 to 12 years old exhibited poor motor performance.

A. H. Ismail, N. Kephart, and C. C. Cowell, utilizing motor aptitude tests, found that I.Q. and academic success could be predicted from these tests, with balance and coordination items the best predictors for estimating achievement.

Other studies indicate that the child's first learnings accrue from an interaction with his physical and social environment. Physical action provides the experience to clarify and make meaningful concepts of size, shape, direction, and other characteristics. In addition, through physical activities he experiences sensations, he has new feelings, and he develops new interests as well as satisfies old curiosities.

The importance of physical fitness was stressed by Lewis Terman more than 25 years ago. After working with gifted children he stated, "Results of physical measurements and medical examinations provide a striking contrast to the popular stereotype of the child prodigy, so commonly depicted as a pathetic creature, an overserious, undersized, sickly, bespectacled child." He went on to say that physical weakness was found nearly 30% fewer times in children of higher intelligence than in those of lower intelligence.

Many research studies since Terman have supported the contention that physical fitness is related to academic achievement.

H. H. Clarke and Boyd O. Jarman, in a study of boys of ages 9, 12, and 15, found a consistent tendency for the high groups on various strength and growth measures to have higher means on both academic achievement tests and grade-point averages than low groups. Studies conducted at the universities of Oregon and Iowa and at Syracuse and West Point have shown a significant relationship between physical fitness and academic success and between physical fitness and leadership qualities. David Brace, F. R. Rogers, Clayton Shay, Marcia Hart, and others have done extensive research showing relationships between scholastic and academic success and physical fitness.

Through the development of desirable attitudes and the application of health knowledge, the student achieves his maximum strength, energy, endurance, recuperative power, and sensory acuity. Furthermore, the effective physical education program helps boys and girls to understand and appreciate the value of good health as a means of achieving their greatest productivity, effectiveness, and happiness as individuals.

Some research has shown a relationship between scholastic success and the degree to which a student is accepted by his peer group. Similarly, the boy or girl who is well grounded in motor skills usually possesses social status among his or her peers.

For example, J. B. Merriman found that such qualities as poise, ascendency, and self-assurance were significantly more developed in students of high motor ability than in those with low motor ability.

Other research shows that popularity in adolescent boys is more closely associated with physical and athletic ability than with intelligence; that leadership qualities are most prevalent among school boys (and West Point cadets) who score high on physical fitness tests; and that well-adjusted students tend to participate to a greater extent in sports than poorly adjusted students.

Physical education not only affects social development but emotional development as well. Games provide release from tension after long periods of study: furthermore, achievement in physical activities gives students a sense of pride which pays dividends in emotional satisfaction and well-being.

In this sense, the value of physical education may be greater for educationally subnormal students than for average boys and girls. James N. Oliver, lecturer in education at the University of Birmingham, England, has done much research on educationally subnormal boys and has found that systematic and progressive physical conditioning yields marked mental and physical improvement. He believes such improvement resulted from the boys' feelings of achievement and of consequent improved adjustment.

The value of physical education will depend largely upon whether or not they meet the following criteria:

The physical education program includes a variety of daily movement experiences and instruction in many basic motor activities, aimed not at making the student a superior performer in one or two, but stressing a modest performance in all, consistent with his developmental level. It also helps each student to achieve physically according to desirable standards.

The physical education program provides boys and girls with accurate and significant health knowledge related to their individual needs and interests. There is also concern for health services and a healthful physical and emotional environment.

The physical education program is accorded educational respectability so that students and parents will more readily appreciate its value and seek the benefits it offers.

By providing these essentials, the school will help to ensure a high standard of academic achievement on the part of all boys and girls.

## GETTING AT THE "WHY" OF THE ACTIVITY

There is the beginning of a trend in physical education to get at the "why" of the activity as well as the activity itself. This is evidenced by the publication of high school textbooks; assignments given to students to investigate various physiological, psychological, and sociological factors related to the role of physical activity and human development; findings of some research studies that indicate that mental practice is effective in skill learning; the provision for classroom activity in state syllabuses, and the emphasis upon conceptualized teaching with a realization that the most effective way to help students form general concepts is to present the concepts in many different and varied situations. Watson* indicates this and points out, in addition, that the formation of concepts can be furthered by providing many different experiences, some of which will be contrasting—some that include and some that do not include the desired concept—and then to encourage the formulation of the general concept and its application to specific situations that are different from those in which the concept was learned.

For many years physical educators have been primarily activity oriented. Programs have been centered around calisthenics, games, sports, obstacle courses, dance, and other physical activities. There has been little classroom activity where assignments are given, discussions held, laboratory experiences conducted, questions answered, scientific principles of physical activity presented and interpreted, history of sports revealed, as well as rules, strategies, and other subject matter related to physical education presented. Some physical educators have discussed with high school students the subject of physical education in order to determine what knowledge, for example, they had regarding the physiological basis for physical activity. Unfortunately, most of these students did not know why physical education is important to them as individuals and the contributions it makes to their physiological, psy-

chological, and sociological betterment. They did not know why exercise is important on a regular basis in planning their week-to-week schedules. Some students felt that physical activity is desirable to provide a break between classes and a means of having fun. Girls found it difficult to see the relationship between beauty and physical activity. Most students did not understand why physical education should be a requirement in our schools and colleges. Most of our students have not been physically educated in this sense. It is the feeling of more and more persons in the profession that all students who graduate from our schools and colleges should understand and appreciate the scientific values that accrue to the person who includes physical activity as part of his routine throughout life. It is the feeling of this group that the carry-over values of school and college physical education programs will be much greater if such subject matter is presented. These persons would hasten to explain, however, that they would continue to stress activity, but at the same time provision would be made periodically for classroom experiences and for reading and mental problem-solving experiences.

## NEW DEVELOPMENTS AFFECTING LEARNING PROCESS

There are several new developments on the educational scene that portend to influence the learning process. These include programmed instruction, team teaching, emphasis on creativity, educational television, ability grouping, and class reorganization. Because of the impact these trends may have on physical education, a short discussion is devoted to each.

### Programmed instruction

Programmed learning is available in many forms, but the advent of teaching machines is the best known of the various kinds of mechanical devices that utilize

*Watson, Goodwin: What do we know about learning, NEA Journal 52:20, March, 1963.

programmed materials. The first person believed to have experimented with teaching machines was Sidney L. Pressey at Ohio State University in the 1920's. Recently, B. F. Skinner, a psychologist at Harvard University, has given new impetus to this method of teaching. It is being used in several subject-matter areas and in some schools across the country. It has implications for physical education, especially in the area of getting across knowledge, understanding, and appreciation associated with such factors as physiological facts, rules of games, techniques, and health materials.

The basic psychological principles that seem to make the teaching machine a valuable auxiliary aid to the teacher are as follows:

1. *Learning appears to progress best when acquired in small steps.* Programmed learning is based on the principle that subject matter should be broken down into small doses and that the student should be led from the simple to the complex in the learning process.

2. *The learning process encourages the student to actively participate.* Each student participates by answering questions, analyzing his progress, and progressing as he achieves. He cannot be a passive spectator. He becomes actively involved in the learning process.

3. *Rewards reinforce learning.* The student is immediately informed if his answer is correct, if he is making progress, and if he can go on to more difficult material. This reward usually proves to be a satisfying experience and enhances the learning process.

4. *The student sets his own pace.* Programmed learning is tailored to either the fast or the slow learner. The individual proceeds at his own rate, but in either case he learns.

Teaching machines usually function by asking questions of the student through the medium of an item, a sentence that appears in a small window, or some other method of presentation. If a space is left for a missing word, for example, the student would answer the item and then by manipulating a lever determine the right answer. The student knows immediately if his answer is correct. He then moves on to the next question. Some machines repeat questions at the end of the lesson.

The results from programmed learning have been encouraging and augur well as an effective means of instruction. In some cases a programmed text is used rather than the teaching machine. Subject matter fields such as psychology, logic, music, and foreign language have been utilized with some degree of success. There is a feeling that programmed learning will never eliminate or replace teachers but that it will free them from routine drills and other forms of robot learning concerned with such things as basic skills.

## Team teaching

In its barest essentials, team teaching takes place whenever more than one teacher has responsibility for the same group of children at a given time. In its more highly organized existence, team teaching involves an instructional team of teachers who are specialists in certain areas, together with some who are nonprofessional. The team usually varies from three to six teachers responsible for 150 children or more. The students instructed by the team may all be in the same grade or in different grades and the classes in one subject or groups of subjects. The teaching team is responsible for the planning, teaching, and evaluation of the educational program for the group of children with whom they are working. One of the teachers is named the team leader and is responsible for program coordination.

Hundreds of communities throughout the United States are engaged in or planning some form of team teaching. It has

## GRADE 10 — DECEMBER 3-7 — PERIOD 2

| GROUP | MONDAY | TUESDAY | WEDNESDAY | THURSDAY | FRIDAY |
|---|---|---|---|---|---|
| "A" Weight Classification 0-110 lbs. | HEALTH LECTURE (Auditorium) Instructor IV | Health (Classroom) Inst. IV | Basketball Round Robin Tournament (Station A) Inst. II Student Leaders | Basketball Round Robin Tournament (Station A) Inst. II Student Leaders | Basketball Round Robin Tournament (Station A) Inst. II Student Leaders |
| "B" Weight Classification 111-125 lbs. | | Wrestling Round Robin Tournament (Balcony) Inst. I Student leaders | Health (Classroom) Inst. IV | Wrestling Round Robin Tournament (Balcony) Inst. I Student Leaders | Wrestling Round Robin Tournament (Balcony) Inst. I Student Leaders |
| "C" Weight Classification 126-150 lbs. | | Weight Training Isometrics (Station B) Inst. III Student Leaders | Weight Training Isometrics (Station B) Inst. III Student Leaders | Health (Classroom) Inst. IV | Weight Training Isometrics (Station B) Inst. III Student Leaders |
| "D" Weight Classification 151-over lbs. | | Basketball Round Robin Tournament (Station A) Inst. II Student Leaders | Wrestling Round Robin Tournament (Balcony) Inst. I Student Leaders | Weight Training Isometrics (Station B) Inst. III Student Leaders | Health (Classroom) Inst. IV |

## GRADE 11 — MAY 27-31 — PERIOD 6

| GROUP | MONDAY | TUESDAY | WEDNESDAY | THURSDAY | FRIDAY |
|---|---|---|---|---|---|
| "A" Weight Classification 0-125 lbs. | FIRST AID LECTURE (Auditorium) Instructor III | First Aid (Classroom) Inst. III | Softball (Athletic Field) Inst. V Student Leaders | Track & Field: Shot Put Discus (Track Areas) Inst. I Student Leaders | Track & Field: Broad Jump High Jump (Track Areas) Inst. II Student Leaders |
| "B" Weight Classification 126-145 lbs. | | Track & Field: Broad Jump High Jump (Track Areas) Inst. II Student Leaders | First Aid (Classroom) Inst. III | Softball (Athletic Field) Inst. V | Track & Field: Shot Put Discus (Track Areas) Inst. I Student Leaders |
| "C" Weight Classification 146-165 lbs. | | Track & Field: Shot Put Discus (Track Areas) Inst. I Student Leaders | Track & Field: Broad Jump High Jump (Track Areas) Inst. II Student Leaders | First Aid (Classroom) Inst. III | Softball (Athletic Fields) Inst. V Student Leaders |
| "D" Weight Classification 166-over lbs. | | Softball (Athletic Fields) Inst. V Student Leaders | Track & Field: Shot Put Discus (Track Areas) Inst. I Student Leaders | Track & Field: Broad Jump High Jump (Track Areas) Inst. II Student Leaders | First Aid (Classroom) Inst. III |

*Physical Education Newsletter,*
*March 12, 1963.*

Indoor and outdoor team-teaching schedules, Evergreen Community High School, Evergreen Park, Ill.

*Saks-Evergreen Studio.*

Team teaching at Evergreen Park High School, Evergreen Park, Ill. Physical education instructors meet daily in a common planning period.

been utilized in the field of physical education with success.

Franklin School in Lexington, Massachusetts, is a community that pioneered in team teaching at the elementary school level. Each team teaches two grades. The pupils spend the day in varying-sized groups, and each member of the teaching team has some responsibility for each child.

Norwalk, Connecticut, has also pioneered in elementary school team teaching. There are fourteen elementary schools involved in the project. One team, for example, teaches language arts and social studies in grades seven and eight. Another team is working with mentally handicapped children.

The University of Wisconsin has used team teaching in the training of teachers. Teams have been placed in cooperating schools in various communities. Student teachers or teacher-interns form part of the teams.

Seven high schools in Jefferson County, Colorado, utilize team teaching involving 3,000 students, 50 teachers, and 9 clerks.

Evergreen Park High School in Evergreen Park, Illinois, utilizes team teaching in physical education.* In this community large-group instruction is utilized in such areas as warm-up drills, special programs and tournaments, and health instruction. These large groups are broken down into smaller groups for discussion of certain health instruction and matters that can be handled effectively in this manner. It has been found that team teaching in this community has resulted in greater flexibility. Changes can be made as the need arises; each teacher in the department plays a part in each class; outside resources, such as teachers from other departments, and the community, are utilized more frequently; the needs of students are better met; the planning period provides for better teaching and evalua-

*Clein, Marvin I.: Journal of Health, Physical Education, and Recreation **33:**34, Nov., 1962.

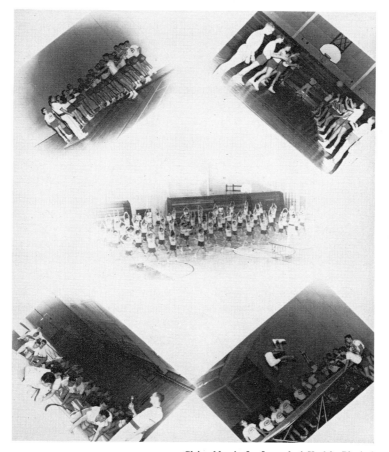

*Clein, Marvin I.: Journal of Health, Physical Education, and Recreation 33:34, Nov., 1962.*

Team teaching at Evergreen Park High School, Evergreen Park, Ill. The large group (center) and its breakdown into small groups. Team members are utilized in areas of their best abilities.

tion; more benefits accrue for the intramural program; members of the department can better exploit their own specialities; better teacher-pupil ratio exists; and there is more effective supervision and control of classes.

## Flexible scheduling

Flexible scheduling, sometimes called modular scheduling because of the time units involved—most frequently about 20 minutes each—is a term used to describe a school schedule in which classes do not meet for the same length of time each day. Flexible scheduling uses blocks of time to build periods of different length. For example, one module might be 20 minutes in length, a double module would be 40 minutes, a triple module would be 60 minutes, and a quadruple module would be 80 minutes. Time is left between each module for purposes of organization of classes.

One advantage of flexible scheduling over the traditional pattern of fixed scheduling, or the same allotment of time per day to a subject, is that flexible scheduling enables subjects to have varying times for instruction. For example, teachers say that usually more time is necessary in a science laboratory than for instruction in a foreign language newly introduced to students. It has been pointed out that a foreign language can be most effectively taught in shorter time periods at more frequent intervals. Flexible scheduling also provides more instructional time, more opportunity for small group instruction, and less time in study halls where learning time is not always put to the best use. With flexible scheduling it is possible to have subject matter and courses presented under more optimum conditions, on an individual basis, and in smaller or larger groups, as best meets the needs of the subject and teacher. Flexible scheduling also helps the teacher by permitting more time for instruction.

It can no longer be assumed that all subject matter and all courses should be taught in the same unit of time to the same number of students. New research shows that some subjects are taught best in shorter periods of time, given more frequently, and with a smaller group of students.

The use of the computer has made flexible scheduling a reality. The principal can tell a 707 computer how many teachers he has, what courses they can teach, how many students there are, and what courses each student wants to take. Within 60 minutes the answers are provided in the form of a complete master schedule and individual schedules for each student enrolled.

Operation GASP (Generalized Academic Simulation Programs) is one example of flexible scheduling. It was developed at the Massachusetts Institute of Technology under a grant from the Ford Foundation's Education Facilities Laboratories. As a result of GASP, time and money have been saved, flexibility in schools has been provided, and preplan-

ning space utilization before construction blueprints are made is much more accurate and meaningful.

One example of a school district where flexible scheduling is carried out is the Anaheim Union High School District in Anaheim, California. It has utilized the Brookhurst Plan, encompassing both team teaching and flexible scheduling. Some of the characteristics of this plan are that the faculty is organized into teams in each subject matter area, teachers submit daily job orders that include number of students desired in a group, length of time needed, facilities required, and method of instruction to be used. A master schedule is developed from the job orders, and students schedule a 14-modular day using the master schedule as a guide. The student's schedule becomes operational three days after the construction of the master schedule, a procedure that is completed each day throughout the year. The method of instruction is determined according to the following criteria: (1) When facts and data are presented, large group instruction is utilized; (2) when it is desired to use information presented in large group discussion as a means of developing insight and effectively using the information, small group discussion is scheduled; and (3) when the goal is to help students develop study habits, use research techniques effectively, and develop self-direction, independent study is utilized.

## Creativity

There is increased interest and stress in education on promoting creativity in the teaching process and in helping to release the creative talents of students. Creativity is the process of giving birth to an idea. It involves thinking, exploring, and examining and a reconstruction of experiences and formation into new patterns.

Creativity can be injected into teaching. Following are some basic principles involved in creative teaching that have been reiterated by Henry, as a result of a lecture he heard.*

1. Creativity is not absolute; there are different levels.
2. Creativity arises from a love of children and helping them to learn.
3. Self-realization is a cardinal principle of creative teaching.
4. Meaningful and aesthetic learning are outcomes of creative teaching.
5. The climate of the classroom must be conducive to creative learning.
6. Problem situations give rise to creativity.
7. A creative teacher is not restricted to a textbook or course of study.
8. A creative teacher helps to direct the creative abilities of children into the right channels.

Certain characteristics contribute to creativity. Strang identifies these qualities as follows†:

1. The creative child *possesses imagination.* All kinds of new ideas and problems cross the child's mind, perhaps not new to adults but original with the child.
2. The creative child *has a purpose.* There is method and an objective in the young person's mind, and creativity stems from this purpose.
3. The creative child *desires experience.* He is curious and wants to explore, and this motivating force should be nourished.
4. The creative child *is puzzled.* The answers to many things in the environment and events that occur are not readily apparent and there is a desire to know.
5. The creative child *exploits the present.* He is not concerned with the past or the future; it is the job at hand that commands his attention—a requisite for creativity.
6. The creative child *enjoys spontaneous play.* There is a desire to toy with different ideas, to see new relationships, and to have fun doing it.

Strang goes on to point out that a child's creativeness is enhanced by the teacher's questions and comments if they

encourage him to participate, choose, and have fun. However, if the reaction is negative, if there are too many "don'ts," if there is too much criticism, this tends to suppress creative tendencies.

Physical educators can be more creative in their own teaching by developing new ideas of presenting material, utilizing facilities, scheduling classes, and evaluating and carrying out other responsibilities. They can also open up the creative reservoirs of their students by encouraging new ideas, new movement ideas, and involving pupils more in the planning of educational experiences.

### Educational television

It has been estimated that today about 6 million of the 33 million elementary school students in the United States are receiving the benefits of educational television. The number of secondary school and college students exposed to educational television is also significant. About 95% of the nation's educational systems either are utilizing or want to utilize educational television. In 1952 the Federal Communication Commission reserved 259 channels for television programs concerned with the schools, colleges, and allied groups. There are more than seventy-five educationally owned television stations in operation. Thirty-two states have passed legislation to encourage such programs. According to David Sarnoff, of the Radio Corporation of America, one teacher can instruct 100,000 students at one time on a national educational network.

Physical education is a subject for which television has great potential. Some of the advantages include the following:

1. Physical education can be interpreted in its correct light to the public. Today, many people do not understand the true meaning of physical education; consequently, there is a great need for better ways of reaching the general public.
2. Physical education can utilize master teachers. By utilizing the very best instruction,

*Henry, Charles D.: The physical educator **15:**58, May, 1958. (Taken from notes from a lecture by Dr. H. L. Richards of Grambling College, Grambling, La.)

†Strang, Ruth: National Parent-Teacher **54:** 14, Feb., 1960.

an excellent job can be accomplished in presenting physical education to the public.

3. Physical education can reach a larger audience. Television reaches into classrooms, play centers, and homes that would never be exposed under ordinary circumstances.

4. Physical education classes in an entire city system or in many systems can benefit from closed-circuit television. New methods can be utilized, new materials demonstrated, new activities introduced, and many other innovations can be accomplished through educational television. New ideas that would not ordinarily be available to many schools, teachers, and people can be disseminated.

5. Physical education can exploit close-up TV techniques to advantage. The "zoom" lens and other techniques make it possible to provide excellent instruction in how to perform skills and other physical activities correctly.

The potential of educational television for physical education is tremendous. Physical educators would be wise to acquaint themselves with the techniques, opportunities, and ways and means by which television can be utilized in their field.

## Ability grouping

Ability grouping is being utilized more and more in the school systems of the United States. Students are being classified according to their intelligence, achievement, and other factors that impinge on their school record. Ability grouping has its advocates and also those who oppose such methods.

Ability grouping, according to some leaders in the field, has potential for grouping physical education classes into meaningful units for instructional purposes. For example, having students with low physical fitness ratings in one group facilitates meeting their needs in this area; having boys and girls of the same skill ability together makes it easier to teach effectively. In other words, a homogeneous grouping rather than a heterogeneous one makes it possible to concentrate on special activities and techniques readily

adapted to the needs of the group in question.

Effective ability grouping depends upon staff, facilities, and valid methods of identifying pupils' abilities. If it is to do the job that is needed, providing better learning experiences for children and youth with a variety of skills, intelligence, physical traits, and mental abilities, then according to Essex, the following items should be kept in mind*:

1. The foremost purpose of the American school should be kept in mind—all children should have some of their school experiences in a typical classroom situation.

2. Ability grouping will be more successful if parents understand individual differences. Mothers and fathers as well as teachers must understand that each child is different from the others.

3. Parents need to understand that ability grouping is aimed at helping all children and not just a few. The aim of ability grouping is to help each child experience challenges that he can meet successfully and not fail.

4. The program should provide for a continuous and comprehensive identification of children's abilities. Children change; therefore, changes in grouping will be necessary from time to time if the child's best interests are to be met.

5. There should be conferences between teachers and parents. Through home and school meetings a better understanding can be created.

6. Patterns of ability groupings will vary from community to community; therefore, the type of ability grouping in any one school system should be developed on the basis of the needs within that educational program.

## Class reorganization

Trump has utilized a report on secondary education in general to forecast a future secondary school health, physical education, and recreation program. Among the new approaches he indicates will take place are the following†:

---

*Essex, Martin: National Parent-Teacher **54:** 16, Sept., 1959.

†Trump, J. Lloyd, and Baynham, Dorsey: Focus on change—guide to better schools, Chicago, 1961, Rand McNally & Co.

1. Class size will vary with the purpose and content of instruction. There will be large, small, and medium-sized classes. There will be large groups of students for lectures and demonstrations and small groups for discussions and for work in the laboratories.

2. A student in the future physical education program will spend once a week as a member of a large group, once a week as a member of a class of fifteen students, and 120 minutes twice a week in the laboratory.

3. Six kinds of staff members will be in charge of the program. These six are professional teachers, instruction assistants, general aides to help with technical services, clerks, community consultants, and professional consultants.

4. Teachers will have more time to plan and evaluate their instruction.

5. The quality of teachers will be improved.

## ADMINISTRATIVE DEVELOPMENTS AFFECTING THE LEARNING PROCESS

The public school system in the United States today is an outgrowth of early Greek methods of education and educational thought. In spite of the changing philosophies and needs of an ever-changing world, present educational curriculums and methods are directly related to the past. Individual and community needs and desires, and social change have had an influence on education, but not an influence profound enough, until very recently, to refashion education and break our centuries-old ties.

Until the nineteenth century, most public education in the United States was conducted in the Little Red Schoolhouse, a structure containing one classroom and one teacher, or, at the most, two classrooms and two teachers. These rooms were filled with pupils of varying ages studying on many different levels. During the latter half of the nineteenth century student enrollment increased tremendously, thus increasing the need for more teachers, more classrooms, and more schools. At this time, the first graded schools in the United States emerged, and units of knowledge were established and given grade labels.

School enrollments again showed a large increase in the early part of the twentieth century, almost doubling in every decade, with the bulk of the increase in the high school age groups. In 1918, the Commission on Reorganization of Secondary Education investigated high school curriculums in an attempt to make this phase of education conform more closely to practical aims. This evaluation resulted in the formulation of the Cardinal Principles of Education, and brought, at least in theory, general education closer to the needs of the masses. However, the standard curriculums were little changed as a result of the report, and all pupils, regardless of ability, were exposed to the same courses and were taught by the same methods. Dissatisfaction with the progress of education led to the founding of the first junior high schools between the years 1910 and 1915.

As the twentieth century progressed, the needs of each individual, rather than the masses, began to dominate educational thought. Researchers pointed out the variations in creativity, ability, need, and interest, and education began to emphasize individual inquiry while placing less stress on the learning of rigid, formalized bodies of knowledge.

Only recently have our schools, and the secondary schools in particular, come under criticism from both educators and parents. Only minor changes in curriculums took place until the start of the space age. Previous to this time, the status quo was almost unequivocally accepted. Many researchers and writers in the educational field currently point out that, although many are criticizing the schools, they are not sure of what role the schools should play nor how the most beneficial changes in education should be accomplished.

Currently, both the federal government and private industry, among other groups, are influencing educational thought through research, experimentation, and the application of technological discoveries and innovations. These are having an effect on curriculums in education by placing an increased emphasis on content, creativity, and school organization.

Some of the most widely applied and discussed innovations are briefly detailed in the following paragraphs. Each educator needs to be aware of not only the newest trends in his own field, but also of those of education in general. Each new trend has an implication, and possibly an application, for every educational field.

### The nongraded school

The nongraded school is the result of a desire on the part of educators and others interested in education to improve the flexibility of the curriculum. The nongraded school is not restricted to a particular educational level, but with certain modifications is adaptable to all levels. In essence, pupils in a nongraded school progress from level to level based on their own readiness. This, then, allows more able students to move toward advanced work more rapidly while slower or less motivated pupils may spend more time on fundamentals.

One of the first attempts at organizing a nongraded elementary school took place in St. Louis, Missouri, in 1868. During the late 1800's communities in New York and Colorado were experimenting with nongraded schools and were giving specialized help for both slow and fast learners. In 1957–1958, nongraded schools were in operation in forty-four communities in twenty-one states, and in 1961, there were nongraded schools in more than 500 communities. Currently, many geographically scattered school systems are experimenting with nongrading, particularly on the elementary school level.

Nongrading is simply the removal of grade labels from some, or all, of the classes in a school or school system, allowing the learner to proceed at his own pace. Appleton, Wisconsin, offers a good example of this kind of educational organization. Under the Appleton Continuous Progress Plan, initiated in 1951, report cards, promotion, and grade retention are eliminated. Each individual is encouraged to work up to the limits of his own capacity, and thus advances at his own most comfortable and practical rate. The Appleton schools retain the traditional kindergarten, but after that year, there follows a nongraded three-year primary program. This is succeeded by a nongraded three-year intermediate school, and a traditional junior high school. Should a child not complete sufficient work in either the primary or intermediate levels to warrant moving to the next higher level, he could spend an additional year at either or both levels, yet conceivably complete his public education at the same time as his faster-moving peers.

The Appleton Plan utilizes the same classrooms and class sizes as most graded schools, grouping children according to maturity within each classroom and regrouping them within each classroom according to subject matter. The flexibility of the plan allows shifting of a child from one classroom to another as the need arises.

Rather than resorting to traditional report cards containing marks only, Appleton's report cards show no marks at all. Instead a comprehensive written analysis of each child's progress is presented. The organizers of the Appleton Plan felt that the report card containing marks only assumed a sameness of direction and ability for each child and disregarded individual differences.

The results of standardized achievement tests showed that Appleton students were surpassing national norms in all test areas, and, encouraged by this, Appleton placed all of its elementary schools on a non-graded basis in 1957.

The role of the teacher in the nongraded school is that of a guide for each student through the learning process. The teacher must select materials suitable to the needs, interests, and abilities of each individual student, and then provide appropriately more difficult material as success is achieved.

The basic premise of the nongraded school is the recognition of individual differences between learners, and within the learner himself, and the need to teach through, rather than around, these differences.

The nongraded school evolved mainly through discontent with existent school organization and curriculums. Other reasons for nongrading have been:

1. To allow for greater flexibility in pupil placement, and for uninterrupted pupil progress
2. To find, and put into use, better educational procedures
3. To provide for irregular pupil progression
4. To remove the stigma of nonpromotion, and relieve the tensions created by skipping
5. To provide for more continuous upward progress of all pupils, regardless of their individual rates of learning
6. To provide a more workable educational framework, centered around the pupil

## The middle school

The question as to what is the most desirable pattern of grade organization is the topic of many discussions among school administrators, teachers, and the lay public. One survey of 366 unified school systems with pupil enrollment of 12,000 or more, conducted by the Educational Research Service, showed that 71% of these school systems were organized on the 6-3-3 plan, 10% on the 8-4 organization, and 6% on a 6-2-4 pattern. Other patterns include 7-5, 6-6, 5-3-4, and 7-2-3.

The pattern of organization being considered by many school systems today is the middle school concept. Most simply, a middle school is for boys and girls between the elementary and high school years—grades six, seven, and eight, and sometimes five. New York City, for example, the nation's largest school system, has decided to eliminate junior high schools, replacing them with middle schools, which will be grouped by grades five to eight or six to eight. The secondary schools will become four-year comprehensive high schools. Other places that are embarked on the middle school pattern are Bridgewater, Massachusetts; Bedford Public Schools in Mount Kisco, New York; Sarasota County, Florida; Saginaw, Michigan; Easton, Connecticut; and Independence, Ohio.

Some of the reasons for the middle school concept are as follows:

1. There is an opportunity for more departmentalization than found in the elementary schools but less than found in the high schools, especially in such fields as science, mathematics, art, and music.
2. There is an opportunity for greater stimulation of students and better facilities and equipment, such as laboratories and shops.
3. There is an opportunity for special teachers and special programs, essential for children passing through the early adolescent period.
4. Students today have subjects that were taught much later in the school program years ago. For example, in terms of the required curriculum, the fourth grader today is in advance of the sixth grader years ago. Therefore, the middle school concept is applicable to the present educational era.
5. There is a better opportunity for student grouping and meeting individual differences.
6. There is a better opportunity for guidance services to be extended into the lower grades.
7. There is a better opportunity for a more personalized approach than is possible under other types of organization.
8. The ninth-grade youngsters are more mature and can fit into the high school program, permitting them to take advanced courses.

9. There is better opportunity for a gradual change from self-sustained classroom to complete departmentalization.

Some of the reasons against the middle school are as follows:

1. There is lack of evidence to support its value because of its relative newness.
2. There are social adjustment problems in placing ninth graders with twelfth graders.
3. Youngsters in the middle school will be pushed too hard academically and socially.
4. Administrative techniques and procedures would need to be altered.

An example of the middle school in operation is the Saginaw Township Community School in Saginaw, Michigan. In Saginaw the administrative plan includes the neighborhood school (grades nine to twelve), the middle school (grades five to eight), and the community high school (grades nine to twelve).

Students at the middle school have a self-contained classroom environment in the fifth grade, where there is an educational climate that provides the needed security with one base and one teacher but at the same time provides for a more open school plan in which there is not complete isolation between fifth-grade classrooms. Also, fifth graders begin to learn how to operate in a more flexible pattern utilized in the succeeding grades. The sixth grade provides for a marked transition that involves a departure from the self-contained classroom, with the teachers working in informal teams, although the student spends most of his time with one teacher in one classroom. Students assume more responsibility for their own and each other's welfare, and become acquainted with several teachers and different groups of children. In the seventh and eighth grades, students spend two periods of each school day in their homerooms but the rest of the time is spent in specialized classrooms receiving instruction from specialists in such areas as physical education, music, arts, mathematics, and science. Students are encouraged to do more independent study in the seventh and eighth grades.

## Year-round school

The need for a year-round school program is increasingly heard whenever educational topics are discussed. Such developments as the child's becoming an economic liability in our modern industrial society, the great technological advance that has resulted in a raising of the minimal requirements for vocational adequacy, the knowledge explosion, and the taking over of many functions of the home by other agencies and institutions have resulted in many people asking the question: Why not have the children in school for a longer period of time?

The year-round school also makes sense to some educators because the school plant is idle during the summer months, although costs for administration, insurance, and capital outlay remain constant. Also, many school-age children do not have constructive programs for the summer months and teachers would be available in many cases.

Some of the plans suggested for extending the school year include the staggered quarter plan, in which the calendar year is divided into four quarters with pupils attending three of four quarters and having a vacation for the fourth quarter. Teachers could be hired for either three or four quarters.

A second suggestion is the 48-week school year which would be divided into four 12-week periods, with the remaining 4 weeks being used for vacation purposes. Teachers would be employed on a 12-month basis.

A third suggestion would be the voluntary summer program which students could attend if they so desired for purposes of remedial work and avocational, recreational, and enrichment type courses.

The fourth suggestion is the summer program for professional personnel plan. Under this arrangement, teachers would be employed on a 12-month basis and would work 48 weeks and have a 4-week vacation. The students would go to school from 36 to 40 weeks. Teachers would spend the other weeks working on curriculum and instructional planning.

## The new curriculums

At the present time, our schools are passing through a rapid state of change. Few people, whether educators, parents, or the leaders of our society, are satisfied with the curriculums we have. Few are content with the outcomes of these curriculums. This unrest has sparked the formulation of new objectives and has led to new curriculums based on these objectives.

New curriculums have been devised and are under almost constant revision by Project English of the United States Office of Education, by the School Mathematics Study Group, by the American Institute of Biological Sciences Curriculum Study, by the National Council for the Social Studies, by the Physical Science Study Committee, by the National Science Foundation, by the Chemical Education Material Study, and by the High School Geography Project, among others.

The new curriculums are designed not to present new facts in place of the old, but to lead today's students toward self-discovery of facts. The new curriculums give incentive to students, beginning in the elementary years, to be inquisitive, to discover knowledge on their own, and to learn through problem solving. The facts of mathematics, for example, do not change. What does change is the teaching approach, the methodology, and the materials used. Rather than memorization, conceptualization is the keynote. The significant concepts of a subject are learned through discovery and thus understood.

Drills and memorization are viewed as the antithesis of learning.

The proponents of the new curriculums believe firmly in a basic and comprehensive education suited to individual needs. They have developed the new curriculums to provide both an enriched and a more significant education. Thus, they have attempted to make the new curriculums as valid as possible. Not only were the effects of these curriculums on learners investigated, but also the effects and demands on the teachers. Comparative pupil progress under new and old curriculums was assessed, as were the goals of the new and the old.

The new curriculums in themselves have presented problems to academicians. While the new materials are widely used in many school systems, other schools have as yet been untouched by the new curriculums. Some academic fields have had vast exposure to the new, while progress in other areas, such as physical education, the arts, and the humanities, have been virtually untouched. Where the new materials have been put into use, the total educational structure has often not been strengthened or revised sufficiently to support the use of the new materials, and teachers are occasionally ill prepared to use them. In some fields, the materials have been updated so frequently that assimilation has been difficult.

However, such groups as the National Curriculum Conference continue to assess and evaluate all of the new curriculums to ascertain that progress is an ongoing product of change.

## Other new trends

Many schools are now placing additional emphasis on special programs for exceptional children and investigating ways in which these children can be aided in becoming useful adults. Some schools participate in distributive education or in sheltered workshop programs, so that vocational training, if even of a limited nature, is assured.

The Elementary and Secondary Education Act of 1965, the first major increase in federal spending for education, provides an on-going opportunity for many school systems to experiment with program improvement and enrichment, and to develop better facilities.

Project Head Start, administered by the U. S. Office of Economic Opportunity, offers an 8-week program for culturally disadvantaged youngsters of pre-kindergarten age. These children, to whom education is often an extremely discouraging experience, are given skills and helped to reach understandings that will help them adjust to the educational process.

In the realm of facilities, school architecture is being modernized. The newest schools are often imaginatively designed, and at times are built in a decentralized form, so that rather than being multistoried, a large school is low and many-winged. Air conditioning, below-ground construction, the use of movable air bubbles, and parklike settings characterize the most recent school construction.

Physical educators interested in playing a key role in the future will equip themselves to utilize their abilities to greatest advantage in the years ahead.

## SUMMARY

Good teachers apply psychological principles to their work. They consider several conditions in fulfilling their duties. They try first to establish rapport between themselves and their students. When this is accomplished, they will be better able to understand, accept, and help each pupil. Their objectives, expectations, and disciplinary methods are clearly stated and understood. Content of material is adjusted to each student's level of learning and made interesting to motivate each pupil. Practice periods are adapted to the subject matter being taught and to the

individual's needs and interests. Good teachers recognize and acknowledge achievements made by students, and then set new goals for the boys and girls to obtain. They give each child a sense of worth by letting him contribute, and give him a sense of belonging. They recognize that repetition of useful and significant information is necessary for retention of material. They know it is important to emphasize the rudiments of physical education so that the students will remember and use their skills, attitudes, and knowledge in furthering learning experiences. Before they examine the students to find out how much and what they have learned in the class, they review the subject content to refresh their pupils' minds.

As teachers, they are firm in their disciplinary approach. They let pupils know what is expected of them. They understand why pupils act in certain ways. They expect courtesy and fair play. They motivate pupils to do their best work and challenge them so they are proud of their achievements. They are sensitive to each pupil's feelings. They are patient, tolerant, and honest.

The physical education instructor should teach the various activities that comprise his profession in accordance with established psychological principles. If the instructor is thoroughly conversant with the best methodology and resources available for skill teaching, physical education skills will be learned better, time will be saved, and the learner will have a more satisfying and all-around better educational experience. Many physical educators today do not interpret their profession from the psychological point of view, and consequently they are not performing their job in the best interests of the consumer and of the profession. The student who is planning to enter this profession should recognize the value of scientific psychological data and use them to perform his work in the most efficient way possible.

## QUESTIONS AND EXERCISES

1. Define the term *psychology* and discuss its implications for the teaching of physical education.
2. Discuss the trial-and-error, conditioning, and whole method theories of learning in respect to the teaching of physical education activities. What points of common agreement are there in these three theories of learning?
3. Why should physical education skills be taught in the most efficient way possible?
4. Identify: reflex arc, connector, sensory nerve, motor nerve, spinal column, "all-or none" principle, and Thorndike.
5. Describe the route over which an impulse travels from the time the organism is stimulated to action by some environmental factor until it responds to the stimulus.
6. Compare the reflex arc to a telephone exchange.
7. What is meant by the law of readiness? How is it related to the teaching of physical education?
8. How is the law of exercise similar to the law of use? What implications does it have for teaching volleyball, handball, and softball?
9. What implications does the law of effect have for coaching a football team?
10. Discuss ten factors or conditions that promote learning in physical education activities.
11. Identify: plateau, initial spurt, learning curve, goals, "whole method," physiological limit, psychological limit, maturation level, visual aids, and overlearned.
12. What is the relationship between leadership and learning?
13. Why is it necessary to overlearn a skill such as swimming?
14. What is meant by concomitant learning? What are some of the concomitants learned in each of the following activities: field hockey, football, basketball, softball, badminton, swimming, and horseback riding?
15. What is meant by the theory of formal discipline? To what extent is it adhered to in present-day education?
16. Under what conditions is transfer of training best accomplished in the field of physical education?
17. How will the psychological principles of learning help you to become a better physical education teacher?
18. Why is motivation sometimes said to be the "heart of the learning process"?
19. Make a list of the things a physical education teacher can do that will act as incentives to pupil learning.
20. Explain how learning takes place, especially relating your discussion to the learning of physical skills.
21. What is the relationship of physical education to academic achievement?
22. How will the new developments in general education, such as educational TV, nongrading, and new grading methods affect physical education?
23. How will the physical education curriculums of the future be affected by new curriculums in general education?

## SELECTED REFERENCES

American Association for Health, Physical Education, and Recreation, Washington, D. C.: Motor learning and motor performance, Fitness Series No. 4, 1959. The growing years—adolescence, 1962.

Association for Supervision and Curriculum Development: Assessing and using curriculum content, Washington, D. C., 1965, The Association.

Brimm, R. P.: The junior high school, Washington, D. C., 1963, The Center for Applied Research.

Broer, Marion: Efficiency of human movement, Philadelphia, 1965, W. B. Saunders Co.

Bruner, J. S.: The process of education, Cambridge, Mass., 1963, Harvard University Press.

Bucher, Charles A., and Reade, Evelyn M.: Physical education in the modern elementary school, New York, 1964, The Macmillan Co.

Bucher, Charles A.: Health, physical education, and academic achievement, NEA Journal **54**:38, May, 1965.

Clark, Leonard H., Klein, Raymond L., and Burke, John B.: The American secondary school curriculum, New York, 1965, The Macmillan Co.

Cratty, B. J.: Movement behavior and motor learning, Philadelphia, 1964, Lea & Febiger.

Cratty, Bryant J.: Psychological bases of physical activity, Journal of Health, Physical Education, and Recreation **36**:71, Sept., 1965.

Davis, Elwood C., and Wallis, Earl L.: Toward better teaching in physical education, Englewood Cliffs, N. J., 1961, Prentice-Hall, Inc.

deGrazia, Alfred, and Sohn, David A.: Revolution in teaching: new theory, technology, and curricula, New York, 1964, Bantam Books.

Dewey, John: How we think, Boston, 1933, D. C. Heath & Co.

Evaul, Thomas W.: The automated tutor, Journal of Health, Physical Education, and Recreation 35:27, March, 1964.

Goodlad, John I., and Anderson, Robert H.: The nongraded elementary school, New York, 1963, Harcourt, Brace, & World, Inc.

Goodlad, John I.: School curriculum reform in the United States, New York, 1964, The Fund for the Advancement of Education.

Goodlad, John I.: Directions of curriculum change, NEA Journal 55:33, Dec., 1966.

Harris, Chester W., editor: Encyclopedia of education research, New York, 1960, The Macmillan Co.

Hermann, Don, and Osness, Wayne: A scientific curriculum design for high school physical education, Journal of Health, Physical Education, and Recreation 37:23, March, 1966.

Hilgard, E. R.: Learning theory and its application. In Schramm, W., editor: New teaching aids for the American classroom, Stanford, Calif., 1960, Institute for Communicative Research.

Johnson, Granville B.: The new physical education, Minneapolis, 1942, Burgess Publishing Co., chaps. 2, 3.

Johnson, Perry B.: An academic approach to college health and physical education, Journal of Health, Physical Education, and Recreation 37:23, March, 1966.

Layman, Emma McCloy: Mental health through physical education, health education and recreation, Minneapolis, 1955, Burgess Publishing Co.

Madigan, Marian East: Psychology, principles and applications, St. Louis, 1963, The C. V. Mosby Co.

Morse, Arthur D.: Schools of tomorrow—today! New York, 1960, Doubleday & Co., Inc.

Murphy, Judith, and Gross, Ronald: The unfilled promise of ITV, Saturday Review, Nov. 19, 1966, p. 88.

National Association of Physical Education for College Women and National College Physical Education Association for Men: A symposium on motor learning, Quest (Monograph VI), May, 1966.

National Congress of Parents and Teachers: PTA guide to what's happening in education, New York, 1965, Scholastic Book Services.

National Education Association: Schools for the sixties, New York, 1963, McGraw-Hill Book Co.

National Society for the Study of Education: Forty-first yearbook, Chicago, 1942, Department of Education, University of Chicago, Part II.

Skinner, B. F.: Reinforcement today, The American Psychologist, March, 1958, pp. 94–99.

Sohn, David A.: Programmed instruction, The PTA Magazine 60:17, Sept., 1965.

Stein, Julian A.: Making school-learned physical education a continued force for future fitness, The Physical Educator 20:126, Oct., 1963.

Stoddard, George D.: The meaning of intelligence, New York, 1947, The Macmillan Co.

Trump, J. Lloyd, and Baynham, Dorsey: Focus on change—guide to better schools, Chicago, 1961, Rand McNally & Co.

Western Society for Physical Education of College Women: The care and treatment of the skilled: do we practice what we know about motor learning? The Physical Educator 17:43, May, 1960.

# Chapter 18

# Sociological interpretations of physical education

Sociology is concerned with a study of people, of groups of persons, and of human activities in terms of the groups and institutions in society. It is concerned with the origin of society. It is a science that is interested in such institutions of society as religion, family, government, education, and recreation. It is a science that is involved in developing a better social order characterized by good, happiness, tolerance, and racial equality.

Persons who work in educational sociology are concerned primarily with three functions: (1) the influence of education upon social institutions and group life upon the individual, such as how the school affects the personality or behavior of an individual, (2) the human relations that operate in the school involving pupils, parents, and teachers, and how they influence personality and behavior of an individual, and (3) the relation of the school to other institutions and elements of society, as, for example, the impact of education upon natural resources.

Physical education can play an important part in the improvement of the democratic way of life. It is applicable to day-to-day living, it is practical, it is functional, it helps in preparing for liv-

ing, and it helps in living a more vigorous and a more interesting life. It also aids in adjusting to the group situation. Play is a socializer. It can do much in promoting the brotherhood of man. To illustrate, the primitive tendency was to strike back if angered by an adversary. Physical education, however, teaches human relationships in accordance with set rules. Participants put forth their best efforts to defeat opponents but in a socially acceptable manner.

## EDUCATORS ARE AGREED ON CERTAIN VALUES

What is important to life, to the American way of life, to life wherever the individual is viewed as having worth? The Educational Policies Commission has listed ten values that are moral and spiritual in character and that represent the foundations upon which a strong society is built.* They are presented here to help clarify the sociological implications for physical educators. Moral and spiritual values are reflected in human relationships

*Educational Policies Commission: Moral and spiritual values in the public schools, Washington, D. C., 1951, National Education Association.

*Flint Public Schools,
Flint, Mich.*

The individual has worth.

and affect a person's emotions and sentiments and ways of behaving.

**Human personality—basic value.** The individual has worth. This represents the basic value in life. Physical education should help each individual to possess a feeling of worth and importance and to achieve within his abilities.

**Moral responsibility.** Each individual must feel responsible for his own behavior. Human beings must exercise rational judgment in making decisions that will not infringe upon the rights of others. They must perform in a manner that is ethical and right according to established codes of conduct. Physical education must use its power to inculcate this responsibility in those individuals who participate in its programs.

**Institutions as servants of men.** Social institutions, whether they are domestic, educational, cultural, or political, must serve people. They should never exist for themselves but, instead, as agencies that help people to realize their goals.

**Common consent.** The popular will must be the key to understanding. Cooperation must exist. Law, justice, and conformance with existing rules and regulations must be a guideline.

**Devotion to truth.** The truth must always be sought and social direction guided thereby. Deception, coercion, and intellectual dishonesty must not exist. Schools and physical educators within the schools must help young people to determine the way to find the truth and how to be guided by its revelation.

**Respect for excellence.** There should be a constant search for excellence of mind, character, and creative ability. Education should help young people to determine their abilities, to select leaders who are most able, and to be excellent producers themselves in all their efforts. Physical education can help people to achieve this important quality by stressing the importance of well-being and good health.

**Moral equality.** All individuals are judged by the same moral standards. The golden rule has been written into all the great religions of the world. Education and physical education must recognize this precept and practice rules of fair play, tolerance, sympathy, and brotherhood.

**Brotherhood.** There must be a feeling of brotherhood for all persons, whether these individuals are ignorant or bright, feeble or strong, experience misfortune or abound in good fortune. This is a moral responsibility of all citizens. Education and physical education must help young people to develop those traits and qualities that will enhance their usefulness to society.

**Pursuit of happiness.** Opportunity must be provided for each individual to pursue and achieve happiness. Education and physical education must promote those qualities that provide lasting happiness— deep personal resources, respect and affection for others, and opportunities for making a contribution to humanity.

**Spiritual enrichment.** The outlook of people is affected by spiritual belief. Their inner feelings and their emotions are tempered by this same belief. Their behavior is also guided by this quality. Education and physical education should encourage and help individuals to have spiritual enrichment, in which beauty and refinement, esthetic appreciation, and creative abilities represent important considerations.

• • •

These moral and spiritual values are important considerations in discussing and considering the sociological interpretations of physical education. The next step is to look at the nature of man to discover what role these values play in his existence and how these values can best be instilled as part of his makeup.

## NATURE OF MAN

The study of sociology shows that man becomes a different type of individual

from his original nature when he takes on acquired characteristics of human nature. The traits and characteristics that result in antisocial conduct and cause fear, hate, and worry in the world are acquired characteristics. Man is not born an antisocial being. Man is not born with traits that lead to power seeking, aggrandizement, and intolerance. These traits are acquired through man's environment. Through a better understanding of human nature and through a meaningful educational experience, it is possible to build a better social order for all mankind. The physical educator should understand these things so that he can utilize his work in the development of a better social order.

### Original nature of man

Man does not start life as a human being. He originates from cells, and cells are not human. The adjective "human" can be applied only after the acquisition of human traits that encompass the sympathies, passions, and failings of men. Such characteristics as jealousy, greed, and insolence are human traits. They are not present in the cells at birth. *Human* is a term that can be applied to an animal species—a name given to a large number of animals. Only in a very limited sense is man born human. He is, in fact, born an animal and becomes a human being. He becomes a human being when he adapts himself to such characteristics of his culture as tools, laws, religions, and words.

The original nature of man is characterized by involuntary or reflex actions, such as crying, sneezing, coughing, blinking an eyelid, sucking, and wiggling. This is animal nature, which under the influence of man's environment becomes human nature.

Original nature is not predestined to take a certain shape or direction. Instead, it can be molded in patterns that permit human beings to live side by side in a peaceful and happy existence. Physical education has the potentialities to contribute much in this molding process.

### Human nature

Human nature is characterized by the acquisition of human traits that are a part of the environment in which an individual lives. It is characterized by intelligence and thinking. Man has a thinking mechanism that enables him to make decisions, to control his behavior, and to adapt himself to various situations.

From birth, man develops as a social being as well as an individual characterized by self-assertiveness and personal interests and desires. Within a few weeks after birth the child shows an inclination to be a social being. His social activities play an important part in his growth. As the maturing process continues, the

child exhibits behavior that is characterized by cooperation and a willingness to be friendly. On the other hand, however, he also exhibits characteristics that display his uniqueness as an individual, his desires, and his likes and dislikes. As time elapses he becomes more cooperative, makes friends, becomes conscious of other people's desires, and acquires to some degree a sympathetic attitude toward the desires of others. Eventually he recognizes the importance of teamwork, develops convictions and loyalties, and becomes interested in the community in which he lives and in the welfare of the nation as a whole. He also feels a certain responsibility for the welfare of all mankind. At the same time, he has certain vested interests that he aims to protect. He becomes a competitor for recognition, prestige, and material possessions, and he spends most of his time in furthering his

As the maturing process continues, the child exhibits behavior that is characterized by cooperation and a willingness to be friendly.

own special and personal interests, which seem to be a prime consideration. Thus an individual develops socially. On the one hand, he is interested in the larger world, in other people, and in the welfare of mankind; but conversely, he is interested in the life that revolves around himself and his personal ambitions. Physical education, through the various activities that it offers, has the potentialities for developing social traits that further personal interests and at the same time stress those characteristics that are necessary for group living.

Man's human nature is also characterized by a progressive advance from involuntary action to one of fixed modes of behavior. At birth the individual possesses certain reflexes, such as crying, sneezing, and coughing. Before long he acquires set patterns of reacting to certain experiences, which soon become habits. The baby cries when he wants certain things. The child acquires the habits of wearing clothes, of brushing his teeth, and of saying his prayers before he goes to bed at night. Eventually, as he grows older, he recognizes that the group of people with whom he is associated in a particular environment act in certain ways and have developed certain folkways and mores. These folkways and mores arise from the needs of the people. People discover in the course of history that certain things give them pleasure and contribute to a more enjoyable existence, whereas other things cause pain and grief. They profit from the experience of previous generations. They find some ways more expedient than others. They adopt certain methods of doing things and turn them into customs, which thus become folkways. Examples of folkways that have developed among some groups of people are the customs of a man's tipping his hat to a lady, going to town on Saturday afternoon, and eating hot dogs at the ball game. Most groups of people

attempt to improve customs or folkways as they progress. Certain ones are abandoned in light of new developments. Folkways that have been lifted to another or higher plane to better serve the needs and interests and desires of a group of people become mores. They are the folkways that through continued experience have been proved right and true and have the force of law. Examples of mores are such things as having one wife or husband and believing in one God.

### Human needs

Another concept that needs the careful consideration of physical educators is what is called the "needs" theory. Whenever a person acts he is trying to satisfy a need. Therefore we should know the needs of our students and of human beings in general and try to satisfy these needs in a constructive manner.

The most obvious human needs are for physical survival and well being. Others may concern themselves with the physiological, psychological, or sociological makeup of the human being.

The physiological aspects include the needs for oxygen, escape from pain-producing situations, and attention to requirements of thirst, sex, intestinal and bladder elimination, rest, sleep, and hunger. These are important to the individual as a means of survival and comfort. They must be satisfied. This fact is generally recognized by almost everyone.

The psychological needs are less obvious and concern themselves with the mind and emotions. They include love, achievement, affection, belonging, approval, recognition, acceptance, and security. A person needs the feeling of belonging, having status, and becoming something. These are not as easily identified by laymen, but they should be known to educators. Teachers can do much to help satisfy these basic needs of every human being.

The sociological needs are those that pertain to the pattern of how a person fits into society. These needs include co-operation, sharing, gregariousness, and love. They take into account the opinions of others, the desire to influence others, and the security one has within the group. A person's self-esteem is affected by his relations with the group.

Human needs can be realized through work, play, and recreation. If not properly nurtured, they may result in an anti-social action and personal maladjustment. Therefore the professional educator should be cognizant of these human needs and plan definite means of meeting them.

## FORCES THAT IMPEL GROUP LIVING

During the course of history there have been many forces that have motivated mankind to live together. These forces have been in the nature of a hostile environment, hereditary influences, and acquired drives.

During man's early history, and to a certain extent during present times, man has sought group life because of a hostile environment. Man's early enemies were wild animals that inhabited the forest and thick underbrush; acts of God, such as floods, hurricanes, and storms; and disease. In order to combat these enemies, it was often necessary to band together for protection. One person found it very difficult to fight alone, but many assured success. Association, rather than an individualistic existence, has proved to be the safer and better expedient in the life struggle that has faced man over the years.

Heredity in itself results in individuals becoming members of certain groups. People are born of a mother and father, and consequently, right from birth a person is a member of a group. Persons are born either males or females, which greatly determines their group associa-

tions during the course of their entire lifetime. A person belongs to a certain race, a certain color, and a certain country, which predestines in some measure his associations. Heredity has placed the sex drive in human beings, which impels them to seek mates. Fear has resulted in group living. The fear of God, the fear of the law, and the fear of enemies are potent factors in stimulating group living. These hereditary forces tend to make man gregarious in nature as a matter of natural circumstances and predestine him to group living.

There are also many acquired factors that impel men to live in groups. These include such desires as hunger, love, and vanity; such wishes as the desire for adventure, security, and recognition; such sentiments as those for the flag, the home, the Bible, the state, or nation; and such interests and values as health, wealth, politics, sociability, knowledge, beauty, and rightness. All of these derivative factors drive men to associate with others. Only through association is it possible to realize such desires, wishes, sentiments, interests, and values.

After becoming a member of a group, certain conditions are necessary for successful adjustment. An individual needs to have affection, the belief that he is liked by other members. He needs to experience a feeling of "belonging," the belief that he has been accepted. He needs independence, which is exemplified by his right to make his own decisions. Finally, he needs social approval and the opportunity to maintain his self-esteem. If these conditions are prevalent, the chances of an individual's becoming a responsible member of a group are very good. The physical educator should keep these needs in mind when organizing and administering his program.

An important hereditary factor that motivates the formation of groups and one in which physical educators are interested is the drive for action that is inherent in a child. A child is a dynamic, active human being who continually wants to be on the move. This is evident whenever an attempt is made to keep a child in a chair, at a school desk, or in one position for any length of time. If an average adult were to follow a child around for a day, performing every movement that the child performed, the adult would be close to the point of exhaustion before half the day had passed. The child is continually cruising, exploring, and getting acquainted with his environment. Physical education, an outlet for the child's abundant energy, comes in as an acquired factor on the part of man. The child, through his natural drive for activity, acquires the desire to participate in many forms of play with other children. It is not necessary to encourage a child to play with another group of children. There is a drive for action present that provides such motivation. The job of physical educators is to establish the program in such a manner that desirable social standards are met through play activities.

## DEVELOPMENT OF SOCIAL UNITY

Social unity is necessary if civilization is to survive, and the key to social unity is cooperation. In this sense cooperation means the merging of the activities of two or more individuals in order to achieve some desirable goal that could not be achieved without their united efforts.

The world needs cooperation today more than ever before. The world is torn with strife, with conflicting ideologies, and with cold wars and hot wars. In every part of the globe we find evidence of discrimination against various classes and races of people. Modern technology is being directed toward developing new types of warfare that will destroy great populated and industrialized areas through atomic bombs, bacteria, and chemicals, that destroy man's will to resist. Considerably more than one half of the budget of the United States is allocated to payment of the costs of past wars and preparation for possible future ones. Many other countries have comparable budgets. Through cooperation, a great deal of this strife, hardship, and unrest that exist around the globe could be eliminated. The United Nations is an example of an attempt at cooperation, but to a great degree its success has been handicapped through the lack of mutual trust and confidence among the nations of the world.

What are the foundations of this cooperation so essential to group living? A sympathetic attitude is necessary so that people do not repel each other. It means that individuals should reflect friendliness and warmth. They should not be self-centered but, instead, should be willing to go more than halfway. They should show that they want to be friends with the other fellow. Only through kindliness and friendliness is it possible to obtain cooperation. If the antithesis of friendliness exists, individuals are hesitant to communicate with one another, and consequently, they fail to coordinate their efforts to achieve some common goal. In order to achieve cooperation there must be group thinking. This means that after mutual friendship has been established there is a getting together of minds so that a usable plan may be evolved. Only through careful thought will a plan be developed that will be in the best interests of all concerned. Finally, there must be a coordination of efforts so that the plan that has been devised can be accomplished. Through an expenditure of time, effort, and personal sacrifice on the part of all, goals can be accomplished that were never thought possible otherwise.

An individual takes from a group in proportion to what he contributes. Effective cooperation can exist only as a

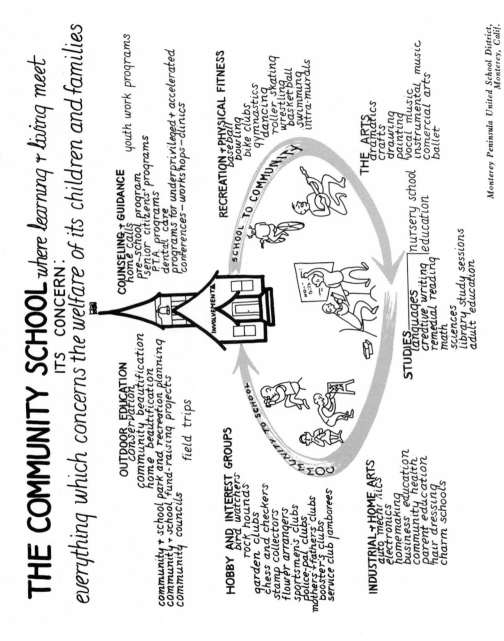

THE COMMUNITY SCHOOL *where learning + living meet*

ITS CONCERN:

*everything which concerns the welfare of its children and families*

**COUNSELING + GUIDANCE**
home calls       youth work programs
pre-school program
senior citizens' programs
P.T.A. programs
dental care
programs for underprivileged + accelerated
conferences—workshops—clinics

**OUTDOOR EDUCATION**
conservation
community beautification
home beautification
community + school park and recreation planning
community + school fund-raising projects
community councils       field trips

**RECREATION + PHYSICAL FITNESS**
baseball
bowling
bike clubs
gymnastics
dancing
roller skating
wrestling
basketball
swimming
intra-murals

**THE ARTS**
dramatics
crafts
drawing
painting
vocal music
instrumental music
comercial arts
ballet

SCHOOL TO COMMUNITY

COMMUNITY TO SCHOOL

INVOLVEMENT

**HOBBY AND INTEREST GROUPS**
bird watchers
rock hounds
garden clubs
chess and checkers
stamp collectors
flower arrangers
sportsmens clubs
police-pal clubs
mothers+fathers'clubs
booster's clubs
service club jamborees

**INDUSTRIAL+HOME ARTS**
auto mechanics
electronics
homemaking
business education
community health
parent education
hair dressing
charm schools

**STUDIES**
languages
creative writing   ⎤ nursery school
remedial reading   ⎦ education
math
sciences
library study sessions
adult education

*Monterey Peninsula United School District,*
*Monterey, Calif.*

The school—focus of social learnings.

person does his part and at the same time realizes that everyone else is doing his part. Cooperation is based on trust, confidence, and assurance. Cooperation is needed in all walks of life. It is needed to combat floods, fires, and storms. It is needed to fight disease and promote health. It is needed to control human beings who prey upon the weak. It is needed to achieve a peaceful world. Cooperation is the most valuable of all the various types of relationships. Through it, progress is made and goals are attained.

Play activities abound with opportunities for cooperation. As a general rule, individuals do not care to play alone. In playing with others, rules are needed and must be observed. This is a form of cooperation. Each member of the team is similar in many respects to the various parts of a machine. When each part is performing its function efficiently and smoothly, the machine achieves its goal. Similarly, when each member of the team cooperates with every other member of the team and each functions as a part of a complete whole rather than as a separate unit, the achievement of the team's goal is much better assured. The desire to play is so strong that participants will abide by rules, give up some of their freedom, and play cooperatively in order to remain in the game. In many ways play is unexcelled as a disciplinarian in the finer aspects of cooperation. It develops attitudes that reflect themselves in all sorts of work and organization. Since play has so many possibilities for developing desirable social traits, further consideration should be given to the question of why people desire to engage in such activity. First, however, the modes of social learning will be considered.

## MODES OF SOCIAL LEARNING

According to Havighurst there are three general modes by which children learn from other people.* All three of these methods of social learning operate in a school situation.

1. **Reward and punishment.** A child wants rewards because of the joy and satisfaction they give him. On the other hand, he does not want punishment because of the pain and dissatisfaction that accrue. Rewards and punishments may be material or nonmaterial in nature. For example, the child may receive some money or a word of praise as a reward, and a slap on the face or a severe scolding as a punishment.

2. **Imitation.** Imitation of other people is a common mode of learning. Such imitation may be conscious or unconscious. A child may learn early in life that rewards accrue when he does what a father or older brother, teacher, neighbor, scout leader, or movie star wants him to do. Gradually, he takes on patterns of behavior that imitate older persons, particularly ones with whom he feels a close emotional bond. The association results in habits of imitation that are repeated frequently and, finally, become unconscious in their application.

3. **Didactic teaching.** When a person with authority or an expert in something tells a child how to perform a particular task or what constitutes desirable behavior under specific situations, learning takes place. Teaching a boy how to bat a ball correctly is an example. This mode of social learning is effective only when accompanied by reward or punishment, or when the teacher, minister, or expert is a model person whom the child desires to imitate. Since this does not always happen, didactic teaching is sometimes a failure. Also, example may have more influence on the child than didactic teaching. For example, if a father smokes

---

*Morris, Van Cleve, and others: Becoming an educator, Boston, 1963, Houghton Mifflin Co., p. 90.

he may find it difficult to teach his boy not to smoke.

## SOME THEORIES OF PLAY

The sociologists have advanced many theories as to why people play. Some of the more outstanding of these theories are the surplus-energy or the Spencer-Schiller theory, the recreation theory, the relaxation theory, the inheritance or recapitulation theory, the instinct or Groos theory, the social-contact theory, and the self-expression theory. It is interesting to examine each of these. From the following discussions it will be seen that there are three possible factors that determine play. These three factors are concerned with the physical environment, the psychosocial environment, and the organism itself. They point to the fact that play is limited by the environment of which the organism is a part; the games the parents played will be the games the child plays; and forms of play are passed down from generation to generation.

### Surplus-energy or Spencer-Schiller theory

Friedrich Schiller, a German poet and philosopher (1759–1805), expressed the idea of play as "the aimless expenditure of exuberant energy." This theory points out that human beings have developed many powers that cannot all act at once. As a result of this phenomenon there is an overabundance of time and vigor not utilized in providing for immediate needs. Therefore many powers are inactive for considerable periods of time. Active, healthy nerve centers during these inactive periods accumulate more and more energy and in time are brought to a point where there must be a letting off of the pressure. Play is an excellent medium of letting off this steam that has developed as a result of the continual bombardment of the organism by a multitude of stimuli. Schiller has also expounded what others

have called the "aesthetic theory." This theory endorses the concept that man plays as an outlet for his creative imagination and in order to create beauty.

### Recreation theory

Guts Muths, the father of physical training in Germany, emphasized the recreative value of play in his book *Games for the Exercise and Recreation of Body and Mind*. This theory has as its premise the idea that the human body needs some form of play as a means of revitalization. Play is a medium of refreshing the body after long hours of work. It aids in the recovery of exhausted energies and is an antidote for tense nerves, mental fatigue, and emotional unrest.

### Relaxation theory

In many ways the relaxation theory is similar to the recreation theory. It holds that today's mode of work, which utilizes the small muscles of the eyes and the hands, is hard, tedious, and very fatiguing. This type of work might lead to nervous disorders if the organism does not have some means whereby it can relax from such an ordeal. Play offers this medium. It helps a person to get out-of-doors and follow such racially old activities as hunting, fishing, hiking, swimming, and camping. These activities relax and rest an individual and leave him refreshed and ready to follow another session of work.

### Inheritance or recapitulation theory

G. Stanley Hall developed the recapitulation theory. This theory maintains that the past is the key to play. Play has been passed down from generation to generation from earliest times. Play and games are a part of each individual's inheritance. Society repeats the fundamental activities of play that were utilized by earliest man. Such activities as running, throwing, striking, climbing, leaping, carrying, and jumping have been part of our daily life

*Recreation Department, Oakland, Calif.*

Surplus energy in children.

for generations. Today, the sports and games that are played are just variations of these racially old activities.

### Instinct or Groos theory

The instinct theory declares that human beings have an instinctive tendency to be active at various stages of their lifetime. A child breathes, laughs, cries, creeps, pulls himself up, stands, walks, runs, and throws at various periods of his development. These are instinctive with him and appear naturally during the course of development. Therefore, play is something that just naturally happens as a matter of growth and development. It is not something that is planned or purposely injected as a means of utilizing time. Instead, it is something that is natural and part of man's makeup.

### Social-contact theory

Human beings are born of parents. The parents are members of a certain group, culture, and society. Consequently, to a great extent, the human being takes on activities from his surroundings. An individual will adopt the games of the group of which he is a part. In the United States this might be baseball; in England, cricket; in Spain, bullfighting; and in Norway, skiing.

### Self-expression theory

Bernard S. Mason expresses a modern theory of play. He points out that man is an active creature, that his physiological and anatomical structure places limits on his activity, that his degree of physical fitness at any time affects the kind of activity in which he engages, and that psychological inclinations that are the result of physiological needs and learned responses, habits, or attitudes propel him into certain types of play activities.

### CAILLOIS' THEORIES OF PLAY

In his book entitled *Man, Play, and Games,** Roger Caillois, a French sociologist, describes four types of play. He

------
*Caillois, Roger: Man, play, and games, New York, 1961, Free Press.

*National Collegiate Athletic Association
Basketball Championship,
Manila, Philippines.*

Play is an excellent medium for letting off steam.

uses the terms *agon, alea, mimicry,* and *ilinx* as the titles of these groups, which may be translated into the categories of *competition, chance, simulation,* and *vertigo.*

1. **Competition.** This type of play may be illustrated by sports and games of individual skill such as tennis, basketball, or chess. The competition may be very simple such as when children try to see who can hold their arms out to the side the longest.

2. **Chance.** This type of play bases the outcome on a decision that is independent of the players such as in dice, lotto, bingo, or perhaps the counting out of nursery rhymes.

3. **Simulation.** This type of play involves simulation or imitation when the player assumes another role from his own such as playing cops and robbers or "farmer in the dell."

4. **Vertigo.** This type of play results in the deliberate production of dizziness or confusion or an attempt to destroy stability and bring about momentary disorientation. Examples of this would be children whirling around and falling down or an adult engaging in tightrope walking.

The first two types of play are more common among older youth, whereas the last two are more common among preschool children. The activities in the four types of play range, on one hand, between the extreme of uncontrolled fantasy involving an imaginative gaiety and, on the other hand, with activity that is planned and purposefully aimed at a specific re-

**Table 18-1.** *Caillois' classification of games**

| Agon (Competition) | | Alea (Chance) | Mimicry (Simulation) | Ilinx (Vertigo) |
|---|---|---|---|---|
| Racing, wrestling, etc., athletics | not regulated | Counting-out rhymes, heads or tails | Children's imitations, games of illusion, tag, arms, masks, disguises | Children "whirling," horseback riding, swinging, waltzing |
| Boxing, billiards, fencing, checkers, football, chess | | Betting, roulette | | Volador, traveling carnivals, skiing, mountain climbing, tightrope walking |
| Contests, sports in general | | Simple, complex, and continuing lotteries | Theater, spectacles in general | |

*From Caillois, Roger: Man, play, and games, New York, 1961, Free Press (see his Table 1, p. 36).

sult through the application of skill and effort. Caillois states that all four forms of play are universal and necessary to human development. Persons engaging in them find contributions basic to physical growth and personality development.

Table 18-1 outlines Caillois' classifications of play.

## BUILDING MORAL CHARACTER IN YOUTH

Physical education has great potential for building moral character in children and youth. However, in order to realize this potential physical educators should be familiar with the stages of character development and the best approaches to achieving this worthy goal.

Havighurst and Peck and associates, with colleagues of the Committee on Human Development at the University of Chicago, studied boys and girls, giving them tests, talking with teachers and parents, and analyzing findings. This study suggests the existence of five stages through which the ordinary person passes in developing character.*

*Peck, Robert F., and others: Psychology of character development, New York, 1960, John Wiley & Sons, Inc.

1. **Amoral, impulsive stage.** This is a period during the first year of life or longer when the individual follows his own impulses and has no moral feelings.

2. **Egocentric, expedient stage.** This period is common among children 2 to 4 years of age. It is characterized by some control over impulses in the interest of making good impressions and also self-protection from physical harm. However, there is still the "I" feeling, with focus on individual pleasures and conveniences.

3. **Conforming stage.** From 5 to 10 years of age there exists a period where the individual attempts to conform to the demands of the social group of which he is a part.

4. **Irrational conscience stage.** This is the period when the example and teaching of parents are dominant, normal for children 5 to 10 years of age and older. Some adults continue in this stage. This period is characterized by a strong feeling that the parental code of morality, whether it is right or wrong, is the one that should be followed in a rigid manner.

5. **Rational conscience stage.** This is the highest level of moral conduct. The individual applies reason and experience

to his moral code, continually trying to see the various avenues of conduct that are open and the consequences of traveling each avenue. A few adolescents get into this stage; some adults are never able to achieve it.

Some aspects of all or a few of the five stages may be noticeable in the conduct of individuals. Physical educators should recognize these various stages in the boys, girls, and adults with whom they associate, and continually strive to develop higher stages of moral conduct. The more the individual can be led to foresee the moral consequences of his own behavior, the higher on the scale he has risen.

In recognition of these five stages, how is character building in youth most effectively realized? Grinnell lists four approaches that have implications for the physical educator. They are as follows*:

1. **Precept.** This method is based on the premise that if young people know what is right they will do it. The church, to a great extent, operates on this principle. There is general agreement that clearly understanding what is right and proper is important knowledge to communicate. However, to be most effective it must be supplemented by other approaches. In physical education it is very important to have children and youth understand clearly what is considered good moral conduct in a class, in a game, away from parents, and in many other situations. No doubt should be left in their minds as to what is the best conduct under many and varied situations.

2. **Study of lives of men and women.** Young people are impressed with great leaders. The lives of Lincoln, Washington, and Benjamin Franklin, for example, have provided the inspiration for others to achieve high moral goals. This approach can be effective if there is reading and dramatization of important moments

*Grinnell, John E.: Character building in youth, Phi Delta Kappan **40**:212, Feb., 1959.

of decision that are recaptured from the lives of great people. Such experiences will have an impact upon the conduct of young people. There are many men and women in the history of sport and physical education whose moral conduct and social dedication offer shining examples of the worth of good social conduct and strong character. Branch Rickey, with his belief in and respect for the worth of each individual and the many trying situations he experienced in attempting to achieve what he knew to be right, will always be a cherished part of American sports history and bring inspiration and behavior changes to many boys and girls.

3. **Teacher's example.** The teacher leaves an imprint upon his or her students, whether it is through his or her sense of fairness, ability to be a regular person, generosity, or unfailing belief in the truth. Many American presidents have pointed to a teacher as having helped mold their lives. The coach and physical education teacher, because of their close relationship to their pupils, play a unique role in helping to mold good behavior and strong character. Through their examples, much good can be done to realize this objective.

4. **Learning to do by doing.** Grinnell points out that the most effective approach is to influence boys and girls in their moral behavior while they are participating in their school activities. They should be shown what is right and what is wrong and what is just and unjust. Many teachable moments occur each day in student government activities, sports, and physical education classes in which elements of character can be strengthened. Whether or not proper moral outcomes accrue will depend largely upon the teacher. Constant supervision, high standards of conduct, strong moral values, and ethical principles will help to make this phase of the educational process a successful venture.

## SOME SOCIOLOGICAL IMPLICATIONS OF ATHLETICS

Since athletics play such an important role in the American culture and in physical education programs, it is interesting to examine some of the sociological implications of sports.

### Influence of American society on interscholastic athletics

Contemporary America likes athletic competition. This has been evident at the professional level, the college level, the senior high school level, and in recent years at the junior high school level. Sports have become a part of the American culture. The interest and popularity of athletics have affected educational programs of schools and colleges.

1. **The place of sports in education has been largely determined by society rather than by educators.** Whether or not a sport is popular in schools and colleges depends to a great extent upon the amount of public interest, spectator approval, and newspaper space it generates. This phenomenon has determined in large measure what the "major" and "minor" sports are today. Basketball, track, football, and baseball have rated higher with the American public than other activities. Samuel M. Cooper,* in a doctoral dissertation at Western Reserve University, indicated that these activities were among the most prominent. This evidence was substantiated further by the National Education Association of the U. S. Department of Secondary School Principals† in a survey of the interscholastic programs in separately organized junior high schools.

It would appear that what the public supports, educators tend to adopt. Young people grow in this type of environment and many times are interested in a sport because society has accented its importance, rather than because of the contributions the sport makes to them as individuals.

2. **Athletics many times have become a medium of entertainment rather than serving to fulfill educational objectives.** The popularity of sports in America is frequently related to their value as entertainment rather than their value as education. Thomas Woody, former Professor of Education at the University of Pennsylvania, made direct reference to this development when he stated, "scholastic contests, despite their best efforts to the contrary, are often spectacles to entertain idle multitudes, rather than to serve educational ends."* Americans thrill to the struggle, competition, and game color that accompanies such spectacles. People love competition and are willing to pay to see it. Once the program becomes popular, the school in all too many cases begins to conform to the wishes of the community. The spectators and the entire community want to see a show and at times the educators either try to please or feel obligated to please.

3. **Community interest in athletics often distorts the program of educational athletics.** In a report on educating children in grades seven and eight, the U. S. Department of Health, Education, and Welfare published an article by Gertrude M. Lewis† on the social and emotional behavior of children at this age. It was reported that society places demands upon

---

*Cooper, Samuel M.: The control of interscholastic athletics, Doctor of Education Dissertation, 1955, Western Reserve University, p. 46.

†National Education Association of Secondary School Principals: A survey of interscholastic junior high athletic programs, Nov., 1958, pp. 2–3.

*Woody, Thomas: School athletics and social good, Journal of Educational Sociology 28:246, Feb., 1955.

†Lewis, Gertrude M.: Educating children in grades seven and eight, U.S. Department of Health, Education, and Welfare Bulletin, 1954, p. 12.

children at a very early age. What is demanded, the article pointed out, varies somewhat from one home, one community, or one social economic group to another, but it is considered important that children learn to think and act in the way that most people who live within the community think and act. In regard to junior high athletics, some school administrators and physical education teachers raised a question as to the advisability of interscholastic athletics at the seventh and eighth grade level, but they refrained from protest since they believed the community, other schools in the region, and the children themselves seem to expect to take part in competitive athletics. The research tended to indicate that the community is indeed a strong motivating force in the shaping of interscholastic athletics.

The interest of the community and the emotional quality and demands of the community in athletics at the high school level were further indicated in a study by Richard Calish* as a master's thesis at the University of Maryland. The purpose of the study was to determine what the problems are among spectators, who cause these problems, in what sports do the problems exist, at what level of the school population do the problems prevail, and in what areas do the problems exist. The results showed that the community, and not the school, was the group from which stemmed the poor behavior among spectators. Thus the community not only assists to shape the program, but to influence how it is conducted during the actual game situation.

4. **Parental interest in schools may increase as a result of athletics.** Athletics may result in an increased interest by the parents in the schools. Mothers and fathers through their interest in sports, may become interested in the schools. They may visit the schools, find out about the educational program, and at times attempt to contribute to educational advancement. As a result, better communication may occur between the school and the community.

Many parents desire their children to participate in a successful athletic program. What parents consider a successful program and what educators consider a successful athletic program may be diametrically opposed. Since athletics often place reflected glory upon the parents and relatives of the youngsters, parents frequently want their children to participate and to win.

In a study of the attitudes of parents, teachers, and administrators concerning athletics in grades four through six, conducted by Phebe Martha Scott* of Bradley University, it was found that parents were most favorable as a group to interscholastic competition. The McCue attitude scale was used and distributed to superintendents in cities of 10,000 or more in the Central District of the American Association of Health, Physical Education, and Recreation. They were sent fifty scales to be distributed to parents, teachers, and school officials. This survey found that 78% of the parents were favorable and 22% were unfavorable to athletics in grades four through six. In comparison, administrators were least favorable with 55% in favor and 45% not in favor of interscholastic competition. The wide range of scores indicated a wide difference of opinion, particularly among teachers and administrators. Parents as a group were more in agreement. Parents sometimes feel that school athletics can improve the social status of their children.

*Calish, Richard: Spectator problems in secondary school athletics, Research Quarterly 25:261–268, Oct., 1954.

*Scott, Phebe Martha: Attitudes toward athletic competition in elementary schools, Research Quarterly 24:352–359, Oct., 1953.

Youth at times can increase their social status through athletic achievement more so than the student of high intellectual ability.

5. **Pressures on girls' athletics are not as severe.** Society has maintained that athletic competition for boys is more important than competition for girls; consequently, the community pressures of an athletic program for girls do not exist to the same degree as those pressures so evident on the boys' programs. Girls are exposed to fewer competitive situations than boys, due primarily to the attitude of society. Eleanor Metheny, Professor of Education and Physical Education at the University of Southern California,* published an article concerning the effect of the cultural mores rather than physical considerations upon participation in athletics for girls. She tells of how the women in Russia put the shot and hurl the javelin with a great degree of skill and no evidence of physical damage. "Since there seems to be no differences in physical structure between Europe and American women, the differences must stem solely from the different concepts of roles appropriate for women in the countries in which they live." She states further that "the resolution of any specific issue relating to girls and athletics is inextricably bound up in these unresolved larger social issues."

Although the pressures are not as great on the girls' programs, this does not mean that they are totally unaffected by the stress placed upon competition for boys. Facilities, leadership, and financial priority for athletics have frequently resulted in a limited program for girls' physical education which places a strain on the class program and the intramural and extramural program. The Educational Policies Commission in *School Athletics*\* lists as one of the weaknesses of an interscholastic program the negligence of the girls' programs.

6. **The need: Proper educational perspective.** Research reveals a need for greater understanding concerning the role of athletics in the school program. Educators, as well as the entire community, need to reevaluate the relation of society to education as it concerns athletics. The manner in which this phase of the school program can best meet the needs of youth should be considered at each educational level.

## Beneficial impact athletics can have upon the student

1. **Good sportsmanship.** Competitive athletics, according to some educators and leaders in the field of sports, can teach the art of winning and losing gracefully, the spirit of being fair to others, observance of the spirit as well as the letter of the rules, and the maintenance of a friendly attitude toward all individuals involved in the game situation.

Walter E. Damon† states that competition contributes to team spirit, motivation, and meets the interests of the boys. A boy has the chance to be more than an individual. He can become a part of something. Damon feels that the strain of tough competition, together with the push to win, is not detrimental, but is actually good for all boys and for delinquent or potentially delinquent boys.

2. **Cooperation.** Competitive athletics, some educators feel, provide a social laboratory for the student to learn how to work with others in a cooperative man-

---

\*Metheny, Eleanor: Relative values in athletics for girls, The Journal of Educational Sociology 28:268-269, Feb., 1955.

\*Educational Policies Commission: School athletics, Washington, D. C., 1954, National Educational Association.

†Damon, Walter E.: Competitive athletics helps delinquent boys, Journal of Health, Physical Education, and Recreation 29:14, Jan., 1958.

ner, to contribute toward the common purposes of the group, to promote a feeling of social consciousness, and to develop an understanding of the rights and feelings of others. Athletics, they further maintain, may help to further a sense of responsibility for one's own actions and for the entire group. The boys learn to conform to acceptable behavior standards.

James B. Nolan, Deputy Commissioner of the Police Department in the City of New York, reported that play becomes a way of learning about life—that respect for the rights of others is impressed upon the child through the rules that he is expected to obey and expects his playmates to obey in turn—that he must get along with his own side and guard the rights of the other side, learn about the importance of individual merit, gain a knowledge of fair play and a knowledge of social behavior, the "shall" and the "shall not"—that, in short, there is no better arena for democracy.

3. **Acceptance of all persons regardless of race, creed, or origin.** Competitive athletics may teach the appreciation and acceptance of all persons in terms of their ability, performance, and worth, according to some educators. Individual attitudes are applauded for their achievements regardless of background and team affiliation. Opportunities are afforded for every person, regardless of economic or social class, to achieve and to be recognized.

In a study by L. W. McCraw,* of the University of Texas, an investigation was made to determine the relationship between sociometric status and general athletic ability among junior high school boys. The conclusions of this study, on

the basis of a statistical analysis of data obtained, revealed that the relationship between sociometric status and athletic ability seemed to be moderately high in almost all of the groups studied. Of the factors included in this study, athletic ability as measured by the athletic index, and participation in interscholastic activities and/or intramural athletics, were probably the predominant factors in conditioning choices of the "best liked."

4. **Traits of good citizenship.** It is believed by some educators that competitive athletics help in developing those traits of good citizenship essential to democratic living. These include such qualities as initiative, trustworthiness, dependability, social consciousness, loyalty, and respect for the individual. Jordan L. Larson,* former president of the American Association of School Administrators, discussed the contributions of athletics to good citizenship. He points out that the ideals of fair play, sportsmanship, and clean living are all a part of athletics and are attributes capable of being carried on into adult life. In describing his team in a small school in Iowa many years ago, Mr. Larson states that a great respect was gained for their metropolitan neighbors, and that their city neighbors in return began to understand better the boys from the country. From his observations as a coach, athletic official, and school administrator, it was his contention that athletics tended to foster respect for the work of the individual regardless of race, creed, or economic background, and that good citizenship qualities could definitely result from competitive play.

5. **Leadership.** Competitive athletics, according to some educators, contribute to qualities of leadership. A study, indicated in an article by Creighton J.

*McCraw, L. W., and Tolbert, J. W.: Sociometric status and athletic ability of junior high school boys, Research Quarterly 24:72–80, March, 1953.

*Larson, Jordan L.: Athletics and good citizenship, Journal of Educational Sociology 28:258–259, Feb., 1955.

Hale,* was made by Jeanne Doyl Lareau of the University of California. It was reported that girls in grades eight and nine were given the UC Interest Inventory tests to determine the relationship between athletic competition and personal and social adjustment. The results revealed that girls with experience in athletic competition showed better personal and social adjustment, were more popular, and exhibited higher leadership qualities. Thus, it may be that through athletics, opportunities are provided for accepting responsibility, making decisions, influencing others, and developing other qualities important to leadership. As a result, the student may achieve prestige and status in the school and community and this, in turn, may make him a still greater force socially. He may be admired, approved, and appreciated, all of which may further open the door of possibilities for additional leadership, perhaps in other areas as well as in the field of sports.

6. **Followership.** Studies by Lareau† and Salz‡ tend to indicate that competitive athletics develop traits of a successful followership, including such qualities as respect for authority and outstanding leadership, abiding by the rules, cooperation with those in command, a recognition of the rights of others, and a sense of fairness. The student may also learn to take criticism without a feeling of hostility or resentment.

7. **Additional avenues for social acquaintances.** Competitive athletics, according to some educators, paves the way to new acquaintances since the athlete appears to be more socially mobile and extroverted than the nonathlete. He has broadened interests, belongs to more organizations, and has many opportunities to meet students from other schools. Some physical educators have stated that interscholastic athletics broadens the social horizon of the child. A wider knowledge of the community may result from the child's contact with children from other schools and neighborhoods.

8. **Social poise and understanding of self.** Competitive athletics contribute to social poise, self-composure, and confidence, according to some educators. This social competence may help him to better make adjustments in new situations. Lowell Biddulph,* in a study concerning high school boys, attempted to determine the personal and social adjustment of those boys with high athletic achievement. The results indicated that the superior athlete at the high school level had a higher mean self-adjustment score on the California Test of Personality than other boys. The superior athletes had a significantly higher mean score on teachers' ratings and sociograms. The athlete also rated considerably higher on the adjustment items as rated by their teachers. The superior athletic group listed more personal friends and were chosen more frequently by others. It was concluded as a result of this study that students ranking high on athletic achievement tests demonstrate significantly a greater degree of personal and social adjustment than those of low athletic achievement.

The athlete may learn to appreciate

---

*Hale, Creighton J.: What research says about athletics for pre-high school age children, Journal of Health, Physical Education, and Recreation 30:19, Dec., 1959.

†Lareau, Jeanne Doyl: The relationship between athletic competition and personal and social adjustment on junior high school girls, unpublished master's dissertation, University of California, 1950.

‡Salz, Art: Comparative study of personalities of little league champions, other players in little league, and non-playing peers, unpublished master's thesis, Pennsylvania State University, 1957.

---

*Biddulph, Lowell G.: Athletic achievement and the personal and social adjustment of high school boys, Research Quarterly 25:1–7, March, 1954.

the uniqueness of each person and more about himself. He is in a position to develop responsibility for his own actions and to acquire a willingness to accept the results of his actions.

9. **Social consciousness with an accompanying sense of values.** According to some physical educators, the athlete develops a concern for his fellow teammates and opponents. He takes increased interest in his school and community. He learns firsthand the importance of sharing with others, adhering to the rules, and the importance of promoting a way of life which fosters morality, ethical behavior, and the concern for individual dignity and worth. He becomes familiar with values concerning what is right and what is wrong, and an adherence to democratic principles and a respect for others is developed.

10. **Better relations with the opposite sex.** Competitive athletics, it is felt, contribute to a masculine image and, consequently, added appeal to the opposite sex. Also, certain physical urges develop at this stage of growth and development. The child begins to develop an interest in members of the opposite sex. Athletics can help in channeling this urge into the proper perspective without creating sudden social and emotional malajustments. Athletic participation serves as a healthy outlet through which this problem, induced by the onset of sexual maturation, can be channeled in a healthy direction.

## Harmful impact competitive athletics may have upon the student

1. **Ego-centered athletes.** There is a great glorification of the star athlete by both the school and the community. These few select youngsters are frequently singled out from the team to receive special publicity and attention. There is a concentration on the few superior players instead of the many. An overemphasis on publicity often results. Consequently, these youngsters may develop inflated ideas about themselves. They begin to assume that they are "special" and should receive extra favors because of their reputations. This desire to be the center of attraction, some educators feel, can very likely grow as they get older and thus continue into adulthood. Samuel Cooper* refers to this glorification of the athlete and indicates that the student is likely to develop false values which he will perpetuate to society.

2. **False values.** False values may very likely be developed because of the emphasis placed upon the star athlete or even athletics in general. The team practice session or the actual game may become more important to the youngster than any other out-of-class activity; the youngster may begin to acquire the attitude that he is destined to become an "all-American," and therefore must give his full time to this endeavor. And, as the community becomes more interested in the program, the youngster may become more concerned that the spectator be pleased than he is concerned about his own needs.

3. **Harmful pressures.** When parents and members of the community develop the kind of interest in interscholastic sports that has as its main objective "winning," pressures are very likely to result which affect the players. A boy may feel the need to win in order to please his public and gain acceptance. Thus, a constant overstimulation of the student progresses as he strives to reach adult goals.

In a study by Elvera Skubic,† of the University of California, concerning little

---

*Cooper, Samuel: The control of interscholastic athletics, unpublished Doctor of Education dissertation, Western Reserve University, 1955, p. 46.

†Skubic, Elvera: Studies of little league and middle league baseball, unpublished thesis, University of California, 1953.

league and middle league baseball, reference was made to the pressures placed upon youngsters in competition. The purpose of this study was to obtain the attitudes of players and their parents toward little league and middle league baseball and elicit suggestions for the improvement of the program. At the close of the season, questionnaires were sent to parents, players, and teachers. Possibly because of the pressures on the players, one third of the parents responding reported that their sons were too excited after winning or too depressed after losing to eat a normal-sized meal. Also, this excitement, in some cases, interfered with their ability to get to sleep. Of the players responding, about one third reported that they began to be excited from one half hour to over five hours before the start of the game; about two thirds of the boys reported that they did not begin to get excited until shortly before the beginning of the game.

The Joint Committee on Athletic Competition for Children of Elementary and Junior High School Age* made direct reference to the harmful effects of the pressures upon young athletes. In their study, they strongly oppose interscholastics of a "varsity pattern or similarly organized competition under the auspices of other community agencies." This type of competition is "definitely disapproved for children below the ninth grade." The committee listed the type of pressures which they considered to be a direct violation of the above principle. The following involve high-pressure elements of which the committee disapproves:

1. High-pressure practices such as highly organized competition in the form of

*Joint Committee on Athletic Competition for Children of Elementary and Junior High School Age: Desirable athletic competition for children, Washington, D. C., 1952, American Association for Health, Physical Education, and Recreation, pp. 4, 13–24.

leagues, publicity, and stress placed upon the individual rather than on the team
2. Tournaments and long seasons
3. Night games
4. Travel beyond the immediate community
5. Partisan spectators
6. "Grooming" of players for the high school
7. Commercial promotions
8. Disproportionate share of facilities and time and attention of staff

4. **Inequitable use of facilities, leadership, and money.** Athletics are only one phase of the total physical education program. Yet the amount of facilities, the number of personnel, and the proportion of money to be spent are often distributed in an unequitable proportion to the interscholastic program. The girls' program, for example, has been known to suffer and be neglected.

5. **Distortion of the educational program leading to overspecialization.** At times, so great an emphasis is placed upon producing successful athletic teams that the entire educational program may suffer. The academic achievement of both the participants and the nonparticipants may begin to diminish as student interests are captured by the constant excitement and tension of their team and their heroes. The young competitive player may become one-sided in his own interests, with athletics becoming all too large and important in his thinking and purposes. This problem is of concern, especially during the junior high school years. In a bulletin published by the U. S. Department of Health, Education, and Welfare,* the preadolescent is described as having endless interests. He wants to become strong and skillful and to excel in group and team games. But he also wants to explore the many different areas in which his interest falls. This should be an exploratory period for the

*Lewis, Gertrude M.: Educating children in grades seven and eight, U. S. Department of Health, Education, and Welfare Bulletin No. 10, 1954, pp. 4–7.

eighth and ninth grader. Yet athletics may result in an overconcentration in one small area. Referring to the study made by Skubic* it was found that youngsters spent a disproportionate amount of time playing and practicing baseball; most of the players responding stated that one half to most of their leisure time during the whole year was spent on baseball.

6. **Leadership.** Untrained coaches and leaders frequently do not understand the needs of junior high school students. Some seem to feel that they are judged by their contribution to the win–loss record rather than their contribution to the growth and development of the children. The game rather than the child begins to become the center of importance. The coach's concern for the team and the team's record sometimes overshadows the importance of the physical education class or the intramural program.

## Conditions under which athletics become valuable sociologically to students

1. **All students—the focus of attention.** There must be equal opportunity for all students to participate in the competitive athletic program, with activities included that are individually adapted to the student. Athletics can be valuable when all students are given the opportunity to learn, to practice, and to play, and when playing facilities and the coach's time are allocated among all students.

In the study by Biddulph† concerning the relation between personal and social adjustment of high school boys of high athletic achievement and the personal and

social adjustment of high school boys of low athletic achievement, his results led him to conclude that athletics should be provided for all boys and not the special few. Since students ranking high in athletic achievement demonstrated significantly a greater degree of personal and social adjustment than those boys with low athletic achievement, Biddulph concluded that it is important for all boys to develop motor ability, with a greater emphasis upon intramural athletic activities rather than upon interscholastic activities which tend to neglect the majority of boys.

2. **Focus on the individual student.** Athletics must be molded and shaped for the student—not the student for athletics. In a study by Katherine Montgomery,* a plan was proposed to determine those principles and procedures in the conduct of competitive athletics for adolescent girls which had been approved by national organizations. Eleven national groups cooperated in this study. Each group recommended individuals qualified by experience and by professional position to serve on a jury of thirty-three to determine the principles. Eighteen states and the District of Columbia were included. It was recommended, as a result of this study, that for athletic competition to be valuable for girls, it should take the form of sports days where no tournaments are played and a few friendly games with neighboring cities make up the schedule of events. To protect the student from pressures, "championships, athletic records, activities of excessive endurance, strength or speed, travel exceeding two hours, gate receipts, publicity featuring the individual, undue emotional stimulation of players, or any practice not re-

---

*Skubic, Elvera: Studies of little league and middle league baseball, unpublished thesis, University of California, 1953.

†Biddulph, Lowell G.: Atheltic achievement and the personal and social adjustment of high school boys, Research Quarterly 25:1–7, March, 1954.

---

*Montgomery, Katherine W.: Principles and procedures in the conduct of interscholastic athletics for adolescent girls, Research Quarterly 23:60–67, March, 1952.

sulting in the welfare of the participants was banned."

In the report by the Joint Committee on Athletic Competition,* the following conditions were revealed as necessary for beneficial effects pertaining to the individual student through participation in competitive athletics: Instruction must be fitted to meet the needs of the players; sports should be included that are appropriate for the age, maturity, skill, stage of growth, and physical makeup of the players; safeguards should be provided for the health and well-being of the participants; the program should be free of undesirable publicity and promotion; and opportunities should be given for a balance of interest and activities on the part of all participants.

3. **Outgrowth of intramurals and extramurals.** The athletic program should represent a natural outgrowth of the intramural and extramural program. The class instructional program and the intramural and extramural programs should be functioning effectively for all students before interschool athletics are considered. Strong physical education classes and intramural programs should form the base of athletic competition in the schools—a base that builds and is finally capped with more highly organized, competitive games of the interscholastic type.

4. **Leadership.** Sound and qualified leadership is essential to the properly functioning athletic program. Elizabeth K. Skinner† states, "if an activity possesses both desirable and undesirable possibilities, then the problem of leadership

becomes of great importance." Leadership plays an important role in setting qualities of fairness, self-control, and honesty. Good coaching, then, together with adequate supervision must serve to prevent undesirable practices and eliminate pressures. Leaders must see that the program is always conducted in regard to the best interests of the students.

## Implications for the physical education program

The impact that society has had upon athletics in education presents a challenge to educators to: (a) properly interpret to the community the role of athletics in education, and (b) to prevent undesirable pressures and practices that are not educationally sound. When conducted in accordance with desirable standards such as those of leadership and program content, athletics have the potential for accomplishing beneficial effects. However, when not conducted in accordance with desirable standards, athletics can be detrimental and harmful to the student.

## A SOCIOLOGY OF SPORT

Sport has become a very important part of the American culture, as well as of other cultures throughout the world. It captures newspaper headlines, usurps television screens, produces billions of dollars a year for entrepreneurs, is a consideration in international affairs, and has social, political, legal, and educational overtones.

As a medium that permeates nearly every important aspect of life, sport has led some physical educators to believe that it should receive intensive study, particularly as it affects the behavior of human beings and institutions as they form the total social and cultural complex of society. They support their premise by pointing out that, according to some anthropologists and psychologists, games affect social processes and human values. However, these advocates hasten to add

*Joint Committee on Athletic Competition for Children of Elementary and Junior High School Age: Desirable athletic competition for children, Washington, D. C., 1952, American Association for Health, Physical Education, and Recreation, pp. 4, 13–24.

†Skinner, Elizabeth K.: The role of the school in competitive sports for girls, unpublished Doctor of Education dissertation, Teachers College, Columbia University, 1951, p. 107.

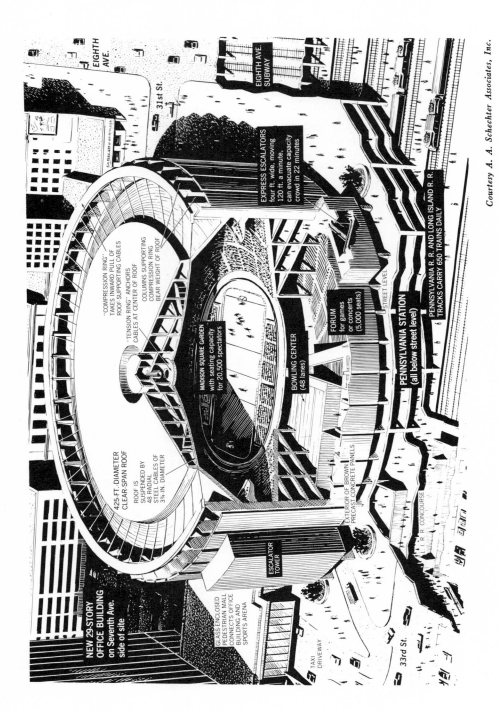

EIGHTH AVE.

31st St.

EIGHTH AVE. SUBWAY

EXPRESS ESCALATORS four ft. wide, moving 120 ft. a minute, can evacuate capacity crowd in 22 minutes

"COMPRESSION RING" TAKES INWARD PULL OF ROOF SUPPORTING CABLES

COLUMNS SUPPORTING COMPRESSION RING BEAR WEIGHT OF ROOF

"TENSION RING" ANCHORS CABLES AT CENTER OF ROOF

MADISON SQUARE GARDEN with seating capacity for 20,500 spectators

425-FT.-DIAMETER CLEAR-SPAN ROOF

ROOF IS SUSPENDED BY 48 RADIAL STEEL CABLES OF 3¾ IN. DIAMETER

BOWLING CENTER (48 lanes)

FORUM for games or concerts (5,000 seats)

STREET LEVEL

PENNSYLVANIA STATION (all below street level)

PENNSYLVANIA R. R. AND LONG ISLAND R. R. TRACKS CARRY 650 TRAINS DAILY

R. R. CONCOURSE

EXTERIOR OF BROWN PRECAST CONCRETE PANELS

ESCALATOR TOWER

NEW 29-STORY OFFICE BUILDING on Seventh Ave. side of site

GLASS ENCLOSED PEDESTRIAN MALL CONNECTS OFFICE BUILDING AND SPORTS ARENA

TAXI DRIVEWAY

33rd St.

*Courtesy A. A. Schechter Associates, Inc.*

Cutaway drawing of new Madison Square Garden Sports Entertainment Center, New York City.

Photograph of model of the new Madison Square Garden Center, New York City.

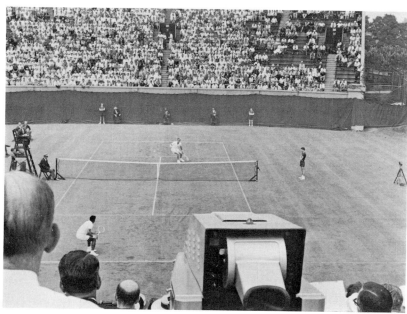

A tennis match at Forest Hills, N. Y.

Professional golf.

that sport sociology should be value-free in that such a science would not be used to influence society or individual behavior for or against sport. Instead, the sport sociologist would look at sport in society in an objective manner and report what he finds.

The advocates of a sociology of sport feel that sport sociologists should have a background of psychology, sociology, anthropology, and other behavioral and social sciences. Another requirement would be a consideration for a background in mathematics and statistics, in order to be able to understand the data analysis and other information that forms a background for such a science.

## YOUTH PROBLEMS IN SPACE AGE

Adolescent problems are a major concern of parents, schools, churches, other social agencies, and police departments in every section of our country. Physical educators should also be very much con-

cerned. These problems are reflected in part by much of the antisocial behavior that has captured the headlines in the nation's press during the last few years.

On a national scale, J. Edgar Hoover, Director of the Federal Bureau of Investigation, has reported that crime is on the increase and that youth is involved in much of this crime and if this crime rate continues for approximately three decades, "youth will commit 7.4 million automobile thefts, 15.8 million burglaries, 2 million robberies, 3 million aggravated assaults, and 200,000 murders."

The country is also concerned with such things as the use of drugs and narcotics, the increase in the number of unwed mothers, and the poor physical condition of youth. Over 170,000 illegitimate births were reported in a recent year to mothers ages 15 to 24, and 50% of the buyers of 9 billion "pep pills" and "goof balls" manufactured annually are teenagers. Many educators feel that these adolescent problems stem from such basic

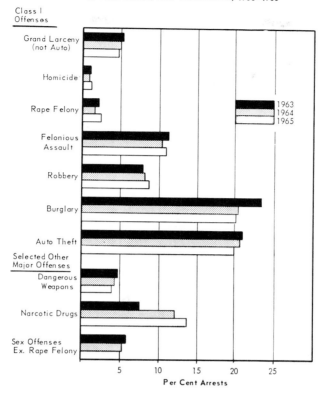

ARRESTS FOR MAJOR CRIMES, CLASS I AND
SELECTED OTHER MAJOR OFFENSES,
AGES 16 THROUGH 20, NEW YORK STATE, 1963-1965*

Class I
Offenses

Grand Larceny
(not Auto)

Homicide

Rape Felony
    1963
    1964
    1965

Felonious
Assault

Robbery

Burglary

Auto Theft

Selected Other
Major Offenses

Dangerous
Weapons

Narcotic Drugs

Sex Offenses
Ex. Rape Felony

        5    10    15    20    25
            Per Cent Arrests

*Jan. 1 through Sept. 30, 1965

*Youth Service News 17:5, Spring, 1966,*
*New York State Division for Youth, Albany, N. Y.*

psychological needs as the necessity for achieving status, gaining economic independence, and being wanted. In order to solve these problems, young people and adults must understand themselves more fully and the culture of which they are a part.

Adolescent problems represent a challenge to every citizen in America. Every community, school, agency, home, or any other organization that has anything to do with young people has been blamed for some of the disorder that exists. These individuals and agencies may be partially at fault, but at the same time it seems that such behavior is also part and parcel

of the times through which we are passing. The day and age in which we are living has much to do with delinquency and other adolescent problems. We cannot expect to have warfare, killing, destruction, and horror running rampant in our society, as they have during the last twenty years, without leaving a very strong impression on the youngster. Today's adolescents have lived during the period of the cold war, which at times has been hot. During this age they have not lived in a vacuum—an ivory tower—protected from all the hate, death, and destruction that have drenched the world. Low morality, stress on material values, and ruthless

**Table 18-2.** *Percent distribution of arrests for major crimes, Class I and selected other major offenses, ages 16 through 20, New York State, 1963–1965\**

| | 1963 | | 1964 | | 1965a | |
|---|---|---|---|---|---|---|
| | Number arrests | Percent | Number arrests | Percent | Number arrests | Percent |
| **All major youth crimes** | 19,392 | 100 | 22,963 | 100 | 17,554 | 100 |
| Class I offenses | | | | | | |
| Homicide | 174 | .9 | 180 | .8 | 154 | .9 |
| Rape felony | 390 | 2.0 | 348 | 1.5 | 379 | 2.2 |
| Felonious assault | 2,146 | 11.1 | 2,382 | 10.4 | 1,915 | 10.9 |
| Robbery | 1,512 | 7.8 | 1,830 | 8.0 | 1,509 | 8.6 |
| Burglary | 4,321 | 22.3 | 4,646 | 20.2 | 3,517 | 20.0 |
| Grand larceny (except auto) | 990 | 5.1 | 1,129 | 4.9 | 836 | 4.8 |
| Auto theft | 4,081 | 21.0 | 4,771 | 20.8 | 3,510 | 20.0 |
| Manslaughter by negligence | 11 | .1 | 18 | .1 | 12 | .1 |
| **Selected other major offenses** | | | | | | |
| Dangerous weapons | 929 | 4.8 | 981 | 4.3 | 648 | 3.7 |
| Narcotic drugs | 1,456 | 7.5 | 2,811 | 12.2 | 2,406 | 13.7 |
| Sex offenses except rape felony | 1,148 | 5.9 | 1,261 | 5.5 | 900 | 5.1 |
| B.T., U.E., and jostling[b] | 627 | 3.2 | 737 | 3.2 | 404 | 2.3 |
| Forgery | 507 | 2.6 | 533 | 2.3 | 454 | 2.6 |

[a]January 1 to September 30, 1965.
[b]Burglary tools, unlawful entry, and jostling.
\*From New York State Division for Youth, Youth Service News **17:**5, Spring, 1966.

competition take their toll. Let's look at a few characteristics of the age in which our youngsters are living.

*It's an age of tension and uncertainty.* The world is divided into armed camps. In spite of meetings at the "summit," disarmament conferences, United Nations sessions, "atoms for peace," and other attempts at friendly relations, there still exists a fear in the minds of most Americans that world war always is a threat as long as power-seeking, hate-inspiring men hold the reins of government in some countries. Atomic-powered submarines and hydrogen bombs are realities with which we must live.

The adolescent is affected by all this talk and action. He can read the papers, listen to the radio, watch television, and hear adult conversation. These threats to civilization affect him. He knows he may be put into uniform at any time—and exposed to some of these scourges of mankind.

Parental tensions cut their niche in youth. These feelings penetrate the minds of young boys and girls and help to shape their thinking. Many times, instead of having a bright, happy, friendly outlook on life, because of these tensions and uncertainties they develop attitudes that are sordid, hateful, and revengeful.

*It's an age of low morality.* Serious crime is on the increase. More than $10 billion worth of liquor is consumed by the American people annually. There are approximately 70 million users of alcohol in the United States, and about 5 million of these drink to excess at one time or another. This is an age when even our conservative newspapers run pictures of girls in bikini bathing suits or V neck

# THE DEVELOPMENTAL TASKS OF THE BOY

**OUR BOYS and YOUTH**

| BASIC TASKS | EARLY CHILDHOOD 3-4-5 YEARS | MIDDLE CHILDHOOD 6-7-8 YEARS About Grades 1-2-3 | LATE CHILDHOOD 9-10-11 YEARS About Grades 4-5-6 | EARLY ADOLESCENCE 12-13-14 YEARS About Grades 7-8-9 | MIDDLE ADOLESCENCE 15-16-17 YEARS About Grades 10-11-12 |
|---|---|---|---|---|---|
| 1. Developing a self-image he can respect | Accepting himself as a separate, distinct individual of worth | Feeling accepted by the person (or persons) in his intimate world who exemplify the ideal way of acting to him | Feeling accepted and effective as a member of his own age and sex contemporaries | Feeling wanted by his contemporaries and feeling able to contribute to them | Feeling equal to becoming an adult |
| 2. Developing a pattern of affection | Having ability to show affection toward others | Having ability to share affection | Beginning to find joy in making others happy | Developing an acquaintance and at-homeness with girls—feeling worthy of love | Being able to attract the one he admires—to give and receive love |
| 3. Achieving independence and self management | Developing a sense of physical independence within a framework of dependence | Reaching toward independence | Responding to the group, yet feeling he can rely upon his home | Being eager and increasingly able to direct his own life | Achieving a working relationship with the family, permitting considerable freedom, yet retaining understanding and affection. |
| 4. Relating one's self to his social group | Enjoying play in the company of others | Enjoying play with a friend | Winning his way with a group | Winning and holding membership in an intimate group of his own age and sex | Achieving a close friendship with some others like himself |
| 5. Learning one's sex role | Becoming aware of sex differences and adjusting to cultural pattern of sex differences | Identifying with a masculine role | Accepting a masculine role in his group life | Understanding his body and developing positive attitudes toward sex life | Understanding sex as a creative force and achieving outlets consistent with his ideals |
| 6. Accepting one's body | Growing—continuing big muscle development and motor abilities | Developing finer muscle control and motor abilities | Being confident of his ability to grow up | Feeling confident that he is normal | Accepting his body with its strengths and weaknesses and feeling able to contribute to life with it. |
| 7. Accepting society's demand for competence | Developing elementary cultural patterns of physical care | Feeling successful in his efforts | Feeling useful to someone or something | Feeling of value to some group or cause | Accepting and meeting society's demand for competence |
| 8. Finding one's place in work | Developing initiative and language communication | Doing small tasks under his own power and direction | Increasing his acquaintance with the adult world | Increasing his experience with the world in which he lives | Having some identification of his place in the world's work and a positive attitude toward work |
| 9. Finding adventure and joy in living | Extending his acquaintance with his environment | Increasing his acquaintance with his environment | Daring to express his feeling for adventure | Finding joy in the active use of his body and mind | Being able to use leisure time creatively |
| 10. Developing a value system | Accepting controls from others—beginning of some self control from a developing conscience | Increasing his ability to take directions from others and direct himself from within. | Increasing his interest in fair play and justice | Becoming articulate about some philosophy of life | Being able and willing to apply religious values to his own life and situations |

## DEVELOPMENTAL TASKS EXPLAINED

As a boy grows, there are special problems that he must solve, and adjustments that he must make to the people and the world about him. The problems he must solve arise out of inner pressures based on his biological maturing. The adjustments he must make arise out of the expectancies of the culture and the peer group in which he lives. All must be met successfully if the boy is to progress satisfactorily with vigor and confidence to the next stage. Because these problems and these adjustments come in a definite pattern and at about the same stage of growth for all boys, they are called developmental tasks.

### TIMING IS IMPORTANT

A boy can meet these tasks based on body maturity only as the organ of the body matures. He meets the tasks based on cultural expectancies most easily when others like himself are working at the same things. To fail in the more crucial of these tasks when others are mastering them makes them more difficult and leaves him reluctant to move ahead in personal growth.

### FALLING BEHIND PRESENTS PROBLEMS

Some phase of the basic task seems to exist at each stage of growth. Each is a stepping stone toward more mature living. These developmental tasks are especially important in infancy, childhood, and adolescence—not only because some of them are related to organic development but because the degree of development needed seems so progressively laid out that each task is achievable. It is only when the personality development falls behind that the achievement load piles up into too large a task. When this occurs, the personality tries to move forward without adequate foundation and becomes weakened or its growth tends to stop behind an insurmountable task (unless assisted by outside help).

### ADULTS MUST HELP THE BOY

The boy is usually not aware of the exact nature of these tasks, for he cannot explain the feelings within himself, nor does he always understand the achievements which his culture is pressing upon him. That is why adults can be so helpful if they will, for they can provide encouragement and guidance as well as arrange opportunities which facilitate the accomplishing of these tasks at the opportune times.

*Moser, Clarence G.: Understanding boys, New York, 1953, Association Press.*

Members of one youth-serving agency solve the problem of insufficient funds by doing their own renovation.

dresses and exotic photographs of every description.

*It's an age when there are signs of family and home disintegration.* One out of every four marriages ends in a divorce court. And 300,000 children are involved in these divorces each year. One out of eight children is not living with both parents. There has been a 50% increase in births outside of marriage in the last decade.

Most studies on delinquency point to broken homes, divorce, and lack of cohesiveness around the hearthstone.

*It's an age of competition.* Businessmen are trying to outsmart their rivals. Competition to get into college is keen. Many times athletic teams are interested only in the loving cup, symbolic of supremacy.

*It's an age of materialism.* This is a day when young people are growing up with the idea that the mink coat, white-walled tire, and mansion on the hill constitute the main goals in life. Many young boys

and girls are growing up drenched in the cult of materialism. This country is in need of new techniques of living and new ideas that will make for happiness.

*It's an age of leisure.* In 1800 the average workweek for Americans was 84 hours; in 1900 it had dropped to 60 hours; in 1925 it was down to 50 hours, and in 1950 it consisted of only 40 hours. Experts predict that with the application of atomic energy to industry it will be reduced to 30 hours a week in the future.

We are living in an age when a tall skyscraper can be clothed with aluminum within one working day. We can board a plane in New York after breakfast and have lunch in Los Angeles. This is an era when, according to Dr. Hurd, consultant to the Atomic Energy Commission, a completely automatic factory is possible. Machines guided by magnetic tapes running through electronic directors are capable of making many selective motions.

Science is achieving great things for

*Youth Services Section, Los Angeles City Schools Facility:*
*Alondra Park Department of Parks and Recreation, Los Angeles, Calif.*

Swimming during leisure hours at Alondra Park, Los Angeles, Calif.

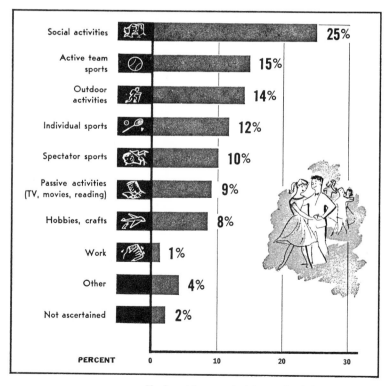

*Needs and interest of adolescent Boys' Clubs members—*
*a national survey of members aged 14 to 18,*
*New York, 1960, Boys' Clubs of America.*

Leisure-time activities most enjoyed by members of Boys' Clubs.

mankind by providing more and more leisure hours. But how are these leisure hours being spent? Children are watching television an average of thirteen hours a week—adults more. The President of the United States has been concerned over the trend of the youth of America to be spectators rather than participants. More money is spent on comic books than on all the books in elementary and secondary schools—more than four times the budget of all public libraries in the United States.

## PHYSICAL EDUCATION MUST HELP IN MEETING THE SOCIAL CHALLENGE OF THE TIMES

Tension, uncertainty, low morality, lack of family cohesiveness, competition, materialism, and increased leisure time are some of the characteristics of the times that must be examined very closely by everyone, especially by physical educators, if adolescent problems are to be solved. We must mobilize our resources to create a totally healthful environment. To solve youth problems it is important for us to know the adolescent during various stages of his development—physical, emotional, mental, and social. It is important to know the influences that are playing upon personality and total being. It is essential to understand clearly the implications of the makeup of the adolescent and these environmental forces. This knowledge is important for each of us in the schools— administrators, teachers, counselors, and physical educators. It is necessary to know the approaches that are most effective in building character. When we understand these things more completely, we will be better prepared to solve some of these adolescent problems.

Physical education can help by establishing a sound foundation of skill in every child. The skill-learning years are the school years. If an adequate program is set up on every educational level, chil-dren will grow into adults who may be helped in forgetting their worries, their fears, their competitors, their materialism, their jealousies, and their hates, at least for short periods of time, while participating in interesting activities.

Physical education can help by stressing in physical education high moral and spiritual standards—the rules of fair play, the golden rule, respect for the rights of others, and those precepts that have been established as basic and foundational to a democratic way of life. Physical educators can be symbols and examples to children and youth of what is the best moral conduct.

It has been pointed out that sociology is concerned with a study of people and their institutions and how a better social order may be established. Sociology depends upon education to help in developing happiness, tolerance, and good will in society. Education plays an important part in solving social problems. Its function is to improve society. Physical education, as part of the total educational process, can contribute to this goal. Physical education is a social experience. Through physical activities great strides can be made in achieving social progress and more satisfaction in living. Juvenile delinquency, race prejudice, intolerance, and discrimination perhaps can be alleviated, and progress can be made toward their elimination from our democratic society. Physical education can help to promote a happier and more cohesive and cooperative type of group living. Finally, physical education can help to promote a happier and a more peaceful world by instilling a spirit of fair play in every child, helping in the development of healthy and physically fit individuals, developing an understanding of the worthy use of leisure time, fostering social equality, furthering democratic procedures, promoting the belief in the dignity of man, and developing an appreciation of the simpler things, as against the collection of great possessions and material wealth.

## QUESTIONS AND EXERCISES

1. Define the term *sociology*. What implications does this field have for physical education?
2. What challenges are confronting educational sociology in modern-day living?
3. How does original nature differ from human nature? What are some of the characteristics of each?
4. Describe how man is interested, on the one hand, in other people and the welfare of mankind and, on the other, is interested in the life that revolves around himself and his personal ambitions. How can both of these interest categories be realized?
5. What are some of the forces that impel group living?
6. Contrast a hermit's life with your own. What are the advantages and disadvantages of each?
7. What do you feel are possible solutions to present world crises from the standpoint of sociology?
8. What are the essential foundations for successful group living?
9. What is social learning, and how does it relate to physical education?
10. Discuss in detail the seven theories of play. In your own thinking which theory is the most descriptive of your definition of play? Discuss.
11. Contrast Caillois' theories of play to the seven theories of play.
12. Discuss the place of sports in education from your own viewpoint.
13. To what extent should physical education activities be provided for the underprivileged youth who inhabit nearly every community in this country? What kind of program should be provided?
14. How can physical education contribute to mental health?
15. Why is it important for physical educators to adapt their program to the older population?

## SELECTED REFERENCES

American Association for Health, Physical Education, and Recreation: Developing democratic human relations through health education, physical education and recreation, Washington, D. C., 1951, The Association.

Bucher, Charles A.: The atomic age strikes youth, Education 76:203, Dec., 1955.

Bucher, Charles A., and Reade, Evelyn M.: Physical education in the modern elementary school, New York, 1964, The Macmillan Co.

Bucher, Charles A., Koening, Constance, and Barnhard, Milton: Methods and materials of secondary school physical education, St. Louis, 1965, The C. V. Mosby Co.

Bucher, Charles A.: Interscholastic athletics at the junior high school level, Albany, New York, 1965, The University of the State of New York, State Education Department.

Caillois, Roger: Man, play, and games, New York, 1961, The Free Press.

Educational Policies Commission: Moral and spiritual values in the public schools, Washington, D. C., 1951, National Education Association.

Harris, Elizabeth and Dale: Let's bring back children's play, The PTA Magazine 60:28, Sept., 1965.

Havighurst, Robert S., and Newgarten, Bernice L.: Society on education, Boston, 1957, Allyn & Bacon, Inc.

Kenyon, Gerald S., and Loy, John W.: Toward a sociology of sport, Journal of Health, Physical Education, and Recreation 36:24, May, 1965.

Morris, Van Cleve, and others: Becoming an educator, Boston, 1963, Houghton Mifflin Co.

National Council, Boy Scouts of America: A study of boys becoming adolescents, New York, 1960, Survey Research Center, Institute for Social Research. The University of Michigan and The Boy Scouts of America.

Oktavec, Frank L.: Physical education as a character builder, Journal of Health and Physical Education 5:12, June, 1934.

Oxendine, Joseph B.: Social development—the forgotten objective? Journal of Health, Physical Education, and Recreation 37:23, May, 1966.

Parker, Franklin: Sport, play, and physical education in cultural perspective, Journal of Health, Physical Education, and Recreation 36:29, April, 1965.

Peck, Robert F., and others: Psychology of character development, New York, 1960, John Wiley & Sons, Inc.

Wannamaker, Claudia: The meaning and significance of social adjustment, Journal of Health and Physical Education 10:12, Jan., 1939.

Wilton, W. M.: An early concensus on sportsmanship, The Physical Educator 20:113, Oct., 1963.

Wood, Thomas Denison, and Cassidy, Rosalind Frances: The new physical education, New York, 1931, The Macmillan Co.

The relay

*Works of R. Tait McKenzie,*
*Courtesy Joseph Brown,*
*School of Architecture, Princeton University.*

**PART SIX**

# Leadership in physical education

# Chapter 19

# Qualities of the teacher

Education as a career is attracting outstanding young people to its ranks. The challenge presented by such events and movements as the explosion of knowledge, the poverty program, the civil rights movement, and the developing nations emerging on the world scene has motivated many young men and women to seek educational careers so they can contribute to the solution of some of the problems that exist in America and throughout the world. Within the field of education, teaching is attracting the greatest number of our youth.

## THE TEACHING PROFESSION

The teaching profession has approximately two million men and women employed at the various educational levels. In the elementary and secondary schools combined, about one third of these teachers are men and two thirds are women. The average age of male teachers is 35 and of female teachers is 41. Contrary to what exists in many fields of endeavor, teachers as a group like their work, as evidenced in a survey conducted by the National Education Association which showed that three fourths of the teachers would choose teaching again if they were starting over in a career. Teachers indicated that the professional relationships

with their colleagues, the intellectual stimulation of their work, and the service they rendered to others were some of the factors that marked their enjoyment of teaching. Surveys show that teachers rank higher on social concerns than does the general population. They rank lower in respect to economic concerns, however. In cognitive abilities, as measured on intelligence tests, students going into teaching rank higher than the general population, but lower than those students going into many other professions.

Teaching is one of the favorite choices of a profession for high school and college students today. Surveys consistently show that teaching has great appeal for young people who are trying to decide on a career that holds challenge and satisfactions for the future.

### New developments affecting the teacher

There are many new trends that will affect the teacher of the future. Rising enrollments at all educational levels will affect the demand for teachers. The emphasis on poverty areas and individualized instruction will result in more teachers being assigned to slum areas. The trend toward urbanism will result in the recruitment of more teachers from the working classes. This, in turn, will result in greater sympathy of these teachers to union membership with resulting greater teacher militancy. The discovery of new knowledge will accelerate the development of new and better ways to keep abreast of this knowledge. It will also mean closer cooperation between institutions of higher learning and the schools. Furthermore, the increase in knowledge will mean greater specialization on the part of teachers and greater departmentalization at all educational levels. Research in all fields of endeavor will continue and be subsidized by federal and foundational grants. The characteristics of effective teachers will be more clearly discerned, with the result that candidates for study in teacher education programs will be more carefully screened. These trainees will find many technological devices, laboratories, and other conditions which will result in their becoming better teachers.

## Rewards of teaching

Teaching offers many rewards. Probably most important of all is that it offers an opportunity to help shape young peo-

*Flint, Michigan, School System.*

The rewards that accrue from teaching depend to a large degree upon the individual and what he makes of his opportunities.

ple's lives. Other rewards include the privilege of being a member of a profession that is growing in respect and importance in the world as well as in America. It offers an opportunity to mingle with some of the great thinkers and leaders of the academic community. It offers opportunities to travel and to better understand the world. It motivates self-improvement and intellectual growth. It provides increasingly better economic benefits in the form of salaries, retirement benefits, sick leaves, insurance, medical help, and sabbatical leaves. It provides security under the tenure laws that exist in most states.

The rewards that accrue from teaching depend to a large degree upon the individual and what he makes of his opportunities. The inner rewards, plus the financial and other benefits, can be great for the person that applies himself diligently and sincerely to assigned tasks.

### Guidelines for making the decision

Some guidelines that may help the college student or other person in deciding whether or not to become a member of the teaching profession include the following:

1. *An individual's interests and aptitudes should be carefully tested.* The person considering teaching should know that he likes to work with children and young people by actually seeking out experiences in a camp or other situation where he can put himself to the test. Also, there are many tests and other instruments that can be used to objectively analyze a person's aptitudes for teaching.

2. *The person should make the decision himself and not permit mother, father, neighbor, or close friend to make it for him.* The guidance and advice of others is important and valuable, but the final decision should be made by the individual himself on what is best for him.

3. *An analysis of personality is an important consideration.* How well a person can interact with young people, with colleagues on the job, and with the community and other groups of persons should be considered. Furthermore,

other aspects of personality such as mental and emotional health, physical health, and prejudices are important considerations.

4. *The decision should not be rushed.* A person should be sure that this is the type of work he wants, is best equipped to do, and is where he can make the greatest contribution to society. Such a decision may take time.

## QUALIFICATIONS FOR TEACHERS IN GENERAL

Many studies have been made of characteristics of a good teacher and the abilities most useful for a teaching career. Six personal traits are discussed by the Future Teachers of America based on the studies that have been conducted.*

1. *Do you like to be with people?* If you like group activities, belong to clubs, enjoy serving on committees, know all types of people and are sympathetic to their peculiarities, have a wide circle of friends, and are always seeking more, you probably meet this criterion essential to success in teaching.

2. *Are you a good scholar? Do you often lose yourself in a book?* Do you enjoy mastering a subject and read because you want to? Are you in the top one third of your class, and do you belong to honor societies? Do you recognize that you must learn before you can teach?

3. *Do you have a good sense of humor?* Can you laugh at yourself, not take yourself too seriously, apply a light approach to ease a tense situation, take a happy view of life, shake off the blues quickly, and see the funny side of a situation?

4. *Are you in good physical and mental health?* Since the hours of teaching are long and the work demanding, do you have plenty of pep, energy, and stamina, are you usually poised and emotionally well balanced, do you take criticism without becoming angry or depressed, and do you keep your voice pleasant and calm even when upset?

5. *Do you like to help others?* Do you have the urge to serve others; enjoy working with youngsters; volunteer to help out in church, schools, hospitals, or orphan homes; and offer your services to local charity drives?

6. *Are you often the leader in group activi-*

*Future Teachers of America: How's your T.Q.—a check-list to explore your aptitude for teaching, Washington, D. C., National Education Association.

ties? Since a good teacher must have leadership qualities, do you ever organize activities in your circle of friends, have you been elected to office in a club or class, and have you demonstrated leadership ability?

---

**A TEACHER'S CREDO**

*This I believe* *

That when we choose to teach, we choose to serve.

That every child is entitled to the best we have to give, regardless of his personality, his mentality, or his situation.

That our discipline should be firm, consistent, and constructive.

That we should remember that kindness and consideration and trust are not a sign of weakness in a teacher.

That children are hurt by the same things that hurt us—sarcasm and ridicule.

That we should not exact a higher standard of conduct in matters of punctuality, responsibility and self-control than we ourselves possess.

That we have limitless opportunities to touch lives for good.

That we should treat every child as if he were our very own.

---

One of the most impressive studies that has been conducted was the one accomplished by Cassel and Johns, of the Fontana Unified School District in California.† The procedure followed was first to analyze more than 1,000 teacher effectiveness reports completed by principals in the Fontana School District. From these

reports were listed critical characteristics of effective and ineffective teachers. In addition to extracting the critical characteristics, the "critical incident" technique was used to compile further critical characteristics of effective and ineffective teachers. More than 22,500 critical characteristics were compiled. Positive statement items were paired with negative items and those mentioned most frequently were recorded. They were then arranged into meaningful groupings pertinent to outstanding qualifications of teachers. The following list embodies many of these qualifications:

*Personal qualities*
  Integrity
  Cooperative
  Dynamic personality
  Enthusiasm for teaching
  Friendly with students and other members of staff
  Good mental and physical health
  Mature
  Sense of humor
  Positive in outlook
  Approachable
  Good intelligence
  Creative and imaginative
  Dependable and reliable
  Ethical in all his activities
  Strong sense of moral obligation to youth
*Professional preparation*
  Possesses a general education
  Well prepared in subject matter field
  Keeps well informed on new trends in education and in special fields
  Has special knowledge and competency in understanding of pupils and methodology at educational level where he teaches
  Has special knowledge of counseling
*Adapts teaching to pupils being taught*
  Makes every effort to know, understand, and appreciate characteristics and needs of adolescent pupils—knows what they are like, how they feel about themselves, their ideals, behavior patterns, and how they get along with others
  Helps students establish a sound standard of values
  Treats each student as a precious and unique personality
  Is sympathetic to all students and the problems they face

---

*By Mary Livingstone, Byram Hills Central Schools, Armonk, N. Y.

†Cassel, Russell N., and Johns, W. Lloyd: The critical characteristics of an effective teacher, Bulletin of the National Association of Secondary School Principals 44:119–124, Nov., 1960.

Helps students evaluate their growth and progress

Takes into consideration the mental, social–emotional, physical needs of students, regardless of his subject matter field

Makes learning activity meaningful to student at his stage of growth and development

Insists that what is good for the student is the main criterion for determining what and how a subject is taught

Provides many and varied experiences for students

*Professional stature*

Active in his profession

Active on school committees

Enjoys teaching

Interested in latest research findings

Participates in community activities

Works well with parents

Interprets professional work to community

Constantly seeks personal and professional improvement

*Leadership qualities*

Is respected by colleagues and students

Bestows credit on those who have done work

Teaches by example as well as by precept

Gets the most from his students and they enjoy doing it

Develops an atmosphere of understanding and mutual trust in his classes

Good organizer and planner

Makes sound decisions

Utilizes democratic processes

Interested in all facets of the educational program

*Human relations qualities*

Observes code of professional ethics at all times

Gets along well with students, administration, and colleagues

Modest in his accomplishments

Keeps educational discussion on professional and not personal basis

Is receptive to constructive criticism

Works for the good of the students

Another study consisted of interviewing several persons as to the qualities and characteristics they thought existed in the best teachers to whom they were exposed. A list of those qualities that were mentioned most frequently are as follows:

1. Teacher knew his subject matter well
2. Teacher took a personal interest in each student

3. Teacher was well respected and respected his students
4. Teacher stimulated his students to think
5. Teacher was interesting and made his subject matter come to life
6. Teacher was an original thinker and creative in his methods
7. Teacher was a fine speaker, presented a neat appearance, and was generally well groomed
8. Teacher had a good sense of humor
9. Teacher was fair and honest in his dealings with his students
10. Teacher was understanding and kind

Another study contrasted effective and ineffective teaching behavior. The information was collected from a survey of supervisors, professors in professional preparing institutions, school principals, student teachers, teachers, and students in education methods courses in professional preparing institutions. Some of the effective behaviors and ineffective behaviors cited were as follows*:

*Effective behaviors*
1. Alert and enthusiastic
2. Interested in pupils
3. Cheerful
4. Shows self-control
5. Sense of humor
6. Admits own mistakes
7. Fair and impartial
8. Patient
9. Sympathetic with pupils
10. Friendly and courteous
11. Helps pupils with personal problems
12. Offers praise for work well done
13. Encourages pupils to do best
14. Work is planned and well organized
15. Stimulates pupils with interesting material and methods
16. Gives clear directions
17. Discipline is quiet and dignified
18. Gives help willingly
19. Classroom procedure is flexible
20. Tries to foresee difficulties

*Ineffective behaviors*
1. Appears bored
2. Not interested in pupils
3. Appears unhappy

*Ryans, David G.: Characteristics of teachers, Washington, D. C., 1960, American Council on Education, Library of Congress.

4. Loses temper
5. Overly serious
6. Does not admit mistakes
7. Has favorites
8. Impatient
9. Uses sarcasm
10. Aloof
11. Appears unaware of personal problems of pupils
12. Is hypercritical
13. No encouragement given
14. Little planning and disorganized
15. Uninteresting materials and methods used
16. Directions are incomplete and vague
17. Ridicules and reprimands at length
18. Does not give help or gives it grudgingly
19. Does not depart from plans—rigid
20. Does not see potential difficulties

## NEA CODE OF ETHICS

The representative assembly of the National Education Association in July of 1963 adopted a Code of Ethics of the Education Profession. The board of directors of the American Association for Health, Physical Education, and Recreation formally endorsed the code in October, 1963.*

The code consists of four principles. *Principle One* outlines the commitment to the *student* and indicates the cooperative, helpful, and professional relationship that exists between the student and teacher. *Principle Two* outlines the commitment to the *community* and spells out the important role of educators in the development of educational programs and policies and their interpretation for the public. *Principle Three* outlines the commitment to the *profession* and indicates the need to raise educational standards, improve the service to people, and develop a worthwhile and respected profession. *Principle Four* outlines the commitment to *professional employment practices* and explains the importance of acting in accordance with high ideals of professional service

---

*Code of ethics of the education profession, Journal of Health, Physical Education, and Recreation 35:36, Feb., 1964.

that embody personal integrity, dignity, and mutual respect.

The code is designed to show the magnitude of the education profession and to judge ourselves and our colleagues in accordance with the provisions of this code.

## QUALIFICATIONS FOR TEACHERS OF PHYSICAL EDUCATION

A young person considering physical education as a career should carefully evaluate his or her qualifications for this field of work.

### Need for well-trained teachers in physical education

The physical education profession needs teachers who believe in such credos; possess the enthusiasm, culture, and other qualities listed in the employer's letter on page 596; and who know subject matter, possess skills, are articulate, and command the admiration and respect of their students, as described in the essay.

The problem of poor teachers is not foreign to the physical education profession. The great growth in the number of teacher education programs throughout the nation is raising a question as to the quality of preparation that is being provided. Carl Nordly, former president of the American Association for Health, Physical Education, and Recreation, pointed out that as of February 2, 1948, there were 390 institutions giving professional education in health education, physical education, and recreation—an increase of forty-eight institutions over the previous year. He then emphasized the fact that there was cause for alarm in that many of the prospective teachers being trained in these specialized areas were being poorly prepared for their future responsibilities. William Hughes pointed out that in 1947 more then 300 leaders in the fields of physical education, health education, and recreation listed the education of well-trained leaders as being the most crucial problem with which these professions were faced.

## AN ESSAY ON THE TEACHER THAT LEFT THE GREATEST IMPRESSION UPON ME*

The teacher that left the most lasting impression on me was a man. I shall never forget the experience of being in his class. After discussing this teacher with other members of my class I found that I was not alone in my opinion of his teaching ability. The few absentees from his classes was proof of this fact.

From the first meeting of the class I sensed that I was truly going to enjoy the course. The classroom atmosphere served as evidence that this man was truly an educator and not merely someone who taught in order to earn a living.

Class interest among the students was so high that you could find groups of students discussing this man, his methods, his ideas, and eagerly awaiting his arrival in the classroom. I can remember a particular incident in which he was twenty-five minutes late for a fifty minute class and no student made a move for the door. I can also remember cutting a class to stay after a lecture to continue a discussion of a topic that he had presented.

Thinking back I will try to relate the manner of teaching this man used and illustrate why I feel he was about the most profound educator I have ever met.

The first point I would like to present is this man's broad scope of knowledge, both in his own subject as well as others. I feel that anyone who is going to educate should have a broad scope of knowledge in his field to provide a background or foundation upon which to build. This man had just that. He was well read. He had not restricted himself in his learning but had, on the contrary, brought together and interrelated the different fields of knowledge that had influenced his own field.

This teacher did not present the material in a manner that would place the facts above the heads of those whom he was trying to contact and educate. He did not try to teach with an air of superiority but strove to present the facts on a level that could be understood by all and at the same time the profound meaning of the material was not in any way slighted.

He always maintained a good contact with the class and encouraged group participation in the lecture. He was in full control of the class and commanded the respect and attention of all. I admired him for his virtue of patience and his willingness to make a point understandable to all. He was always willing to offer his free time to any of his students. In the classroom he used the blackboard and other facilities available. He also made a great amount of reference material available to the students. One other important fact that I feel influenced me was the amazing coordination of his mind and his mouth. He had complete control of his speech and a vocabulary enriched by his background and experience that he could call upon in a split second. He was chosen many times by various clubs on campus because of his ability as a speaker and had the largest following of students on campus. The gift of speech and expression that he had, coupled together with his dynamic personality, is what I feel created this magnetism in him.

This man was truly a person who was sincere in his work. His presentation and vast knowledge offered proof of this fact. His willingness to share this knowledge and his ability to educate had a great influence upon me and many others I am sure, and that is why I chose this man as the educator that has influenced me the most.

By Robert V. Hoffman, Yonkers, N. Y., former graduate student at New York University.

The decade of the 1950's and the years in the 1960's have not solved this dilemma. Leadership is still one of the major problems of the profession.

The problem is not only that of preparing teachers in an adequate manner but also one of making sure that only the best students are allowed to become members of the teaching profession. There is little doubt that many young men and women

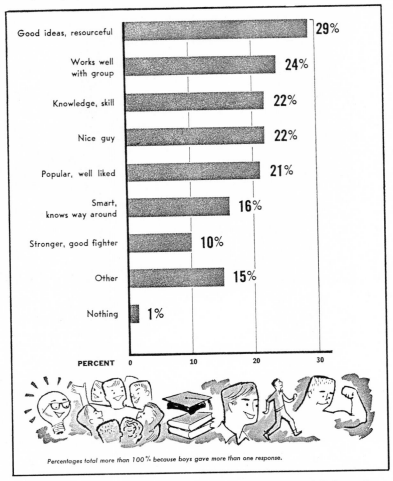

| | |
|---|---|
| Good ideas, resourceful | 29% |
| Works well with group | 24% |
| Knowledge, skill | 22% |
| Nice guy | 22% |
| Popular, well liked | 21% |
| Smart, knows way around | 16% |
| Stronger, good fighter | 10% |
| Other | 15% |
| Nothing | 1% |

PERCENT 0     10     20     30

Percentages total more than 100% because boys gave more than one response.

*Needs and interests of adolescent Boys' Clubs members—*
*a national survey of members aged 14 to 18,*
*New York, 1960, Boys' Clubs of America.*

Qualities that members of Boys' Clubs believed were needed for leadership.

who are capable of becoming superior teachers in our schools never consider the teaching profession as a possible vocation. At the same time, many individuals who are not adequately suited to this profession go through teacher-training institutions. A situation such as this must be changed if our educational system is to carry on its work successfully.

The need for good teachers is obvious. The history of teacher education clearly shows that great care should be exercised in the recruitment and selection of teachers and that the qualifications for potential teachers should be upgraded. It shows that teachers should possess good minds, a broad cultural education, a wholesome personality, and an interest in and understanding of children. Furthermore, it shows that teacher education institutions are responsible to society and not to the individual. It is not their responsibility to admit or graduate all who apply but, instead, to select only those who possess

*Richwoods Community High School, Peoria Heights, Ill.*

Physical educators should have an interest in and understanding of children and youth.

qualifications acceptable to the profession.

## Special qualifications for physical educators

The physical education profession requires special qualifications for those individuals who wish to be considered as candidates for entrance into this specialized field. Many individuals have entered this profession in the past on the basis of their athletic ability alone, without regard for such qualities as intelligence, scholarship, personality, and technical knowledge. Such a practice must end if the physical education profession is to have prestige in the educational world.

The teacher of physical education must possess qualities or traits beyond those normally demanded for the regular teacher in our schools. Such a person is entering a profession where a knowledge of child growth and development, physical skill, physical endurance, enthusiasm, human relations, and leadership are only a few of the essentials. Therefore there should be a careful and rigid selection of all can-

didates in order to ensure that the duties involved will be performed in a manner acceptable to the profession.

Some of the qualifications that have been mentioned and considered most important by leaders in the field are moral character, leadership, honesty, dependability, adaptability, engaging personality, freedom from organic and functional defects, superior motor capacity, motor skill, high native intelligence, high scholarship, superior social ability, interest in teaching as a profession, desire to help others, competency in oral and written English, and the ability to coordinate activities.

The qualification of scholarship is one that is stressed as being especially necessary for our profession. Steinhaus, a leader in the physical education field, made this statement years ago, but it is just as true today: "A major obstacle which confronts physical education today in its struggle to become a mighty profession is its shortage in true scholarship . . . primary reason for this is the fact that virtually our only route for recruiting students into our ranks is through the avenue of their interest in sport or some other physical activity."* If prospective candidates for the physical education profession have a high degree of scholarship along with the other important qualifications, the prestige and respect that physical educators will have in the schools, in the community, and among the professions will be greatly enhanced. Physical educators should be able to hold their ground with other educators or professional people, whether it is in a game of tennis, debating a political issue, or discussing Toynbee's *Study of History*. Scholarship is an essential to the progress of the physical education profession.

### Tests as a selective technique

Some leaders in physical education have stressed the necessity for giving a battery of tests to all prospective candidates and the use of such results as one means of determining who should be allowed to continue their preparation. Nash, a man who contributed much to physical education, cited as qualifications for physical educators: ability, efficiency, intelligence, and physical tests for determining an individual's native ability, rhythmic sense, intelligence, and a degree of physical health. Another leader would give tests to determine emotional stability, intelligence, personality, interests, fitness, motor ability, and academic aptitudes.

### Criteria for selection

The following are criteria that might be used as a basis for selecting candidates: personality, intelligence and special aptitudes, academic achievement, interest in teaching as a profession, competency in oral and written English, skills in physical education activities, and cooperation with individuals and groups.

Some years ago a committee recommended to the Second Conference of In-

*Steinhaus, Arthur H.: Journal of Health and Physical Education 10:141, March, 1939.

---

**LETTER DESCRIBING TYPE OF PHYSICAL EDUCATION TEACHER AN EMPLOYER DESIRES ON HIS STAFF**

Waterloo Public Schools
Waterloo, Iowa

Dear Sir:

Here are some traits that I look for in hiring a teacher of physical education:

I prefer a neat, cultured, enthusiastic person in excellent health with poise and emotional stability.

In checking educational qualifications, I particularly look for the ratings in health, scholarship, discipline and cooperation. It is important that the person is able to cooperate and get along with co-workers. Thus, the individual should be well-adjusted, possess the ability to think practically, and be able to adjust to new situations.

I am interested in a teacher who will be able to have good discipline and at the same time is interested in the welfare of his or her students. It is also important that this person be interested in growing on the job and able to take constructive criticism.

A person with creative ideas who has a wholesome influence on the students as well as his and her fellow teachers is an asset to any faculty.

Once the person is hired and we like his or her work, and he or she is happy in the work, we prefer to have this person stay on the job for a number of years.

Sincerely yours,
Finn B. Eriksen, Director
Health and Physical Education

---

stitutions Giving Professional Training for Physical Education the following qualifications: completion of a four-year high school course, favorable recommendation from the high school director of physical education, passing of a series of efficiency, ability, and intelligence tests, and the passing of a complete medical examination. In addition, after meeting these standards the student would be placed on probation for one year in order to determine whether or not he or she is acceptable to the profession.

The National Study Committee on Professional Education, composed of the state directors of health and physical education, developed standards for the selection of students to be trained. These standards included graduation from a four-year secondary school, an I.Q. of 100 or more, a health examination that shows no impairments that would affect the success of the prospective teacher, a command of oral and written English, and satisfactory motor skill.

Evans and Gans, one a leader in the physical education field and the other a former school administrator, list four areas that should be considered in the selection of physical educators. These are the type of teacher preparation pursued by the candidate, including courses taken, scholastic record, and degrees; the quality and quantity of the candidate's teaching experience; personal qualifications, such as mental and physical health, personal habits, use of the English language, intelligence, scholarship, and hobbies; and finally the importance of professional competence, which includes the candidate's interest in his chosen profession, his desire to improve himself professionally by being acquainted with new techniques, educational developments, and current happenings, and his interest in increasing the prestige of his profession.

The Jackson's Mill National Conference on Undergraduate Professional Preparation in Physical Education, Health Education, and Recreation set forth the following list of personal qualifications that are thought essential to leadership in these professions:

1. Faith in the worth of teaching and leadership
2. Personal concern for the welfare of all people
3. Respect for personality

4. Understanding children, youth, and adults and appreciating their worth as citizens
5. Social understanding and behavior
6. Community-mindedness
7. Interest in and aptitude for teaching and leading
8. Above average mental ability and common sense
9. Above average health status
10. Voice of good quality and power, intelligently used
11. Effective use of language
12. A sense of humor
13. Energy and enthusiasm sufficient to the requirements of effective leadership*

The qualifications for physical educators as set forth by various educators give the student some idea as to the qualifications that are needed to become a member of this profession. A teacher-training program in physical education should provide for the admission of only those individuals who have acceptable qualifications. The establishment of such a policy will go a long way toward dispelling the old theory that the only requirements for a physical educator are a "strong back and a weak mind." The physical education profession has unlimited potentialities for service if the right personnel are selected to guide its destiny.

### Summary of qualifications

The individual desiring to become a member of the physical education profession should be able to meet the following requirements:

1. The candidate should be a graduate of an approved high school and an approved teacher-training institution preparing teachers for physical education. The student should select his college with care. Many are not qualified to train teachers of physical education.

*National Conference on Undergraduate Professional Preparation in Health Education, Physical Education, and Recreation, Jackson's Mill, W. Va., May 16-27, 1948: Report, Chicago, 1948, The Athletic Institute.

2. The candidate should possess that degree of intelligence needed to qualify for successful teaching. This may be determined through standardized tests. Furthermore, since the physical education profession is based upon the foundational sciences of anatomy, physiology, biology, kinesiology, sociology, and psychology, the prospective candidate should have some aptitude for these sciences.

3. The candidate should meet acceptable standards in oral and written English. The candidate's voice should be audible, pleasant, stimulating, smooth, and unaffected and his choice and organization of words should conform with good English usage. The candidate should be able to write in an acceptable manner with special attention to punctuation, choice of words, sentence structure, and logical organization. The speech of physical educators is under continuous scrutiny, and they are frequently called upon to speak in public. The nature of their positions makes it imperative that they use acceptable English in their speaking and writing.

4. The candidate should be able to satisfactorily pass health examinations, including an examination of the skin, teeth, eyes, ears, chest, heart, feet, and posture, and show good personal health history, mental health, and emotional stability. The candidate must be free from any physical or mental defects that would prevent successful teaching in physical education. Because of the important part that a teacher plays in shaping a child's life, it is necessary that a candidate with mental disorders, which would adversely affect the child, not be considered for this profession. Furthermore, physical education is a strenuous type of work, and therefore demands that members of the profession be in a state of buoyant, robust health in order that they may carry out their duties with efficiency and regularity. They should also remember that they are building healthy bodies; therefore they should be a good testimonial for their preachments.

5. The candidate should possess a personality that is suitable for teaching. This may be determined by tests and by interviews with qualified persons. Such personality traits as enthusiasm, friendliness, cheerfulness, industry, cooperation, firmness and forcefulness in supporting one's convictions, dependability, self-control, integrity, social adaptability, and likeableness are factors that can determine in great measure whether an individual will be a success or a failure as a teacher. Whether or not the right social traits are developed in children will depend largely on the personality of the leader. Character is developed through games and other physical education activities. Therefore, it is essential that the teacher of physical education be able to enlist the respect, cooperation, and admiration of the students through his personality, magnetism, and leadership. Frequently one hears teachers described by such phrases as "he has a way with children," or "the children think everything she does is just right." These are the individuals who have personalities that enable them to contribute to a child's "whole" development.

6. The candidate should have a sincere interest in the teaching of physical education as a profession. Unless an individual has a firm belief in the value of physical education and a desire to help extend the benefits of such an endeavor to others, he should not enter this work. Only if he has a deep conviction that he is rendering a service to mankind will the best job be performed. A person sincerely interested in physical education enjoys teaching individuals to participate in the gamut of activities incorporated in such programs, helping others to realize the happiness and thrilling experiences of participation that he himself enjoys, and helping to develop citizenship traits conducive to democratic living. A person must have a

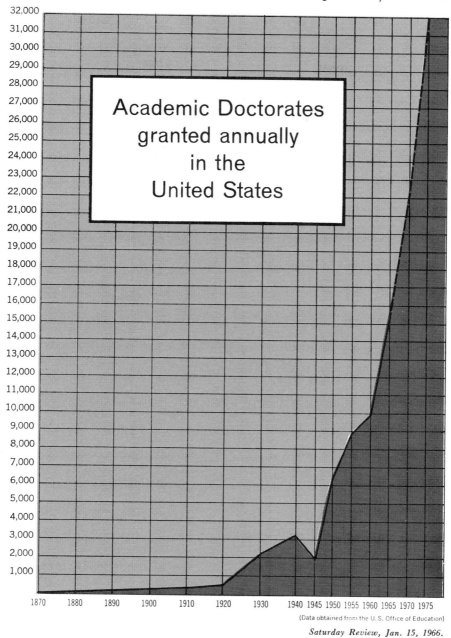

Academic Doctorates
granted annually
in the
United States

(Data obtained from the U.S. Office of Education)

*Saturday Review, Jan. 15, 1966.*

The doctorate is necessary for physical educators who want to qualify for some outstanding leadership opportunities.

sincere love of the out-of-doors and of all the activities that make up the physical education program, either indoors or out in the open. This means that anyone interested in being a member of this profes- sion should enjoy such dual and individual sports as tennis, badminton, swimming, golf, and handball and such team sports as field hockey, football, baseball, basket- ball, and soccer. If an individual does not

Physical educators should have a sincere interest in the teaching of physical education.

enjoy these activities, going into this field of endeavor would be similar to a person becoming a sailor who does not like the water or a veterinarian who does not like animals.

7. The candidate should possess an acceptable standard of motor ability. This may be determined through motor ability tests that meet acceptable test criteria. Physical skills are the basis of the entire physical education profession. In order to play tennis, badminton, football, and basketball effectively, it is necessary to have developed some skill in these activities. If the physical educator is to teach various games and activities to others, it is necessary that he have skill in some of them himself. Otherwise, it would be similar to an individual who does not know how to use a saw planning to be a carpenter, a person who cannot drive, a bus driver, or a person who does not know what a spark plug is, an auto mechanic. Physical skills are basic to the physical education profession. The student should be proficient in many of these skills if he desires to enter this type of work. Coordination, agility, flexibility, strength, and good reaction time aid greatly in the development

of skills. Many of the desirable skills may be developed during the time the prospective teacher of physical education is in college. However, a great amount of time is required in the perfection of skills. Therefore it is important that the individual develop a foundation of skills on the elementary and secondary school levels.

8. The candidate should enjoy working with people. A person is required to associate with human beings when teaching physical education activities. Therefore, a member of the physical education profession should get along well with others, be interested in people, be able to adapt to various social settings, be able to attain respect, and should enjoy working with children and young people. To satisfy this qualification he should possess such traits as patience, loyalty, tactfulness, sympathetic attitude, sincerity, friendliness, tolerance, reliability, industry, self-control, and good temperament. These are very important qualifications for those desiring to enter this profession. In order to be a success, a person must be able to work with others in a manner conducive to happiness, cooperation, and a spirit of

friendship. The effectiveness of the work performed rests upon good human relations. If such relations do not prevail, the objectives for which the profession strives will not be realized.

9. The candidate should have a sense of humor. The teachers who never crack a smile, tell a joke, or get a "kick" out of life well deserve the label students have associated with such individuals, "sour puss." Good mental health for both the student and the teacher is dependent upon a sense of humor. The teacher who can see the humor in numerous classroom incidents, a joke told by a colleague, or a remark made by a student possesses a trait that helps him to get along better with others, makes life more interesting for his students and himself, and aids in the dispelling of gloom. Good teachers possess a sense of humor.

The qualifications listed are necessary for all who desire to enter the physical education profession. In establishing such standards it is understood that all individuals are not qualified to be physical educators any more than all are qualified for careers in medicine, law, or social work. A person's future happiness depends upon making the right decision. A poet said it this way:

> Each is given a bag of tools . . .
> A carving block and a book of rules.
> Each must make ere life be done
> A stumbling block or a steppingstone.*

## RECRUITING QUALIFIED TEACHERS OF PHYSICAL EDUCATION

Several suggestions may be set forth that, if followed, will bring about better recruitment and selection on the part of our teacher-training institutions. The qualifications they establish for prospec-

---

*Quoted from Committee on Vocational Guidance, American Association for Health, Physical Education, and Recreation, Research Quarterly, AAHPER **13:**145, May, 1942.

tive teachers will determine whether children will be subjected to the right type of leadership.

### Closer working relationships among educational institutions

A recommendation that has been made during recent years stresses a closer relationship between the colleges and the secondary and elementary schools. This cooperative working arrangement ensures better recruitment and selection of prospective teachers. Among other things, a program of general vocational guidance can do much to interest individuals who are superior intellectually, socially, emotionally, and physically. If students are allowed to reach college before the advantages of the teaching profession as a career are brought to their attention, many superior candidates will be lost. If education is to be a dignified profession, its members must be willing to urge outstanding students with whom they work from day to day to become teachers.

### Meaningful records

Along with the closer relationship between colleges and public schools, it is important to keep meaningful records. Cumulative records containing information relative to scholarship, intelligence, personality, and educational history, as well as home conditions, will aid in determining whether or not an individual is suitable for the teaching profession.

### Scholarship

Scholarship should be taken into consideration as a qualification for prospective teachers. Wood, an expert in education, stated that students in teacher-training institutions were lower in academic ability than those in other professions, with the possible exception of the ministry. He further stated that such professions as medicine, law, and engineering

take only students that have met established standards, with the result that those
of lower academic ability go into teaching. Peik, a specialist in research in the
field of education, after analyzing several
studies, pointed out that research conducted over a fifteen-year period showed
the need for upgrading the selection of
teachers in respect to scholarship. In one
state all prospective teachers are required
to take a state psychological test. Any
student who falls below the thirtieth percentile is forbidden to enter training. This
procedure has resulted in the teaching
profession ranking above all others in that
state, with the exception of medicine and
law, in respect to the intelligence and
achievement levels of its personnel. Several years ago, the Educational Testing
Service at Princeton, New Jersey, gave
more than 400,000 examinations as part
of its Selective Service College Qualification Test Program. As a result of these
tests, evidence was presented that persons
preparing to be teachers are among the
poorest students attending institutions of
higher learning. Education ranked at the
bottom of the occupations represented.
Furthermore, teachers of health and physical education were the poorest of all education students. One of the major criticisms against the schools is the poor
quality of the students preparing for the
teaching profession.

The use of scholarships and other incentives has been advocated by some educators and professional organizations as a
means of attracting superior talent into
the profession. Intelligence, personality,
ability, and other desirable characteristics are not limited to the higher income
brackets. They are found among all types
of people. Therefore, those prospective
students who would be unable to attend
college because of economic means should
be provided with scholarships so that their
contribution to the profession will not be
lost.

## Selection

Selection must be made from among
those who propose to become teachers. It
cannot be presumed that all who enter
teacher-training institutions should be allowed to continue and graduate as full-
fledged teachers. Instead, it can be anticipated that many will be found lacking in
such qualities as personality, intelligence,
and ability to understand and work with
children. Therefore, it will be necessary to
select those who can meet acceptable standards and to eliminate the rest. A student
should be dismissed whenever he indicates
a lack of interest in teaching, ability to
teach, or other factors essential to success.
Selection should be a continuous process
since pertinent information is accumulated during the course of an individual's
training. Furthermore, the student should
participate in this process of selection.
Conferences should be held, and accumulated evidence that has a bearing on the
prospective teacher's suitability for the
profession should be discussed. Such a
procedure is more democratic and will
make for a more wholesome solution to
the problem.

## HOW TEACHERS ARE EVALUATED

Teacher evaluation has become an important consideration in determining promotions, in-service education, tenure,
merit salary raises, and most important,
the improvement of teaching. Some general guidelines for the evaluation of teachers include the following:

1. *Appraisal should involve the teachers
themselves.* Evaluation is a cooperative venture and teachers should be involved in the
development of the criteria for evaluation and
should understand the process.
2. *Evaluation should be centered on performance.* The job that is to be accomplished
should be the point of focus, with other extraneous factors omitted.
3. *Evaluation should be concerned with
helping the teacher to grow on the job.* The
purpose of evaluation is to help the teacher

# Teacher evaluation

**TEACHER: Socrates**

## A. Personal qualifications

| | Rating (high to low) | Comments |
|---|---|---|
| | 1 2 3 4 5 | |
| 1. Personal appearance | ☐ ☐ ☐ ☐ ☑ | Dresses in an old sheet draped about his body |
| 2. Self-confidence | ☐ ☐ ☐ ☐ ☑ | Not sure of himself—always asking questions |
| 3. Use of English | ☐ ☐ ☐ ☑ ☐ | Speaks with a heavy Greek accent |
| 4. Adaptability | ☐ ☐ ☐ ☐ ☑ | Prone to suicide by poison when under duress |

## B. Class management

| | | |
|---|---|---|
| 1. Organization | ☐ ☐ ☐ ☐ ☑ | Does not keep a seating chart |
| 2. Room appearance | ☐ ☐ ☐ ☑ ☐ | Does not have eye-catching bulletin boards |
| 3. Utilization of supplies | ☑ ☐ ☐ ☐ ☐ | Does not use supplies |

## C. Teacher-Pupil relationships

| | | |
|---|---|---|
| 1. Tact and consideration | ☐ ☐ ☐ ☐ ☑ | Places student in embarrassing situation by asking questions |
| 2. Attitude of class | ☐ ☑ ☐ ☐ ☐ | Class is friendly |

## D. Techniques of teaching

| | | |
|---|---|---|
| 1. Daily preparation | ☐ ☐ ☐ ☐ ☑ | Does not keep daily lesson plans |
| 2. Attention to course of study | ☐ ☐ ☑ ☐ ☐ | Quite flexible—allows students to wander to different topics |
| 3. Knowledge of subject matter | ☐ ☐ ☐ ☐ ☑ | Does not know material—has to question pupils to gain knowledge |

## E. Professional attitude

| | | |
|---|---|---|
| 1. Professional ethics | ☐ ☐ ☐ ☐ ☑ | Does not belong to professional association or PTA |
| 2. In-service training | ☐ ☐ ☐ ☐ ☑ | Complete failure here—has not even bothered to attend college |
| 3. Parent relationships | ☐ ☐ ☐ ☐ ☑ | Needs to improve in this area—parents are trying to get rid of him |

RECOMMENDATION: Does not have a place in Education. Should not be rehired.

to evaluate his strengths and weaknesses and to maintain his strengths and reduce his weaknesses.

4. *Evaluation should look to the future.* It should be concerned with developing a better program and a better school system.

5. *Evaluation of teachers should be well organized and administered.* It should be clearly outlined and every teacher should know the step-by-step approach to be followed.

Some of the methods of evaluation of teachers include the following:

1. *Observation of teachers in the classroom or in the gymnasium.* The National Education Association Research Division, in studying this method, reported that the median length of time for the most recent observation was 22 minutes; about 25% of the teachers were notified one day in advance that the observation would take place; and about 50% of the teachers reported that a conference followed the observation period with the teacher's performance being discussed and evaluated. Nearly one half of the teachers reported that the observation was helpful to them.

2. *Student progress.* With this method, standardized tests are used to determine what progress the student has made as a result of exposure to the teacher.

3. *Ratings.* Ratings vary and may consist of an overall estimate of a teacher's effectiveness or consist of separate evaluations of specific teacher behavior and traits. Self-ratings may also be used. Ratings may be conducted by the teacher's peers, by students, or by administrative personnel, and may include judgments based on observation of student progress. Rating scales, in order to be effective, must be based on such criteria as objectivity, reliability, sensitivity, validity, and utility. At college and university levels the evaluation of teacher performance is sometimes more difficult than at precollege levels because of the unwillingness of the faculty to permit members of the administration, or other persons, to observe them in the classroom, or some other place, for this purpose. Various methods have been devised in institutions of higher learning to rate faculty members, including statements from department heads, ratings by colleagues, ratings by students, and ratings by deans and other administrative personnel. A question that frequently arises in the development of any system of teacher evaluation is: What constitutes effectiveness as it relates to a teacher

in a particular school or college situation? Several studies have been conducted with some interesting findings. For example, there is only a slight correlation between intelligence and the rated success of an instructor. Therefore, the degree of intelligence a teacher has, within reasonable limits, seems to have little value as a criterion. The relation of knowledge of subject matter to effectiveness appears to relate most in particular teaching situations. A teacher's demonstration of good scholarship while in college appears to have little positive relationship to good teaching. There is some evidence to show that teachers who have demonstrated high levels of professional knowledge on national teachers' examinations are more effective teachers. However, the evidence here is rather sparse. The relationship of experience to effectiveness also seems to have questionable value. Experience during the first five years of teaching seems to enhance teacher effectiveness and cultural background, socioeconomic status, sex, and marital status. Finally, there is little evidence to show that any specified aptitude for teaching exists. The studies indicate that more research needs to be done in order to establish what constitutes teacher effectiveness on the job.

## THE BEGINNING TEACHER

Beginning teachers need considerable encouragement and help. A survey of fifty teachers indicated the following as some of the problems that beginning teachers face:

1. Difficulties arising as a result of the lack of facilities
2. Large size of classes, making it difficult to teach effectively
3. Teaching assignments in addition to the primary responsibility of teaching physical education
4. Discipline problems with students
5. Conflicting methodology between what beginning teachers were taught in professional preparing institutions and established patterns of experienced teachers
6. Clerical work—difficulty in keeping records up to date
7. Problems encountered in obtaining books and supplies
8. Problems encountered in obtaining cooperative attitude from other teachers

9. Lack of departmental meetings to discuss common problems
10. Failure to find time for personal recreation

## QUESTIONS AND EXERCISES

1. In approximately 250 words discuss your qualifications for the physical education profession in the light of the standards set forth in this chapter.
2. How would you describe the qualifications for the teaching profession to someone who is considering making teaching his career?
3. To what degree do you feel there is a relationship between the qualifications for a profession and the prestige held by a profession?
4. What is meant by the "crisis in American education"?
5. Why is there a need for well-trained teachers in physical education?
6. What recommendations can be made for the better recruitment and selection of physical educators?
7. Why should selection be a continuous process in respect to physical education teachers?
8. Why is scholarship important to physical education work?
9. Prepare a list of standards that could be used as a basis for selecting individuals for training in physical education work.
10. In approximately 250 words discuss the implications of the list of personal qualifications for leadership as presented by the Jackson's Mill National Conference on Undergraduate Professional Preparation.
11. Why is it important for the physical educator to meet acceptable standards in oral and written English?
12. Why is it important for the physical educator to possess an acceptable standard of motor ability?
13. Describe and contrast the various methods of teacher evaluation. Which do you feel might be the most effective and objective? Why?

## SELECTED REFERENCES

American Association for Health, Physical Education, and Recreation: Professional preparation in health, physical education and recreation, Washington, D. C., 1962, The Association.

American Council on Education: Teachers for our times. A statement of purposes on teach-

---

**PROUD TO BE A TEACHER***

Teaching is an art which requires long periods of training, high qualifications, and dedicated service. Any person can be proud to be a teacher because:

*The teacher is a prophet*

He lays the foundations of tomorrow.

*The teacher is an artist*

He works with the precious clay of unfolding personality.

*The teacher is a friend*

His heart responds to the faith and devotion of his students.

*The teacher is a citizen*

He is selected and licensed for the improvement of society.

*The teacher is an interpreter*

Out of his maturer and wider life he seeks to guide the young.

*The teacher is a builder*

He works with the higher and finer values of civilization.

*The teacher is a culture-bearer*

He leads the way toward worthier tastes, saner attitudes, more gracious manners, higher intelligence.

*The teacher is a planner*

He sees the young lives before him as a part of a great system which shall grow stronger in the light of truth.

*The teacher is a pioneer*

He is always attempting the impossible and winning out.

*The teacher is a reformer*

He seeks to remove the handicaps that weaken and destroy life.

*The teacher is a believer*

He has abiding faith in the improvability of the race.

*Dr. Joy Elmer Morgan, FTA Founder and Chairman, 1937–1954.

er education, Washington, D. C., 1944, The Council.

American Council on Education: The improvement of teacher education. Final report of the Commission on Teacher Education, Washington, D. C., 1946, The Council.

Biddle, Bruce J., and Ellena, William J.: Contemporary research on teaching effectiveness, New York, 1964, Holt, Rinehart, and Winston, Inc.

Bucher, Charles A.: Administration of school health and physical education programs, St. Louis, 1967, The C. V. Mosby Co.

Bucher, Charles A., Koening, Constance, and Barnhard, Milton: Methods and materials of secondary school physical education, St. Louis, 1965, The C. V. Mosby Co.

Conference on the Undergraduate Professional Preparation of Students Majoring in Health Education, Washington, D. C., 1949, Office of Education.

Gilbin, Robert L., and Vogel, Stefan: So you're going to be a teacher, Great Neck, New York, 1962, Barron's Educational Series, Inc.

National Commission on Teacher Education and Professional Standards: Invitation to teaching, Washington, D. C., 1966, National Education Association.

National Conference on Undergraduate Professional Preparation in Health Education, Physical Education, and Recreation, Jackson's Mill, Weston, W. Va, May 16-27, 1948: Report, Chicago, 1948, The Athletic Institute.

National Study Committee on Professional Education: Report on standards: national study of professional education in health and physical education, Research Quarterly, AAHPER 6:48, Dec., 1935.

Nordly, Carl L.: Quantity versus quality (editorial), Journal of Health and Physical Education 19:334, May, 1948.

Nordly, Carl L.: Unifying the profession, Journal of Health, Physical Education, and Recreation 21:14, Oct., 1950.

Peik, W. E.: The preservice preparation of teachers, review of educational research 13: 228, June, 1943.

Ryans, David G.: Characteristics of teachers, Washington, D. C., 1960, American Council on Education, Library of Congress.

Snyder, Raymond, and Scott, Harry: Professional preparation in health, physical education and recreation, New York, 1953, McGraw-Hill Book Co.

Steinhaus, Arthur H.: The next step in teacher training, Journal of Health and Physical Education 10:138, March, 1939.

Tyler, Ralph W.: Trends in the preparation of teachers, The School Review 51:207, April, 1943.

Chapter 20

# Duties of physical education personnel

In considering the duties of physical education personnel some initial questions might be: Duties to whom? Where do the responsibilities lie? For whom do you perform the duties?

## GROUPS TO WHOM PHYSICAL EDUCATORS ARE RESPONSIBLE

One way of answering the questions listed above might be to say that the physical education teacher performs duties for the student, the department, faculty and school, community, and the profession.

### The student

The teacher's first responsibility is to the student. The teacher should know the student physically, mentally, emotionally, and socially. He should know the student's background, his needs, and his characteristics. The teacher should view the student as a growing and maturing human being who can be shaped by the teacher and helped to progress toward worthwhile educational goals. The teacher has the responsibility to help the student develop the skills, master the knowledge, and acquire the attitudes and social qualities that will help him become all that he is capable of becoming.

### The department

The teacher is usually one member of a team—the members of the department of physical education. The duties that befall the department, such as program planning, grading, testing, counseling, caring for equipment and facilities, and keeping records, must be shared with other members of the department. There should be harmonious interrelationships among members of the department. There should be ethical standards of conduct and mutual support of colleagues. The department will be as strong as its weakest human link, so each member of the staff should strive to be a valuable and important member of the team.

### The faculty and school

The teacher must also recognize that he is a member of a school faculty. This position carries with it many responsibilities that are a part of administering a program for children. All teachers must share in this endeavor, which includes obligations in regard to upholding school policies, sharing mutual responsibilities such as supervising student activities, and respecting the total curriculum. Teachers of physical education must see the total educational plan and how all parts of it contribute to the education of young people. Physical education is an important part of the total plan, but at the same time is only one part. Faculty meetings also represent an important medium for school planning, discussion of problems, and interpreting to colleagues each area of the curriculum, so physical educators have a responsibility to be in attendance at faculty meetings.

### The community

Another responsibility of the physical education teacher is to the community. The support a physical education teacher gains for the program depends largely on the program itself and the way in which the citizens interpret it. The responsibilities of the physical education staff in promoting this community relationship include presenting a sound program, joining community-sponsored activities, and supporting worthwhile community endeavors.

### The profession

Each physical educator owes some time and effort to the profession of which he is a part. This obligation can be carried out by joining professional organizations, serving on committees and as officers of the associations, and supporting professional endeavors. Physical educators should also be in attendance at professional meetings, and keep up with the literature and developments related to the profession.

### RANGE OF DUTIES

The duties performed by physical education personnel are many and varied. They include such functions as coaching sports, administering physical fitness tests, teaching games and first aid, monitoring study halls, and performing routine administrative duties. They are not limited to physical education alone. They are also concerned with a wider range of duties

essential to the functioning of a school, voluntary agency, camp, church, athletic club, or other organization.

Although the functions of physical educators are performed in various institutions, they are, nevertheless, very similar in nature. If this were not true, nearly as many teacher-training curricula would be needed in colleges and universities as there are different types of positions. As a general rule, most positions involve some combination of teaching, administrative, community, and other duties that are miscellaneous in nature. Since the majority of students preparing themselves for work in physical education anticipate work in the public schools, it seems necessary to emphasize this area of employment.

Before discussing the specific duties performed by physical educators, it seems important to consider certain general responsibilities they have in respect to the objectives of their profession, the program of activities, effective leadership, a measurement and evaluation program, and a reevaluation of the program periodically. Only if an individual knows the standards that form the basis for teacher responsibilities will he be able to interpret meaningfully the various duties performed by physical education personnel.

### GENERAL RESPONSIBILITIES OF THE PHYSICAL EDUCATOR

There are certain responsibilities that each teacher must assume upon accepting a position. These responsibilities are as follows:

1. Knowing the objectives of the profession of physical education
2. Planning and administering a physical education program in the light of these objectives
3. Providing effective leadership in order to achieve these objectives
4. Scientifically measuring and evaluating the physical education program in order to determine if the objectives are being accomplished

## Today's teachers are expected to . . .

1. Remain alert to significant developments in academic specialty and continue general education in order to avoid obsolescence of knowledge
2. Be a continuing student of the educative process and keep current with respect to innovations in teaching methods and materials
3. Plan with students and fellow teachers
4. Work with curriculum committees
5. Experiment with different content, methods, and materials and keep systematic records of such studies
6. Read and evaluate student work
7. Confer with students and parents regarding pupil progress
8. Counsel and advise students on academic, vocational, and personal concerns
9. Maintain a cumulative file of significant data on each student
10. Develop reading lists, outlines, study guides, drill sheets, and visual materials
11. Prepare tests appropriate to the range of objectives established
12. Type and duplicate tests and other materials for classroom use
13. Arrange for field trips, outside speakers, and other programs relevant to the learning objectives of the class
14. Supervise homeroom, study hall, or lunchroom
15. Supervise playground or recess periods
16. Advise student extracurricular groups, chaperon school functions
17. Keep attendance and academic records
18. Collect money for various drives and sell tickets for school events
19. Order and return films and other visual aids and operate equipment involved
20. Participate in professional-association and learned-society activities
21. Maintain an active interest in civic and community affairs and represent the school in the community effectively
22. Orient and assist beginning teachers
23. Supervise student teachers and cooperate with area colleges in providing opportunities for observation and demonstration.

*George W. Denemark, NEA Journal 55:19 Dec., 1966.*

Duties assigned to teachers in today's schools.

5. Reevaluating the program of physical education in the light of results obtained through measurement and evaluation techniques

### Knowing objectives of profession

In the first place, the physical education person must know and fully understand the objectives of the physical education profession. These objectives include the long-term goals (Chapter 6) as well as the more immediate and specific objectives. By the more immediate and specific objectives are meant those goals toward which one works during one lesson, over the course of a week, or during

**JOB ANALYSIS FOR AN ELEMENTARY
SCHOOL PHYSICAL EDUCATION TEACHER**

Mrs. Jacobi of Lafayette Elementary School in Waterloo, Iowa, lists the following as some of her duties:

I teach physical education grades four, five, and six. Many activities are included in the program: games, sports, tumbling, rhythms, rope jumping, ball bouncing, track and field, posture improvement, marching, and exercises for physical fitness. The sports include modified football (football-kickball), soccer (kickball), modified volleyball, modified basketball (captain ball), and softball.

The sixth grade plays several games with other schools each year. An arrangement is made to have members from both schools on the same team. The sixth graders do not compete on a school-against-school basis.

We try to check for physical fitness once a week, i.e., chinning, sit-ups, squat thrusts. The children help check each other in their squads.

After playing a game or after any physical activity we usually discuss what we've done. Suggestions are given for improving our next activity. We discuss what we thought we did well. I stress good sportsmanship and we comment on that. Sometimes I make and give tests over such sports as softball and basketball.

I teach art, literature, and music to grades four, five, and six; and also, fourth grade spelling and social studies.

Some of the things I specifically try to do in my physical education classes are:

1. Offer proper incentives and ideals
2. Help build better citizens—physically, mentally, and morally
3. Develop health habits—posture and exercise
4. Help each child to feel he is needed and has a very important part in everything we do
5. Help each child to work for improvement
6. Help to organize and direct big-muscle activity

tigue, to understand the importance of milk in one's diet, to know the rules of baseball, or to assist a less-skilled player in badminton. These more immediate or specific objectives, along with the long-term goals, should be present in nay physical educator's mind, whether he is teaching a class in the public schools, in a Young Men's Christian Association, a camp, or a settlement house. They will aid in keeping continually in mind the things he is striving to accomplish today, tomorrow, next year, and ultimately. Through a knowledge and understanding of the objectives of physical education, the program is better planned, the leadership is superior, and the results obtained are much more fruitful.

**Planning physical education program**

In the second place, the physical educator has the responsibility for planning and administering a program in the light of its objectives. This means that the interests and needs of the individuals whom it will serve, as well as other acceptable criteria, will be taken into consideration. It means that a varied program of activities will be selected that will include rhythmics and the dance, dual and individual activities, team games, games of low organization, relays, field days,* outdoor sports, aquatics, and gymnastics. The percentage time of the program devoted to these various activities will depend on the age or grade level concerned. In planning and administering a program in the light of the objectives such factors as facilities, personnel, equipment, state legislation, size of class, time allotment, and climatic conditions will be taken into consideration. Provisions will be made for the physical, social, skill, and intellectual development of the participant, and safety factors will be considered. A core and

a unit of work. Some examples are the ability to throw with accuracy, to run the 220-yard dash without excessive fa-

*See also Bucher, Charles A.: Field days, Journal of Health and Physical Education 19: 22, Jan., 1948.

elective program will be utilized at certain age and grade levels.

There has been considerable research on the types of programs that are most suited to various levels of instruction. For example, a national physical education curriculum has been developed based on a committee's research covering a period of nine years and summarized by LaPorte. This national physical education program may be suitable for adoption in some elementary and secondary schools and colleges throughout the country. Irwin devoted an entire book to the subject of the curriculum in health and physical education. Other authors, too numerous to mention, have spent considerable time construcing curricula. Many states have developed syllabi that provide guidance and help in establishing a program for particular geographical regions. The armed forces, voluntary agencies, and various institutions where physical education activities are carried on have developed programs that may be utilized in whole or in part. There is a wealth of material available. The physical education instructor should appraise this material in the light of the objectives of physical education and in terms of his local situation. As a result, it will be possible for him to develop a program that meets the needs and interests of the group or groups with whom he is working.

### Providing leadership

In the third place, the physical educator has the responsibility for providing effective leadership in order to achieve the objectives of physical education. Leadership is a quality or attribute that is possessed by the efficient teacher. It influences the way students react to his personality, association, and guidance. The functions of leadership are to aid each person to develop to his greatest possible capacity—physically, neuromuscularly, intellectually, and socially.

The program in physical education requires competent leadership. This leadership may be provided only if a person has adequate professional training; understands the problems involved; and has such essential physical, mental, social, and personality characteristics as vitality, enthusiasm, intelligence, keen powers of observation, respect for the dignity of the individual, belief in the golden rule, sympathy, patience, and loyalty. A teacher should also be alert to the possibilities in games and other physical education activities for developing situations in which the proper responses evolve for the participant.

The teacher of physical education should realize that his responsibility extends beyond the immediate group with which he is working to the rest of the school, institution, or agency with which he is associated and out into the community of which he is a part. He should never get to the point where he becomes encased in an ivory tower and feels that he has no responsibility for the rest of mankind. Every teacher should feel that the wider his associations, the greater his personal enjoyment and happiness and the greater the extension of the benefits of physical education.

The informal and play type of physical education program that exists today offers an opportunity for the indolent physical educator to conduct a program without providing good leadership. He can throw out a ball or pass out the equipment and then loaf. In order to provide effective leadership, the physical educator must be on the job every minute. He must be alert to every opportunity that arises so that he may aid in developing the individual to his optimum capacity. A person must experience success and happiness if he is to make the right adjustment. If good leadership is provided in physical education, the correct adjustment will take place. However, good leadership will not be provided if a ball is thrown out to a physical education class and the instruc-

The physical educator has the responsibility for providing effective leadership.

tor goes back to his office to rest or work out a new football play with which he hopes to defeat his rival by seven points. Good leadership will not be provided in competitive sports if winning is stressed as the main objective instead of courtesy, sympathy, teamwork, truthfulness, honesty, respect for authority, fairness, and abiding by the rules. Good leadership will not be provided if physical education classes are neglected and the teacher's entire efforts are put into coaching. Good leadership will be provided only by working full time with the group and conscientiously attempting to help each member. Through good leadership the objectives of physical education will be brought nearer to realization.

The teacher's example has a tremendous weight in providing good leadership. Whether or not his teachings bear fruit will depend to a great degree on what he does out of class. The following poem well depicts this lesson:

*I'd rather see a sermon*
*Than hear one any day;*

*I'd rather one should walk with me*
*Than merely show the way.*
*The eye's a better pupil,*
*And more willing than the ear;*

*Fine counsel is confusing,*
*But example's always clear.*
*And best of all the preachers*
*Are the men who live their creeds;*
*For to see good put in action*
*Is what everybody needs.*

*I soon can learn to do it,*
*If you'll let me see it done;*
*I can see your hands in action,*
*But your tongue too fast may run.*
*And the lectures you deliver*
*May be very fine and true,*

*But I'd rather get my lesson*
*By observing what you do.*
*For I may misunderstand you*
*And the high advice you give,*
*But there's no misunderstanding*
*How you act and how you live!*

—Edgar Guest

## Utilizing measurement and evaluation techniques

In the fourth place, the physical educator has the responsibility for utilizing measurement and evaluation techniques in order to determine whether the objectives of physical education are being accomplished.

If the teacher is to evaluate the various types of programs and instruction, if he is to know what he is achieving through these programs and instruction, and if he is to know whether he is meeting the objectives that have been set, it seems imperative that he utilize acceptable measurement and evaluation techniques. These will enable him to better determine individual and program weaknesses, quality of instruction, and progress achieved.

In the utilization of such techniques, however, it should be kept in mind that many of those in use today have been developed by individuals who have failed to use or interpret scientific methods of instruction correctly. As a result, there are materials being used that either have

failed to be scientifically evaluated or else have fallen below acceptable standards. In view of these conditions, it is necessary to assure oneself that only materials that meet acceptable criteria will be used.

Measurement and evaluation techniques enable a teacher to determine an individual's physical condition, traits, or characteristics in respect to physical, motor, intellectual, and social development. Furthermore, they enable him to evaluate practices concerned with such items as program administration, leadership, facilities, and activities. They may be utilized for purposes of guidance, motivation, diagnosis, pupil classification, prognosis, research, grading, and determining achievement. They should, however, be considered as tools and not as ends in themselves.

**Reevaluating program periodically**

In the fifth place, the physical educator has the responsibility for reevaluating the program in the light of measurement and evaluation results. The results that are compiled, tabulated, and analyzed should aid the teacher in determining whether or not the program being followed and the teaching techniques being used are satisfactory and accomplishing the objectives of physical education. If, through a careful analysis, it appears that progress is not being made, the program and/or the teaching techniques should be reevaluated in light of the findings and the necessary changes made. Such a procedure places physical education more and more on a scientific basis and enables it to render a greater service to all concerned. As has been previously pointed out, however, measurement and evaluation techniques should not become ends in themselves. The tests should not be given just for the sake of testing and the results placed in a file and allowed to gather dust. Instead, they should be utilized in furthering the program and in

---

**JOB ANALYSIS FOR A SECONDARY SCHOOL PHYSICAL EDUCATION TEACHER**

Mr. Buck, a secondary school physical education teacher in McKinstry School in Waterloo, Iowa, points out that in his job he performs the following:

1. Teaches physical education classes in such activities as touch football, soccer, rope climbing, rope jumping, handball, dodgeball, crabball, pinball, wiffleball, wrestling, basketball, marching to music, square dancing, softball, track, swimming, and diving
2. Teaches four health classes
3. Gives practical and written tests in physical education activities, physical fitness, attitudes, and lifesaving.
4. Coaches football, wrestling, and basketball
5. Conducts intramurals on a homeroom basis
6. Supervises recreation room on days when there are no intramurals
7. Supervises Elks basketball program on Tuesday evenings and swimming on Saturday mornings (programs last about 12 weeks each)

helping the individuals who are participating. Furthermore, they should not take
up too much of the time allotted to the
program. The activity program should
not be sacrificed for a measurement and
evaluation program. Instead, it should be
aided and strengthened thereby.

## TYPES AND DUTIES
## OF POSITIONS IN WHICH
## PHYSICAL EDUCATORS SERVE

The types and duties of positions in
which physical educators serve may be
discussed under the following headings:

1. Capacities in which physical education
   teachers serve
2. Intramural and/or interschool activities
3. Physical education activities
4. Measurement and evaluation techniques
5. Health education
6. Safety education
7. Driver education
8. Other subjects
9. Research
10. School levels of instruction
11. Other duties

The findings of a national survey conducted by the author show that physical
educators perform in several capacities,
coach many sports, teach various activities, utilize measurement and evaluation techniques, teach health education
and other subjects along with their physical education duties, conduct research,
and perform many other miscellaneous
duties.

### Capacities in which physical
### education teachers serve

Teachers of physical education throughout the United States serve in an administrative and/or teaching capacity and
frequently have health education duties
as part of their work, according to a survey conducted by the author.

The distribution of administrative and
teaching positions showed that a mean
average of 50.3% of the men and 41.2%
of the women have a *combination of ad-*

*ministrative and teaching positions.* Many
physical educators work in small towns
where it is common to find in the public
schools one man, the director and teacher
of boys' physical education, and one
woman, the director and teacher of girls'
physical education. This results in the performance of administrative and teaching
duties.

Although many physical educators have
a combination of administrative positions,
others have teaching positions or administrative positions only. The larger
the physical education program, the greater the need for personnel whose sole
function is teaching and for personnel
whose primary responsibility is administration.

According to this survey, a mean average of 44.2% of the men and 55.5% of
the women had *teaching positions only.*
A mean average of 5.5% of the men and
3.3% of the women had *administrative
duties only.*

Physical educators may have physical
education duties only or they may, in
addition, have health education responsibilities. Although health education is
making great strides toward having specialized personnel handling the health
duties, there is still a lack of adequately
trained personnel to take over all of the
health duties in the country. Furthermore, many towns are too poor finan-
cially to assume the responsibility of having both physical educators and health
educators. It is in cases such as these that
physical educators are assuming health
education responsibilities. A survey of the
nation showed that a mean average of
39.6% of the men and 37.1% of the
women had *physical education duties only.*
On the other hand, a mean average of
60.3% of the men and 62.9% of the
women had *health education duties combined with their physical education
duties.*

Some of the capacities in which physical

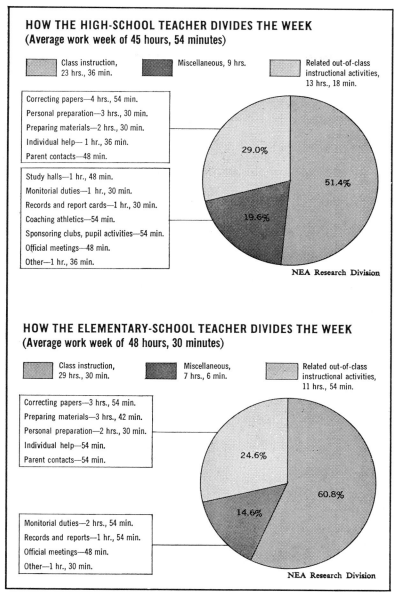

**HOW THE HIGH-SCHOOL TEACHER DIVIDES THE WEEK**
(Average work week of 45 hours, 54 minutes)

Class instruction, 23 hrs., 36 min.    Miscellaneous, 9 hrs.    Related out-of-class instructional activities, 13 hrs., 18 min.

Correcting papers—4 hrs., 54 min.
Personal preparation—3 hrs., 30 min.
Preparing materials—2 hrs., 30 min.
Individual help— 1 hr., 36 min.
Parent contacts—48 min.

Study halls—1 hr., 48 min.
Monitorial duties—1 hr., 30 min.
Records and report cards—1 hr., 30 min.
Coaching athletics—54 min.
Sponsoring clubs, pupil activities—54 min.
Official meetings—48 min.
Other—1 hr., 36 min.

29.0%
51.4%
19.6%

NEA Research Division

**HOW THE ELEMENTARY-SCHOOL TEACHER DIVIDES THE WEEK**
(Average work week of 48 hours, 30 minutes)

Class instruction, 29 hrs., 30 min.    Miscellaneous, 7 hrs., 6 min.    Related out-of-class instructional activities, 11 hrs., 54 min.

Correcting papers—3 hrs., 54 min.
Preparing materials—3 hrs., 42 min.
Personal preparation—2 hrs., 30 min.
Individual help—54 min.
Parent contacts—54 min.

Monitorial duties—2 hrs., 54 min.
Records and reports—1 hr., 54 min.
Official meetings—48 min.
Other—1 hr., 30 min.

24.6%
60.8%
14.6%

NEA Research Division

*NEA Research Division,
NEA Journal, April, 1963.*

How high school and elementary school teachers divide the week.

education teachers served, as revealed by this nationwide survey, are the following:

Supervisor of health and physical education
Director of physical education and health
Supervisor and teacher of health and physical education

Director and teacher of health and physical education
Supervisor, director, and teacher of physical education, and coordinator and teacher of health
Director and teacher of physical education and coordinator and teacher of health

Director and teacher of physical education and teacher of health
Teacher of health and physical education
Director of physical education, health, and recreation

Following are some of the positions throughout the country concerned solely with physical education activities, as revealed through this survey:

Teacher of physical education
Supervisor and teacher of physical education
Director and teacher of physical education
Supervisor, director, and teacher of physical education
Coach of varsity sports
Director of athletics
Physical educator in the YMCA, YWCA, YMHA, YWHA
Resource physical educator on the elementary level
County supervisor of physical education
Research worker
Supervisor of physical education on the elementary level
Supervisor of physical education on the secondary level
Director of intramurals
Coordinator of physical education
Chairman of the department of physical education

## Intramural and/or interscholastic activities

Both men and women are called upon to coach intramural and interscholastic sports. Such duties are very common in the public schools, increasing progressively from the elementary to the college levels, and are also functions of the individual who works for other agencies.

A study of the status of physical education in Michigan secondary schools, for example, conducted by the Michigan Association for Health, Physical Education, and Recreation, showed that 87.3% of the physical education instructors in the junior high schools and 97.4% of those in the senior high schools of the state had coaching duties. A survey of intramural and/or interscholastic activities that physical educators are called upon to coach

---

**JOB ANALYSIS FOR A COLLEGE PHYSICAL EDUCATION TEACHER**

The author, as a Professor of Education at New York University, has duties such as the following in the Division of Health, Physical Education, and Recreation:

1. Director of Graduate Study involving meetings with staff members, development of curriculums, revision of courses, initiating research projects, answering correspondence from prospective graduate students and active students, and keeping graduate records
2. Supervises research projects
3. Teaches four classes per week
4. Attends faculty meetings of School of Education and Division of Health, Physical Education, and Recreation
5. Advises students
6. Attends professional conventions and conferences
7. Serves on All-University, School of Education, and Division committees
8. Teaches one off-campus course
9. Prepares brochures and other materials
10. Serves as graduate student organization advisor

---

showed that an individual preparing to follow this profession should be familiar with many activities. The activities that are most commonly assigned to physical educators as coaching responsibilities are basketball, softball, volleyball, baseball, track, touch football, swimming, tennis, soccer, field hockey (women only), football (men only), speedball, cross country (men only), golf, and bowling. A listing of activities coached by men and women as revealed in this survey is as follows:

*Men*

| | |
|---|---|
| Archery | Polo |
| Baseball | Rifle |
| Basketball | Skish |
| Bowling | Soccer |
| Boxing | Softball |
| Crew | Speedball |
| Cross country | Squash racquets |
| Fencing | Swimming |

| | |
|---|---|
| Flag football | Tennis |
| Football | Touch football |
| Golf | Track and field |
| Gymnastics | Tumbling |
| Ice hockey | Volleyball |
| Lacrosse | Wrestling |
| *Women* | |
| Archery | Skish |
| Basketball | Soccer |
| Baseball | Softball |
| Bowling | Speedball |
| Fencing | Swimming |
| Field hockey | Tennis |
| Golf | Touch football |
| Ice hockey | Track and field |
| Rifle | Volleyball |

## Physical education activities

Physical educators are called on to teach many and varied forms of physical activity. For purposes of convenience, they may be grouped under the following headings:

1. Team games
2. Dual and individual sports
3. Rhythms and dancing
4. Formal activities
5. Aquatic activities
6. Outdoor winter sports
7. Gymnastics
8. Other activities

The most popular team games on all levels of instruction in the schools (men and women) are baseball, softball, basketball, touch football, volleyball, soccer, and field hockey. The most popular on the elementary level (men and women) are softball, basketball, and volleyball; on the junior high school level, baseball, softball, basketball, soccer, touch football, and volleyball for the men and softball, volleyball, and basketball for the women; on the senior high school level, volleyball, basketball, baseball, softball, football, touch football, and soccer for the men and volleyball, basketball, softball, and field hockey for the women; on the college level, volleyball, baseball, basketball, softball, and touch football for the men and volleyball, basketball, and field hockey for the women.

There is a variety of dual and individual sports offered. Among the ones most frequently included in physical education programs are track, badminton, table tennis, deck tennis, handball, horseshoes, tennis, archery, golf, and shuffleboard. From the widespread use of activities in this category, it seems that greater and greater stress is being placed on this area so as to prepare for many years of enjoyable participation.

There are various types of rhythms and dancing included in most programs. Social dancing, folk dancing, rhythms, gymnastic dancing, square dancing, tap dancing, and modern dancing are offered. Men, as well as women, utilize these various types of rhythms and dancing. In the schools, folk dancing, rhythms, social dancing, and square dancing are most popular with both sexes. Only in the area of modern dancing do the men seem to have some hesitancy.

Formal activities are extensively utilized in programs of physical education. Of these activities, calisthenics is the most frequently mentioned, with marching second. Although it is evident that the games type of program is very popular, it still can be seen that many physical educators also utilize some of the more formal activities in their classes.

When facilities make it possible, aquatic activities are a phase of many physical education programs. However, in the public schools the lack of swimming pools makes such an activity impossible for many boys and girls throughout the country. Other agencies, such as the Young Men's Christian Association, frequently have pools as part of their physical plant. The enormous cost involved in including a swimming pool as part of a school plant makes it appear a luxury to many laymen. When aquatic activities are a part of the program, swimming, diving, lifesaving, water games, and sometimes canoeing, sailing, and rowing are offered.

*Seattle, Washington, Public Schools.*

Girls' archery class.

*Toledo, Ohio, Public Schools.*

Developing a sense of balance.

Outdoor winter sports form a group of activities that are included in most programs. Climatic conditions in certain parts of the country and the desire to stay indoors during inclement weather cause many physical educators to omit these sports. When such activities are a part of the program, skating, snow games, ice hockey, skiing, and tobogganing are the most popular.

Gymnastics are included in the majority of physical education programs. Such activities as tumbling, pyramid building, apparatus, rope climbing, and acrobatics are popular.

Some of the other activities offered, which do not seem to fit logically into the previous groupings, are self-testing activities, relays, games of low organization, correctives, and camping. Each of these is very popular throughout the public schools and other agencies of the country that utilize physical education activities in their program.

A complete list of activities physical educators are called upon to teach, as revealed by this survey, is given below:

*Team games*
  Baseball
  Basketball
  Code ball
  Field hockey (women only)
  Flag football (men only)
  Football (men only)
  Soccer
  Softball
  Speedball
  Touch football
  Volleyball

*Dual and individual sports*
  Archery
  Badminton
  Bait and fly casting
  Bowling
  Boxing (men only)
  Checkers (women only)
  Darts (women only)
  Deck tennis
  Fencing
  Fishing
  Golf

*Dawson County High School, Glendive, Mont.*

Pyramid building.

Handball
Horseback riding
Horseshoes
Paddle tennis (men only)
Rifle
Rope skipping
Shuffleboard
Skish
Table tennis
Tennis
Tether ball
Track and field
Wrestling (men only)
*Rhythms and dancing*
Folk dancing
Gymnastic dancing
Modern dancing
Rhythms
Square dancing
Social dancing
Tap dancing
*Formal activities*
Calisthenics
Marching
*Aquatic activities*
Canoeing
Diving
Lifesaving
Rowing
Swimming
Sailing
Water games
*Outdoor winter sports*
Ice hockey
Roller skating
Skating
Skiing
Snow games
Snowshoeing
Tobogganing
*Gymnastics*
Acrobatics
Apparatus
Obstacle course
Pyramid building
Rope climbing
Stunts
Trampoline
Tumbling
*Other activities*
Camping and outdoor education
Combatives
Correctives
Fly-tieing
Games of low organization
Relays
Self-testing activities

## Measurement and evaluation techniques

The more popular measurement and evaluation techniques used by physical educators are those that measure the health, physical fitness, knowledge, skill, and adaptability of their students.

The medical examination continues to be the most common procedure for checking on an individual's health status. This is utilized by schools as a routine procedure in examining students periodically and for participation in interscholastic sports and by various agencies and institutions for checking on the advisability of an individual's participating in physical activity. It is conducted by medical doctors.

Other techniques, which are also utilized extensively for determining various physical traits and characteristics, are organic, skill, knowledge, and adaptation tests. Organic tests are designed to measure such things as the efficiency and quality of an individual's cardiovascular system, nutritional status, strength, and physical fitness. Skill tests measure such things as an individual's general motor ability, general motor capacity, motor educability, and skill in specific activities. Physical education and health education knowledge tests include such areas as rules, strategies, techniques, health knowledge, and attitudes. Adaptation tests are concerned with measuring certain character and personality traits.

Another evaluation technique that is utilized to some extent has to do with program evaluation. This is concerned with such administrative items in the conduct of a program as leadership, time element, facilities, and participation.

## Health education

The health education subjects and activities that physical educators are asked to teach and conduct are similar for both men and women. These facts were pointed out in the author's national survey on duties of physical educators and the capacities in which they serve. The most common health education subjects are first aid, safety, community health hygiene, nutrition, physiology, and home nursing. However, such subjects as sight saving and personal regimen were also listed in this survey. Besides the teaching of health subjects, the responsibility for holding guidance conferences, administering vision and hearing tests, giving home-bound instruction, and teaching crippled children play an important part in many programs. As the emphasis on health education becomes more and more pronounced, physical educators increasingly may be called upon to assume responsibilities in this area.

### Safety education

Safety education has become an important part of the programs of school systems, and in many cases physical educators are asked to assume duties in this field of endeavor. Duties include bringing to the attention of teachers, parents, children, and others proper protective procedures; organizing safety patrols; instructing a unit of safety in the health curriculum; cooperating with community agencies interested in promoting a safe community; supervising playgrounds and athletic facilities in a manner that will promote safety; and other responsibilities involving the promotion of safe living in the educational program. In some school systems safety education supervisors are appointed to coordinate the entire safety program.

### Driver education

Driver education is becoming a common responsibility of teachers of physical education. The great expansion of this type of education is readily apparent. Studies have shown the effectiveness of driver education in reducing automobile accidents. As a result, some insurance companies offer reduced rates for persons who have pursued this training. Other studies have shown that programs are more effective when offered as a separate course and when the teacher has had special preparation in teaching driver education and traffic safety. The American Driver Education Association recommends at least 30 hours of classroom instruction and, in addition, 6 hours behind the wheel for each student.

Physical educators who are interested in teaching this special subject should find it helpful to take special training in this field.

### Other subjects

The teacher of physical education, if planning to work in the public schools, should consider preparation in areas other than physical education. Especially in smaller schools, administrators frequently hire physical educators who can also teach some other subject. This procedure is followed because of financial limitations, small staffs, and low enrollments in some school systems.

This national survey in determining the duties of physical educators found that general science and biology are the subjects most often assigned to physical educators. The second most frequently assigned area is social studies, with such subjects as American history, civics, ancient history, problems of American democracy, and geography on the list. English also ranks high. Such subjects as mathematics, drawing, design, representation, speech correction, industrial arts, lip reading, chemistry, physics, home economics, arts and crafts, agriculture, commercial subjects, and music are also assigned as part of a physical educator's duties in many schools. A prospective physical educator should therefore take these facts into consideration in planning a second field of interest.

## Research

Teachers of physical education are becoming increasingly research conscious. There are many opportunities for physical educators, regardless of where they serve, to conduct some meaningful research and thus contribute to new knowledge concerning physical education and the contribution it makes to human betterment. Research studies being conducted at the present time relate to such things as: teaching techniques that yield greatest student progress toward designated class goals, relationship between physical activity and scholastic success, most effective ways of organizing physical education classes, social qualities developed in athletics, relationship of certain learning theories to the teaching of motor skills, and the role of physical education in contributing to the handicapped student. In conducting research, sound research methodology should be utilized. In this way, physical educators can pioneer and be put on the cutting edge of their profession, and helping to insure for it more respect and a more important place in the educational structure.

## School levels of instruction

Teachers of physical education perform duties on all levels of instruction. The high school level has the most teachers of physical education, the junior high school level next, and the elementary level least. Furthermore, there is a marked similarity in the distribution of men and women on the various levels.

The majority of teachers have duties on one level of instruction only. However, there are many who have responsibilities on two levels of instruction, and some who have responsibilities on all three levels. Approximately 60% of the men and women perform duties on one level of instruction only, whereas approximately 40% have duties on more than one level of instruction. Also, about one third of these men and women physical educators perform part of or all their duties on the elementary level; one half perform part or all of their duties on the junior high school level; and more than one half perform part or all of their duties on the high school level. These findings show that opportunities are available for physical educators on all three levels of instruction in the schools. There are also opportunities in higher education.

## Other duties

Health and physical education teachers are required to perform many duties other than teaching and coaching. Some of these duties are closely related to their field of endeavor and others are not. The physical educator should realize that they are a part of his job and should endeavor to carry them out just as faithfully as he would his teaching or coaching duties. All are necessary for the efficient operation of a school or other agency. Listed below are some of the duties assigned to physical education teachers.

*Administrative duties*
  Supervision of plant equipment
  General maintenance and repair of equipment and facilities
  Establishing office regulations and procedures, and carrying out departmental policies
  Formulating and administering budget
  Conducting inventories
  Preparing reports on various phases of work
  Maintaining records
  Administering intramural program
  Making arrangements for athletic events
  Securing officials
  Organizing and administering field and play days
  Organizing and administering interschool athletic program
  Preparing attendance reports
  Procuring supplies
  Planning in-service education programs
  Preparing notices and announcements
  Coordinating program with other departments
  Interviewing salesmen
  Developing curriculum materials

Preparing schedule for classes

Developing plan for determining pupil marks

Developing program for evaluation

*Special services and activities*

Administering first aid

Maintaining adequate sanitation

Speaking at various public gatherings

Writing for periodicals

Playground work

Establishing safety regulations and precautions

After-school recreation

Working with athletic association

Evening recreation

Working with such organizations as sport clubs, bowling clubs, leaders' clubs, Hi-Y, varsity clubs, booster clubs, and health clubs

Training cheerleaders

Organizing assembly programs concerned with health and physical education

Taking charge of a homeroom

Taking charge of a study hall

Directing school plays

Working with Parent–Teachers Association

Serving on faculty committees

Supervising cafeteria

Supervising noon-hour recreation

Serving as a school bus driver

Supervising student and faculty parking of cars

Chaperoning school affairs

Planning in-service education programs

Working with official and voluntary health agencies

## Implications that may be drawn from job analysis survey

Conclusions based upon the findings of this study, concerning the types and duties of positions in which physical educators serve may be summarized as follows:

1. The prospective teacher of physical education should be trained to assume administrative as well as teaching duties.

2. The number of positions in the country that involve health education as well as physical education duties is such that the prospective teacher should have adequate preparation in both areas. Health education should not be taught without adequate preparation.

3. Teachers of physical education should be familiar with the methods and materials in-volved in the coaching of basketball, softball, volleyball, baseball, track, touch football, swimming, tennis, soccer, field hockey (women only), football (men only), speedball, cross country (men only), golf, and bowling.

4. Teachers of physical education should be familiar with the methods and materials involved in the teaching of the following activities:

*Team games*—baseball, softball, basketball, touch football, volleyball, soccer, and field hockey (women only)

*Dual and individual sports*—track, badminton, table tennis, deck tennis, handball, horseshoes, tennis, archery, golf, and shuffleboard

*Rhythms and dancing*—social dancing, folk dancing, rhythms, gymnastic dancing, square dancing, tap dancing, and modern dancing

*Formal activities*—calisthenics and marching

*Aquatic activities*—swimming, diving, lifesaving, and aquatic games

*Outdoor winter sports*—skating, snow games, ice hockey, skiing, and tobogganing

*Gymnastics*—tumbling, pyramid building, apparatus, rope climbing, and acrobatics

*Other activities*—self-testing activities, relays, games of low organization; correctives, and camping and outdoor education

5. The teacher of physical education should be familiar with measurement and evaluation techniques in physical education, with especial emphasis on acceptable materials in each of the following areas:

*Organic tests*—cardiovascular, nutritional status, strength, physical fitness, etc.

*Skill tests*—general motor ability, general motor capacity, motor educability, achievement, etc.

*Physical education knowledge tests*—rules, attitudes, etc.

*Health education knowledge tests*—health knowledge, attitudes, etc.

*Adaptation tests*—character, personality, etc.

*Medical examinations*

*Program evaluation*—leadership, activities, time, etc.

6. The teacher of physical education should be prepared in subject-matter fields concerned with the following topics: first aid, safety, driver education, community health, hygiene, nutrition, physiology, and home nursing. In addition to such preparation, the teacher should also be familiar with the best procedures for conducting guidance conferences and administering vision and hearing tests.

7. The prospective teacher should be prepared to teach an academic field in addition to physical education. General science, biology, social studies, English, or mathematics is recommended.

8. The teacher of physical education should be well grounded in research methodology.

9. The teacher of physical education serves on all levels of instruction in the public schools.

10. The teacher of physical education should be prepared for duties other than teaching and coaching, including supervision of plant equipment, establishing office regulations and procedures, formulating and administering the budget, conducting inventories, preparing reports, maintaining records, making arrangements for athletic events, administering the intramural program, public speaking, writing, playground and recreation work, and scheduling.

## TIME ALLOTMENT FOR PHYSICAL EDUCATION IN THE UNITED STATES

Table 20-1 shows the results of a national survey of twenty public school systems in respect to: number of days per week for physical education, minutes of time usually allocated for physical education per period, and the total time granted to physical education per week. The table provides information on this basis for the elementary, junior high, and senior high schools in each school system surveyed. From a study of this table the prospective physical education teacher can better understand the place of physical education in the nation's schools.

## SECOND JOBS

According to the National Education Association Research Division survey, about one fifth of the teachers in this country have second jobs during the school year. This survey covered all teachers and positions and was not limited to those in physical education.

Although second jobs may be necessary

**Table 20-1.** *Time allotment in physical education*

| School systems | High school | | | Junior high | | | Elementary | | |
|---|---|---|---|---|---|---|---|---|---|
| | *Days/ week* | *Minutes/ period* | *Total/ week* | *Days/ week* | *Minutes/ period* | *Total/ week* | *Days/ week* | *Minutes/ period* | *Total/ week* |
| No. 1 | 2½ | 48 | 120 | 2½ | 48 | 120 | 1½ | 20 | 30 |
| No. 2 | 2 | 53 | 106 | 3 | 65 | 195 | 2½ | 30 | 75 |
| No. 3 | 2 | 45 | 90 | 3 | 45 | 135 | 1 | 45 | 45 |
| No. 4 | 2 | 46 | 92 | 2 | 46 | 92 | 2 | 45 | 90 |
| No. 5 | 2½ | 45 | 112 | 2½ | 45 | 112 | 2 | 30 | 60 |
| No. 6 | 5 | 40 | 200 | 5 | 40 | 200 | 2 | 38 | 76 |
| No. 7 | 3 | 42 | 126 | 3 | 42 | 126 | 2 | 30 | 60 |
| No. 8 | 5 | 48 | 240 | 3 | 45 | 135 | 2½ | 35 | 88 |
| No. 9 | 3½ | 44 | 154 | 3 | 45 | 135 | 2 | 35 | 70 |
| No. 10 | 2 | 45 | 90 | 3 | 45 | 135 | 5 | 30 | 150 |
| No. 11 | 5 | 50 | 250 | 5 | 30 | 150 | 5 | 30 | 150 |
| No. 12 | 5 | 60 | 300 | 3 | 60 | 180 | 5 | 30 | 150 |
| No. 13 | 5 | 52 | 260 | 5 | 52 | 260 | 5 | 40 | 200 |
| No. 14 | 2 | 45 | 90 | 2 | 45 | 90 | 2 | 45 | 90 |
| No. 15 | 2 | 43 | 86 | 2 | 40 | 80 | 2 | 30 | 60 |
| No. 16 | 5 | 55 | 275 | 5 | 55 | 275 | 2 | 45 | 90 |
| No. 17 | 2 | 45 | 90 | 2 | 45 | 90 | 5 | 25 | 125 |
| No. 18 | 2 | 50 | 100 | 2 | 50 | 100 | None | Recess only | |
| No. 19 | 3 | 60 | 180 | 3 | 45 | 135 | 5 | 30 | 150 |
| No. 20 | 2 | 53 | 106 | 2 | 50 | 100 | 1 | 45 | 45 |

in order to support a family when wages are low, this practice is discouraged except in emergency cases. This statement refers to second jobs during the school year and not during vacation periods.

Teaching physical education is a full-time job, not a part-time responsibility. Class preparation, conferences with students and parents, and intramurals and interschool athletic programs will utilize all the time and energy that a teacher has available. A teacher, like any human being, can give his or her best efforts only so many hours a day. When this limit has been reached, the law of diminishing returns sets in, and inferior services are rendered. The national survey of the National Education Association Research Division showed that all teachers, on the average, work 47.3 hours per week, with an average number of pupils per teacher in elementary school of 29 and in secondary school of 156. Probably physical education teachers exceed the national average in both instances.

## COMMUNITY DUTIES

Most physical education teachers throughout the country have community responsibilities. These are usually engaged in voluntarily. However, the special qualifications and skills of a physical education teacher make them a likely target for requests from community groups to assist with youth and other programs. Some of the more common agencies in which all teachers are affiliated are church activities, social or recreational clubs, fraternal or lodge activities, service clubs, civic welfare organizations, and political clubs.

Physical educators should be interested in providing leadership for their communities in programs involving sports, athletics, and recreational activities. By exercising a leadership role they can help to ensure that such programs are organized and administered in the best interests of youth and adults. It also offers an opportunity to interpret physical education to the public in general. In so doing, they become respected and important

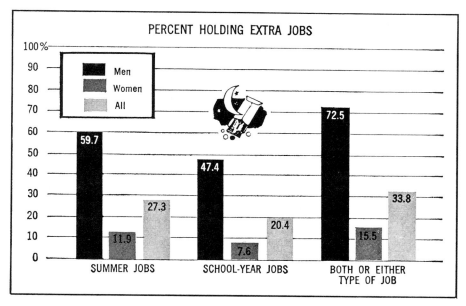

*NEA Research Division,*
*NEA Journal, April, 1963.*

Teachers holding extra jobs.

leaders in the community and gain greater support for their school program.

## BEGINNING TEACHER OF PHYSICAL EDUCATION

The beginning teacher of physical education is not going to find an ideal teaching situation when he or she assumes the first job. Many times the theory that prospective teachers have learned in the classroom is not applicable in a practical situation. The facilities may be limited, the community uninformed, the pupils disinterested, administrators and colleagues uncooperative, and other obstacles to be hurdled one at a time. However, new teachers should never lose the enthusiasm that prompted them to go into teaching. In time, through hard work and a whole-

some attitude, changes will occur and a more desirable teaching situation develop.

A few factors the beginning teacher should recognize in taking the first job are as follows:

1. *The workday and workweek will be long.* The physical education teacher can expect to work fifty, sixty, or seventy hours weekly. The many duties that need to be performed, students to see, obligations to render, all make for a long day and week. The beginning teacher should expect long hours, but if a good job is done, the rewards will be great.

2. *The daily schedule is strenuous.* The new teacher may find that she or he has to work through an entire day with the exception of a small break for lunch. Some schools require teachers of physical

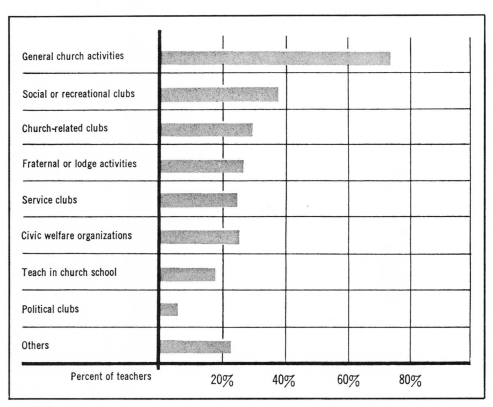

Teachers regularly take part in community activities.

education to supervise the parking lot before school, watch the lunch room at the noon hour, see students that need to be disciplined after school, monitor detention halls, and perform a hundred and one tasks. The new teacher should take these extra responsibilities with a smile. However, after a period of time has been spent on the job, there should be an attempt to eliminate some of these undesirable tasks so that more time can be given to the business of teaching.

3. *The clerical work is heavy.* The beginning teacher will find herself or himself completing monthly attendance forms, grade slips, requisitions for equipment, excuses, plus many other records requiring clerical work. All of these take time away from teaching and working with pupils and, as such, cannot be fully justified. However, the teacher should recognize this as part of the job and undertake the responsibility. A new trend called "teacher's aides" may be of help. Some communities are bringing in mothers and interested parents and citizens to take over some of the clerical work so that teachers can spend more time with their professional duties.

4. *The materials and facilities may be inadequate.* Certain materials, in the form of equipment and supplies, as well as adequate facilities in terms of teaching stations for physical education classes are essential. However, due to the cost, in many communities they are not provided. The beginning teacher should be sympathetic and understanding but, nevertheless, should strive to interpret the need for new materials and facilities so that a better teaching job can be accomplished. The American public must understand that if they want excellence in education it will cost money.

## QUESTIONS AND EXERCISES

1. Outline the duties of a teacher of physical education in a school where the enrollment consists of approximately 100 boys and 100 girls.
2. Visit an elementary, junior high, or senior high school and do a job analysis study of one of the physical education positions.
3. Why is it essential that the physical educator be prepared in areas other than physical education?
4. What are the responsibilities of physical educational personnel in respect to each of the following: (a) objectives, (b) program, (c) leadership, (d) measurement and evaluation, and (e) reevaluation?
5. Why is good leadership essential to the realization of the objectives of physical education?
6. In what capacities do physical education teachers serve? What implications does this have for a student's preparation?
7. For what coaching responsibilities should the potential teacher of physical education prepare?
8. What physical education activities are taught in the public schools? To what extent is your teacher-training institution preparing you to teach these activities?
9. Why is a knowledge of measurement and evaluation techniques essential to the student training for the profession of physical education?
10. What duties do many physical education teachers have in the field of health education?
11. For what duties, in areas other than physical education, should the student be trained?
12. Why is a well-rounded, general education background essential to a teacher of physical education in the light of the duties he or she will perform?
13. What implications for the student of physical education may be drawn from the job-analysis survey reported in this chapter?
14. Write an article of approximately 250 words describing the extent to which your training is preparing you to discharge the duties as outlined in this chapter.

## SELECTED REFERENCES

American Association for Health, Physical Education, and Recreation: Fit to teach, Washington, D. C., 1957, The Association.
American Association for Health, Physical Education, and Recreation: Careers in physical education for girls: a key to your future, Washington, D. C., 1964, The Association.
American Association for Health, Physical Edu-

cation, and Recreation: Physical education and coaching as a career, Washington, D. C., The Association.

Bucher, Charles A.: A professional curriculum in health and physical education for the State Teachers College at New Haven, Connecticut, Doctoral Thesis, 1948, New York University, pp. 56-77.

Bucher, Charles A.: Field days, Journal of Health and Physical Education **19:**22, Jan., 1948.

Bucher, Charles A.: Administration of school health and physical education programs, St. Louis, 1967, The C. V. Mosby Co.

Bucher, Charles A., and Reade, Evelyn M.: Physical education in the modern elementary school, New York, 1964, The Macmillan Co.

Bucher, Charles A., Koening, Constance, and Barnhard, Milton: Methods and materials of secondary school physical education, St. Louis, 1965, The C. V. Mosby Co.

Cassidy, Rosalind: Counseling in the physical education program, New York, 1959, Appleton-Century-Crofts, Inc.

Evans, Ruth, and Gans, Leo: Supervision of physical education, New York, 1950, McGraw-Hill Book Co.

Fischer, John H.: Should you be a teacher? New York, 1964, Career Information Service, New York Life Insurance Co.

Graybeal, Elizabeth: A consideration of qualities used by administrators in judging effective teachers of physical education in Minnesota, Research Quarterly, AAHPER **12:** 741, Dec., 1941.

Hindman, Darwin A.: An analysis of the ac-tivities of physical education teachers in high schools, Research Quarterly, AAHPER **7:**117, May, 1937.

Johnson, Ralph H.: Selection of men students for professional training in physical education, Research Quarterly, AAHPER **20:**307, Oct., 1949.

LaPorte, William Ralph: A job analysis of the functions of the physical education teacher, Journal of Health and Physical Education **7:** 550, Nov., 1936.

LaPorte, William Ralph: A job analysis of the functions of the physical education teacher, Los Angeles, 1951, The University of Southern California Press.

Latchaw, Marjorie, and Brown, Camille: The evaluation process in health education, physical education, and recreation, Englewood Cliffs, N. J., 1962, Prentice-Hall, Inc.

Meyers, Carlton R., and Blesh, T. Erwin: Measurement in physical education, New York, 1962, The Ronald Press Co.

Phi Delta Kappa: Teaching as a man's job, Bloomington, Indiana, 1963, Phi Delta Kappa.

Snyder, Raymond, and Scott, Harry: Professional preparation in health, physical education, and recreation, New York, 1954, McGraw-Hill Book Co.

Stinnett, T. M., and Haskew, L. D.: Teaching in American schools: a handbook for the future teacher, New York, 1962, Harcourt, Brace & World.

United States Department of Health, Education, and Welfare, Office of Education: Teaching as a career, Circular No. OE-2604, Pamphlet No. 122, Washington, D. C., 1965, Government Printing Office.

# Chapter 21

# Professional preparation in physical education

Many years ago, Johann Heinrich Pestalozzi, the great Swiss educator, pointed out the responsibility that rests with the teaching profession. He stressed the fact that the educator must understand the full significance of man himself and human nature, and that no profession requires greater skill in order to guide human nature properly. What is true of the professional preparation of all teachers is true of the preparation of physical education teachers as well.

The student of physical education, as well as physical education personnel in the field, should be familiar with all aspects of professional preparation in physical education. Such information will help interested persons to realize what constitutes adequate training for physical education leaders. In turn, they can bring their influence to bear upon teacher-training institutions so that proper preparation will be provided. To a great degree teacher-preparing institutions have decided—on their own—how physical education teachers should be selected and trained. Many have failed in this responsibility and consequently physical education has lost prestige and respect in the eyes of the public. Good leadership is one of the basic needs in this field today.

## OBJECTIVES OF PROFESSIONAL PREPARATION

The goals of professional preparation have been set forth by many professional organizations. These goals include the need to graduate educated men and women who are prepared and committed to teaching, to influence not only the intellectual life of students, but also the emotional and ethical aspects of their professional careers, and to acquaint these prospective teachers with the rights and responsibilities of professional service.

According to the American Association for Health, Physical Education, and Recreation, the objectives of professional preparation are as follows[*]:

1. Professional preparation should assist students to see the relationship between their field of work and the philosophy of a free democratic society.

---

[*]American Association for Health, Physical Education, and Recreation: Professional preparation in health education, physical education, and recreation education, Washington, D. C., 1962, The Association.

Goals of professional preparation should include the need to graduate educated men and women.

2. Professional preparation should have as one of its goals the development of broadly educated persons.

3. Professional preparation should be a responsibility of the college or university—not some subdivision of the institution.

4. Professional preparation is a responsibility of the profession, the preparing institution, and also those organizations that employ the trained specialists.

5. In the final analysis, the profession itself has the responsibility for the training of its practitioners.

6. The preparing institution should be given increased authority in the process of certifying school personnel.

7. Professional-preparing programs should have as one of their goals the maintenance and improvement of professional standards.

8. Professional-preparing programs should assist the teacher to become as effective as possible on the job.

9. Five years of preparation are desirable in the training process.

10. Professional preparation is a continuous process and does not terminate when a student graduates and receives his degree.

11. Professional-preparing programs must be sensitive to societal changes.

12. Professional-preparing programs should be evaluated periodically.

13. Professional-preparing programs should instill in each student a personal philosophy

that embraces a dedication to the service of mankind.

## BEGINNINGS OF TEACHER EDUCATION IN PHYSICAL EDUCATION

Since the first class of teachers was graduated from the Normal Institute of Physical Education in Boston in 1861, the preparation of teachers in physical education has progressed rapidly. The ten weeks' course at this institution, founded by Dio Lewis, had regular instruction in hygiene, physiology, anatomy, and gymnastics, in addition to an interpretation of and practical work in the "Swedish Movement Cure."

The North American Turnerbund, the second normal school for the training of teachers in physical education, opened its doors in 1866 in New York City, offering a one-year course. Of the nineteen men who started in attendance, only five received diplomas at the end of the first course. Later the school was moved to Chicago, back to New York, and then to Milwaukee until 1888. In 1889 the school was transferred to Indianapolis for two years, was then moved back to Milwaukee, and, finally, in 1907 it was situated permanently in Indianapolis. Gymnastics and gymnastic nomenclature were emphasized, with much concern for medical gymnastics as well as for fencing and swimming.

Dr. Dudley Allen Sargent, one of the early leaders in physical education in America, brought his influence to bear on teacher preparation starting in 1881. The Sargent School, as it was called, trained almost exclusively women who planned to teach physical education. From 1887 to 1919 Dr. Sargent also directed the Harvard University summer courses in physical education.

The Brooklyn Normal School for Physical Education, under the directorship of Dr. William C. Anderson, came into existence in 1886. This school placed principal emphasis upon training the student in the theory and practice of gymnastics. Shortly after the opening of the school in Brooklyn, Dr. Anderson was named to the position of Associate Director of the Yale University Gymnasium in New Haven. With this appointment, the Normal School was moved to New Haven and became the Anderson Normal School of Gymnastics. Dr. Ernst H. Arnold became the director in 1896, and in 1901 the school was named the New Haven Normal School of Gymnastics, eventually to become the Arnold College of Hygiene and Physical Education.

In the year of 1886 the start of the International Young Men's Christian Association College at Springfield, Massachusetts, was witnessed. This college, better known as Springfield College, offered a professional course for young men who expected to teach physical education in the Young Men's Christian Association. Later the degrees of Bachelor of Physical Education, Master of Physical Education, Bachelor of Science, Master of Education, and Doctor of Physical Education were granted, and many of its graduates accepted positions in public school teaching, as well as other related fields. In 1890 a similar training school was opened in Chicago.

In 1889 Mrs. Mary Hemenway established, and later endowed, the Boston Normal School of Gymnastics, which in 1909 became the Department of Hygiene and Physical Education of Wellesley. Baron Posse, a teacher in this Normal School, organized his own gymnasium in 1890, calling it the Posse Normal School of Gymnastics. The school remained under his direction until his death in 1895, at which time Baroness Rose Posse carried on as director. In 1915 Mr. Hartvig Nissen was secured as its president, and the school became known as the Posse-Nissen School of Physical Education.

Previous to World War I, physical educators received their professional preparation primarily in normal schools. A study made by Ruth Elliot in 1927 lists the private normal schools of physical education engaged in training physical education personnel, the date of their establishment, and the length of curricula. This list, shown in Table 21-1, is significant since it indicates the gradual lengthening of curricula in the training of prospective physical education teachers.

## TEACHER EDUCATION IN COLLEGES AND UNIVERSITIES

The colleges and universities soon followed the normal schools in the preparation of teachers in physical education. The University of Washington, with a professional course in physical education organized in 1896, is usually thought of as the first of the state universities to offer work in this area. However, in 1894 Bowen, at the State Normal School at Ypsilanti, Michigan, was responsible for the first attempt to train teachers in physical education in a state-controlled institution.

The University of California, Indiana University, and the University of Nebraska initiated courses in this area from 1897 to 1898, placing particular emphasis upon the areas of anthropometry, physical examinations, anatomy, physiology of exercise, hygienic gymnastics, and the history of physical culture.

In the early 1900's privately endowed colleges and universities began to consider training for leadership in physical education. Oberlin College in 1900, Teachers College, Columbia University, in 1903, and Wellesley College in 1909 were among the first of these.

In the early part of the twentieth century, the larger secondary schools began to call for full-time teachers of physical education. State legislation and requirements had much to do with this demand for more emphasis upon teacher training in physical education. Shortly after the First World War, approximately thirty-five states passed legislation requiring the teaching of health and physical education in the public schools. Such legislation was a tremendous stimulant to teacher preparation in the field of physical education. Until this time, efforts along this line were mainly directed at training gymnastic teachers. The typical curriculum in many of the earlier schools consisted of some theoretical courses, such as anatomy of the bones and muscles, gymnastic nomenclature, and methods in gymnastics and marching. These were included in the program in order to supplement the training received on the gymnasium floor.

A few outstanding leaders in the field of education began to look beyond the mere teaching of gymnastics and subjects related to it and emphasize subjects rich in cultural background, foundation sciences, and courses in the general field of education. In the early 1920's courses in education began to be introduced, as well as courses concerned with psychology, fundamental sciences, and methodology. The education of the physical education teacher became an important consideration.

With the advent of courses in physical education in some of the larger universities, leading to a bachelor's degree with a major in physical education, more and more of the graduates found their way into elementary schools and subsequently into the secondary field. An increasing number of teachers were being prepared, which brought forth a steady upgrading of requirements for teachers' certificates.

One by one the various states began to require four years of training with a degree, and it was not unusual to find minimum requirements in courses in education, psychology, and foundation sciences, as well as courses in physical education.

**Table 21-1.** *Normal schools of physical education**

| Name of school | Date established | Length of present curricula in years | Degrees granted | Affiliation with college or university |
|---|---|---|---|---|
| Normal College of the American Gymnastic Union, Indianapolis, Ind. | 1866 | 1,2,3,4 | BPE, MPE | |
| Sargent School of Physical Education, Cambridge, Mass. | 1881 | 3 | | |
| Arnold College of Hygiene and Physical Education (New Haven Normal School of Gymnastics) | 1886 | 2,3 | BPE | |
| International Y.M.C.A. College, Springfield, Mass. | 1886 | 2, 4 | BPE, MPE | |
| Chautauqua School of Physical Education, Chautauqua, N. Y. | 1888 | 1, 3 | BS, M ED | New York University |
| Formerly Boston Normal School of Gymnastics, Boston, Mass. | 1889 | 2, 5† | MS, AB | 1909 became Department of Hygiene and Physical Education, Wellesley College |
| School of Physical Education, Y.M.C.A. College, Chicago, Ill. | 1890 | 4 | BPE | |
| Posse-Nissen School of Physical Education, Boston, Mass. | 1890 | 1, 3 | | |
| Savage School of Physical Education, New York, N. Y. | 1898 | 3 | | |
| Chicago Normal School of Physical Education, Chicago, Ill. | 1903 | 1,2,3 | | |
| American College of Physical Education, Chicago, Ill. | 1908 | 2,3,4 | BPE | |
| Battle Creek College, School of Physical Education, Battle Creek, Mich. | 1909 | 3,4 | BS in PE | |
| Boston School of Physical Education, Boston, Mass. | 1913 | 3 | | Boston University |
| Columbia Normal School of Physical Education, Chicago, Ill. | 1913 | (3 mo., 2-6 mo., 9 mo.) | | |
| Newark School of Hygiene and Physical Education, Newark, N. J. | 1917 | 2,3 | | |
| Central School of Hygiene and Physical Education, New York, N. Y. | 1919 | 3 | | New York University |
| Marjorie Webster School Expression Physical Education, Washington, D. C. | 1920 | 1,2 | BPE | |
| Ithaca School of Physical Education, Ithaca, N. Y. | 1923 | 3,4 | BPE | |
| Bouve School of Physical Education, Boston, Mass. | 1925 | 3 | | |

*Elliot, Ruth: The organization of professional training in physical education in state universities, New York, 1927, Teachers College Contributions to Education, No. 268, Columbia University, p. 9.
†For college graduates only.

*Sargent Camp, Boston University, Boston, Mass.*

A phase of the teacher education program.

More and more the schools began to ask for full-time specialists in physical education, and both men and women interested in this field rushed to the teacher-training institutions.

The rapid influx of prospective teachers in this area, together with the renewed emphasis upon teacher training, resulted in the abandonment of two-year and three-year training courses and the establishment of four-year curricula. Many normal schools became teachers' colleges with degree-granting privileges, and, in general, the quality of training improved. The period from 1920 to 1930, when institutions such as New York University, Teachers College, Columbia University,

and Springfield College began to offer courses beyond the first four years of college, was indeed a milestone in the advancement of the professional preparation of teachers of physical education.

A noticeable change took place in the field of education when in 1930 the financial depression began to be felt in the schools. The teaching of physical education was discontinued in many schools or combined with the teaching of other subjects. Few new teachers were hired, and this resulted in an oversupply of those trained in this field. Teacher-training institutions revised their programs and began to make a more careful selection of students, and some states raised the certification requirements to five years of study. The inevitable result was a decided improvement in the training of teachers in physical education.

Important in professional-preparing programs after 1920 until the present was the initiation of more stringent admission requirements by teacher-training institutions. Selective admission, guidance, entrance examinations, and a more careful look at candidates became considerations at several institutions of higher learning.

Another point of concern was professional curricula. More emphasis on general education, together with a closer examination of the professional education and specialization courses, became evident. The need for a broad training in all aspects of physical education, rather than just in coaching or other specialty, came into being. Furthermore, since 1926 there has been a definite trend away from medical training for specialists directing physical education programs in colleges.

The Cooperative Study in Teacher Education sponsored by the American Council on Education, 1938 to 1943; the reviving of the American Association for Health, Physical Education, and Recreation's Cooperative Study Committee, including representatives from many professional organizations; the Miami University, Oxford, Ohio, Conference in 1947; and the Report on Teacher Education by the American Association of Teachers Colleges in 1948 helped to raise professional standards in physical education.

A series of professional-preparing conferences have been held in recent years, starting with the Jackson's Mill Conference in 1948. One of the most important meetings was the Professional Preparing Conference held in January, 1962.* The

purpose of the conference was to improve the training of teachers in health and safety education, physical education, and recreation and outdoor education, at the undergraduate level, and to give some direction to graduate study. The conference accomplished such things as the following:

1. Developed principles and standards for each of the special areas in respect to philosophy and objectives, organization and administration, student personnel, faculty, curriculums, professional laboratory experiences, and facilities and instructional materials for teacher education
2. Outlined the professional competencies needed in each area
3. Defined ways of improving the professional stature of personnel
4. Identified the kinds of experience by which trainees could develop the essential knowledge and skill needed for outstanding leadership
5. Outlined guidelines for the implementation of the conference report

The complete report is available from the American Association for Health, Physical Education, and Recreation.

Another report, by James B. Conant,* also represented a milestone in the training of teachers. This report recommended some new departures from the traditional pattern of training and certifying teachers by suggesting such procedures as the following:

1. The university should assume the responsibility for endorsing and attesting that the student was properly trained for teaching, and that the president of the institution, on behalf of the faculty, certifies that the candidate is adequately prepared to teach.
2. The institution of higher learning should establish, in conjunction with a public school system, a state-approved, practice teaching arrangement.

*American Association for Health, Physical Education, and Recreation: Professional preparation in health education, physical education, and recreation education, Washington, D. C., 1962, the Association.

*Conant, James Bryant: The education of American teachers, New York, 1963, McGraw-Hill Book Co.

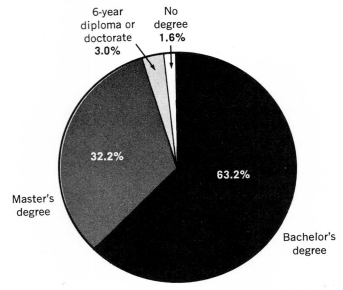

6-year diploma or doctorate 3.0%

No degree 1.6%

32.2%

Master's degree

63.2%

Bachelor's degree

*NEA Research Bulletin 45:12, March, 1967.*

Professional preparation of male teachers in respect to degrees held, 1965-1966.

3. An institution offering programs in art, music, or physical education should award a teaching diploma in these fields without grade distinction.
4. Graduate preparation in physical education was not necessary.
5. There should be an all-university approach to teacher training, with the liberal arts professors and departments sharing with the education professors the professional preparation of teachers.
6. Clinical professorships should be established where the professors would work with student teachers in the school internship program.
7. Physical education should not be given credit in elementary and secondary schools.

There were also several other recommendations in the Conant report in respect to the composition of accrediting agencies, certification reciprocity among states, revision of salary schedules by local boards of education, financial assistance to teachers for study in summer schools, and master's degree programs.

A new type of program for the professional preparation of teachers is being conducted by Northwestern University. It is a clinical and tutorial program designed to provide students who are going to be teachers with a firm foundational education in the arts and sciences. The program includes seminars and tutorials and clinical work in elementary schools and high schools. Methods courses as traditionally known have been eliminated. Much of the program is designed after the recommendations set forth by James B. Conant in his book *The Education of American Teachers*. Participating at Northwestern University from the faculty are two new types of staff members: (1) an education professor of interdisciplinary studies who plans and coordinates the work of the school of education and the college of arts and sciences, and (2) a clinical professor who works with the public schools as a teacher and also conducts seminars on classroom problems as part of the faculty of Northwestern University.

Another new type of program exists in nine Oregon colleges, where students going into teaching have a more extensive opportunity to do classroom teaching, and thus to correlate and integrate theory with practice. These experiences are in the form of internships where the colleges place intern–teachers in the public schools of the state of Oregon, and where they have the opportunity to find out what actual teaching is like and the problems involved in such an experience.

A conference on graduate education in health education, physical education, recreation education, dance, and safety was held in January, 1967. The purpose of this conference was to suggest principles and standards to improve graduate education in the special areas. The conference accomplished such tasks as the following:

1. Defined the nature of graduate education at the master's and doctoral levels, the functions of graduate education, and the competencies needed in research and other areas
2. Developed guidelines for the organization of graduate programs in respect to such things as student personnel, curriculum, instructional methodology, laboratory experiences, and facilities and materials
3. Explored new programs
4. Reviewed research completed in the area of professional preparation
5. Suggested new graduate program possibilities

Teacher education in physical education has continued to expand. After World War I and again after World War II great eras of expanding teacher education programs have developed in various colleges and universities. In 1918 there were twenty institutions preparing teachers of physical education; in 1929, 139; in 1944, 295; in 1946, approximately 361; and today, over 700.

Along with the growth of teacher education institutions in physical education there has developed a growing concern as to the type of preparation that is needed for training potential physical education personnel. In the future a better selection and a better training of physical educators should be seen. This will be in keeping with the objectives of the physical education profession to serve society in the best way possible.

## CURRENT STATUS OF PROFESSIONAL PREPARATION PROGRAMS

More than half of the approximately 2,200 institutions of higher learning in the United States prepare teachers for the elementary and secondary schools. Approximately one third of those teachers graduated each year are graduates of schools of education located in about 160 major universities. Another third of the graduating teachers are graduates of institutions of higher learning that have as their primary responsibility the preparation of teachers. The remaining third of graduating teachers are trained in departments of education in some 900 liberal arts colleges. A noticeable trend in those institutions primarily geared to training teachers is that they have become, and are becoming, liberal arts colleges with names and titles such as state colleges or even state universities.

In respect to certification of teachers and the implications for professional preparing programs, forty-five states require four years of college for elementary teaching and all states require at least four years for a teaching certificate at the secondary school level. Better than 90% of public school teachers have bachelor's degrees and approximately 25% have master's degrees. Most states issue temporary certificates for teaching.

A study conducted by the American Association for Health, Physical Education, and Recreation Professional Panel* identified 5,000 physical educators, health educators, and recreation education persons whose primary responsibility was in

---

*American Association for Health, Physical Education, and Recreation: Professional preparation, Journal of Health, Physical Education, and Recreation **36**:71, April, 1965.

the area of professional preparation. Furthermore, more than 700 institutions of higher learning were identified that offer a major preparation program in one or more of the three special areas. The Identification Summary was as follows:

**IDENTIFICATION SUMMARY**

1. Number of institutions responding to the request — 680
2. Members of institutions identified and not responding to the request — 50
3. Number of professional preparation personnel by area of specialization:
   a. Administrative — 650
   b. Health education, physical education, and recreation education — 350
   c. Health education — 400
   d. Physical education — 2,600
   e. Recreation education — 175
   f. Health education and physical education — 600
   g. Physical education and recreation education — 225

Total professional persons identified — 5,000

In respect to qualifications for teaching in professional preparing programs, the author conducted a survey of administrators who did the hiring in 65 institutions of higher learning. The survey revealed that, in respect to degrees attained, 76% of the administrators felt it was *very important,* 20% considered it *important,* and 4% *not very important* that staff members hold at least a master's degree. Fifty-six percent of the administrators felt it was *very important,* 42% felt it was *important,* and 2% felt it was *not very important* for professional preparing programs in health, physical education and recreation to have staff members who are specialists in a particular phase of the special field, such as adapted physical education. In respect to teacher qualifications, 56% of the administrators surveyed indicated that they felt it *very important,* 38% felt it was *important,* and 6% *not very important* for staff members to have knowledge of educational methods and psychological principles related to

what they were teaching. Fifty percent of the hiring administrators felt it was *very important,* 40% felt it was *important,* and 10% felt it was *not very important* for staff members to have previous teaching experience in elementary and secondary schools. Thirty-two percent of the administrators wanted staff members to have previous college teaching. In respect to qualifications for coaches, 40% of the administrators felt it was *very important,* 38% felt it was *important,* and 22% felt it was *not very important* that the candidates have expert knowledge and experience in coaching a particular sport and the techniques involved.

Recently, the author participated in a survey of the professional preparation curriculums in physical education at ten selected colleges and universities throughout the United States. This survey considered the degree offered, undergraduate admission requirements, courses offered in the area of general education and educational theory, and specialized courses required in physical education.

All of the colleges and universities in the survey awarded the bachelor's degree to men, and nine of these schools also offered a bachelor's degree program for women. One school awarded a combined degree in health and physical education for men on both the bachelor's and the master's levels. Of the ten schools, nine also had graduate programs leading to the master's degree, and two had programs on the doctoral level.

All of the schools surveyed required a high school diploma for admission. Seven required that the applicant take the Scholastic Aptitude Test of the College Entrance Examination Board, and an additional school required this test for nonresidents of the state only. One of the schools required applicants to take both a state admissions test and a test of physical skills, but did not require the Scholastic Aptitude Test. High school units required for entrance totaled fifteen or sixteen units, depending on the college or university, and included such academic courses as English, social studies, mathematics, science, and foreign languages.

Courses required in general education during the undergraduate years by the colleges and universities in the survey included English and speech, mathematics and statistics, the humanities, art, music, philosophy, social sciences, psychology, sociology, history, foreign languages, natural and physical sciences, zoology, chemistry, physics, anatomy, bacteriology, and physiology.

All but one of the schools surveyed required three credit hours in educational psychology. Other educational theory courses included requirements ranging from two to six credit hours in such areas as adolescent psychology, educational sociology, history and philosophy of education, organization and administration of schools, and methods of teaching.

In the area of professional specialization, nine of the schools surveyed required from two to six credits in physical education methods, while eight schools required courses in physical education for the atypical child. All ten institutions required courses in the introduction to physical education, the organization and administration of physical education, tests and measurements in physical education, physical education skills courses, and a student teaching experience. Nine of the schools required from two to four credits in applied anatomy, and nine schools required from two to five credits in the history and principles of physical education. Other courses in the field of specialization required in the various schools were: the physical education curriculum, physiology of exercise, care and prevention of athletic injuries, methods of coaching, health courses, first aid, safety education, and courses in recreation and camping. Two schools included a twelve-credit teaching

minor in its requirements, while one school included a thirty-credit teaching minor.

Of the ten colleges and universities surveyed, one school required a total of 120 points for graduation with a bachelor's degree in physical education, four schools required 124 credits, one school required 125 credits, one school listed 130 credits, and one listed 131 credits. Two of the schools required a total of 192 credits for graduation.

In a study of methods used by professors in teacher training programs in physical education, health and recreation, the following methods were utilized: lecture method, group reports and discussions, problem-solving techniques, guest lecturers, laboratory experiences, and audiovisual aids.

An article in the *NEA Journal** indicated the reactions of several hundred college students in respect to methods that were used in the college classroom. These are presented in adapted form as follows:

1. Professors should not read from lecture notes.
2. Professors should not repeat in lectures what is in the textbook.
3. Better planning is needed and professors should not ramble so much.
4. Departments should coordinate better different sections of the same course.
5. Professors should get to know their students, especially the level of their experience and their backgrounds.
6. Professors should involve all the students in discussions.
7. Professors should cultivate the skill of lecturing.
8. Professors should base quizzes on significant material.
9. Assignments should be less vague and hasty.
10. Repetition of course content should be avoided.
11. Small classes should be taught differently than large ones.

---

*Shane, Harold G.: How do they rate you, professor? NEA Journal 54:18, Nov., 1965.

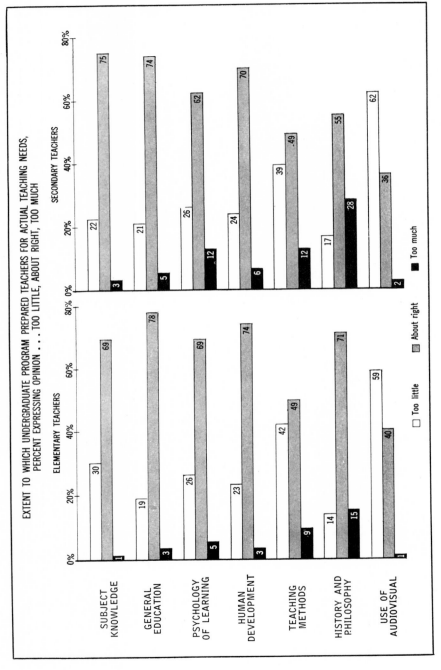

EXTENT TO WHICH UNDERGRADUATE PROGRAM PREPARED TEACHERS FOR ACTUAL TEACHING NEEDS, PERCENT EXPRESSING OPINION . . . TOO LITTLE, ABOUT RIGHT, TOO MUCH

ELEMENTARY TEACHERS

SECONDARY TEACHERS

□ Too little    ▨ About right    ■ Too much

SUBJECT KNOWLEDGE
GENERAL EDUCATION
PSYCHOLOGY OF LEARNING
HUMAN DEVELOPMENT
TEACHING METHODS
HISTORY AND PHILOSOPHY
USE OF AUDIOVISUAL

12. Contemporary courses should be more up to date.
13. Rote learning should not be stressed where it is not necessary.
14. Professors should not make life unnecessarily difficult for their students.

The National Education Association Research Division surveyed a cross section of public school teachers to find out whether they thought teacher preparation programs were geared to actual teaching needs. The results are charted in the illustration on page 640.

## ACCREDITATION

Accreditation in the area of professional preparation is a system or evaluation procedure that vouches for officially or certifies that certain colleges and universities have approved programs for training physical education teachers. Three ways in which accreditation can take place is by governmental agencies such as state departments of education, regional accrediting agencies such as the Northcentral Association for Colleges and Secondary Schools, and professional associations. The American Association for Health, Physical Education, and Recreation has long been interested in accreditation and has tried to develop an effective system. However, it was not until the representative assembly and the board of directors of this association approved recommendations for accreditation that strength was put into the process. The official action in 1960 provides for such important regulations, as the following:

1. The National Council for Accreditation of Teacher Education (NCATE) is the official accrediting organization for physical education, health education, and recreation, and AAHPER recognizes programs approved by NCATE.
2. State departments of education are encouraged to grant teacher certification only to graduates of institutions accredited by NCATE.
3. Professional organizations, such as the American Association of School Administrators, are urged by AAHPER to hire only teachers of health, physical education, and recreation who graduate from institutions accredited by NCATE.
4. Professional membership in AAHPER is contingent upon evidence of an earned bachelor's degree or advanced degrees from institutions accredited by NCATE. Student professional membership is contingent upon attending such institutions. Furthermore, state associations are urged to follow the example set by the national association.

These requirements represent a major stride forward in preparing leaders for the professions of physical education, health, and recreation who are qualified and adequately prepared for their work.

What does NCATE accreditation mean to the graduate of an accredited school? This is a question that every student should ask. First of all, school and college administrators will be very hesitant to hire any person who has not graduated from an accredited school. Second, it helps in moving from one state to another and taking a position in another section of the country. In fact, some states do not require the applicant to meet all the detailed state certification regulations if he has graduated from a college that has NCATE endorsement. Third, NCATE-endorsed programs are better planned, have higher standards of admission and retention, better staff, higher professional requirements in general, and render more outstanding professional services to their students and graduates. These are a few reasons why each student and teacher has a personal stake in, and responsibility for, the accreditation of teacher education programs.

## SELECTED CURRENT DEVELOPMENTS IN TEACHER EDUCATION PROGRAMS

Selected current developments in teacher education which have strong implications for the training of physical education teachers are discussed in the following paragraphs.

### Teacher education—a campus-wide concern

As a result of the Conant report and other reports, teacher education is becoming a campus-wide concern. This is evidenced by faculty members in all departments of a college and university playing key roles in professional preparing programs. This is being accomplished by courses being taught by experts in the various disciplines throughout a college and university, rather than confining the staff to merely the school of education or to educationists. Professors and administrators in various departments and colleges are serving on planning committees, administrative councils, and other groups, to advise and plan teacher education programs. All-university and all-college committees are evaluating teacher education programs and making recommendations for their upgrading. Admission requirements and professional standards that are college-wide and university-wide are being applied to those students who are preparing to be teachers, as well as to students in other departments, schools, and colleges. Students in professional teacher preparing programs are able and encouraged to take courses in general psychology, philosophy, and courses in other departments, schools, and colleges throughout the university.

By becoming a campus-wide concern, teacher education in physical education should benefit. Majors in physical education should become better educated, have a broader background, be exposed to the teachings of outstanding professors, and have the backing and approval of a much larger segment of the academic community.

### Stress on general education

The world is experiencing an age of specialization, and the prospective teacher must have training in the various phases of his particular field. However, there is still a genuine need for a broad background of knowledge in all areas of learning. In order that an individual may assume his duties and responsibilities as a good teacher and also as a good citizen, he should be able to understand, think, and talk intelligently about his profession and the complexities of life as a whole.

Teachers need a broad cultural background instead of the limited educational background. If they are to be leaders in a society that desperately needs good leadership, they must not only have a knowledge of the total educative process but also a broad view and mastery of such things as the achievements of the human race; the fine arts; the English language; current political, social, and economic factors; the physical environment; and human institutions in general. The teacher must realize that he is not an isolated factor in a brick school building but, instead, is a dynamic force, possessing potentialities that will aid in solving local, state, national, and international problems.

**Functions of general education.** To be more specific, what are some of the functions of a broad, general education that will enable the teacher to be a more potent force toward bettering the society in which the student lives?

First, a broad, general background is especially necessary in our society because of the American way of life. A democracy such as ours provides for the election of public officials and leaders by the public. The teacher can do much toward laying the foundations for an informed citizenry. Through such a medium, our form of government will better serve the welfare of the constituents for which it has been established.

Second, a broad, general background will help the teacher to recognize his responsibility as a worker, a parent, a citizen, and a human being. With an accumulation of knowledge that concerns various areas of learning comes a better understanding of the place of the individual in society. A broad, general background respects and cultivates such desirable characteristics as initiative, responsibility, and integrity. It produces citizens who reason things out for themselves, weigh controversial issues from all angles, and act only after careful thought and deliberation. It recognizes the dignity of labor, no matter how menial the task. It recognizes the important place of the home and parents in the preservation of a well-ordered society. Finally, it promotes human equality and recognizes that talent, intelligence, and individual accomplishment are no respecters of race, creed, or economic status.

Third, a broad, general education can enrich the meaning of life and the social service of the individual. A broad, general background is concerned with individuals who live together, work together, and strive to accomplish common goals together. It stresses the importance of an individual's living more satisfactorily with himself and with others. It aids in promoting an understanding of one's fellowmen that is based on human ideals. It aims at an understanding of the individual in relation to contemporary institutions and problems of American and world life. Finally, it emphasizes an appreciation of selective fields of cultural material that makes life more satisfying and enjoyable.

**General education for teacher of physical education.** Although it has been previously indicated that teachers in general need a broad educational background, evidence points to the fact that this is especially true for the teacher of physical education. Such a specialist holds a strategic position. The nature of his work, his close personal contact with students, his place of leadership in the community, and the necessity for the coordination of

his field with other phases of the school program have implications that in many ways do not exist for the general classroom or subject-matter teacher.

Persons who are specialists in the curricula of teacher-training institutions agree that the training must prepare this prospective teacher to adjust to new and changing social conditions and to fit into a complex society. Such training will not accomplish this purpose unless the student is given a broad background in the various areas of learning. In this way he may become aware of the history of current social, economic, and political problems; he will appreciate the accomplishments of man, will have a mastery of the means of communication, will understand human relations, and will have an understanding of educational offerings other than his own specialty. Such training will make provisions for such things as a mastery of the English language, both oral and written, the social studies, the biological and physical sciences, and the fine arts.

Teachers of physical education possess many commendable qualities that make them stand out in the field of education. Many members of the profession occupy positions of leadership throughout the country. When they assume such responsible positions, the prestige of the profession should not be lessened through their use of crude and careless language expressions, promotion of physical education as an end in itself, inability to converse or write in an intelligent manner, or a lack of knowledge of current world affairs.

The evidence is ample that the prospective teacher of physical education should receive a broad background in the various areas of knowledge. The curriculum should be flexible to ensure that deficiencies in such important areas as English, social studies, science, and the fine arts may be made up whenever necessary to provide adequate preparation for the profession.

If those who carry on the physical education program are to be leaders in society, they must possess a cultural training that will gain them the respect of the students, faculty, administration, and the community. The individual who has secured his position primarily because he was an outstanding athlete on some college team, despite the fact that he may have language difficulties and lack breadth of knowledge, must become a thing of the past if the profession is to continue growing. Teacher education should guarantee a health and physical education teacher who is enlightened, purposeful, and productive of good results. This is an age when a man must be an expert in the performance of his duties as an intelligent citizen as well as in some particular vocation.

### Importance of understanding child growth and development

At no time in our educational history has there been so much talk about "knowing the child" as there is at present. Therefore, there is a feeling among leaders in teacher education that more emphasis should be placed upon child growth and development in the training of future teachers. Teachers should know and understand the children with whom they spend so much time. Teachers should know why children behave in certain ways and under what conditions they learn best. A teacher cannot be successful in her job unless she is acquainted with this basic knowledge. Many of the faults of schools today come from the fact that teachers have been appointed to positions on school faculties because of their knowledge of subject matter and without reference to their knowledge of child growth and development.

This emphasis upon child growth and development cannot be limited to the incorporation of one course in the curriculum. Instead, it must saturate the entire training period. There must be a feeling on the part of all instructors and students that a knowledge of the child is of prime importance. However, there may be a course or sequence of courses to aid in rounding out a program and to aid in crystallizing the student's understanding of children.

### Stress on student teaching

It is believed that student teaching is one of the most important parts of the preparation of teachers and that this period should be lengthened to a point where the prospective teacher is well oriented in the life of the school and the community.

The student teaching experience should be supervised by skilled and competent school and college personnel in a program that has been cooperatively worked out by the two. Supervising teachers should be the best teachers in the school. They should be given a reduced load in order to carry out their responsibilities in an efficient manner. The college supervisors should also be well qualified, both by preparation and experience, to assume this most important responsibility.

Although educators have recognized the need for such an experience, only in the last few years has there developed an emphasis on a longer period. Three reasons exist why a longer period in this phase of professional preparation is necessary. In the first place, a longer period is necessary so that the student may observe the total growth of the child. This means growth or progress, not only in academic subjects but also organically, socially, intellectually, and emotionally. Only if the student is allowed to be with the same children over a longer period of time will such an experience be possible. In the second place, a longer period is necessary because practice teaching is the core of the professional program and, as such, is necessary to develop the competence that will be needed when the teacher assumes complete responsibility in her first job after graduation. In the third place, a longer period is necessary so that the student may actually live in the community and participate in its various activities. Furthermore, he should feel a part of the school and become well acquainted with the children, the staff, and the total picture of school life.

Many educators are advocating that the student meet the practice teaching requirements by serving a period of internship. Such a trend will make the practice teaching experience more realistic and similar to the actual work the prospective teacher will perform on the job. It will also provide additional opportunities for developing the ability to think out the solution to pertinent problems under wise supervision. It is gener-

ally agreed that during the internship period the prospective teacher would become an integrated part of community and school life. Instead of coming back to the college every day, he would make his home in the community where he may have the experience of an actual teaching situation.

Finally, there is the question of when the student teaching should take place in the training of the teacher and how much time should be allotted to it. The majority of educators favor placing this experience in the latter part of the training period when the knowledge and experience that have been accumulated in the first few years of preparation may be put to good use. As to the length of time that should be allotted, there is wide variance of opinion, ranging from ninety clock hours to one full year. The most common trend as advocated by current thinking, is for eight to fifteen weeks of full-time student

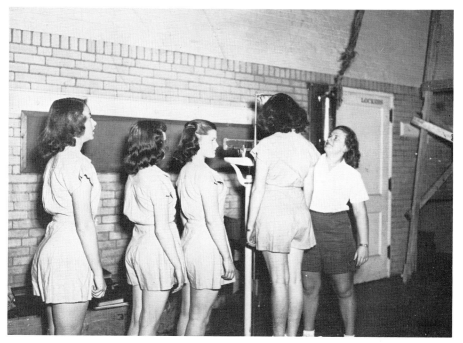

*Lawrence Central High School, Indianapolis, Ind.*

Weighing and measuring children.

teaching experience. If the teacher is to adequately experience school and community life and is to observe the total growth of the child, the period of student teaching should be adequate to accomplish the realization of this objective.

Another recent emphasis in teacher education is the recommendation that an internship take place following the regular preservice program of teacher education, which includes student teaching. This internship would be planned by both the schools and colleges concerned. Although such an arrangement is beyond the reach of many states and colleges at present, it is a development that will be more frequently seen in the future.

### Need for a five-year program

The Professional Preparing Conference of 1962, sponsored by the American Asso-

ciation for Health, Physical Education, and Recreation, reaffirmed the need for increasing the preparation of physical education, health, and recreation leaders to a period of five years. Although World War II and the teacher shortage resulted in a temporary halt to the extension of preservice preparation, the emphasis at present is again in that direction. Educators stress the fact that the elementary school teacher also needs the same amount of preparation as the secondary school teacher and should therefore have a similar period of preparation. Others point out that teaching is as complex as the medical profession and therefore reach the conclusion that the profession of teaching needs many years of intensive preparation—perhaps five, six, or seven years. Some states, such as California and New York, require five years of preparation in cer-

*Richwoods Community High School,*
*Peoria Heights, Ill.*

The physical educator should be able to teach motor skills effectively.

tain subjects before they can be taught on the high school level.

The five-year program of teacher education will result in a much broader and more intensive preparation. It will enable teacher-training institutions to offer programs that take into consideration more adequately the general education of teachers by providing more preparation in the areas of the fine and practical arts, English, social sciences, physical sciences, biological sciences, and mathematics. It will make possible a more thorough background in various subject-matter fields. It will make provision for more preparation in the professional education area by making it possible to extend the student-teaching period, by providing for more direct experiences with children, and by developing a broader understanding of child growth and development.

### Emphasis on broad health knowledge

All teachers should be concerned with the health of students, and therefore should have some understanding of this subject matter field. The teacher of physical education must have a thorough grounding in health education knowledge as well as a knowledge of physical education activities. If the prospective teacher is to be successful in his work, teacher-training institutions must provide adequate preparation in both areas.

Although the teacher of physical education is primarily concerned with his field of specialization, it is nevertheless essential that he have a thorough knowledge in health education as well. Such an important phase of the total educational process needs special consideration in that the work of physical educators is so closely related to the work of those engaged primarily in health education work. Physical education contributes to the health of the individual. The physical educator should also be concerned with other factors that are essential to the maintenance

and improvement of an individual's health. A complete and accurate knowledge of all factors involved in the health of an individual will enable him to realize more fully his place in the total program. Only through an adequate health education background will it be possible for the physical educator to handle his responsibilities efficiently.

### TWO-YEAR COLLEGES AND PROFESSIONAL PREPARATION

The two-year college has become a very important factor on the American educational scene. This type of institution is expanding at a rapid rate and will continue to do so as the number of college-bound students rises. This means that more and more high school boys and girls will find their educational opportunities in this kind of college. Though there are exceptions, most junior colleges (and by this term the community college is included) have the following three functions:

1. *Two years of preprofessional training or general education.* A student may graduate with a degree of associate in the arts or sciences after two years, or transfer to a four-year institution for a bachelor's degree. This transfer program is sometimes called the university parallel curriculum. Most four-year colleges and universities will accept transfer students from accredited junior colleges if the academic achievement of the student is high and if the subjects studied mesh with the curriculum of the higher institution.

2. *Provision for a complete program in a semiprofessional field such as secretarial work, home economics, medical laboratory techniques, and business education.*

3. *Provision for classes for adults who want more education to help them in their jobs, or who simply want to study subjects they never had a chance to study before.*

The type of curriculums offered by junior colleges is usually controlled by the needs and interests of the students they serve. Some junior college curriculums are planned almost entirely for students who want a general education and who plan to transfer to a four-year institution. Other junior colleges enroll the majority of students in semiprofessional courses.

Physical education service programs are being developed in most of the two-year colleges. Most of these institutions require physical education for two hours each week for two years.

With more and more students taking their two years of higher education in the two-year colleges and with many of these students vitally interested in sports and physical education, the question naturally arises, what part should the two-year college play in the professional preparation of teachers of physical education? One guideline might be the one recommended by the National Conference on Professional Preparation in Health Education, Physical Education, and Recreation held by the American Association for Health, Physical Education, and Recreation in 1962, which stressed that the freshman and sophomore years should be viewed primarily as general education. However, several leaders in physical education have pointed out that the student who has made a vocational choice by the time he enters college should be offered some professional education during the first two years, and that it is not realistic to insist that this vocational interest should be delayed until the junior year in college. These leaders agree that a major share of the program should be devoted to general education, but at the same time, they point out, it is possible in the remaining time to orient the student to the whole field of specialization by providing such experiences as an introductory course in his professional field and, in addition, to strengthen the basic skill background of the student. These leaders, however, point out that a prerequisite to such experience should be a qualified staff and adequate facilities, in order to do the job properly.

The two-year college should help each student in accordance with his interests, abilities, and needs, so that he may become a mature citizen and contribute to his own happiness and the good of his community.

## GRADUATE WORK

Graduate work in all areas of education is receiving increasing emphasis. Some of the developments in this area stress that graduate students should be very carefully selected on the basis of their backgrounds, degree of motivation, intellectual competence, and maturity. In most cases, the student should be prepared for advanced study by having a good grounding in his specialty. Graduate courses would therefore extend beyond the normal undergraduate experiences and would be developed upon a foundation of research that had been conducted, and would be concerned with principles, history, philosophy, and research, rather than skills and techniques. A feature that should be common to all graduate courses is the emphasis upon mature thinking, extensive reading, and original work.

Professional preparation is a continuous process. It does not end with commencement and the conferring of the bachelor's degree. It continues throughout one's professional career. The next step in improving qualifications for physical education work after leaving the undergraduate ranks is graduate study toward advanced degrees. In order, these usually are the master's degree, sixth-year or professional certificate, and doctor's degree. The master's degree usually requires the equivalent of one full year's work above the bachelor's degree; the sixth-year or professional certificate requires one full year beyond the master's; and the doctor's degree varies usually from two to three years beyond the sixth-year or professional certificate. Frequently, physical educators omit the sixth-year or professional certificate and work directly on the doctor's degree following the conferring of the master's degree.

Graduate work offers opportunities such as getting help in solving many practical problems that exist in the field, increasing one's knowledge and skills as a teacher, doing research, studying under some leader in the field, specializing in some facet of the physical education program in which one is interested, improving one's general education, and obtaining a better understanding of the total educational picture.

In addition to the educational improvement that accrues to the graduate student, there are also material benefits. Some states grant provisional certificates after graduation from undergraduate programs and then permanent certification after a certain number of graduate credit hours have been taken. Most school systems recognize graduate work in their salary schedules so that, with additional professional preparation, there is increased income.

The student who finds that additional financial aid is needed to pursue graduate work should investigate four kinds of financial aid:

1. *Fellowships.* Many graduate schools in physical education offer grants of money for further study. This grant may include teaching some service skill or other classes or doing some form of work as a means of obtaining aid.

2. *Scholarships.* An outright grant of money for graduate work not requiring service or repayment is termed a scholarship. These are awarded to outstanding physical educators who have demonstrated merit and leadership qualities and who require financial assistance to pursue graduate study.

3. *Grant-in-aid.* A grant-in-aid is usually thought of as an outright grant of money for a specialized purpose. For example, it could be given to a graduate student to work on a specific research project in physical education.

*New York University, New York, N. Y.*

Graduate work in physical education in a camp setting.

4. *Loans.* Colleges, universities, state governments, banks, and the national government, through the National Defense Education Act, offer loans to students at moderately low interest rates to pay for educational needs.

A person going into physical education work and desiring to have a successful career should take some graduate work in this special field. It will assist him in his personal growth and in rendering a greater service.

## CONSIDERATIONS IN SELECTING A COLLEGE PROFESSIONAL-PREPARING PROGRAM IN PHYSICAL EDUCATION

There are many factors that should be taken into consideration when selecting a teacher-training institution to prepare for work in physical education. The institution of higher learning should meet desirable standards as established by the profession. The physical educator's chances for employment and for success on the job will depend, to a great extent, on the experiences and opportunities that are provided during this training period. In order that there may be some logical basis for making this important decision, some of the factors to be considered when evaluating the training institution will be discussed in the following sections.

### Selecting teacher-training institution

There are many teacher-preparing institutions throughout the United States that train students for the profession of physical education. However, all the institutions that prepare teachers for this specialized work do not adhere to the highest standards of the profession. A careful analysis of various institutions will acquaint the prospective physical educator with their qualifications for preparing teachers of physical education. Such items as faculty, facilities, purposes, quality and length of curricula, accreditation, reputation, and placement are a few of the factors that should be taken into consideration.

### Reviewing college entrance requirements

As a general rule, an individual desiring to prepare for the teaching of physical education is required to meet college entrance requirements. The standard high school college-preparatory course should be taken by all high school students who want to prepare for this work. Usually this means a minimum of fifteen to sixteen high school units of credit, as defined by the particular state. Frequently, five to ten units of the total number required should be in academic subjects, including English, mathematics, natural science, and social science. Foreign languages are required by an increasing number of teacher-preparing institutions. There are also general requirements as to character, physical fitness, and personality. Entrance requirements vary from state to state, and interested individuals should consult the institution or institutions in which they are interested.

### Analyzing the cost

The cost of preparing for the teaching of physical education varies with the institution. Usually the cost is lower in tax-supported institutions such as state teachers colleges and state universities. The expenses incurred by the student of physical education are similar to those of students preparing in other fields. In most teacher-preparing institutions it would be wise for the student to set aside approximately $3,000 per year to allow for tuition, board, room, and fees. The actual tuition fee varies from $20 to $50 in some tax-supported institutions to $500 to $2,500 or more in some privately endowed colleges and universities. The student with limited financial resources may supplement his income through scholarships, fellowships, loan funds, and part-time employment.

## Determining financial aid for teacher education

Since the cost of a college education is skyrocketing, physical educators should be familiar with various programs for financial aid. Two that will be mentioned here are the National Defense Education Act and the AAHPER scholarship program.

**National Defense Education Act.** Congress provides, under the National Defense Act, funds to assist institutions of higher education in the establishment of low-interest, long-term student loan funds.

To qualify for a loan a person must be enrolled or have been accepted as a full-time student in an institution of higher education, must be capable of maintaining good standing, and must be in need of the loan. Applications for funds are filed at the college or university where the student is enrolled. At present, funds can be borrowed up to $1,000 a year or a total of not more than $5,000 to complete the bachelor's or the master's degree. The loan bears interest at the rate of 3% per year on the unpaid balance. The repayment period of the loan, plus interest, begins one year after the student graduates or ceases to pursue a full-time course of study. Ten years are allowed for repayment. For those students who go into teaching in public elementary or secondary schools, up to 50% of the principal plus interest may be cancelled at the rate of 10% a year for each complete academic year of full-time teaching service in any state or territory.

**AAHPER scholarship program.** The American Association for Health, Physical Education, and Recreation has established a new service to the profession—scholarship grants. Scholarships are awarded to outstanding students who have demonstrated professional zeal, are highly recommended, and possess other necessary qualifications. Scholarships have been established such as The AMF–W. J. Voit Youth Fitness Scholarship in Physical Education, Brunswick Youth Fitness Scholarship, and the E. R. Moore Scholarships in Physical Education for Women. The Association's scholarship program is expanding continuously, and interested high school students should be encouraged to make application by writing to the Scholarship Department, AAHPER, 1201 Sixteenth Street, N. W., Washington, D. C.

## Recognizing the need for degrees

A college degree should be held by all who plan to teach physical education in the public schools. Without this minimum preparation there will be few opportunities for employment. At the present time most college and university courses are four years in length, but in some states, such as New York and California, the period is equal to five years for high school teaching. Furthermore, the trend is more and more in the direction of an extended period of training. The degree usually granted at the end of the four-year period is that of Bachelor of Science, Bachelor of Science in Education, or Bachelor of Arts. The Master of Education or Master of Arts degree is frequently granted at the end of the fifth year of training.

## PROFESSIONAL CURRICULUM

The professional preparation that is given in the various institutions of higher learning should prepare the physical educator adequately for the duties that will be assumed after graduation.

### Competencies to be developed

Professional competencies are important to all physical educators. The essential professional competencies needed are: a knowledge of the school and community, including their growth and structure; a knowledge and understanding of child growth and development; a sound knowledge of the process and theories of learning; the knowledge of and ability to use pertinent resource materials; the ability to apply proper teaching techniques, and a knowledge of capable leadership; the ability to objectively evaluate the progress of each student; the ability to meet the needs and interests of each student; and the ability to cooperate and work with colleagues, administrators, parents, students, and the community at large for the good of all concerned.

### Training experiences

Those students who successfully meet the entrance requirements should pursue a curriculum that includes work in the academic area, foundation science area, professional education area, and specialized area of physical education. The professional preparation that is given in each of these four general areas should apply to the elementary, junior high, senior

high school, and college levels of instruction.

In order to ensure that each prospective teacher receives the preparation that is best suited to his needs, it is necessary to recognize that the curriculum should be flexible to the extent that individual differences are taken into consideration. A blanket requirement for all students should not be listed. Some individuals, for example, may need more work in the academic area and less in the foundation science area, whereas others may need more in the specialized area and less in the academic area. A prospective teacher's capacity, educational background, and interests should be given careful consideration before his program is prescribed. Furthermore, the student should participate in the evaluation of his record and help in planning the prescribed work. The amount of preparation that is prescribed for each individual should be determined as a result of a study of school records, which takes into consideration

*Courtesy Dr. Gunsun Hoh,*
*Republic of China.*

Professional preparation of physical educators at Normal University, Taiwan.

the extent and quality of his previous preparation; conferences with the prospective teacher; and standardized tests that meet accepted test criteria and that should be selected by the admissions committee of the college.

The preparation of the student of physical education should include work that centers on adequate training in the academic, foundation science, professional education, and specialized areas. A description of such preparation and also some of the reasons for these recommendations are given in the paragraphs that follow. Through a careful study of the requirements as outlined it is possible to evaluate professional-preparing institutions and their ability to meet desirable professional standards for training physical education teachers. The National Conference on Professional Preparation in Health Education, Physical Education, and Recreation Education identified the experiences that a person should have in order to develop the competencies necessary for effective work in the field of physical education.* Interested persons should examine this report at first hand. In large measure, however, the experiences outlined at this national conference are embodied in the following discussion.

### Experiences in academic area

Each prospective teacher of physical education should, upon completion of his period of preparation, have a mastery of certain elements in the fields of English, fine and practical arts, social sciences, and mathematics.

**English.** The prospective teacher of physical education occupies a position in which the ability to speak and write the

English language and appreciate and understand the best in the field of literature is an essential. In speaking to students or to the public and in writing assignments or articles, the teacher must conform to the best in English usage and be able to converse intelligently.

The prospective teacher should be able to speak the English language with proficiency before a group. He should be able to present his views in a logical sequence and with good diction. Furthermore, his voice should have a pleasing tone quality and should be used effectively without strain and fatigue.

The prospective teacher should be able to write clearly and effectively, using vivid and significant words and having the ability to organize material in a logical sequence. He should be familiar with several essay selections, be able to write with correctness and express his ideas with clarity, and be adept in outlining, preparing bibliographies, and assembling material for papers.

Furthermore, the prospective teacher should be able to appreciate and understand the best in the field of literature. He should have the necessary background for making literary and artistic discriminations of intelligence. He should be familiar with selections from the best literature of all ages. He should be concerned with the emotional life of characters, with their attitudes, with the psychology of their acts, with their personal conflicts, with their spiritual aspirations as individuals, and with their way of saying and doing things.

**Fine and practical arts.** The prospective teacher should be familiar with the fine and practical arts of music, painting, drawing, handicrafts, and dramatics. These arts will afford a means of expression, a means of releasing the emotions, a medium for a richer understanding of life, and a medium for promoting mental health. The prospective

---

*American Association for Health, Physical Education, and Recreation: Professional preparation in health education, physical education, and recreation education, Washington, D. C., 1962, The Association, pp. 65–68.

teacher should use his hands in some form of expression. This may be accomplished in a variety of ways, such as playing a musical instrument, artistic work with paints or clay, or constructive work with wood, paper, or metals. Through such media of expression, he will inwardly partake of higher forms of human activity and will consequently be able to understand human nature better. The prospective teacher should be able to appreciate the architecture, sculpture, painting, and crafts, from prehistoric times to the present, and the development of music composition as it is related to the great composers in history.

The prospective teacher of physical education should be especially familiar with handicrafts. This knowledge should be designed to promote the student's interest and enjoyment in creative and individual expression. It should include the techniques of working with metal, wood, and leather. It should also include needlework for women. Through such a medium students should be encouraged to develop skills and hobbies they can pass on to their pupils and that they themselves may enjoy in their homes, apart from any group, throughout their entire lives. Projects should be selected according to abilities, interests, and capacities of the members of the group. Individuals should be encouraged to create their own designs rather than to follow patterns worked out by others.

**Social sciences.** The prospective teacher should have an understanding of the world in which individuals must work together, live together, and strive to accomplish worthwhile goals together.

The student should be familiar with the various social sciences with a resulting understanding and appreciation of human society. The various political, social, and economic factors that have influenced man's history should be understood, with emphasis on an understanding

of the interdependence of different peoples and of the individual's responsibility to live more satisfactorily with himself and others.

The prospective teacher should have a knowledge of the accomplishments and problems of man from earliest times to the present and their relation to the complex world of today.

The prospective teacher should understand the importance of the community, its relation to the teaching profession, the procedures for studying and developing it, and how to utilize effectively what is learned. He should realize that an understanding of the community is basic to a knowledge of his pupils, to leadership in the school and the wider environment that surrounds the school, and to successful living in that particular environment.

**Mathematics.** The prospective teacher of physical education should have a knowledge of the fundamentals of mathematical computation. This is necessary because of its utility in modern-day living and as a basis for a more thorough knowledge in the field of science.

The student who shows, through standard tests that meet accepted criteria, a knowledge of the fundamentals of mathematical computation and whose interests lie in other areas should not be required to take additional work in this field.

For the student whose educational background does not include a foundation in the fundamentals of elementary mathematics, training should be provided to the point where it is possible for him to meet successfully the established standards of performance. After this requirement has been met, the student's interests should determine whether or not more work should be taken in this field of study.

**Modern languages.** The prospective teacher of physical education should have a mastery of at least one language other than English. With the increased realization that this is a "one world" era, it is increasingly important that one be able to converse with people of other countries. It is to be hoped that this command of modern languages will have been acquired before the student attends college. It seems that the best years for learning the languages of other countries are on the elementary and secondary school levels.

### Experiences in foundation science area

The content of the foundation science area should be concerned with providing the student with a general education, other than that included in the academic area, and with the basic knowledge in science needed for his specialized field of physical education. The content of this area should not necessarily be the same for all students. The individual's interests and educational background should determine the amount of preparation needed.

Each prospective teacher of physical education should, upon completion of his period of preparation, have a mastery of certain elements in the fields of physical and biological sciences.

**Physical sciences.** The prospective teacher of physical education should have a general knowledge of the fields of astronomy, geology, physics, and chemistry. Furthermore, such knowledge should include the development and appreciation of the contributions and limitations of science with a realization that increased knowledge is needed.

The emphasis in science teaching should be functionally related to the world in which people live. Such emphasis should point out factors concerning the earth and its place in the universe, the nature of matter in terms of modern theories of atomic structure, the nature of energy and the significance of energy changes, and the application of science to industry, invention, and day-to-day living.

**Biological sciences.** The student should have an appreciation of the principles fundamental to an understanding of the structure, function, and behavior of living things and the relationship and interdependence between plant and animal life. The student should receive a meaningful orientation to the field and discover how closely related and basic it is to the specialized area of physical education.

For those students whose interests, educational background, and time permit, more experiences should be provided in the fields of biology, zoology, and botany.

The biological sciences are basic and closely related to the specialized field of physical education. For this reason certain specified fields of knowledge should be included in this area and a more detailed description required. The following specific fields should be included in the preparation of the prospective teacher of physical education:

1. *Personal health.* Experiences concerned with personal health should be designed to establish high standards of personal living through a study of correct living habits. The student should be presented with the underlying reasons for good health, the principles and practices of personal hygiene, and the sociological, psychological, economic, and physiological implications of health practices that prevent adequate sleep, rest, exercise, and nutrition. This information will help him to discover his own health needs and meet them understandingly. Popular fallacies should be corrected, self-medication should be discouraged, and students should be taught to evaluate the claims of health extremists. The outcomes of such experiences should help in the development of desirable health attitudes.

2. *Community health.* A study of community health is designed to present a comprehensive study of facts of community hygiene as related to group living. It should include a survey of community

health problems, with their social and economic aspects; a knowledge of the services performed by public health organizations, whether they be volunteer, school, municipal, state or federal; a knowledge of the means of controlling and preventing communicable diseases; a knowledge of the methods and media of community health education, including publicity through visual and auditory means; a knowledge of the means of protecting food and water supplies; a knowledge of measures utilized in home nursing; and an understanding of the need for cooperation between school and community health agencies.

3. *Mental health.* An understanding of mental health is designed to equip the major student with the principles, factors, and conditions underlying this phase of total fitness. It should deal with emotional problems, attitudes, conflicts, neurotic behavior, and conduct disorders in both the child and the adult. The emphasis should be on the beginnings of undesirable attitudes and habits and methods of treating them rather than upon the more serious cases of maladjustment. The methods of building a wholesome personality should be stressed more than an analysis of extreme disorders. The outcome of such knowledge should aid the prospective teacher to recognize mental maladjustment early so that the persons with serious problems may be referred to professional personnel and those with minor ones corrected through the knowledge he has at his command.

4. *General bacteriology.* Work in the field of bacteriology should show the relationship between bacteria and human welfare. It should include a study of yeasts, molds, and bacteria; industrial, economic, and sanitary applications; effects of physical and chemical agencies upon bacteria; biochemical activities of bacteria; microscopical examination and cultivation of bacteria; the bacteria of air, water, soil, milk and dairy products, and other foods; and disease-producing bacteria.

5. *Human anatomy and physiology.* Human anatomy and physiology should acquaint the student with a knowledge of cell and tissue structure of the human body, visceral anatomy, bones, joints, and muscles. It should acquaint the student with a knowledge of the chemical composition of the body and its relation to the various systems and parts of the human body. It should include a study of the nervous system and its relation to the control and coordination of the various body mechanisms; the circulatory system, including a study of the physiological anatomy of the heart and the composition of the blood; the digestive system, including a study of the bile and pancreatic juice, the intestines, the liver and spleen, and the salivary glands; and the respiratory system, including the mechanics of respiration, chemistry of respiration, and control of respiration.

Provisions should be made for extensive laboratory work in this area of knowledge. Through such a medium, visual aids such as slides, charts, prints, living models, and manikins will clearly impress upon the student the anatomy and physiology of the human body. Furthermore, dissections should be made of animals and cadavers to further aid the student in getting a grasp of this knowledge.

6. *Nutrition.* A study of nutrition is designed to furnish the student with a knowledge of food and nutrition since they are related to the health of an individual. It should involve a study of foods in regard to their selection, nutritive value, care, cost, composition, and digestibility. It should bring out the factors in the planning and preparation of well-balanced meals as influenced by such things as age, sex, size, activity, and health. It should point out the energy value of foods in the light of chemistry and physiology of digestion and the nu-

tritive properties of protein, fat, carbohydrates, vitamins, and other constituents.

## Experiences in professional education area

The professional education area should be selected in view of the preparation that is needed to instill in the prospective teacher sound educational principles and practices in regard to teaching and learning. It should stress the following: orientation, child growth and development, evaluation, student teaching, methodology, and seminar.

**Orientation.** An introduction to the area of professional education that will provide the student with a broad overview of the field of education should stress in particular the following:

1. The role of education in a free society, including the purpose, organization, and administration of the school system
2. The old and present philosophies, theories, practices, principles, and objectives of education
3. The problems encountered in elementary, junior high, and senior high school education
4. The psychological factors affecting progress in learning
5. Observation and participation in guiding children

This knowledge should be presented by specialists from the various educational areas, and one individual should be responsible for coordinating the total program. A portion of the time devoted to this experience should be utilized in observation of various school situations in the training schools of the college and public schools.

**Child growth and development.** The prospective teacher of physical education should have a knowledge of child growth and development. Such a knowledge should include information pertinent to human growth from conception through adolescence, with reference to the psychological foundations of behavior and effective adjustment. It should also include physical, mental, social, and emotional development and their relation to the school, home, and community. As a means of procuring this knowledge, emphasis should be placed on direct experiences with children in varying types of relationships. Although a study of general and educational psychological principles of learning should be a part of a student's training, direct experiences with children in the classrooms, on the playgrounds, in various youth organizations, or any place where they congregate should be emphasized as one of the most vital means by which one may gain an understanding of behavior patterns. As a result of such experiences, generalizations about the child will become pronounced.

The material that is presented and the experiences that are provided should give the prospective teacher a thorough knowledge and understanding of child growth and development. Such training should result in a knowledge of why children behave in certain ways and what are the best conditions for learning.

**Evaluation.** The prospective teacher should have a knowledge of the methods and techniques of evaluating the educational program so as to be able to estimate objectively individual development and program effectiveness. The prospective teacher should be provided with a knowledge that will show how results of evaluation may be used as a basis for better guidance and curriculum revision, how they may be used in identifying individual differences, and how they may be used as a basis for sound teaching procedures.

**Student teaching.** The prospective teacher should possess the understanding and confidence that come as a result of actual teaching experience under supervision in the field of physical education.

The prospective teacher should serve a period of internship in a situation similar to the one he will experience upon graduation. This practice teaching should cover a period of time sufficient for allowing the prospective teacher to observe the total organic, social, intellectual, and emotional growth of the child; to develop the competence that will be needed when he assumes complete responsibility in his first job; and to experience community life. Such an experience should allow for teaching on more than one level of instruction.

**Methodology.** The chief purpose of this phase of the professional education area is to provide those prospective teachers who have pursued work in some academic field in addition to physical education with the proper educational methodology in the teaching of these subjects. It should acquaint the prospective teacher with the educational objectives of these areas of learning in the public schools; review the best courses of study that have been prepared; consider the important characteristics of instruction on the elementary, junior high, and senior high school levels; give the student familiarity with the chief aids to instruction; critically evaluate teaching in these fields; and provide for the study of the relationships of the subjects to other areas on the various levels of instruction.

**Seminar.** The prospective teacher should be provided with the opportunity to evaluate critically the experiences of the educational sequence he has pursued and to focus these experiences upon an understanding of the professional character of teaching. Emphasis should be placed upon problems that have arisen during the student's period of training.

### Experiences in area of specialization

The content of the physical education area should provide the prospective teacher with that specialized knowledge which will be essential for the successful performance of his duties after graduation.

There are two main divisions in this area, physical education experiences that also have implications for health education and physical education experiences.

**Physical education experiences with implications for health education.** In this division of the specialized area, experiences should be offered that have implications for health education as well as physical education duties.

1. *Orientation in physical education and health education.* The prospective teacher should have experiences that introduce him to the fields of physical education and health education. A general overview of the fields should include the place of physical education and health education in the educational process, the objectives of physical education and health education, the scientific foundations of physical education and health education, the opportunities for service, the qualifications and training of physical education and health education personnel, the program of activities, and the relation of physical education to the field of recreation.

2. *Measurement and evaluation.* The nature and scope of measurement and evaluation in physical education and health education should be an important part of the teacher's training. Organic, skill, knowledge, and adaptation measurement techniques, as they are used for purposes of classification, ascertaining achievement, diagnosis, prognosis, grading, motivation, and research, should be studied. Evaluation of administration, leadership, facilities, activities, time, participation, and research should be discussed. A recommended program of measurement and evaluation should be established for the various institutional levels and the minimum and desirable standards brought out. The health examination as it relates to this field in respect to purposes, techniques involved, records, and follow-up should be considered. Direct experience should be provided through the medium of sending major students into schools,

Physical fitness testing program in United States Air Force.

under supervision, to administer various measurement and evaluation techniques and then to interpret the results. This direct experience should also include observation and participation in the health examination.

3. *Education and care of the handicapped.* A study should be made of the program in physical education and health education especially adapted and beneficial to the handicapped person. The abnormal conditions of posture should be brought out, including weak feet, lordosis, kyphosis, and scoliosis; the causes and symptoms of malnutrition, including conditions of underweight and overweight; and the causes and care of cardiac disturbances that are prevalent among pupils. Other items that should receive consideration are the education and care of the crippled, the blind and deaf, the mentally handicapped, the speech handicapped, and the environmentally handicapped and how they may be aided in living as normal a life as possible, in developing emotional security, and in developing a sense of belonging to the group. Direct experience should be provided by

assigning major students to observe and work with atypical children in the training schools of the college and the public schools.

4. *Applied anatomy and physiology.* The student should be acquainted with a knowledge of bodily movement, including a study of muscles, their isolated action, how movements are performed, and the practical application of knowledge to bodily movement and activity as expressed in gymnastics, sports, and occupational activities.

The major student should also know the physiological factors in bodily movements, especially those involved in physical education activities. Laboratory experimental research in analyzing the physiological effects of activity should be included. Special consideration should be given to the general effects of exercise and the effects of special types of exercise upon bodily functions as they affect the circulatory, respiratory, and neuromuscular mechanisms. Due consideration should be given to the phenomena of fatigue, recovery, and conditioning as they relate to programs of physical activity.

5. *Organization and administration.* Experiences should be provided to inform the major student about the various factors necessary for the successful administration of a physical education program and also the health education and recreational aspects of such a program. It should be concerned with such a program on the elementary, junior high, and senior high school levels of instruction. Some of the factors that should be considered are the importance and essentials of good leadership, office management, care and maintenance of facilities, sanitation, supervision of instruction, scheduling, intramural and interscholastic sports programs, classification of students, legal aspects, program organization, budget and finance, special events, health instruction, health services, and playground and recreational work.

6. *Prevention and emergency care of injuries.* Knowledge and skill should be provided for the proper and immediate care of the injured until the services of a physician can be obtained. Such knowledge and skill should include bandaging, splinting, transportation, and procedures to alleviate bleeding and shock. The prospective teacher should also have a knowledge of the injuries common among athletes, such as sprains and knee cartilage dislocations, and the precautionary measures that may be taken to avoid such accidents. Furthermore, an analytical study should be made of the causes of accidents on the highways, in the home, in the school and gymnasium, and on the playground. The emphasis should be on the means of prevention, involving legal controls and developing the right habits and attitudes in children and adults.

Practical work should become a valuable part of this experience through the planning of safety projects and routines, demonstrations, and special pupil activities on the various levels of instruction.

7. *The health service program.* This experience is designed to equip the prospective teacher with knowledge concerning the part that he may play in the health service program. It should point out the responsibilities of the teacher in regard to the health examination of all students, whether it is made by the student health service or the family physician; the follow-up, counseling, and corrective program; and the inspection of such enviromental factors as lighting, ventilation, seating, sanitation, water, sewage, and waste disposal, playgrounds, and housing. It should provide the prospective teacher with an understanding necessary for conducting inspection of children in order that communicable diseases and physical defects may be detected, with an understanding of the proper technique in the administration of vision and hearing tests, and with an understanding of the importance and procedure to be followed in counseling. It should also bring out the necessity of cooperating with such community and private health agencies as the health department, hospitals, and voluntary health agencies. Furthermore, it should equip the prospective teacher with an understanding of the procedures necessary for dealing with the handicapped child and for both preventing and caring for injuries.

Each major student should be assigned to observe the periodical health examinations of pupils. The student should also have the experience of assisting the school physician, nurse, and health and physical education staff by checking weight, height, vision, and hearing and keeping records.

**Physical education experiences.** This division of the specialized area is concerned with those experiences peculiar to the field of physical education alone.

1. *History and principles of physical education.* The prospective teacher should be familiar with the history and principles of physical education as related to changing, social, religious, and political condi-

tions. The emphasis in history should be on the training given in Sparta and Athens, the Panhellenic games, modern revival of the Olympics, rise of gymnastics in Germany, Sweden, and Denmark, growth of physical education in American schools and colleges, and modern trends in physical education in Europe and America. The emphasis on principles should deal with the biological, psychological, and sociological factors that influence the organic, skill, interpretative, and emotional development of the individual.

2. *Methods and materials in physical education.* The methods and materials for teaching and coaching physical education activities should be stressed. The development of performance skill should not be considered a part of this experience. A knowledge of all these activities, with performance skill in most, is a prerequisite. This experience should include the methods and materials in the teaching and/or coaching of the following:

1. Methods and materials for both men and women
   (a) *Team games:* softball, basketball, touch football, volleyball, soccer, speedball
   (b) *Dual and individual sports:* track and field, deck tennis, ping-pong, horseshoes, badminton, archery, shuffleboard, bowling, tennis, golf, fencing, paddle tennis, fishing
   (c) *Rhythms and dancing:* social dancing, folk dancing, square dancing, rhythmics, tap dancing, modern dancing
   (d) *Water activities:* swimming, diving, lifesaving, canoeing, rowing, water games
   (e) *Outdoor winter sports:* skating, snow games, skiing, tobogganing
   (f) *Formal activities:* calisthenics, marching
   (g) *Gymnastics:* tumbling
   (h) *Self-testing activities*
   (i) *Relays*
   (j) *Games of low organization:* ring games and tag and "it" games, for example

2. Methods and materials for men only
   (a) *Team games:* baseball, football
   (b) *Dual and individual sports:* handball, boxing, wrestling, squash
   (c) *Outdoor winter sports:* ice hockey
   (d) *Gymnastics:* apparatus, acrobatics, pyramid building
3. Methods and materials for women only
   (a) *Team games:* field hockey

A desirable standard of performance skill, to be determined by the department of health and physical education, should be required in the following activities: apparatus work (men only), archery, softball, baseball (men only), basketball, folk dancing, square dancing, rhythmics, social dancing, modern dancing, football (men only), games of low organization, handball (men only), relays, badminton, bowling, ping-pong, soccer, speedball, swiming, tennis, track and field, tumbling, volleyball, golf, and touch football.

A knowledge of the following activities, the extent of which should be determined by the department of health and physical education, should be required: calisthenics, fencing, hiking, indoor games, lifesaving, marching, pyramid building, deck tennis, paddle tennis, shuffleboard, riding, rowing, skating, skiing, social games, squash (men only), water polo (men only), wrestling (men only), and horseshoes.

A student should be required to take instruction, for purposes of performance skill, in only those physical education activities in which he fails to achieve an acceptable standard of performance or knowledge as determined by the physical education department. However, physical activity should be a requirement for majors of physical education, as it should for all students, throughout the entire training period.

3. *Nature and function of play.* The major student should have at his command a knowledge of the laws of normal growth and development of the child, including the child's natural drives, hun-

Oakland Recreation Department, Oakland, Calif.

Folk dance group. The physical educator should be qualified to teach dance.

gers, and attitudes and their relation to play. A study of the child's nature in relation to his play and the functions and values of these activities should be part of this experience. The age and sex characteristics and individual differences from birth through adolescence should be studied as a basis for the classification of play activities.

4. *Recreation, camping, and outdoor education.* A knowledge and understanding of the areas of recreation, camping, and outdoor education should be a part of the training of every physical education teacher. This should include a study of the role of recreation, camping, and outdoor education in the total educational process, the aims and objectives, procedures essential in the conduct of a recreational program or camp, qualifications and duties of the recreator and camp counselor in his relation to the di-

rector and to the campers, safety precautions and procedures, the program of activities for all types of weather conditions, and facilities. This experience should include visits to various recreation programs and camps, and also actually living in a camp situation for a period of time. Experiences should also be required in various aspects of the outdoor education program.

• • •

The experiences just listed represent many of the essential needs of the student training for the physical education profession. Such experiences in a professional curriculum will equip the physical educator with the necessary knowledge to successfully cope with the problems that will arise when he gets on the job, and he will be capable of making an outstanding contribution to the welfare of children and youth.

## COLLEGES AND UNIVERSITIES OFFERING PROFESSIONAL TRAINING IN PHYSICAL EDUCATION

The prospective teacher of physical education should be interested in selecting a qualified college or university. The various institutions in the United States that offer this specialized training can be determined by consulting qualified physical education personnel in the field, teacher-training institutions, the executive secretary of the American Association for Health, Physical Education, and Recreation, or the Office of Education of the Department of Health, Education, and Welfare.

By consulting a list of colleges and universities, the student may discover the ones in which he is interested. Then, the professional program offered by each institution should be checked against the standards established for the physical education profession to see how well they will prepare him to carry out successfully the duties that he will encounter on the job.

## PROFESSIONAL PHYSICAL EDUCATION CURRICULUMS

To provide further information, professional-preparing curriculums are listed.

### Physical education in schools and colleges
#### Curriculum for men and women

Below are listed two professional preparing programs. The first is a curriculum for both men and women desiring to teach at any level. The second is designed to prepare for teaching physical education in secondary schools.

**FIRST YEAR**

| | Semester hours |
|---|---|
| Biology: Introductory Zoology and Botany | 8 |
| Oral English | 4 |
| Written English | 4 |
| Personal and Community Hygiene | 2 |
| Introduction to Psychology | 4 |
| Introduction to Camp Leadership | 2 |
| Man in Society: The Western Tradition | 4 |
| Introduction to Physical Education | 2 |
| Music in Physical Education (women) | 1 |

**SECOND YEAR**

| | Semester hours |
|---|---|
| Mammalian Anatomy and Physiology | 8 |
| Introductory Chemistry or Introductory Physics | 8 |
| Introduction to Religion and Philosophy | 4 |
| Expressive Arts | 2 (women) 4 (men) |
| Community Service Experience | 2 |
| Social Science Electives (men) | 4 |
| Literature (women) | 4 |
| Physical Education in Elementary Schools (women) | 2 |

**THIRD YEAR**

| | Semester hours |
|---|---|
| Foundation of Education | 4 |
| Social Science Electives (women) | 4 |
| Educational Psychology | 2 |
| First Aid and Safety | 2 |
| Analysis of Motion | 2 |
| Tests and Measurements in Health Education and Physical Education | 4 |
| Physiology of Exercise | 2 |
| Administration of the Secondary School Physical Education Curriculum (women) | 2 |
| Methods and Materials in Sports (women) | 3 |
| Physical Education Methods and Materials (men) | 6 |
| Rhythmic Activities (women) | 2 |
| Teaching and Coaching Swimming and Diving (women) | 1 |
| Gymnastics Coaching (women) | 1 |
| Literature (men) | 4 |
| Nonrestricted Elective | 2 |

**FOURTH YEAR**

| | Semester hours |
|---|---|
| Supervised Student Teaching | 10 |
| Physical and Health Inspection | 2 |

| | |
|---|---|
| Physical Education for Atypical Children | 3 |
| Organization and Administration of Physical Education | 3 |
| Philosophy and Principles of Physical Education | 2 |
| Contemporary Problems | 3 |
| Expressive Arts (women) | 2 |
| Prevention and Care of Athletic Injuries (men) | 2 |
| Organization and Administration of Community Recreation (men) | 3 |
| Nonrestricted Elective | 3 (women) |
| | 2 (men) |

*Note:* In addition to the above requirements, a total of 16 semester hours of Skills and Techniques courses is required.

## Physical education major for teaching in secondary schools

**FIRST YEAR**

| | Semester hours |
|---|---|
| English | 6 |
| Biology | 4 |
| Social Science | 6 |
| Mathematics | 3 |
| Physics | 4 |
| Physical Education | 2 |
| History and Introduction to Health and Physical Education | 2 |
| Team Sports Skills and Techniques | 2 |
| Practical Instruction in First Aid Methods | 1 |

**SECOND YEAR**

| | Semester hours |
|---|---|
| English | 2 |
| Social Science | 3 |
| Humanities | 6 |
| Minor | 8 |
| Physical Education | 5 |
| Team Sports Skills and Techniques | 2 |
| Fundamentals of Dance | 2 |
| Electives in area of Concentration | 6 |

**THIRD YEAR**

| | Semester hours |
|---|---|
| Humanities | 3 |
| Psychology | 6 |
| Minor | 3 |

| | |
|---|---|
| School Health Education | 3 |
| Physical Education | 6 |
| Anatomy | 3 |
| Kinesiology | 3 |
| Organization and Administration of Health and Physical Education | 2 |
| Programs in Health and Physical Education | 2 |
| Introduction to Tests and Measurements in Health and Physical Education | 2 |

**FOURTH YEAR**

| | Semester hours |
|---|---|
| General Education Courses | 19 |
| Adapted and Developmental Physical Education | 2 |
| Minor | 7 |
| Electives in area of Concentration | 4 |

### QUESTIONS AND EXERCISES

1. Prepare a list of criteria that you would recommend as a means of selecting a teacher-training institution in preparing for physical education work.
2. Draw up a list of training experiences that you feel are essential in preparing for work in physical education.
3. How is it possible for a student with limited financial resources to go to college?
4. What is meant by the academic, foundation science, professional education, and specialized areas of preparation?
5. Prepare a chart showing the essential preparation that should take place in each of the academic, foundation science, professional education, and specialized areas.
6. Why is it important for the physical educator to have preparation in each of the following areas: English, fine and practical arts, social sciences, mathematics, modern languages, and physical sciences?
7. What are some of the subdivisions of biological science that are especially important for the teacher of physical education?
8. Why are many experiences needed in the professional education area?
9. Show how training in the following will be of help to you out on the job: measurement and evaluation, education and care of the handicapped, applied anatomy and physiology, organization and administration, prevention and emergency care of injuries, methods and materials, and school health problems.

10. What are the current developments in teacher education especially applicable to the teacher of physical education?
11. Make a list of as many reasons as possible to show the need for a general education.
12. Write an essay on the implications of the statement, "Those who can, do; those who can't, teach," in regard to physical education skills.
13. Why is a broad health knowledge essential to the physical educator?
14. What progress has been made in recent years in establishing recreation, camping, and outdoor education as an important part of the school program?
15. How will a knowledge of the community help you to perform a better job in teaching physical education?

## SELECTED REFERENCES

American Association for Health, Physical Education, and Recreation: Professional preparation in health education, physical education, and recreation education, Washington, D. C., 1962, The Association.

Bucher, Charles A.: A professional curriculum in health and physical education for the State Teachers College at New Haven, Connecticut, Doctoral thesis, 1948, New York University.

Bucher, Charles A.: Administration of school health and physical education programs, St. Louis, 1967, The C. V. Mosby Co.

Bucher, Charles A., and Reade, Evelyn M.: Physical education in the modern elementary school, New York, 1964, The Macmillan Co.

Campbell, Ronald F.: Tomorrow's teacher, Saturday Review, Jan. 14, 1967.

Conant, James Bryant: The education of American teachers, New York, 1963, McGraw-Hill Book Co.

Drews, Frederick R.: Selection of the college physical education teacher, The Physical Educator 21:147, Dec., 1964.

Esslinger, Arthur A.: Professional preparation, Journal of Health, Physical Education, and Recreation 37:63, Nov.-Dec., 1966.

Harvard Committee: Report. General education in a free society, Cambridge, 1945, Harvard University Press.

Hetherington, Clark W.: Professional education in physical education, Journal of Health and Physical Education 5:3, Nov., 1934.

National Conference on Undergraduate, Professional Preparation in Physical Education, Health Education, and Recreation, Jackson's Mill, Weston, W. Va., May 16-27, 1948: Report, Chicago, 1948, The Athletic Institute.

Pearson, George B.: Trends in professional preparation for physical education in three districts of the AAHPER, Proceedings, National College Physical Education Association, 1964.

Professional preparation for health, physical education, and recreation, A special journal feature prepared by the AAHPER Professional Preparation Panel, Journal of Health, Physical Education, and Recreation 35:31, May, 1964.

Richardson, Deane E.: Professional preparation, Journal of Health, Physical Education, and Recreation 36:71, April, 1965.

Shane, Harold G.: How do they rate you, professor? NEA Journal 54:18, Nov., 1965.

Snyder, Raymond, and Scott, Harry: Professional preparation in health, physical education, and recreation, New York, 1953, McGraw-Hill Book Co.

The icebird

*Works of R. Tait Mc Kenzie. Courtesy Joseph Brown,*
*School of Architecture, Princeton University.*

**PART SEVEN**

# The profession

# Chapter 22

# Professional organizations*

A survey of the field of physical education indicates the prevalence of many professional organizations. Such an imposing list of associations shows the field to be wide in scope and important in nature. These societies exist for specific purposes, and these purposes have a bearing on the work, welfare, and public appraisal of the physical educator. All physical educators should belong to their state and national associations and to others, as far as it is practical and possible. The fact that many physical educators do not belong to their national association, for example, is indicated by statistics that show there are probably more than 200,000 persons in the field today and approximately 50,000 members of the national association. Yet, the thousands who are not members accept, experience, and participate in the advances, better working conditions, and benefits that the association has accomplished. This should not be the case. If all physical educators belonged to and worked for their professional organizations, the concerted effort of such a large professional group would result in greater benefits and more prestige for the profession.

The physical educator should become familiar with the role of professional organizations in his work. He should realize that these associations promote professional ethics, scholarship, leadership, and high educational standards. They are interested in doing more than just improving a member's personal welfare, although this is definitely accomplished. Professional organizations such as the American Association for Health, Physical Education, and Recreation are also interested in developing a healthier, more physically fit, more democratic, and more intelligent citizenry. They seek to enrich the lives of people everywhere. They need help in accomplishing these noble purposes. If all practitioners unite and work together, there is a great future for physical education.

## WHY BELONG TO A PROFESSIONAL ASSOCIATION?

There are many advantages in belonging to a professional organization. This is especially true of associations that give their strength and support to worthwhile programs of education. The publications, meetings, workshops, seminars, and social occasions represent a few of the benefits that can be derived. Factors that every physical educator should recognize about

---

*International professional organizations are discussed in Chapter 14.

membership in professional associations include the following:

1. *They provide opportunities for service.* Through the many offices, committee responsibilities, and program functions that professional associations provide, the individual has an opportunity to render a service for the betterment of his or her field of work.

2. *They provide a channel of communication.* Communication in a profession is essential in order that members may know about what is going on, the latest developments in teaching techniques, new emphases in program content, and many other trends that are happening continuously in a growing profession. Through associations, an effective channel of communication exists via the publications, meetings, and announcements that are periodically made.

3. *They provide a means for interpreting the profession.* There is a need to interpret one's profession to the public on national, state, and local levels. This interpretation is essential if public support is to be achieved for the services rendered by the professional practitioner. The professional association provides an opportunity for the best thinking and ideas to be articulately interpreted far and wide. Through such endeavors, recognition, respect, prestige, and cooperation with other areas of education, professions, and the public in general can be achieved.

4. *They provide a source of help in solving one's professional and personal problems.* Each physical educator has problems—both professional and personal. In solving these problems, professional associations, through their officers, members, conferences, and other media can play an important role. If a person is a member of an association he does not "go it alone" but, instead, is surrounded by professional help on all sides. These groups are interested in helping and rendering a service. The associations can be of assistance, for example, in solving a professional problem involving the administration of an adapted program or a personal problem of life insurance.

5. *They provide an opportunity for fellowship.* Through association conferences and meetings the physical educator gets to know others doing similar work, and this common denominator results in friendships and many enjoyable professional and social occasions. A person literally gets a "shot in the arm" by associating with other persons who are dedicated to the same field of endeavor.

6. *They provide an organ for research.* Professions must continually conduct research to determine how effective their programs are, how many contributions they are rendering to human beings, how valid their techniques are, and the answers to many other questions that must be known if the profession is to move ahead and render an increasingly larger service.

7. *They yield a feeling of belonging.* A basic psychological need is to have a feeling of being part of a group and accomplishing work that is recognized and important. A professional association can contribute much in meeting this human need.

8. *They provide a means for distributing costs.* The work accomplished by a professional association is designed to help the members who belong to the association. The work accomplished requires financial means. By joining a professional association, a physical educator helps to share the expenses that he rightfully has the responsibility to share. If he participates in the benefits, he should also want to share in the costs of achieving these benefits.

## PROFESSIONAL ORGANIZATIONS

It would be difficult to discuss all of the organizations that pertain to the physical education profession. However, some of these organizations with which the physi-

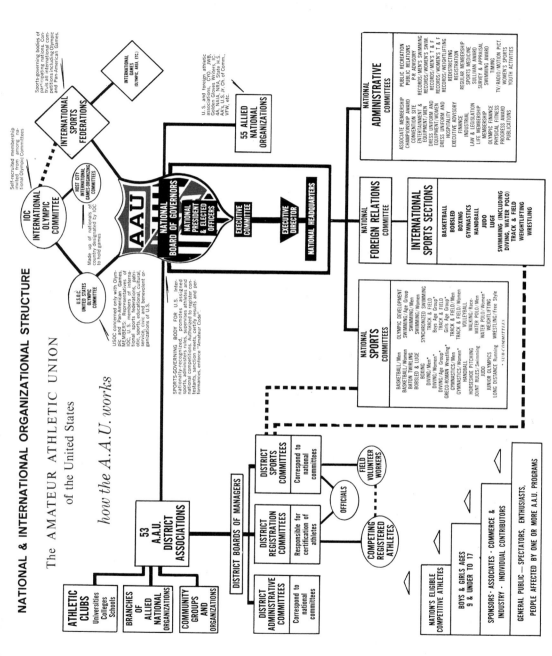

Organizational chart of the Amateur Athletic Union.

cal educator should be familiar are discussed. Items concerned with the history, purpose, membership, organization, and publications of these organizations are considered in order to give the reader a brief description of these associations.

## Amateur Athletic Union

The Amateur Athletic Union (AAU) was founded in 1888. It serves as the governing body in the United States for thirteen amateur sports: basketball, baton twirling, bobsled and toboggan, boxing, gymnastics, handball, horseshoe pitching, judo, luge, swimming (including diving and water polo), track and field, weight lifting, and wrestling.

The objectives of the AAU include:

1. The encouragement and development of amateur sport and physical fitness
2. Maintaining integrity in competitions
3. Making facilities and opportunities available to all
4. Providing the best possible contestants to represent America in international competitions

The AAU is composed of fifty-three associations serving 175,000 registered athletes. Its activities also serve more than five million boys and girls. It sponsors many adult programs, including fitness classes, and has developed an isometric fitness development program, as well as a physical fitness and proficiency test. The AAU conducts pre-Olympic trials to aid with the selection of competitors, and is the official representative of the United States in many international sports federations. Since 1949, it has sponsored an annual Junior Olympics for boys and girls between the ages of 9 through 17.

Headquarters are at the AAU House, 231 West 58th Street, New York.

## American Academy of Physical Education

The American Academy of Physical Education was established "to advance knowledge, uplift standards, and bestow honors in the fields of physical education, health education and recreation." This Association was established in 1930, and Clark W. Hetherington, R. Tait McKenzie, Thomas Storey, William Burdick, and Jay B. Nash were the first members.

Individuals are elected to membership in this Association as a result of such factors as making significant contributions to these specialized fields through research, writing, or exceptional service, providing trust funds for research purposes, recruiting promising students, making awards for outstanding contributions to these fields, sponsoring legislation, and spreading information of note from other countries. The principal types of fellows or memberships are designated active and associate fellows, fellows in memoriam, and associate fellows in the United States and corresponding fellows from other countries. The dues are $15 per year.

The Academy is committed to the function of furthering scholarship and excellence in the field of physical education. Through its meetings and work it provides an avenue of communication for new ideas and creative thinking, not only among leaders in the United States but throughout the world as well. It confers awards for excellent literary, administrative, and research contributions to individuals and citations to organizations or institutions. The address of the American Academy of Physical Education is Women's Gymnasium, University of Iowa, Iowa City, Iowa.

## American Association for Health, Physical Education, and Recreation

The American Association for Health, Physical Education, and Recreation was established in 1885 under the title of American Association for Advancement of Physical Education. The leaders in this initial organization were some thirty-five physicians, educators, and individuals.

They were called together by Dr. William G. Anderson, then on the staff of Adelphi Academy. Other physical education leaders who were prominent in the early history of the Association were Dr. Hitchcock of Amherst, Dr. Sargent of Harvard, Dr. Gulick of the Young Men's Christian Association, Dr. Arnold of Arnold College, and Dr. Savage of Oberlin College. In 1903 the name of the Association was changed to American Physical Education Association. In 1937 the Departments of School Health and Physical Education of the National Education Association were combined to form the American Association for Health and Physical Education, a department of the National Education Association. In 1938 the term *recreation* was added to the title of the Association.

The purpose of the Association is to bring about a closer relationship among the various members, improve the standards of the professions, dispense materials and information of interest and value to members, and stimulate interest in and understanding of the work being performed by these professions.

The six districts of the American Association for Health, Physical Education, and Recreation and the states or areas that come under each of these divisions are as follows:

*Central district*
Colorado
Iowa
Kansas
Minnesota
Missouri
Nebraska
North Dakota
South Dakota
Wyoming
*Eastern district*
Connecticut
Delaware
District of Columbia
Maine
Maryland
Massachusetts
New Hampshire

West Virginia
Wisconsin
*Northwest district*
Alaska
Idaho
Montana
Oregon
Washington
*Southern district*
Alabama
Arkansas
Florida
Georgia
Kentucky
Louisiana
Mississippi
North Carolina
Oklahoma

New Jersey
New York
Pennsylvania
Puerto Rico
Rhode Island
Vermont
*Midwest district*
Illinois
Indiana
Michigan
Ohio

South Carolina
Tennessee
Texas
Virginia
*Southwest district*
Arizona
California
Hawaii
Nevada
New Mexico
Utah

There are seven main divisions of the American Association for Health, Physical Education, and Recreation: health education, physical education, recreation, men's athletics, girls and women's sports, safety and driver education and the general division. The administrative staff of the Association includes a president, president-elect, past president, vice-president of health, vice-president of physical education, vice-president of recreation, vice-president of men's athletics, vice-president of girls and women's sports, vice-president of safety and driver education, and executive secretary-treasurer. The two principal governing bodies are the board of directors, which conducts much of the business of the Association, and the representative assembly, which is made up of the state association delegates, chairmen of divisions, district presidents, delegates from affiliated organizations, and members of the board of directors. There are fifty-two state association affiliates, including Puerto Rico and the District of Columbia.

Some of the general sections of the Association are Administration and Supervision, Measurement and Evaluation, Professional and Public Relations, Professional Education, Research, and Student.

Some of the organizations affiliated with the Association are as follows:

1. American Academy of Physical Education
2. American College of Sports Medicine
3. American Physical Therapy Association
4. American School Health Association
5. American Youth Hostels, Inc.

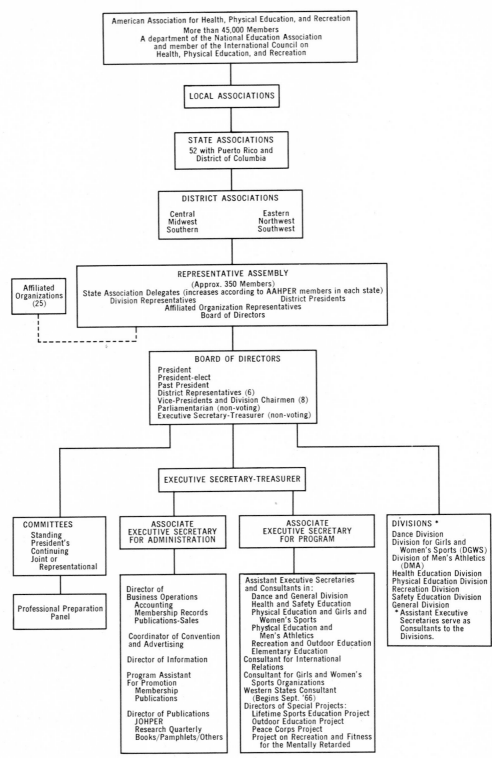

American Association for Health, Physical Education, and Recreation
More than 45,000 Members
A department of the National Education Association
and member of the International Council on
Health, Physical Education, and Recreation

LOCAL ASSOCIATIONS

STATE ASSOCIATIONS
52 with Puerto Rico and
District of Columbia

DISTRICT ASSOCIATIONS

Central               Eastern
Midwest               Northwest
Southern              Southwest

REPRESENTATIVE ASSEMBLY
(Approx. 350 Members)
State Association Delegates (increases according to AAHPER members in each state)
Division Representatives                    District Presidents
Affiliated Organization Representatives
Board of Directors

Affiliated
Organizations
(25)

BOARD OF DIRECTORS
President
President-elect
Past President
District Representatives (6)
Vice-Presidents and Division Chairmen (8)
Parliamentarian (non-voting)
Executive Secretary-Treasurer (non-voting)

EXECUTIVE SECRETARY-TREASURER

COMMITTEES
Standing
President's
Continuing
Joint or
    Representational

Professional Preparation
Panel

ASSOCIATE
EXECUTIVE SECRETARY
FOR ADMINISTRATION

Director of
Business Operations
    Accounting
    Membership Records
    Publications-Sales

Coordinator of Convention
and Advertising

Director of Information

Program Assistant
For Promotion
    Membership
    Publications

Director of Publications
    JOHPER
    Research Quarterly
    Books/Pamphlets/Others

ASSOCIATE
EXECUTIVE SECRETARY
FOR PROGRAM

Assistant Executive Secretaries
and Consultants in:
    Dance and General Division
    Health and Safety Education
    Physical Education and Girls and
        Women's Sports
    Physical Education and
        Men's Athletics
    Recreation and Outdoor Education
    Elementary Education
Consultant for International
    Relations
Consultant for Girls and Women's
    Sports Organizations
Western States Consultant
    (Begins Sept. '66)
Directors of Special Projects:
    Lifetime Sports Education Project
    Outdoor Education Project
    Peace Corps Project
    Project on Recreation and Fitness
        for the Mentally Retarded

DIVISIONS *
Dance Division
Division for Girls and
    Women's Sports (DGWS)
Division of Men's Athletics
    (DMA)
Health Education Division
Physical Education Division
Recreation Division
Safety Education Division
General Division
* Assistant Executive
    Secretaries serve as
    Consultants to the
    Divisions.

Organizational chart of the American Association for Health, Physical Education, and Recreation.

6. Association for Physical and Mental Rehabilitation
7. Boys' Clubs of America, Inc.
8. Canadian Physical Education Association
9. College Physical Education Association
10. Delta Psi Kappa
11. National Association for Intercollegiate Athletics
12. National Association of Physical Education for College Women
13. National Board of the Young Women's Christian Association of the United States
14. National Collegiate Athletic Association
15. National College Physical Education Association for Men
16. National Committee for Health and Physical Education of National Association of Jewish Center Workers
17. National Intramural Association
18. Phi Delta Pi
19. Phi Epsilon Kappa
20. Physical Education Society of the Young Men's Christian Associations of North America
21. Society of State Directors of Health, Physical Education, and Recreation

The national office of the American Association for Health, Physical Education, and Recreation is located at 1201 16th Street, N.W., Washington, D. C.

The publications of the Association are many and varied. Starting in 1896, the *American Physical Education Review* was the official publication. This was discontinued in 1929 when it was combined with the *Pentathlon*, the publication of the Middle West Society of Physical Education. Then, the new publication of the Association became known as the *Journal of Health and Physical Education*. This periodical is known at the present time as the *Journal of Health, Physical Education, and Recreation*. The Association also publishes the *Research Quarterly*, a magazine devoted to research in health, physical education, and recreation. In addition, it publishes many other pamphlets, books, and materials pertinent to the work of the Association.

The services performed by the Association are numerous. Some are listed below.

1. The American Association, with its membership of 50,000, the largest organization of its kind in the world, influences professional standards.
2. Individual inquiries regarding health, physical education, and recreation are given expert attention.
3. The official publication of the Association contains articles on health, physical education, and recreation, book reviews, news sections, and professional news items; it is published ten times per year.
4. State, district, and national conventions are held periodically.
5. This is the largest department of the National Education Association, and it shares National Education Association services.
6. The Association serves as a clearing house for information on positions in health, physical education, and recreation.
7. Pamphlets, brochures, reprints, bibliographies, and conference and convention reports are made available.
8. Individual and group sports guides are published by the Association, for the Division on Girls and Women's Sports.
9. Fifty-two state, six district, and many local associations compose the national association.
10. The American Association for Health, Physical Education, and Recreation, as a democratic organization, influences public opinion.
11. The research medium for the profession is published four times per year.
12. Field service is given on professional problems in health, physical education, and recreation.
13. The Association has national prestige in health, physical education, and recreation.

Members in the Association are designated as professional members, associate members, fellows, life members, life fellows, student members, honorary members, emeritus members, and contributing members. Professional members are persons working actively in one of the specialized fields of the association; associate members are those persons not professionally engaged in one of the specialized fields. Fellows, life fellows, and life members are the same as professional members with the exception of dues payment and

# The Association's Dollar

## where it comes from...

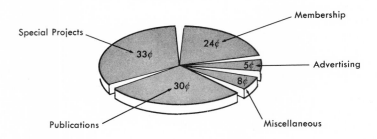

## where it goes...

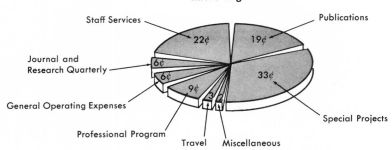

How the American Association for Health, Physical Education, and Recreation spends its funds.

variety of publications received. Student members include students attending professional and teacher-education institutions preparing for one or more of the specialized fields in the Association. Honorary members are persons outside of the professions but who, because of unusual interest and meritorious services, are nominated to membership. Emeritus membership is open to those who have reached a certain age and meet other criteria. A contributing member is one who has contributed an annual payment of $100 or more to the Association.

The annual dues for professional members are $20 and $15; associate members, $20 and $15; fellows, $20 and $15; and student members, $8 and $5.

All new professional, fellow, life, and life fellow members must have at least one graduate or undergraduate degree, with a major or minor in health, physical education, and recreation from an institution accredited by the National Council for the Accreditation of Teacher Education. Students must be enrolled in an NCATE-accredited institution offering work in one of the special fields.

### American College of Sports Medicine

On April 23, 1954, a few outstanding leaders in the fields of medicine, physiology, and physical education met in New York City and founded the American College of Sports Medicine. The purposes this group set forth for the association are as follows:

1. To promote and advance scientific studies dealing with the effect of sports and other motor activities on the health of human beings at various stages of life
2. To cooperate with other organizations concerned with various aspects of human fitness
3. To sponsor meetings of physicians, educators, and other scientists whose work is relevant to sports medicine
4. To make available postgraduate education in fields related to the objectives of the College
5. To initiate, encourage, and correlate research
6. To publish a journal dealing with scientific aspects of activity and their relationship to human fitness
7. To establish and maintain a sports medicine library

This association is rapidly being recognized as an important force for bringing together the best thinking in the fields of medicine, physiology, and physical education. In addition to encouraging research in all aspects of physical fitness, it is setting up a number of workshops in different sections of the country where advanced studies and outstanding programs are being conducted.

The membership of the College is comprised of approximately one-third physical educators, including coaches and trainers, one-third physicians, and one-third scientists in various fields, but principally in physiology.

The College is affiliated with the Federation Internationale de Medicine Sportive, an organization that has played an important role for many years in Europe and South America. The official publication of the International Federation of Sports Medicine and hence of the College is *The Journal of Sports Medicine and Physical Fitness,* which is published in Italy but printed in the English language with French, Italian, and English summaries. The College maintains a speakers' bureau and a postgraduate program of workshops for its members.

The activities of the College and the research papers cover such topics as the treatment and prevention of athletic injuries, the effects of physical activity on health, and the scientific aspects of training.

The constitution of the American College of Sports Medicine provides for various types of membership. They are listed with the annual dues for each as follows:

1. Fellows—$16
2. Members—$16
3. Student members—$6

The American College of Sports Medicine has its national office at the University of Wisconsin, 1440 Monroe Street, Madison, Wisconsin.

## American Physical Therapy Association

The American Physical Therapy Association was founded in the year 1921 as an organization for qualified physical therapists in this country. It was incorporated in 1930. The functions of the Association, as stated in the by-laws, are as follows:

1. To define functions of physical therapists and promote standards of physical therapy service
2. To provide leadership in physical therapy education by promoting sound principles of education; stimulating the development of programs and opportunities for growth; guiding and evaluating the organization and administration of curricula; and directing the maintenance of standards
3. To promote legislation and to speak for physical therapists in regard to legislative action concerning general health and welfare programs
4. To promote and protect the economic and general welfare of physical therapists
5. To provide consultation and other services within the purview of the American Physical Therapy Association to individuals, agencies, schools, and communities
6. To represent physical therapists and to serve as spokesman with allied professional, governmental, and international groups and

with the general public in regard to matters relating to the object of the American Physical Therapy Association

7. To promote scientific research in physical therapy

Members are of six classifications—active, life, honorary, associate, inactive, and student. Active members pay dues of $35 per year; life and honorary members pay no dues; associate members, $10; and inactive and student members, $10 and $2, respectively, each year, with an additional $5 assessment if they desire the official publication. Currently there are more than 8,500 active members, 2,400 inactive members, and 170 life members.

The national office of the Association is situated at 1790 Broadway, New York City, and through the media of office work and field visits it performs the following services:

1. Furnishes consultation and guidance to members, chapters, schools of physical therapy, and allied organizations.
2. Supplies educational guidance to prospective students as well as members.
3. Maintains placement services for members and for organizations needing qualified physical therapists.
4. Publishes and distributes reprints, bulletins, handbooks and other informational material in the field of physical therapy.
5. Issues News Letters to members on the activities of the association.
6. Carries out policies established by the Executive Committee and the House of Delegates.
7. Coordinates the work of the committees.*

The official publication of the American Physical Therapy Association is *The Journal of the American Physical Therapy Association*. This is a monthly publication and contains information and material pertinent to all aspects of physical therapy. Articles presented are written by prominent physicians, scientists, and physical therapists. Every member of the Asso-

*American Physical Therapy Association: Our Association, New York, The Association.

ciation receives a copy of this publication.

The American Physical Therapy Association is responsible for many achievements and activities in this specialized field. It has helped to establish high standards for the profession; has established professional classification for physical therapists employed in United States Civil Service, Veterans Administration, and United States Public Health Service; and has gained prestige for physical therapists in the Army, state agencies for crippled children, and among members of the medical profession.

## American School Health Association

The American School Health Association is interested in improving health services, health instruction, and healthful living in the nation's schools. It was organized in 1927 as the American Association of School Physicians, and for some time only physicians were eligible to become members of that Association. The number of persons who belonged to the organization in its early years was small, but the Association grew very rapidly. In 1929 the membership was 494. In 1946 it was more than 2,000. Currently it is over 8,000. In 1927 the Association's name was changed to the School Physicians Association, and a journal was published called the *School Physicians' Bulletin*. In 1937 the name of the organization was changed again to the American School Health Association. The membership requirements were broadened to include not only physicians but also dentists, nurses, nutritionists, public health workers, and others whose professional training included the premedical sciences and who were engaged in school health work. During this transition period, the name of the official publication was changed from the *School Physicians' Bulletin* to the *Journal of School Health*.

The American School Health Association works very closely with the American Public Health Association. Annual meetings are held jointly, and ideas are exchanged at this time. Much of the work performed by the Association is done through committees. The study and standing committees are concerned with such subjects as tuberculosis, professional standards, in-service training, dental program, nutrition, health services, physical fitness, nursing policies, and school health.

The dues are $5 per year, which includes the *Journal of School Health*. This periodical is published ten times each year and contains professional activities pertinent to the medical health professions; reviews of books, reports, and studies; abstracts of current literature; queries and answers; editorials on matters pertinent to school health work; and other material of value to anyone interested in health. Membership in the Association, in addition to providing a subscription to the *Journal*, offers other advantages, including informational service and the opportunity to help in promoting higher standards for the profession and to participate in other work to advance the profession. The address of the American School Health Association is 515 East Main Street, Kent, Ohio.

## American Youth Hostels, Inc.

American Youth Hostels, Inc., is a non-profit corporation whose purpose is to encourage hosteling within and outside the United States. This organization is designed to help all persons, especially young people, to a greater understanding of the world and its people through outdoor activities, educational and recreational travel, and creative group programs; to develop healthy, self-reliant, well-informed citizens; to provide youth hostels (simple overnight accommodations) in scenic, historic, and cultural areas with supervising houseparents and local sponsorship.

Youth hosteling is a special way of traveling. First, it is travel "under your own steam"—bicycling, hiking, canoeing, skiing, or horseback riding. Second, it is friendly travel, initiated for the purposes of getting acquainted with one's own or any country and gaining practical understanding and appreciation of nature and of how people live.

Hosteling takes its name from simple accommodations—hostels—which help make this kind of travel possible. Hosteling offers the chance to travel informally and on a low budget. Through hosteling a person gains new friends, is exposed to new ideas, and gains perspective. It also is a lot of fun.

In the United States each hostel is sponsored by a local community and chartered by American Youth Hostels, Inc. Resident houseparents supervise hostels, which they usually own. Each hostel has separate sleeping quarters and washrooms for fellows and girls, a common kitchen where hostelers cook their food, and, usually, space for recreation. Hostels provide blankets and cooking utensils.

Most hostels in the United States are in the New England, Middle Atlantic, Great Lakes, and West Coast states. In many sections one can hike or bike from hostel to hostel. The annual *AYH Hostel Guide and Handbook* lists each American hostel and shows temporary accommodations in some regions where hostels do not exist.

There are hostels in more than thirty-six countries outside the United States. Handbooks and other information are available through the American Youth Hostels Councils and National Headquarters. The American Youth Hostels has a national office at 14 West 8th Street, New York.

Anyone may use hostels who holds a pass, travels under his or her own power, and observes youth hostel customs. An American Youth Hostels' pass is a membership card in American Youth Hostels, Inc. It entitles the member to use hostels and commits him to follow youth hostel custom when traveling as a passholder.

American Youth Hostel passes may be used in thirty-six different countries. For those under 18 years of age, a youth pass is $4; for those age 18–20, a senior youth pass is $6; an adult pass is $7; and a family pass, good only in the United States and Canada, but including all children to 18 years of age, is $9.

Most hostelers travel on their own, but both the American Youth Hostels national headquarters and chartered councils sponsor hostel trips. Headquarters trips, usually taking about two summer months, go all over Europe, Asia, across the United States, and into North Africa, Canada, Mexico, or Alaska. Councils sponsor shorter trips throughout the year within the United States and parts of Canada and Mexico, but particularly in their own areas.

## Association for Physical and Mental Rehabilitation*

The Association for Physical and Mental Rehabilitation is a nationwide, incorporated, professional organization operated for educational and scientific purposes.

The Association was formally organized in October, 1946, by a group of corrective therapists attending a special course of instruction at the Veterans Administration Hospital, Topeka, Kansas.

This formation was a natural and necessary outgrowth of the tremendous expansion of the fields of corrective physical rehabilitation, as organized by the Veterans Administration, and the reconditioning units developed by the United States Armed Forces during and immediately following the Second World War.

---

*Information taken from promotional literature of the Association.

The objectives, as listed in the Association's constitution, are:

1. To promote the use of medically prescribed exercise therapy and adapted physical education

2. To advance the professional standards of education and training in the field of medically prescribed exercise therapy and adapted physical education

3. To promote and sponsor medically prescribed exercise therapy programs of the highest scientific and professional character

4. To encourage research and publication of scientific articles dealing with medical rehabilitation

5. To engage in and encourage those activities related to medically prescribed activity which might prove advantageous to medical rehabilitation and/or the Association

Membership in the Association for Physical and Mental Retardation, Inc., is divided into four categories:

1. *Active* ($20)—for those actively engaged in corrective or exercise therapy working under the supervision of a licensed physician, whether in hospitals, schools, rehabilitation clinics or colleges, and who meet the standards set up by the Professional Standards Committee of the Association

2. *Professional* ($7)—for those persons working in allied professional fields who wish to share and contribute to the educational and scientific progress of the Association

3. *Associate* ($7.50)—for those persons who are interested in the work of corrective therapy and wish to receive the Journal and other pertinent information relating to Association matters

4. *Student* ($3)—for students enrolled in accredited schools of health and physical education

The Association through its recruitment and placement committee has much to offer its membership in the following areas of rehabilitation employment:

1. Adapted or corrective physical education in public and private schools, colleges, and universities

2. Special schools and camps for handicapped and atypical children

3. Government, public and private rehabilitation clinics and hospitals: (a) general medicine and surgery, (b) neuropsychiatric, and (c) domiciliary

4. Armed services hospitals
5. Nursing homes
6. Recreational programs for the handicapped
7. Research

The Association publishes *The Journal of the Association for Physical and Mental Rehabilitation,* a bimonthly magazine that contains information on education and scientific research, the *APMR Information Bulletin,* issued three times a year, and the yearly *Association Brochure.*

The Association for Physical and Mental Rehabilitation is located at 105 St. Lawrence Street, Rehoboth Beach, Delaware.

## Boys' Clubs of America

Boys' Clubs were first established in the New England states during the 1860's. Some of the cities where they were developed include Hartford and New Haven in Connecticut; Providence, Rhode Island; and Salem and New Bedford in Massachusetts. The popularity of these organizations for youth increased rapidly from the time they first appeared until 1900.

Boys' Clubs are mainly interested in youth who are from indigent families. Therefore these clubs are located in those sections of cities and towns inhabited by such youth. They are exclusively for boys, who usually range from 8 to 21 years of age. These clubs offer recreation, companionship, and wholesome activity at a very low cost or no cost. Facilities and personnel are commonly provided for such activities as games and sports, reading, health education, handicrafts, vocational guidance, parties, movies, and camping.

The national organization, Boys' Clubs of America, was created as a means of organizing the various clubs that were formed throughout the country. In 1906 a Federated Boys' Club was established. The title was changed to Boys' Club Federation in 1915, to Boys' Club Federation of America in 1929, and in 1931 to Boys' Clubs of America, Inc.

Prominent men have been associated with this organization since its inception. Jacob Riis was the first president, and Herbert Hoover served from 1936 until recently as chairman of the board of directors. The purposes of the Boys' Clubs of America are outlined in the constitution: "The purposes of the Corporation shall be to promote the health, social education, vocational and character development of boys throughout the United States of America; to receive, invest and disburse funds and to hold property for the purposes of the Corporation."*

The business affairs of the Boys' Clubs are assumed by a board of directors which is elected by the members of a national council. The national council consists of delegates from the various Boys' Clubs in the organization. The national office is at 771 First Avenue, New York.

The various services provided by the national office of the Boys' Clubs of America are as follows:

1. It establishes policies, standards, principles, and procedure for the guidance of Boys' Clubs.
2. It furnishes a service to Boys' Clubs in all matters of organization, administration, operation, and expansion.
3. It furnishes a service to community groups in the establishment of Boys' Clubs.
4. It studies and keeps abreast of the problems and needs of boys and of events, legislation, and movements affecting boys. It represents the Boys' Clubs in discussions with other organizations, agencies, and groups. It cooperates with other organizations, agencies, and groups in planning to meet the needs of boys.
5. It collects and furnishes general and specific information.
6. It promotes a knowledge and understanding of Boys' Clubs through interpretive publicity carried on both national and local

---

*Constitution, New York, Boys' Clubs of America.

levels. It prepares and furnishes publicity and interpretive material to Boys' Clubs for local use.

7. It provides a field service by trained men who give information, guidance, and assistance to Boys' Clubs in their plans, operation and financing, and who aid community groups in the organization of Boys' Clubs.

8. It carries on a continuous study of programs, activities, and methods, and furnishes program material and information through the field service, publications, special bulletins, institutes, and conferences.

9. It plans and promotes national programs, projects, contests, and events.

10. It recruits, trains, and places men in Boys' Club work. It establishes job classifications and qualifications. It furnishes information about salaries.

11. It provides an informational, planning, and consultation service in the alteration, expansion, and construction of buildings, furnishings, and equipment, and in the care and upkeep of buildings.

12. It publishes papers, booklets, leaflets, and bulletins of value to Boys' Clubs and the promotion of the movement.

13. It plans, organizes, and conducts institutes for training workers in various parts of the country. It plans, organizes, and conducts a national convention.

14. It promotes the organization of Area Councils made up of lay people and professional representatives from Boys' Clubs in a particular geographical area for discussion and planning. It furnishes information, guidance, and assistance to these councils.

15. It administers national group and retirement insurance plans for Boys' Club workers.*

A quarterly magazine, *The Journal,* provides new ideas in programming, discusses educational and psychological ideas of interest in work with boys, and gives tips on how to conduct and maintain good programs.

Two comparatively recent developments in Boys' Club work is the expanded program for scholarships for young men to train for Boys' Club work. Since 1957 scholarships have been provided to over 500 individuals. This has been made possible through foundation grants. The sec-

ond development is a program of certification of professional workers in order to raise the level of Boys' Club leadership.

Today, there are more than 660 Boys' Clubs in the Boys' Clubs of America organization. Their assets amount to more than $135 million. They are doing an excellent job in directing youth into proper leisure-time activities and in developing boys into useful citizens.

## Canadian Association for Health, Physical Education, and Recreation

The Canadian Association for Health, Physical Education, and Recreation (CAHPER) was organized originally as the Canadian Physical Education Association in 1933 through the joint efforts of the Quebec Physical Education Association and the Toronto Physical Education Association. The "father" of physical education in Canada was the late Dr. Arthur S. Lamb of McGill University, which was the alma mater of Dr. James Naismith and Dr. R. Tait McKenzie.

In 1948 the Association changed its name to the Canadian Association for Health, Physical Education, and Recreation. In 1951 it became an incorporated body, the original signing officers being John Lang, Iveagh Munro, and Gordon Wright, three outstanding Canadian physical educators. The constitution of the Association was given a major revision in 1960 under the chairmanship of Dr. M. L. Howell of Alberta, Canada.

The aims of the Association are as follows:

1. To encourage the improvement of the standards of those engaged in the furtherance of health education, physical education, and recreation

2. To provide such means of promotion as will service the establishment of adequate programs under the direction of approved leadership

3. To stimulate a wide, intelligent, and active interest in health education, physical education, and recreation

4. To acquire and disseminate accurate information concerning it

---

*Hall, Walter M.: Journal of Health and Physical Education **17:**387, June, 1946.

5. To cooperate with kindred interests and organizations in the furtherance of these aims

Yearly dues in the Canadian Association for Health, Physical Education, and Recreation are $15 for a fellow membership, $10 for a professional membership, $10 for an associate membership, and $3 for student memberships. The address of CAHPER is 703 Spadina Avenue, Toronto 4, Ontario, Canada.

The publication of the CAHPER is the *Journal of the Canadian Association for Health, Physical Education, and Recreation.* It is published six times a year. The membership of the Association has increased to about 1,200, each province of Canada having representation. The Association meets biennially.

## Delta Psi Kappa

Delta Psi Kappa is a professional organization for women majors or minors in health, physical education, and recreation. The purpose of this organization is to stimulate fellowship among women in these specialized areas, to promote high educational standards, and to promote opportunities and mutual service among the women in these professions.

Delta Psi Kappa was founded in 1916 with thirteen members and was incorporated by the state of Indiana. Chapters have gradually been established in various colleges and universities throughout the United States and alumnae organizations have been set up in some cities. There were twenty-six college chapters and ten alumnae chapters as of March, 1963, with more applications to be processed.

Meetings of this fraternity are held biennially, and since all the work of this fraternity cannot be accomplished at these meetings, a great percentage of it is performed by the grand council of seven members.

Through various funds and awards, Delta Psi Kappa helps to stimulate high educational standards and worthwhile projects. It supports an Educational Loan Fund for promising members who wish to use it for study. It also has a biennial Research Fellowship Fund which is used to make an award to a woman doing some outstanding research in health, physical education, and recreation.

Delta Psi Kappa promotes national and chapter projects. For example, in 1939 many pieces of equipment were presented to the Nashville, Tennessee, Home for Crippled Children. The various chapters of the organization also carry on worthwhile projects, such as sponsoring radio programs, maintaining hospital beds, and conducting playdays.

The official publication of Delta Psi Kappa is *The Foil*, which is published semiannually in the months of January and May. *The Foil* contains news and articles from the various chapters, contributions from outstanding leaders in the profession, and workshop and book review sections.

Membership in Delta Psi Kappa is limited to women in major departments of health, physical education, and recreation. The school, however, must meet the standards established by the American Association for Health, Physical Education, and Recreation. These are as follows:

1. Be an accredited member of a recognized association of higher educational institutions
2. Be listed by the State Department of Education as approved for the training of health and physical education teachers for secondary schools
3. Have established an organized curriculum of health education and physical education
4. Require a minimum of four years for completion of preparation for teaching in secondary schools
5. Have an efficient student health service program
6. Conduct recreational activities including physical education programs*

*National Committee Report on Standards: Research Quarterly, AAHPER 6:56, Dec., 1955.

A minimum of ten women must constitute a group petitioning the national organization for membership. There are six kinds of membership, active, alumnae, inactive, honorary, alumnae associate, and active associate.

## National Association of Intercollegiate Athletics

The National Association of Intercollegiate Athletics (NAIA) is a group of colleges and universities organized for the purpose of attacking cooperatively the problems that face them in the administration of a sound, challenging intercollegiate athletic program.

The organization has grown from a membership of approximately thirty institutions in 1940 to over 465. It is recognized as a "small college" organization. The enrollment of the institutions in this organization ranges from a few colleges, with under 200 students, to many institutions, with enrollment between 3,000 and 6,500 students. The average enrollment of the institutions with the NAIA, however, is approximately 1,172 students.

Within the membership are all types of institutions, from the private college and university, of which many are controlled and financed by religious denominations, to the state college and university.

Membership in the NAIA is based on the size of the undergraduate male enrollment of the member college, and is on a sliding scale. Full membership is from $50 to $150, while associate membership ranges from $30 to $90.

The objectives of this Association as stated in its constitution are the following:

1. To establish a code of ethics and standards for the best interests of athletics
2. To establish uniform officiating and interpretation of rules
3. To establish uniformity of equipment
4. To issue a monthly bulletin throughout the school year devoted to furthering of NAIA and intercollegiate athletics

5. To cooperate with other national or state organizations in standardizing rules
6. To establish an eligibility code which is in conformity with the best interests of intercollegiate athletics
7. To take united and prompt action against any of the evils which may creep up to prevent the proper development of intercollegiate athletics and NAIA
8. To establish working committees and cooperate in the solution to problems for the improvement of intercollegiate athletics and NAIA. A few of these problems would include:
   A. Selection of officials for National Tournaments and Meets
   B. Establishing uniformity of procedures in districts throughout the organization
9. To publicize our national association throughout the United States by means of press, radio, motion picture, television, and any other medium which seems wise
10. To carry on research projects in athletics through the NAIA in order to assist in the over-all development of the athletic sports
11. To constantly seek to expand and enlarge the activities and the influence of NAIA
12. To set up committees for the purpose of carrying out any objectives deemed necessary by the Executive Committee and secretary to furtherance of NAIA
13. To establish strong and functioning district committees, aiding these districts in every way possible with respect to organization, and so far as practicable to determine the best method of carrying on the activities of the district and selecting the best team to represent the district at the National Championship Sports
14. To establish and use every means possible for the improvement of public relations between NAIA, the general public, and other sports groups
15. To establish a financial structure which will be sound for future growth, which will allow full expenses to all participating teams and an added amount for activities necessary to the development of NAIA and intercollegiate sports

The NAIA has a national office in the Aladdin Hotel, 106 West 12th Street, Kansas City, Missouri.

## National Association of Jewish Center Workers

The National Association of Jewish Center Workers (NAJCW) has its offices at 145 East 32nd Street, New York City. The Association is an organization of professional workers in Jewish Community Centers, camps, and youth groups. Its objectives are to maintain and improve the standards, techniques, practices, scope, and public understanding of Jewish Community Center and kindred work.

Membership in the NAJCW means better placement, work, and advancement conditions; job security; acceptable salary standards and retirement plans; personal emergency loans and scholarships; the opportunity for collective study, research, and action; automatic membership in the National Conference of Jewish Communal Service; and a subscription to the quarterly *Journal of Jewish Communal Service*.

Types of membership include the following:

1. Full membership, which is open to professionally qualified men and women employed in Jewish Community Center or kindred work
2. Associate membership, which is open to former workers in the Jewish Center field and current workers in related fields
3. Student membership, which is open to students attending professional schools of social work or the graduate divisions of other approved schools offering preparation for service in Jewish Community Centers and/or related areas
4. Emeritus membership, which is open to those who have been Association members for a minimum of twenty years and who have retired from full employment

Membership dues are based on salary, ranging from $8 for those earning under $3,000 to $32 to $65 for those earning $9,000 or over. Student membership dues are $5 and associate membership dues are $15.

## National Association of Physical Education for College Women

The National Association of Physical Education for College Women, although formally organized in 1924, had its beginning before this time. In 1909 Miss Amy Morris Homans issued an invitation to directors of physical education to meet at Wellesley College. This group continued to meet annually after this first meeting with Miss Homans and gradually grew into the Eastern Society, which was organized in 1915. Later, in 1917 and 1921 the Midwest and Western Societies, respectively, were organized. Then, in 1924 these three societies united and formed a national association at a meeting in Kansas City. At the present time the national Association represents five district associations, Eastern, Southern, Midwest, Central, and Western. Each district association is to a great extent autonomous in its own section.

The purpose of the National Association of Physical Education for College Women is to investigate and study problems that characterize departments of physical education for women in the various colleges and universities. Since its inception, this organization has concerned itself with such problems as establishing standards for policies, equipment, and programs; promoting research studies and making findings available to all; promoting sane athletic policies in institutions of higher learning; and developing an interest in women's health, skill development, and proper emotional adjustment.

Originally membership in this women's association was restricted to women directors of physical education. However, as physical education has grown, so has this organization, with a broadening of membership requirements. At the present time, membership is open to all women teachers of physical education in colleges and universities. This includes teachers' colleges and junior colleges. To be a member of the national organization, one must be a member of the district organization. Honorary members of the National Association of Physical Education for College Women pay no dues. Active and associate members pay $4 yearly. This organization is located at 1201 16th Street, N.W., Washington, D. C.

The national Association holds meetings biennially, whereas the districts hold their meetings annually. The agenda for such meetings includes such items as discussion of topics pertinent to the profession, reports of research studies, leadership problems, and international problems. Once a year the Association sends newsletters to all its members, and after the biennial meeting a report is usually sent out concerning the meeting and important items that transpired at the conference.

### National Collegiate Athletic Association

The history of the National Collegiate Athletic Association (NCAA) began in the early 1900's. Due to the alarming number of football injuries and the fact that there was no uniform or national control of the game of football, a conference of representatives of universities and colleges, primarily from the eastern section of the United States, was held December 12, 1905. Preliminary plans were made for a national body to assist in the formulation of sound requirements for intercollegiate athletics, particularly football, and the name of Intercollegiate Ath-

## GROWTH OF MEMBERSHIP

Total NCAA membership stands at an all-time record of 626 colleges and universities, athletic conferences and associations (as of March 1, 1965). Since 1950, NCAA membership has increased by 97 percent.

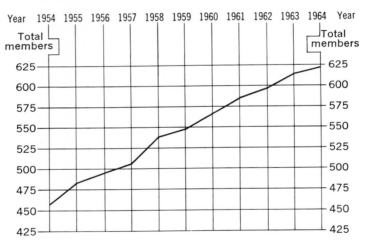

| Year | Active | Associate | Allied | Affiliated | Total |
|------|--------|-----------|--------|------------|-------|
| 1954 | 420 | 6 | 19 | 11 | 456 |
| 1955 | 436 | 7 | 23 | 11 | 477 |
| 1956 | 449 | 5 | 24 | 11 | 489 |
| 1957 | 467 | 4 | 25 | 13 | 509 |
| 1958 | 491 | 5 | 24 | 11 | 539 |
| 1959 | 497 | 8 | 31 | 13 | 549 |
| 1960 | 510 | 11 | 32 | 14 | 567 |
| 1961 | 524 | 10 | 32 | 16 | 582 |
| 1962 | 534 | 13 | 32 | 20 | 597 |
| 1963 | 548 | 14 | 32 | 20 | 614 |
| 1964 | 553 | 13 | 37 | 20 | 623* |

*626 as of March 1. 1965.

*The National Collegiate Athletic Association: The story of the NCAA, Kansas City, Mo., 1965.*

Growth of membership of the National Collegiate Athletic Association.

letic Association was suggested. At a meeting March 31, 1906, a constitution and bylaws were adopted and issued. The first annual convention of the Intercollegiate Athletic Association was held at the Murray Hill Hotel, New York City, on December 29, 1906. On December 29, 1910, the name of the Association was changed to the National Collegiate Athletic Association.

The purposes of the NCAA are designed to uphold the principle of institutional control of all collegiate sports; to maintain a uniform code of amateurism in conjunction with sound eligibility rules, scholarship requirements, and good sportsmanship; to promote and assist in the expansion of intercollegiate and intramural sports; to formulate, copyright, and publish the official rules of play (in eleven sports); to sponsor and supervise regional and national meets and tournaments for member institutions (presently the NCAA conducts national meets and tournaments in many sports); to preserve collegiate athletic records; and to serve as headquarters for collegiate athletic matters of national import.

To achieve membership in the NCAA, a college must be accredited, and compete in a minimum of four sports each year, on an intercollegiate level. At least one sport must be engaged in during the normal three major sport seasons. Dues are scaled according to the enrollment of the college, and range from $37.50 to $200.

The NCAA is a voluntary association of more than 625 member institutions and affiliated associations. Its services include the following:

1. Serving as a discussion, legislative, and administrative body for college athletics
2. Maintaining a national headquarters staff
3. Publishing official guides in nine sports
4. Conducting national championship events in many sports
5. Participating in United States Olympic and Pan American athletic events
6. Maintaining a central clearing and coun-

seling agency in the field of college athletic administration
7. Providing a film library covering play in national meets and tournaments
8. Administering group travel and medical insurance programs for its member institutions

Some of the publications of the NCAA are as follows:

1. Guides (all "guides" include the official rules):
    *Official Collegiate Baseball Guide*
    *Official NCAA Collegiate Football Guide*
    *Official NCAA Collegiate Basketball Guide*
    *Official NCAA Collegiate Track & Field Guide*
    *Official NCAA Collegiate-Scholastic Soccer Guide*
    *Official NCAA Collegiate-Scholastic Lacrosse Guide*
    *Official NCAA Collegiate-Scholastic Ice Hockey Guide*
    *Official NCAA Wrestling Guide*
    *Official NCAA Collegiate-Scholastic Swimming Guide*
2. Rule books (these publications contain the rules of the sport, only):
    *Official NCAA Football Handbook*
    *Official NCAA Basketball Handbook*
    *Official NCAA Boxing-Gymnastics-Skiing Rules*
3. The *NCAA Yearbook:*
    Contains the annual year-end reports of the district vice-presidents and Tournament and Rules Committees, the list of officers and committees, the proceedings of the annual convention, the proceedings of special committees, and the annual financial reports of the Association

The NCAA has an office in the Fairfax Building, 11th and Baltimore Streets, Kansas City, Missouri.

## The National College Physical Education Association for Men

In 1897 the National College Physical Education Association for Men (NCPE-AM) was founded under the name of the Society of College Gymnasium Directors. In 1909 it became known as the Society of College Directors of Physical Education and in 1933 as the College Physical Education Association.

The men present at the organization in 1897 included Dr. Anderson of Yale, Dr. Sargent of Harvard, Dr. Seaver of Yale, Dr. Linhart of Ohio State, Dr. Savage of Columbia, Professor Goldie of Princeton, Mr. Marvel of Wesleyan, Mr. F. H. Cann of New York University, and Mr. Sharp of Yale.

The Association was formed for men performing health and physical education work in colleges. The purpose of the organization is the advancement of college health, physical education, and recreation in institutions of higher learning. Many areas of these professions are represented and have sectional meetings, such as required physical education, adapted physical education, recreational activities, intercollegiate athletics, teacher education, and administration and supervision. The Association meets annually.

The work of the organization is largely carried on by committees. Some of the important committees that have been in operation at various times during the history of the Association are the following: Committee on Relationships of College Physical Education to National Preparedness, Committee on Constitution and Material Equipment, Committee on Curriculum Research, and Committees on Teacher Education, Research, and Physical Education and Athletics.

The National College Physical Education Association for Men has three types of members. First there are active members, or those who are directly engaged in some phase of college health, physical education, or recreation; second, associate members, or those to whom the Association has extended membership by reason of work related to the fields of health, physical education, and recreation, but who are not teaching in a college; and, third, honorary members, or those who have been selected by the Association and

who may be active or former active members. The dues for a member are $10 annually. Represented in the Association are more than 300 different colleges in five countries, with approximately 700 members.

The official publication of the National College Physical Education Association for Men is *The Proceedings of the College Physical Education Association.* This material is published once a year. Also available are such publications as *College Facilities for Health Education, Physical Education, and Recreation,* which sells for $2 a copy, and *Fit for College,* which sells for 50 cents. The NCPEAM also publishes the monograph *Quest* in conjunction with the National Association for Physical Education of College Women.

The NCPEAM has its headquarters at 205 Huff Gymnasium, University of Illinois, Urbana, Illinois.

### National Education Association

Every physical educator associated with the schools in this country should be familiar with the National Education Association (NEA). It has reportedly the greatest number of members of any professional organization in the world and is very active in promoting the cause of education. Its central offices are located at 1201 16th Street, N.W., Washington, D. C.

T. W. Valentine and D. B. Hager were the two educators who were largely responsible for calling the first meeting of the National Teachers Association in 1857. This was the organization that later became known as the National Education Association. The first meeting of the National Teachers Association was on August 26, 1857, in Philadelphia. Forty-three educators, representing twelve states, were in attendance.

Some highlights in the history of the National Education Association have been the lecture delivered by Horace Mann in

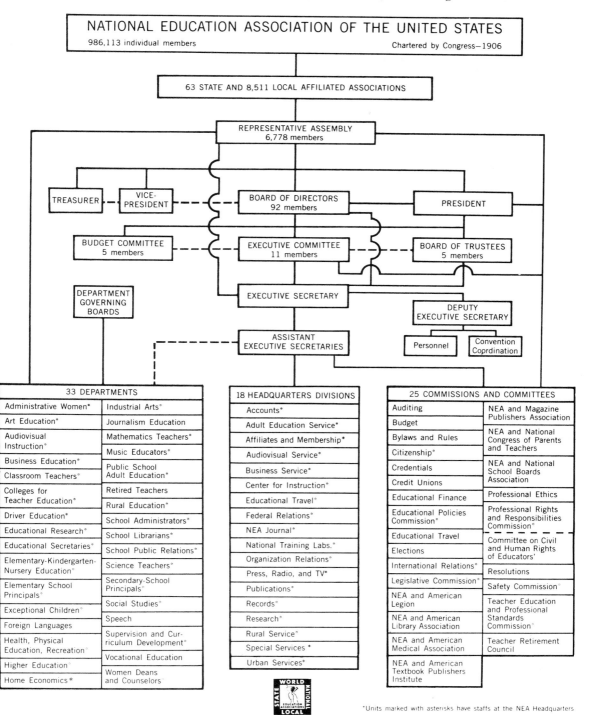

# NATIONAL EDUCATION ASSOCIATION OF THE UNITED STATES

986,113 individual members     Chartered by Congress—1906

63 STATE AND 8,511 LOCAL AFFILIATED ASSOCIATIONS

REPRESENTATIVE ASSEMBLY
6,778 members

TREASURER

VICE-PRESIDENT

BOARD OF DIRECTORS
92 members

PRESIDENT

BUDGET COMMITTEE
5 members

EXECUTIVE COMMITTEE
11 members

BOARD OF TRUSTEES
5 members

DEPARTMENT GOVERNING BOARDS

EXECUTIVE SECRETARY

DEPUTY EXECUTIVE SECRETARY

ASSISTANT EXECUTIVE SECRETARIES

Personnel

Convention Coordination

| 33 DEPARTMENTS | |
|---|---|
| Administrative Women* | Industrial Arts° |
| Art Education° | Journalism Education |
| Audiovisual Instruction° | Mathematics Teachers° |
| | Music Educators° |
| Business Education° | Public School Adult Education° |
| Classroom Teachers° | |
| Colleges for Teacher Education° | Retired Teachers |
| | Rural Education° |
| Driver Education* | School Administrators° |
| Educational Research° | School Librarians° |
| Educational Secretaries° | School Public Relations° |
| Elementary-Kindergarten-Nursery Education° | Science Teachers° |
| Elementary School Principals° | Secondary-School Principals° |
| | Social Studies° |
| Exceptional Children° | Speech |
| Foreign Languages | Supervision and Curriculum Development° |
| Health, Physical Education, Recreation° | Vocational Education |
| Higher Education° | Women Deans and Counselors° |
| Home Economics* | |

| 18 HEADQUARTERS DIVISIONS |
|---|
| Accounts* |
| Adult Education Service* |
| Affiliates and Membership* |
| Audiovisual Service* |
| Business Service* |
| Center for Instruction° |
| Educational Travel° |
| Federal Relations° |
| NEA Journal° |
| National Training Labs.° |
| Organization Relations° |
| Press, Radio, and TV* |
| Publications° |
| Records° |
| Research* |
| Rural Service° |
| Special Services * |
| Urban Services* |

| 25 COMMISSIONS AND COMMITTEES | |
|---|---|
| Auditing | NEA and Magazine Publishers Association |
| Budget | |
| Bylaws and Rules | NEA and National Congress of Parents and Teachers |
| Citizenship° | |
| Credentials | NEA and National School Boards Association |
| Credit Unions | |
| Educational Finance | Professional Ethics |
| Educational Policies Commission° | Professional Rights and Responsibilities Commission° |
| Educational Travel | Committee on Civil and Human Rights of Educators' |
| Elections | |
| International Relations° | |
| Legislative Commission° | Resolutions |
| NEA and American Legion | Safety Commission° |
| NEA and American Library Association | Teacher Education and Professional Standards Commission° |
| NEA and American Medical Association | Teacher Retirement Council |
| NEA and American Textbook Publishers Institute | |

°Units marked with asterisks have staffs at the NEA Headquarters

THE NATIONAL EDUCATION ASSOCIATION IS THE ONLY ORGANIZATION THAT REPRESENTS OR HAS THE POSSIBILITY OF REPRESENTING THE GREAT BODY OF TEACHERS IN THE UNITED STATES.

Organizational chart of the National Education Association of the United States.

1858, entitled "The Teacher's Motives"; President James Buchanan's recognition of the National Education Association and his attendance at one of its sessions; the incorporation of the National Education Association by a bill signed by President Theodore Roosevelt in 1906; the appointment of Willard E. Givens as executive secretary of the National Education Association in 1935; the establishment of the Education Policies Commission; and the establishment of the American Association for Health, Physical Education, and Recreation as a department of the National Education Association.

The purposes and services of the National Education Association are concerned with promoting education in this country. In doing so, it works toward the advancement of the interests of those in the teaching profession, helps to better care for the welfare of all American youth, and is interested in and strives to provide for the education of all individuals.

The services of the National Education Association are primarily to members only; however, indirectly it is of service to youth, to parents, and to the public and nation as a whole.

Membership in the National Education Association started with forty-three active members in 1857 and is approaching the million-member mark today and has almost one million affiliated members. The dues for the annual membership are $10. In addition, there is a $225 life membership. Any student enrolled in a teacher education program in a college or university may become a student NEA member by joining a chapter of the student National Education Association. The dues are $1 per year. The membership year is from September 1 to August 31.

The publications of the National Education Association are too numerous to list in this chapter. However, the one that has the widest circulation and that is representative of the Association is the *Journal of the National Education Association*. It is published monthly, with the exception of June, July, and August, and is sent to all members of the Association. This periodical contains discussions of recent developments in the field of education, reports from teachers on work they are doing, articles by outstanding leaders, and other material of interest and value to the physical educator.

### National Intramural Association*

In the school year 1948–1949 William Wasson, an instructor at Dillard University in New Orleans, received a Carnegie grant-in-aid to study intramural programs in twenty-five colleges and universities. It was from this study that he conceived the idea of having the intramural directors meet annually and of developing a medium through which an exchange of information and ideas could take place.

The first meeting was held at Dillard University on February 22 and 23, 1950. At this meeting the National Intramural Association was formed.

The National Intramural Association is an affiliate member of the American Association for Health, Physical Education, and Recreation.

The objectives of the National Intramural Association are stated below:

1. To provide a common meeting ground for intramural directors and members of their staff to discuss current problems and policies
2. To provide an opportunity to exchange ideas and thoughts for improvement in the operation of the intramural program
3. To determine policy, principles, and procedures to guide intramural directors in performance of their duties
4. To promote and encourage intramural and recreational programs
5. To serve as a medium for the publication

---

*The information on the National Intramural Association was contributed by Ellis J. Mendelsohn.

of research papers on intramurals, of both members and nonmembers

6. To work in close cooperation with the American Association for Health, Physical Education, and Recreation, the National Recreation and Park Association, and the Educational Policy Committee of our respective institutions

The official publication of the National Intramural Association is *The Proceedings of the Annual Intramural Conference.*

Membership in the National Intramural Association started with the eleven charter members who attended the first intramural conference held at Dillard University in New Orleans in 1950, rose to 250 by 1959, and has a much higher membership today. Membership in the Association, in addition to providing a subscription for a copy of the annual conference proceedings, offers other advantages, including information service and an opportunity to help in promoting higher stands for the profession.

## National Recreation and Park Association

The National Recreation and Park Association (NRPA) had at least part of its beginnings in 1906 when the Playground Association of America was organized. At the time of the founding of this Association, only forty-one cities reportedly had playgrounds with qualified leadership. One of the main objectives of this Association was to achieve the goal of having adequately trained men and women conducting play and recreation programs on a community basis. It also furthered the cause of spending leisure in a wholesome, profitable manner.

The National Recreation Association, as the Playground Association of America later came to be known, received support from such individuals as President Theodore Roosevelt, Jane Addams, Jacob Riis, Felix Warburg, Joseph Lee, and Luther Gulick. These persons helped the Associa-

tion in achieving many of its aims. In 1965, the American Association of Zoological Parks and Aquariums, the American Institute of Park Executives, the American Recreation Society, the National Conference on State Parks, and the National Recreation Association united to form the National Recreation and Park Association.

The Association has conducted an educational program that has brought to the attention of the public the necessity for playgrounds; the need for recreation, especially in a highly industrialized society; the need for conservation, beautification, and purification of water supples; and the need for qualified leadership to conduct programs in such areas as sports, arts and crafts, drama, and dance.

The National Recreation and Park Association serves such groups as board members, park executives, Green Spaces committees, recreation departments, volunteer leaders, government agencies, armed forces, students, educational institutions, camps, hospitals, child care institutions, religious groups, and the general public.

The services rendered by the Association include leadership training, program planning and ideas, planning areas and facilities, recreation surveys, research, publishing a recreation magazine, and providing library conferences, and public information and education.

The Association is responsible for many publications, ranging from books to mimeographed bulletins. The content of the published material covers the entire field of recreation, including philosophy, administration and operation, facilities, layout and equipment, leadership and leadership training, public relations, parks, recreation for special groups, home play and activities material covering the various fields of arts and crafts, camping and nature, drama, games, tests and special activities, holiday and special day ma-

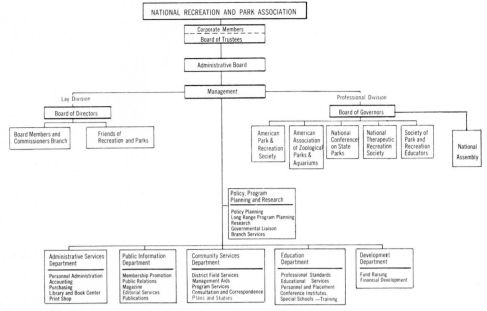

**Organizational chart of the National Recreation and Park Association.**

terial, music, radio, dancing, and social recreation.

The national headquarters of the Association is at 1700 Pennsylvania Avenue, N.W., Washington, D. C. (See also Chapter 9, Recreation, for more information on NRPA.)

## Phi Delta Pi

Phi Delta Pi is a national professional education fraternity for women. It was organized in 1916 at the Normal College of the American Gymnastic Union, Indianapolis, Indiana. The objects of Phi Delta Pi are listed below:

1. To provide a national physical education affiliation for women
2. To promote the progressive development of physical education
3. To emphasize and develop effective leadership*

This fraternity for women has a na-

tional convention every two years and a national council meeting every year. Sectional meetings are held in connection with the district meetings of the American Association for Health, Physical Education, and Recreation. Committees perform much of the work for this organization. Committees have been established that are concerned with such problems as alumnae expansion, documents and rituals, history, necrology, scholarship loan, publicity, and professional standards.

This association has sponsored many national projects. It has had a camp project as a service for underprivileged children. Camps for this purpose have been held at Elkhart Lake, Wisconsin; Johnstown, New York; Salt Lake City, Utah; Medford, New Jersey; and Cincinnati, Ohio. This fraternity has sponsored many projects in forms of symposiums. These have been held for a discussion of such problems as posture and dysmenorrhea. Other projects include scholastic loans, magazine agency, professional standards,

---

*Phi Delta Pi, national professional physical education fraternity for women: Phi Delta Pi, The Fraternity, p. 2.

and round and square dances at the national convention of the American Association for Health, Physical Education, and Recreation. The fraternity is reorganizing its scholarship program and is developing close relations with the Professional Panhellenic Association. A national alumnae bureau is being organized to serve members throughout the country.

Phi Delta Pi has four types of membership. The active membership is for majors in physical education in a school where a chapter of the fraternity exists. The alumnae membership exists when an active member graduates and becomes an alumna member. The honorary membership is for individuals who are outstanding in fields of health, physical education, or recreation. The special membership is for educators active in health, physical education, or recreation work. The membership in the fraternity is now 3,000. Dues are $3.50.

The publications of Phi Delta Pi include *The Professional Physical Educator* and the *Handbook for Student Teachers.*

Active chapters in Phi Delta Pi may be installed in colleges or universities where there is a major course in physical education and upon approval of the National Council of Phi Delta Pi.

The address of Phi Delta Pi is 5850 N. 13th Street, Apt. 410, Philadelphia, Pennsylvania.

## Phi Epsilon Kappa

Phi Epsilon Kappa is a fraternity for men engaged in the professions of health, physical education, and recreation. It was founded in 1913 at the Normal College of the North American Gymnastic Union, Indianapolis, Indiana. Carl P. Sputh, M.D., who is referred to as the "father of the national organization" and who was national president from 1920 to 1936, contributed greatly toward the expansion and growth of this fraternity. The purpose of

its founding was for reasons of social and professional companionship. Since the granting of the first chapter charter to the American College of Physical Education in Chicago in 1920, this fraternity has grown very rapidly. Chapters have been installed in various colleges and universities in every section of the country. There are more than 45 active collegiate chapters and 17 alumni chapters.

The objectives of the fraternity are stated as:

1. To inculcate the principles of peace, friendship, and brotherly love
2. To promote and enhance the happiness of its members
3. To elevate the standards, ideals, and ethics of those engaged in teaching in the fields of health, physical education, and recreation
4. To support the active chapters
5. To perpetuate itself as a fraternal organization and to provide for its government*

More than 12,500 members have been initiated in Phi Epsilon Kappa. The current active membership is over 3,000. There are four types of membership in the fraternity. The active membership in collegiate chapters is for students and teachers in colleges and universities where a chartered chapter has been installed and in alumni chapters for men in physical education work. The honorary membership is for prominent persons in physical education work, who have received the approval of the Grand Chapter. The extraordinary membership is for individuals who have retired from active physical education work and have been approved by an alumni chapter. Life membership is for alumni members who pay a prescribed fee. Annual membership dues are $3 for undergraduates and $4 for graduate students, staff members, and alumni members. A life membership is $60.

The publications of Phi Epsilon Kappa include *The Physical Educator,* which is published four times annually, and ab-

---

*Phi Epsilon Kappa Fraternity: Pledge manual, 1953, The fraternity, p. 12.

stracts of foreign physical education literature which are published annually.

New chapters of Phi Epsilon Kappa may be installed in colleges and universities that have four-year courses in physical education and are approved by the fraternity. A new chapter will be considered only if at least fifteen men organize and conduct business in a satisfactory manner for a period of one year after the first petition. Alumni chapters may be organized with a minimum of seven members.

## Physical Education Society of the Young Men's Christian Associations of North America

The Physical Education Society of the Young Men's Christian Associations of North America was founded in 1903. The purposes of this organization, as originally established, are as follows:

1. To unite in one body those professional workers in the Young Men's Christian Association who are related to physical education
2. To promote a fraternal spirit and fellowship among the members
3. To engage in original research
4. To study technical and professional problems
5. To cooperate with constituent or related bodies*

The Society has chapters in both states and other areas and holds a triannual convention. In addition to the conventions, meetings are also held in conjunction with the American Association for Health, Physical Education, and Recreation. A great part of the business for the Society is performed by an executive. Also, commissions are appointed periodically to study pertinent problems in regard to physical education. A few of these commissions that have been appointed are the following: Commission on a Progressive Program of Physical Education for Boys, Commission on Mental Hygiene and Phys-

ical Education, Commission on Leadership and Leaders' Clubs, and the Professional Recognition Committee.

The Society includes over 800 persons in the YMCA's of North America. There are 20 chapters of the Society divided geographically throughout the nation, such as Southern Area and New England. The dues are $7 per year.

The Society, through its program, attempts to help in the realization of the objectives of the Young Men's Christian Association. These objectives may be stated as follows:

1. Respect for personality
2. Application of the Golden Rule to human relationships
3. Recognition of the Fatherhood of God and the brotherhood of man
4. Need for cooperative effort in trying to apply the principles of Christ in everyday living*

When the Young Men's Christian Association was founded in London in 1844, physical, as well as spiritual, educational, and social, needs were recognized as being an essential for youth. Consequently, gymnasiums, swimming pools, and recreational facilities are found in Young Men's Christian Associations, as well as provision for spiritual, educational, and social programs.

The first meeting of physical directors was held at Jamestown, New York, in 1902. In this same year the periodical *Physical Training* was published. This was later changed to the *Journal of Physical Education* and is published bimonthly.

## Society of State Directors of Health, Physical Education, and Recreation

The idea and the initial impetus for the Society may be credited to James E. Rogers. The first meeting of the association was held in 1926, with Dr. Carl L. Schrader, State Director of Massachusetts, as the first president. James Rogers was

---

*Walters, M. L.: Journal of Health and Physical Education **18**:311, May, 1947.

*Walters, M. L.: Journal of Health and Physical Education **18**:312, May, 1947.

elected secretary and served in this capacity for fifteen years. The constitution for this organization was adopted in 1944 with Bernice Moss as chairman of the constitution committee. At first, the Society met twice a year—once with what is known as the American Association of School Administrators and once in conjunction with the council meeting of the American Physical Education Association. At present the meeting of the Society is held in conjunction with the American Association for Health, Physical Education, and Recreation.

The purposes of the Society have been described as follows:

1. To promote a more general understanding and a better appreciation of the importance of health, physical education, and recreation
2. To promote the establishment of a physical and health education program in each of the states by legislative enactment, or otherwise
3. To promote the development of physical and health education programs in states in which such programs have been established
4. To promote a closer and more cooperative relationship among persons engaged in physical and health educational service
5. To promote the adoption of wise policies and procedures in matters relating to state, interstate, and intersectional athletic contests
6. To promote the professional and official efficiency of members of the Society

Some of the accomplishments of the Society, since its inception in 1926, are as follows:

1. The Society has helped in the publication of the physical achievement standards for boys and girls.
2. It has worked with certification groups.
3. It has helped in campaigns for national legislation regarding health and physical education.
4. It has contributed to the upgrading of state legislation and standards.
5. It has made contributions to teacher-training programs, curriculums, and standards.
6. Widespread interest in the subjects of health and physical education has been developed.

7. Athletic ideals and practices in schools have been greatly elevated and improved.
8. Physical education activities for girls, taught and supervised by women teachers and directors and suited to their physiological and social needs, have been promoted.
9. Intra-school program rather than inter-school contests have been encouraged.
10. Participation in physical education by all rather than by a minority of the pupils has greatly increased.
11. A closer relationship with other education organizations has been effected.*

The Society has also passed many resolutions during its history that have been pertinent to programs of health, physical education, and recreation. Some of these were concerned with the supervision of state programs; the preparation of guides, manuals, and materials; the promotion of in-service training for teachers; the establishment of certification standards; the promotion of sports and playday programs; and the maintenance of library and reference files. The Society has also assisted in planning new facilities; written professional articles; and cooperated with various official and nonofficial agencies.

An active membership in the Society of State Directors of Health, Physical Education, and Recreation is $5, while an associate member pays $2. The Society may be reached at the Office of Education, U. S. Department of Health, Education, and Welfare, Washington, D. C.

## Young Women's Christian Association

The Young Women's Christian Association was one of the first organizations for women to be founded in this country. It dates back to 1858, and since that time it has spread rapidly to more than 400 towns and cities in the United States. Today, there are YWCA's in 72 countries. In the United States alone more than 1,600 YWCA's have a membership of

*Ayars, George W.: Journal of Health and Physical Education **17**:69, Feb., 1946.

**Table 22-1.** *Composite of professional organizations*

| Name | Membership | Selected liaison organizations | Method of finance | Services |
|---|---|---|---|---|
| Amateur Athletic Union | Open to all engaged or interested in amateur athletics | U. S. military services<br>U. S. Figure Skating Association<br>Catholic Youth Organization<br>American Turners<br>AAU of Canada<br>AA Federation of Japan | Contributions<br>Endowments<br>Registration fees<br>Revenue from events<br>Sanctioning of meets | Encourages and promotes amateur sports and physical fitness |
| American Academy of Physical Education | Limited to 100 active fellows who have made significant contributions | American Association for Health, Physical Education, and Recreation | Dues | Advances knowledge in health, physical education, and recreation through research, publications, meetings, lectures |
| American Association for Health, Physical Education, and Recreation | Open to all qualified persons interested in health, physical education, and recreation | World Confederation of Organizations of the Teaching Profession<br>International Council on Health, Physical Education, and Recreation | Dues<br>Sales of publications | Advances knowledge in and promotes health, physical education, and recreation; encourages research, assumes a leadership role |
| American College of Sports Medicine | Fellows must have graduate degrees in health, physical education, or recreation or related fields, and five years of service. Members must have graduate degree plus two years of service | Federation Internationale de Medicine Sportive | Dues | Promotes research and studies concerned with the effect of sports and physical activities on health and fitness |
| American Physical Therapy Association | Graduates of accredited schools of physical therapy and others interested in the field | World Confederation for Physical Therapy<br>National Health Council<br>American Medical Association | Dues<br>Sales of materials | Acts as a clearinghouse; gives assistance with programming, placement, and recruiting; sponsors research |
| American School Health Association | Those professionally engaged or otherwise interested in school health programs | American Public Health Association | Dues | Promotes school health programs, conducts research, sponsors committees, publishes literature in the field |

**Table 22-1.** *Composite of professional organizations—cont'd*

| Name | Membership | Selected liaison organizations | Method of finance | Services |
|---|---|---|---|---|
| American Youth Hostels, Inc. | Open to all willing to abide by hosteling customs | International Youth Hostel Federation | Memberships Program fees Contributions Income from special events | Promotes a spirit of friendship and understanding on an international basis |
| Association for Physical and Mental Rehabilitation | Those professionally engaged in adapted physical education, corrective therapy, or interested in these areas, and meeting the standards of the Association | President's Council on Physical Fitness American Association for Health, Physical Education, and Recreation American Academy of Physical Medicine and Rehabilitation | Dues | Promotes and oversees corrective programs, offers aid in building curricula in the field |
| Boys' Clubs of America | Boys | American National Red Cross American Association for Health, Physical Education, and Recreation | Contributions Investments Endowments Fees and dues | Provides boys with a chance to put their leisure time to wholesome use |
| Canadian Association for Health, Physical Education, and Recreation | Those professionally engaged in health, physical education, and recreation | Canadian Medical Association Park and Recreation Association of Canada | Dues | Promotes health, physical education, and recreation in Canada |
| Delta Psi Kappa | Women in health, physical education, and recreation | American Association for Health, Physical Education, and Recreation | Dues | Educational Loan Fund Research Fellowship Fund |
| National Association of Intercollegiate Athletics | Four-year accredited colleges and universities | NAIA Coaches Association National Alliance Athletic Association Amateur Athletic Union | Dues Radio and television rights Advertising Programs Concessions Ticket sales | Opportunity for all colleges and universities to compete on an intercollegiate basis, regardless of size or budget |
| National Association of Jewish Center Workers | Professional workers in Jewish Community Centers, camps, and youth groups | National Conference of Jewish Communal Service National Jewish Welfare Board YMHA-YWHA | Dues Publications Interest on savings | Holds workshops, conferences, and promotes professional education in the field |

**Table 22-1.** *Composite of professional organizations—cont'd*

| Name | Membership | Selected liaison organizations | Method of finance | Services |
|------|-----------|-------------------------------|-------------------|----------|
| National Association for Physical Education of College Women | Women | Athletic and Recreation Federation of College Women<br>Western Society<br>National College Physical Education Association for Men | Dues | Offers professional leadership, promotes research and international understanding |
| National Collegiate Athletic Association | Eligible four-year colleges and universities | American Association for Health, Physical Education, and Recreation<br>Olympic Committee | Dues<br>Radio and television rights<br>Advertising | Acts as a watchdog agency on intercollegiate competitions, player recruitment, and eligibility |
| National College Physical Education Association for Men | Men engaged in physical education or interested in the field | American Association for Health, Physical Education, and Recreation<br>National Association for Physical Education of College Women | Dues | Offers professional leadership, promotes research and international understanding |
| National Education Association | Classroom teachers, school administrators, college professors, educational specialists, and others | World Confederation of Organizations of the Teaching Profession<br>American Association of School Administrators<br>National Retired Teachers Association | Dues<br>Investments | Promotes legislation, distributes information, gives professional support to teachers |
| National Intramural Association | Intramural directors | American Association for Health, Physical Education, and Recreation | Dues | Information service, publications, clearinghouse for programs, policies, and standards |
| National Park and Recreation Association | Those interested in, or professionally engaged in the field | American Camping Association<br>International Recreation Association<br>National Rifle Association<br>Lifetime Sports Foundation | Gifts<br>Dues<br>Community chests<br>Foundations<br>Trusts | Promotes worthy use of leisure time, conducts studies on facilities, programs, recruits leaders, serves in an advisory capacity |
| Phi Delta Pi | Women | American Association for Health, Physical Education, and Recreation<br>Professional Panhellenic Association | Dues | Camp projects for underprivileged children, conducts symposiums |

**Table 22-1.** *Composite of professional organizations—cont'd*

| Name | Membership | Selected liaison organizations | Method of finance | Services |
|---|---|---|---|---|
| Phi Epsilon Kappa | Men | American Association for Health, Physical Education, and Recreation | Dues | Attempts to raise the standards of health, physical education, and recreation through meetings and publications |
| Physical Education Society of the YMCA | Interested professionals | American Association for Health, Physical Education, and Recreation | Dues | Studies problems pertinent to physical education |
| Society of State Directors of Health, Physical Education, and Recreation | Limited to state directors | American Association for Health, Physical Education, and Recreation and affiliated organizations | Dues | Studies programs in physical education, cooperates with other organizations to promote and improve programs |
| Young Women's Christian Association | Women | World YWCA Student YM-YWCA | Fees Sales of publications Sales of YWCA jewelry | Furthers mutual understandings and cooperation between people of diverse cultures, races, and nationalities |

more than two million girls and women. Its national headquarters is at 600 Lexington Avenue, New York City.

The Young Women's Christian Association has as its objectives the furthering of democratic living and promoting educational and recreational programs to enrich the lives of girls and women. The activities program is designed in part to develop and maintain health and physical fitness so that routine tasks may be performed efficiently. Whereas the program of the Young Women's Christian Association was originally referred to as physical education, since 1920 it has been referred to as health education.

The Young Women's Christian Association works for community health through a program that improves the health and welfare of girls and women. Members may participate in activities designed to im-

prove one's knowledge of body mechanics, sex education, nutrition, family life, various diseases, and other areas necessary for healthful living. It encourages health examinations as a prerequisite for participation in physical education activities, for health counseling purposes, and as a basis for educational programs. Through health education committees, it has done research in respect to girls and women. It furthers coeducational activities.

Hundreds of health education leaders are employed by the Young Women's Christian Association in this country. Approximately one half of these employees are located in small or medium-sized associations. The rest act in the capacity of assistants or as heads of programs in cities of greater size. In each separate Young Women's Christian Association the health education leaders have the responsibility for developing programs that will meet the needs of girls and women in their particular community. Health education leaders are required to have a bachelor's degree in health and physical education as a minimum requirement.

## QUESTIONS AND EXERCISES

1. Prepare a chart listing all the organizations in this chapter, the physical education personnel that should belong to each, and essential factors about each association.
2. In an essay of around 250 words, discuss the reasons why physical educators should be members of their national association.
3. What is the National Education Association? What are some of the purposes for which it was founded?
4. Describe in detail the history, purposes, organization, and services of the American Association for Health, Physical Education, and Recreation.
5. What are some of the services available to members of the National Park and Recreation Association?
6. Why is membership in the American Academy of Physical Education a coveted goal of many physical educators?
7. Discuss the history of the American School Health Association.
8. Who is eligible for membership in the College Physical Education Association?
9. What is the purpose of the National Association of Physical Education for College Women?
10. Why should a student interested in the field of physical therapy as a career become a member of the American Physical Therapy Association?
11. What have been some of the accomplishments of the Society of State Directors of Health, Physical Education, and Recreation?
12. Discuss American Youth Hostels, Inc., bringing out: the meaning of hosteling, types of membership in American Youth Hostels, history of hosteling in the United States, and the present organizational set-up of this association.
13. What are the objectives of the Young Women's Christian Association?
14. What are the purposes of the Physical Education Society of the Young Men's Christian Association of North America?
15. What are the qualifications for membership in the Boys' Clubs of America, Inc.?
16. What are the services performed by the National Collegiate Athletic Association?
17. Describe the history of the Canadian Physical Education Association.
18. How do the following organizations contribute to physical education: Delta Psi Kappa, Phi Delta Pi, and Phi Epsilon Kappa?

## SELECTED REFERENCES

Ainsworth, Dorothy S.: The National Association of Physical Education for College Women, Journal of Health and Physical Education 17:525, Nov., 1956.

American Association for Health, Physical Education, and Recreation: Annual Report, Washington, D. C., The Association.

American Physical Therapy Association: Our Association, New York, The Association.

American Youth Hostels, Inc.: By-laws of American Youth Hostels, Inc., New York, National Headquarters.

Association for Physical and Mental Rehabilitation, Constitution, New York, The Association.

Ayars, George W.: The Society of State Directors of Health and Physical Education, Journal of Health and Physical Education 17:68, Feb., 1946.

Boys' Clubs of America, Inc.: Constitution, New York, Boys' Clubs of America, Inc.

DeTurk, Wilbur C., and Foertsch, Fred E.: Phi Epsilon Kappa Fraternity, Journal of Health and Physical Education 18:11, Jan., 1947.

Fenner, Mildred Sandison: National Education Association history, Washington, D. C., The Association.

Gable, Martha A., and Christaldi, Josephine: Phi Delta Pi, Journal of Health and Physical Education 17:598, Dec., 1946.

Gilman, Estelle: Delta Psi Kappa, Journal of Health and Physical Education 17:482, Oct., 1946.

Hall, Walter M.: The Boys' Clubs of America, Journal of Health and Physical Education 17:343, June, 1946.

Howell, Maxwell L.: The Canadian Association for Health, Physical Education, and Recreation, Inc., Journal of Health, Physical Education, and Recreation 36:24, April, 1965.

Keene, Charles H.: The American School Health Association, Journal of Health and Physical Education 17:147, March, 1946.

McCloy, C. H.: Do you belong to your national association? Journal of Health and Physical Education 12:241, April, 1941.

McKenzie, R. Tait: The American Academy of Physical Education, Journal of Health and Physical Education 3:14, June, 1932.

Miller, Ben W.: The role of the professional organizations, Journal of Health and Physical Education 16:551, Dec., 1945.

Nash, Jay B.: The American Academy of Physical Education, Journal of Health and Physical Education 17:8, Jan., 1946.

National Association of Intercollegiate Athletics: Constitution and by-laws, The Association.

National Collegiate Athletic Association: Purposes, services, history, The Association.

National Education Association of the United States: Charter, by-laws, and standing rules, Washington, D. C., The Association.

National Education Association of the United States, NEA Handbook, Washington, D. C., The Association.

Palmer, Grace M.: The Young Women's Christian Association, Journal of Health and Physical Education 18:150, March, 1947.

Phi Delta Pi: The Fraternity.

Phi Epsilon Kappa: Pledge manual, 1953, The Fraternity.

Plewes, Doris Willard: The Canadian Physical Education Association, Journal of Health and Physical Education 17:273, May, 1946.

Rogers, James E.: History of the Society, 1945, The Society of State Directors of Health and Physical Education.

Society of State Directors of Health and Physical Education: Constitution, The Society.

Stevenson, Jessie L.: The American Physiotherapy Association, Journal of Health and Physical Education 17:212, April, 1946.

Walters, M. L.: The Physical Education Society of the Young Men's Christian Associations of North America, Journal of Health and Physical Education 18:311, May, 1947.

# Chapter 23

# Certification requirements for employment in physical education

This chapter has been written for the purpose of discussing various aspects of certification requirements for the teaching of physical education. This is of interest and importance to physical educators.

The teacher is the major factor in the educational process. Whatever happens in the school experience of a child is due largely to the kind of teacher who has guided his destiny. If a child has a happy and profitable educational experience, the teachers with whom he has come in contact can be given a major share of the credit. On the other hand, if a child has an unhappy and unprofitable educational experience, the teachers with whom he has come in contact should assume a major share of the blame. Therefore the teacher occupies a key position in the schools.

The educational process in which the teacher holds this key position has been a function of each state since the Tenth Amendment was made a part of the Constitution of the United States. If the state is responsible for education, it must establish certain minimum standards for those who desire to teach. Years ago teachers of physical education received little training and were required to meet very few standards for teaching. Gradually, however, as various states passed legislation incorporating physical education as part of the school programs, as the length of the preparatory period for teachers of physical education increased, and as the work of physical education became recognized as a vital experience in the education of the child, more stress was placed on the importance of having adequately trained teachers in physical education positions.

Certification requirements represent a first step in any system that attempts to fill positions on the basis of merit. The minimum requirements for teaching, which comprise the rules and regulations concerning state teachers' certificates, are designed primarily to secure teachers who are professionally and personally well equipped. They are designed to protect children from poorly prepared and inefficient teachers. They are designed to protect the teaching profession from unqualified teachers whose standards are so low that instruction suffers, and, finally, they are designed to protect administrators from local pressures urging the appointment of teachers who are not qualified for teaching positions.

Certification requirements are designed to ensure that only qualified persons teach physical education.

There is a recognized need for certification requirements as a means of maintaining and ensuring the quality of physical education teachers in the various states. They are necessary to ensure that children in the schools will have well-prepared and efficient teachers of physical education guiding their day-to-day activities. At the present time, teacher-training institutions have prospective teachers who are looking forward to obtaining positions. The certification standards that have been established determine, in some measure, the type of preparation that is offered in the various states, and thus, in the final analysis, these standards also determine to some degree whether or not teachers being prepared in physical education are qualified to guide the school activities of children.

An examination of the training of men and women shows that the average male teacher has had more college education than the typical female teacher. About 41% of the men but less than 16% of the women have two college degrees. Taking into account all public school teachers, it is found that slightly over 85% have a bachelor's degree or higher, approximately 23% a master's degree or higher, and four teachers in 1,000 a doctor's degree. Nine men in 1,000 have a doctor's degree, as compared to one woman in 1,000.

A survey of the teacher certification requirements indicates a general lack of uniformity for the certification of teachers in general and physical education teachers in particular. At the same time there are some general conclusions and trends that may be drawn from a survey of the various requirements. The teacher may be able to obtain a clearer picture of the requirements for the various states by examining Table 23-1, which lists minimum requirements for lowest regular teaching certificates; Table 23-2, which lists specific minimum requirements for elementary school certificates based on degrees; Table 23-3, which lists specific min-

**Table 23-1.** *Minimum teaching certification requirements by states and in the District of Columbia and Puerto Rico*

| State | Elementary school | | | High school | | |
|---|---|---|---|---|---|---|
| | Degree or semester hours | Semester hours of professional education | Student teaching semester hours | Degree or semester hours | Semester hours of professional education | Student teaching semester hours |
| 1 | 2 | 3 | 4 | 5 | 6 | 7 |
| Alabama | B | 27 | 3 | B | 21 | 3 |
| Alaska | B | 21 | C | B | 15 | C |
| Arizona | B | 24 | 6 | B[a] | 16 | 6 |
| Arkansas | B | 12 | 6 | B | 12 | 6 |
| California | B[b] | 16 | 8 | B[c] | 18 | 6 |
| Colorado | B | AP | AP | B | AP | AP |
| Connecticut | B | 24 | 6 | B | 12 | 6 |
| Delaware | B | 24 | 6 | B | 12 | 6 |
| District of Columbia | B | 18 | 6 | MA | 12 | 6 |
| Florida | B | 14 | 6 | B | 14 | 6 |
| Georgia | B | 12 | 6 | B | 12 | 6 |
| Hawaii | B | 18 | AP | B | 18 | AP |
| Idaho | B | 14 | 6 | B | 14 | 6 |
| Illinois | B | 11 | 5 | B | 11 | 5 |
| Indiana | B | 19 | 8 | B | 13 | 5 |
| Iowa | B | 20 | 5 | B | 20 | 5 |
| Kansas | B | 19 | 5 | B | 15 | 5 |
| Kentucky | B | 16 | 8 | B | 9 | 8 |
| Louisiana | B | 20 | 4 | B | 14 | 4 |
| Maine | B[d] | 22 | 8 | B | 12 | 6 |
| Maryland | B | 18 | 8 | B | 12 | 8 |
| Massachusetts | B[e] | 16 | 2 | B | 10 | 2 |
| Michigan | B | 15 | 5 | B | 15 | 5 |
| Minnesota | B | 24 | 6 | B | 14 | 4 |
| Mississippi | B | 12 | 6 | B | 12 | 6 |
| Missouri | B | 15 | 5 | B | 15 | 5 |
| Montana | B | AP | AP | B | AP | AP |
| Nebraska | 40 | 15 | 3 | B | 15 | 3 |
| Nevada | B[f] | 14 | 4 | B | 14 | 4 |
| New Hampshire | B | 15 | 6 | B | 6 | 6 |
| New Jersey | B | 18 | 150[g] | B | 18 | 150[g] |
| New Mexico | B | 18 | 6 | B | 12 | 6 |
| New York | B | 14 | 4–8 | B | 14 | 4–8 |
| North Carolina | B | 18 | 6 | B | 12 | 6 |
| North Dakota | B | 13 | 3 | B | 13 | 3 |
| Ohio | B | 22 | 6 | B | 11 | 6 |
| Oklahoma | B | 15[h] | 6 | B | 15[h] | 6 |
| Oregon | B | 20 | AP | B[i] | 24 | AP |
| Pennsylvania | B | 30[j] | 6 | B | 12 | 6 |
| Puerto Rico | 68 | 53 | 6 | B | 29 | 5 |
| Rhode Island | B | 12 | 6 | B | 12 | 6 |
| South Carolina | B | 15 | 6 | B | 12 | 6 |
| South Dakota | B | 20 | 6 | B | 14 | 6 |
| Tennessee | B | 20 | 4 | B | 20 | 4 |
| Texas | B | 12 | 6 | B | 12 | 6 |
| Utah | B | 14 | 8 | B | 22 | 10[k] |

**Table 23-1.** *Minimum teaching certification requirements by states—cont'd*

| State | Elementary school | | | High school | | |
|---|---|---|---|---|---|---|
| | Degree or semester hours | Semester hours of professional education | Student teaching semester hours | Degree or semester hours | Semester hours of professional education | Student teaching semester hours |
| *1* | *2* | *3* | *4* | *5* | *6* | *7* |
| Vermont | B | 9 | 9 | B | 12 | 6 |
| Virginia | B | 12 | 6 | B | 11 | 4–6 |
| Washington | B | AP | AP | B¹ | AP | AP |
| West Virginia | B | 15 | 5 | B | 15 | 5 |
| Wisconsin | Bᵐ | 21 | 5 | B | 13 | 5 |
| Wyoming | B | 23 | AP | B | 20 | AP |

*Key: AP* means approved program; *B* means bachelor's degree of specified preparation; *MA* means master's degree of specified preparation; *C* means a course.

ᵃ*Arizona.* Teaching on the secondary level requires a master's degree or 30 points beyond the bachelor's degree.

ᵇ*California.* On the elementary level, a fifth year of postgraduate work is required.

ᶜ*California.* On the secondary level, 6 hours of postgraduate work is required.

ᵈ*Maine.* A bachelor's degree in an approved program may be accepted in lieu of the required semester hours.

ᵉ*Massachusetts.* Completion of bachelor's degree or graduation from an approved 4-year normal school.

ᶠ*Nevada.* In rural schools, a minimum of 60 hours of degree work is required.

ᵍ*New Jersey.* Practice teaching requirement is 150 clock hours, 90 of which must be in actual classroom teaching.

ʰ*Oklahoma.* For standard certificate; for temporary certificate the requirement is 6 semester hours.

ⁱ*Oregon.* Provisional certificate only; 5 years required for standard certification. Fifth year must be completed within 5 years after provisional certificate is issued.

ʲ*Pennsylvania.* Eighteen in professional; 18 in elementary content subjects.

ᵏ*Utah.* The 10 hours includes both student teaching and methods courses.

ˡ*Washington.* Requires 1 year of advanced study beyond the bachelor's degree.

ᵐ*Wisconsin.* For graduates of 2-year teacher preparation courses, a bachelor's degree must be obtained within six years; within 7 years for graduates of 3-year courses.

imum requirements for high school certificates based on degrees; Table 23-4, which lists general requirements for teaching certificates; and Table 23-5, which lists types of certificates issued.

In respect to minimum special requirements for certification of teachers of physical education, there are no uniform qualifications from state to state. They range anywhere from thirty-six semester hours in specific courses plus requisites in New York State to sixteen semester hours in Massachusetts. The requirement is listed in semester hours. Some require graduation from an approved four-year teacher-training course, and others say all that is required is "blanket certification," meaning that any teacher who holds a regular certificate can also teach any special field for which he is qualified. Some states have only a major certification requirement, and others have major and minor listings.

## GENERAL AREAS FOR CERTIFICATION REQUIREMENTS

There are ten general areas in which states have governing regulations for teacher certification. Since states differ in their requirements, however, the prospec-

*Text continued on p. 713.*

**Table 23-2.** *Minimum certification requirements for elementary schools*

| State | Degree required | Semester hours of general education | Semester hours of professional education | Semester hours of student teaching |
|---|---|---|---|---|
| 1 | 2 | 3 | 4 | 5 |
| Alabama | B | 36 | 27 | 3 |
| Alaska | B | NS | 21 | AP |
| Arizona | B | 40 | 24 | 6 |
| Arkansas | B | 48 | 12 | 6 |
| California | B[a] | 45 | 16 | 8 |
| Colorado | B | AP | AP | AP |
| Connecticut | B | 40 | 24 | 6 |
| Delaware | B | 40 | 24 | 6 |
| District of Columbia | B | NS | 18 | 6 |
| Florida | B | 45 | 14 | 6 |
| Georgia | B | 40 | 12 | 6 |
| Hawaii | B | 18 | 18 | AP |
| Idaho | B | 42 | 14 | 6 |
| Illinois | B | 42 | 11 | 5 |
| Indiana | B | 73 | 19 | 8 |
| Iowa | B | 100 | 20 | 5 |
| Kansas | B | 50 | 19 | 5 |
| Kentucky | B | 45 | 16 | 8 |
| Louisiana | B | 46 | 20 | 4 |
| Maine | B | —[b] | 22 | 8 |
| Maryland | B | 80 | 18 | 8 |
| Massachusetts | B | NS | 16 | 2 |
| Michigan | B | 60 | 15 | 5 |
| Minnesota | B | NS | 24 | 6 |
| Mississippi | B | 48 | 12 | 6 |
| Missouri | B | 25 | 15 | 5 |
| Montana | B | AP | AP | AP |
| Nebraska | B | 60 | 15 | 3 |
| Nevada | B | 30 | 14 | 4 |
| New Hampshire | B | NS | 15 | 6 |
| New Jersey | B | 36 | 18 | 150 |
| New Mexico | B | 48 | 18 | 6 |
| New York | B | NS | 14 | 4–8 |
| North Carolina | B | 48 | 18 | 6 |
| North Dakota | B | AP | 18 | 3 |
| Ohio | B | 60 | 22 | 6 |
| Oklahoma | B | 50 | 15 | 6 |
| Oregon | B | 30 | 20 | AP |
| Pennsylvania | B | 60 | 30 | 6 |
| Puerto Rico | B | 16 | 20 | 6 |
| Rhode Island | B | 30 | 12 | 6 |
| South Carolina | B | 45 | 15 | 6 |
| South Dakota | B | 30 | 20 | 6 |
| Tennessee | B | 40 | 20 | 4 |
| Texas | B | 60 | 12 | 6 |
| Utah | B | 40 | 14 | 8 |
| Vermont | B | AP | 9 | 9 |
| Virginia | B | 60 | 12 | 6 |
| Washington | B | AP | AP | AP |
| West Virginia | B | 36 | 15 | 5 |
| Wisconsin | B | AP | 21 | 5 |
| Wyoming | B | 40 | 23 | AP |

*Key: AP* means approved program; *NS* means the information is not specified by the state; *B* means a bachelor's degree in the specified field.

[a]*California.* One year of postgraduate work beyond the bachelor's degree is required.

[b]*Maine.* Courses in general education must make up 50% of the undergraduate curriculum.

**Table 23-3.** *Minimum certification requirements for secondary schools*

| State | Degree required | Semester hours of general education | Semester hours of professional education | Semester hours of student teaching |
|---|---|---|---|---|
| *1* | *2* | *3* | *4* | *5* |
| Alabama | B | 36 | 21 | 3 |
| Alaska | B | NS | 15 | AP |
| Arizona | B | 40 | 16 | 6 |
| Arkansas | B | 48 | 12 | 6 |
| California | B[a] | 45 | 18 | 6 |
| Colorado | B | NS | AP | AP |
| Connecticut | B | 40 | 12 | 6 |
| Delaware | B | 40 | 12 | 6 |
| District of Columbia | MA | 30 | 12 | 6 |
| Florida | B | 45 | 14 | 6 |
| Georgia | B | 40 | 12 | 6 |
| Hawaii | B | 36 | 18 | AP |
| Idaho | B | 50 | 14 | 6 |
| Illinois | B | 42 | 11 | 5 |
| Indiana | B | 50 | 13 | 5 |
| Iowa | B | 40 | 20 | 5 |
| Kansas | B | 50 | 15 | 5 |
| Kentucky | B | 45 | 9 | 8 |
| Louisiana | B | 46 | 14 | 4 |
| Maine | B | 48–50 | 12 | 6 |
| Maryland | B | 24 | 12 | 6 |
| Massachusetts | B | 27 | 10 | 2 |
| Michigan | B | 54 | 15 | 5 |
| Minnesota | B | NS | 14 | 4 |
| Mississippi | B | 48 | 12 | 6 |
| Missouri | B | 25 | 15 | 5 |
| Montana | B | NS | AP | AP |
| Nebraska | B | NS | 15 | 3 |
| Nevada | B | NS | 14 | 4 |
| New Hampshire | B | NS | 6 | 6 |
| New Jersey | B | 36 | 18 | 150 |
| New Mexico | B | 48 | 12 | 6 |
| New York | B | 60 | 14 | 4–8 |
| North Carolina | B | 48 | 12 | 6 |
| North Dakota | B | NS | 13 | 3 |
| Ohio | B | 30 | 11 | 6 |
| Oklahoma | B | 50 | 15 | 6 |
| Oregon | B | 24 | 24 | AP |
| Pennsylvania | B | 60 | 12 | 6 |
| Puerto Rico | B | NS | 29 | 5 |
| Rhode Island | B | 18 | 12 | 6 |
| South Carolina | B | 45 | 12 | 6 |
| South Dakota | B | NS | 14 | 6 |
| Tennessee | B | 40 | 20 | 4 |
| Texas | B | 60 | 12 | 6 |
| Utah | B | 40 | 22 | 10 |
| Vermont | B | NS | 12 | 6 |
| Virginia | B | 48 | 11 | 4–6 |
| Washington | B[b] | NS | AP | AP |
| West Virginia | B | 36 | 15 | 5 |
| Wisconsin | B | 56 | 13 | 5 |
| Wyoming | B | 40 | 20 | AP |

*Key: NS* means that the information was not specified by the state; *AP* refers to an approved program in the educational field.

[a]*California.* Requires 6 hours of postgraduate work in addition to the bachelor's degree.

[b]*Washington.* Requires 1 year of advanced work beyond the bachelor's degree.

**Table 23-4.** *General requirements for teaching certificates[1]*

| State | United States citizenship | Oath of allegiance or loyalty | Must secure employment | Recommendation (college or employing officer) | Minimum age required | Fee required for certificate | General health certificate required | Chest x-ray required | Special course required |
|---|---|---|---|---|---|---|---|---|---|
| *1* | *2* | *3* | *4* | *5* | *6* | *7* | *8* | *9* | *10* |
| Alabama | No | No | No | Yes | 17 | $2.00 | No | Yes | No |
| Alaska | Yes | No | Yes | No | 18 | 5.00 | No | No | No |
| Arizona | Yes | Yes | No | No | 18 | 4.00 | No | Yes | Yes |
| Arkansas | No | No | No | Yes | 18 | None | Yes | Yes | No |
| California | Yes[a] | Yes | No | No | 18 | 10.00[b] | Yes | No | Yes[c] |
| Colorado | No | Yes | No* | Yes | None | 5.00 | No | No | No |
| Connecticut | Yes | No | No | Yes | 18 | None | Yes | No | Yes[d] |
| Delaware | No | Yes | Yes[e] | Yes | None | None | Yes | Yes[f] | No |
| District of Columbia | Yes | Yes | No | Yes | None | None | Yes | Yes | No |
| Florida | Yes | Yes | No | Yes | 20 | 5.00 | Yes | No | No |
| Georgia | No | No | No | Yes | None | None | No | No | No |
| Hawaii | Yes | Yes | No | Yes | None | None | Yes | Yes | No |
| Idaho | Yes[g] | No | No | Yes | 18 | 5.00 | No | No | No |
| Illinois | Yes | Yes | No | No | 19 | 4.00 | No | No | Yes[h] |
| Indiana | No | Yes | No | Yes | None | 1.00 | Yes | No | No |
| Iowa | No | No | No | Yes | 18 | 2.00 | No | No | Yes[i] |
| Kansas | No | Yes | No | Yes | None | 5.00 | No | No | No |
| Kentucky | No | No | No | Yes | 18 | None | No | No | No |
| Louisiana | No | No | No | Yes | None | None | No | No | Yes[j] |
| Maine | No | No | Yes[k] | Yes | 17 | None | No | No[l] | No |
| Maryland | Yes | Yes | Yes | Yes[m] | 18 | None | No | No | No |
| Massachusetts | Yes | No | No | No | None | None | Yes | No | No |
| Michigan | Yes | Yes | No | Yes | 18 | None[n] | No | No | No |
| Minnesota | No | No | No | Yes | None | 3.00 | Yes | No | No |
| Mississippi | Yes | Yes | No | Yes | 18 | None | Yes | No | No |
| Missouri | No | No | No | Yes | None | None | Yes | No | No |
| Montana | Yes | Yes | No | Yes | 18 | 2.00[o] | Yes | Yes[p] | No |
| Nebraska | Yes | Yes | No | Yes | None | 2.00 | Yes | No | No |
| Nevada | Yes[q] | Yes | No | No | 18 | 3.00 | Yes | Yes | Yes[r] |
| New Hampshire | No | Yes | Yes | Yes | None | 5.00 | No | No | No |
| New Jersey | Yes | Yes | No | No | 18 | 5.00 | Yes | No | No |
| New Mexico | Yes | No | No | Yes | 18 | 1.00 | Yes | Yes | No |
| New York | Yes | No | No | No | 18 | 5.00 | No | No | No |
| North Carolina | No | No | Yes[s] | No | 18 | None | Yes | Yes | No |
| North Dakota | Yes[t] | Yes | No | Yes | 18 | $3-$5 | No | No | No |
| Ohio | No | No | No | Yes | None | 2.00 | No | No | No |
| Oklahoma | Yes[u] | No | Yes[v] | Yes | None | 1.00 | Yes | No | Yes[w] |
| Oregon | Yes | Yes | No | No | 18 | 5.00 | No | Yes | No |
| Pennsylvania | Yes[x] | No | No | Yes | 18 | None | Yes | No | Yes |
| Puerto Rico | Yes | Yes | Yes | No | 18 | None | Yes | Yes | No |
| Rhode Island | Yes | Yes | Yes | Yes | 19 | None | Yes | No | Yes[y] |
| South Carolina | Yes | No | No | Yes | 18 | None | Yes | Yes | No |
| South Dakota | Yes | Yes | No | Yes | 18 | $6-$10 | No | No | No |
| Tennessee | No | No | No | Yes | 18 | 2.00 | No | No | No |
| Texas | Yes | Yes | No | Yes | 18 | $2-$3 | No | No | Yes[z] |

**Table 23-4.** *General requirements for teaching certificates—cont'd*

| State | United States citizenship | Oath of allegiance or loyalty | Must secure employment | Recommendation (college or employing officer) | Minimum age required | Fee required for certificate | General health certificate required | Chest x-ray required | Special course required |
|-------|------|------|------|------|------|------|------|------|------|
| *1* | *2* | *3* | *4* | *5* | *6* | *7* | *8* | *9* | *10* |
| Utah | No | No | No | Yes | None | 1.00 | No | No | Yes^aa |
| Vermont | No | Yes | Yes^bb | Yes | 19 | None | No | No | No |
| Virginia | Yes | No | Yes | Yes | 18 | None | No | No | No |
| Washington | Yes^cc | Yes | No^dd | Yes | 18 | 2.00 | No | Yes | Yes^ee |
| West Virginia | Yes | No | No | Yes | 18 | 1.00 | No | No | No |
| Wisconsin | No | No | No | Yes | None | 2.00 | No | No | Yes^ff |
| Wyoming | Yes^gg | No | No | Yes | None | None | No | No | Yes^hh |

[1]Armstrong, W. Earl, and Stinnett, T. M.: A manual on certification requirements for school personnel in the United States, Washington, D. C., National Education Association. Adapted.

[a]*California.* Filing for declaration of intention will qualify for citizenship.

[b]*California.* There is a $4 fee for transcript evaluation which will be credited toward a credential if one is issued within a 5-year period.

[c]*California.* Constitution of United States and audiovisual education required for renewal of regular certificate.

[*]*Colorado.* Except for vocational and some special services certificate.

[d]*Connecticut.* History of the United States.

[e]*Delaware.* Except for graduates of in-state colleges or Delaware high schools.

[f]*Delaware.* Not prerequisite, but required by law some time during first year and each year of employment.

[g]*Idaho.* Must be citizen or have taken out first papers.

[h]*Illinois.* American history and/or government.

[i]*Iowa.* American history or American government.

[j]*Louisiana.* American history, biological and physical science. Louisiana history for upper elementary teachers only.

[k]*Maine.* Required only of out-of-state, initial applicants who apply under reciprocity.

[l]*Maine.* Not required for certificate, but law requires chest x-ray examination every 2 years. Responsibility of employing superintendent.

[m]*Maryland.* Recommendation of employing officer required.

[n]*Michigan.* Out-of-state applicants are charged a fee of $3 for investigating credentials.

[o]*Montana.* Registration fee of $2 charged for initial certificate and $1 for each year of validity.

[p]*Montana.* Can use Montana TB test.

[q]*Nevada.* Or have filed declaration of intention.

[r]*Nevada.* Nevada school law, Constitution of State of Nevada, and United States Constitution (by credit or examination).

[s]*North Carolina.* Applies only to out-of-state applicants.

[t]*North Dakota.* Must be citizen or have declared intention.

[u]*Oklahoma.* Must be citizen or have taken out first papers.

[v]*Oklahoma.* For temporary certificate only.

[w]*Oklahoma.* Oklahoma history and 6 semester hours of American history and government.

[x]*Pennsylvania.* Citizenship may be waived for exchange teachers and teachers of foreign languages.

[y]*Rhode Island.* Rhode Island education; may be completed within 3 years of initial teaching in the state.

[z]*Texas.* Texas and federal governments.

[aa]*Utah.* School health education.

*Footnotes continued on next page.*

Footnotes to Table 23-4—*cont'd*

[bb]*Vermont.* Required of nonresidents.

[cc]*Washington.* Must be citizen or have declared intention.

[dd]*Washington.* Required of nonresidents.

[ee]*Washington.* Washington state history and government or Pacific Northwest history and government (may be satisfied by examination).

[ff]*Wisconsin.* Cooperatives required of teachers of economics, social studies, and agriculture. Conservation required of teachers of science and social studies.

[gg]*Wyoming.* Must be citizen or have taken out first papers.

[hh]*Wyoming.* United States and Wyoming Constitutions (may be satisfied by credit course or passing an examination).

**Table 23-5.** *Types of certificates issued by states**

| State | Life or permanent certificate | General or blanket high school certificate | Academic fields endorsed on high school certificate | Special fields endorsed on high school certificate | Separate certificate issued for each special field |
|---|---|---|---|---|---|
| 1 | 2 | 3 | 4 | 5 | 6 |
| Alabama | Yes[1] | No | Yes | Yes | No |
| Alaska | Yes[2] | Yes | No | No | No |
| Arizona | No | Yes | No | Yes | Yes[3] |
| Arkansas | No | No | Yes | Yes | No |
| California | Yes[4] | Yes | No | No | Yes |
| Colorado | No | Yes | Yes | Yes | No |
| Connecticut | Yes[5] | No | Yes[6] | Yes[6] | No |
| Delaware | No† | No | Yes | No | Yes |
| District of Columbia | Yes[7] | No | Yes | No | Yes |
| Florida | No | No | Yes | Yes | No |
| Georgia | Yes[8] | No | Yes | Yes | No |
| Hawaii | No | No | Yes | Yes | No |
| Idaho | No | No | Yes | Yes | No |
| Illinois | No | Yes | Yes | Yes | Yes |
| Indiana | Yes[9] | No | Yes | Yes | Yes[10] |
| Iowa | Yes[11] | Yes[12] | No | No[12] | No[12] |
| Kansas | No[13] | Yes | No[14] | No | No |
| Kentucky | Yes[15] | No | Yes[16] | Yes | No |
| Louisiana | No[17] | No | Yes | Yes | No |
| Maine | No | Yes | Yes[18] | No | Yes |
| Maryland | No | No | Yes | Yes | No |
| Massachusetts | Yes[19] | No[20] | Yes | No | Yes |
| Michigan | No | No | Yes | Yes | No |
| Minnesota | Yes[21] | No | Yes | Yes | No |
| Mississippi | No[22] | No | Yes | No | Yes[23] |
| Missouri | Yes[24] | No | Yes | Yes | No |
| Montana | No | No | Yes | Yes | No |
| Nebraska | No | Yes | No | No | No |
| Nevada | No | Yes | No | Yes | No |
| New Hampshire | No | No | Yes | Yes | No |
| New Jersey | Yes[25] | No | Yes | Yes | Yes |

**Table 23-5.** *Types of certificates issued by states—cont'd*

| State | Life or permanent certificate | General or blanket high school certificate | Academic fields endorsed on high school certificate | Special fields endorsed on high school certificate | Separate certificate issued for each special field |
|---|---|---|---|---|---|
| 1 | 2 | 3 | 4 | 5 | 6 |
| New Mexico | No | No | Yes | Yes | Yes |
| New York | Yes | No | Yes | No | Yes[26] |
| North Carolina | No | No | Yes | Yes | No |
| North Dakota | Yes[27] | Yes | Yes[28] | Yes | No |
| Ohio | Yes[29] | No | Yes | Yes | —[30] |
| Oklahoma | No | No | Yes | Yes | No[31] |
| Oregon | No[32] | Yes | No | No | Yes[33] |
| Pennsylvania | Yes[34] | No | Yes | Yes | No |
| Puerto Rico | Yes[35] | No | Yes | Yes | Yes |
| Rhode Island | Yes[36] | No | Yes | Yes | No |
| South Carolina | No | No | Yes | Yes | No |
| South Dakota | No | No | Yes | Yes | No |
| Tennessee | No | No | Yes | Yes | No |
| Texas | Yes[37] | Yes | No | No | No[38] |
| Utah | No | Yes | No | No | No |
| Vermont | No | Yes | No | —[39] | —[39] |
| Virginia | No | No | Yes | Yes | No |
| Washington | No | Yes | Yes | Yes | No |
| West Virginia | Yes[40] | No | Yes | Yes | No |
| Wisconsin | Yes[41] | No | Yes | Yes | No |
| Wyoming | No | No | Yes | Yes | No |

*Armstrong, W. Earl, and Stinnett, T. M.: A manual on certification requirements for school personnel in the United States, Washington, D. C., National Education Association. Adapted.

[1]*Alabama.* Class AA certificate is issued for life, based on 30 semester hours beyond the master's degree in a planned program leading toward the doctor's degree. Applicant must have completed enough work to be within one year of doctor's degree.

[2]*Alaska.* Applicant must have a master's degree and 5 years of successful teaching experience in Alaska.

[3]*Arizona.* Only for music, art, home economics, vocational, and specialized service.

[4]*California.* Forty-eight months of service—21 months in the public schools of California. Teaching service acceptable across the board. Nonteaching service must be in area of credential applied for.

[5]*Connecticut.* After 3 years of successful teaching and completion of 30 semester hours beyond the bachelor's degree; valid so long as the holder does not leave Connecticut public school teaching for 5 consecutive years.

[6]*Connecticut.* The state has no high school certificate as such; provisional certificate may be endorsed for all teaching fields—elementary, secondary, or special—for which applicant is eligible.

†*Delaware.* Professional status certificate may be renewed provided teacher shall have been employed for at least 3 school years during 5-year term of certificate in position for which certificate was issued.

[7]*District of Columbia.* Permanent teacher may continue until retirement; appointed permanently after 2 years of successful probationary period.

[8]*Georgia.* Five years of professional certification based on teacher training program from an approved college plus 5 years of teaching experience. This certificate remains valid so long as the teacher remains in service. Life certificates may be reinstated by two courses—10 quarter or 6 semester hours.

*Footnotes continued on next page.*

## Footnotes to Table 23-5—*cont'd*

[9]*Indiana.* (a) First-grade license and 5 years of experience subsequent to its issue. (b) Five-year professional certificate based on bachelor's degree—converted to first-grade on 5 years of experience and master's degree, then converted to permanent on 5 years of experience subsequent to issuance of the first-grade certificate.

[10]*Indiana.* If enough credit for special certificate.

[11]*Iowa.* Permanent professional certificate which never expires is issued to teachers with a master's degree in an approved program of preparation and 4 years of successful experience.

[12]*Iowa.* Except for certain special-subject or special-service certificates, such as art, industrial arts, music, physical education, education of exceptional children, and librarianship, all Iowa certificates carry no subject endorsement. However, every high school teacher does receive a list of subjects which he is approved to teach. Annual reports from the schools are checked to guarantee adherence to such approval standards.

[13]*Kansas.* Former life certificates are in use. The state issues no original life or permanent certificates.

[14]*Kansas.* Trade and industrial arts is an exception. The state also has in use a music special certificate which was formerly issued.

[15]*Kentucky.* Since September 1, 1935, all life certificates for elementary, secondary, and administrative positions have required completion of a 5-year program including the master's degree and 3 years of successful teaching. At present, all administrative certificates are on a continuing basis and a program of 24 semester hours beyond the master's degree.

[16]*Kentucky.* Only major and minor fields or areas of concentration are shown on certificate.

[17]*Louisiana.* Type A and type B certificates valid for life for continuous service.

[18]*Maine.* When applicant does not qualify for the general certificate but can qualify in one or more teaching subjects or fields.

[19]*Massachusetts.* All certificates are permanent.

[20]*Massachusetts.* No certificates are issued which would cover all fields, but certificates entitled "Social Studies," "General Science," etc. cover a number of academic fields.

[21]*Minnesota.* Applicant must have 5 years of experience in Minnesota, at least one of which must have been within 2-year period preceding application. (Experience on a limited certificate, a provisional certificate, or an ungraded elementary school certificate does not apply on the above experience requirement.)

[22]*Mississippi.* Life certificates issued to administrators who have completed Ed.D. in administration.

[23]*Mississippi.* Special fields are endorsed on one type of special-subject certificate.

[24]*Missouri.* Bachelor's degree required.

[25]*New Jersey.* Fulfillment of all academic requirements, plus 3 years of successful experience "within the scope of the certificate in New Jersey Public Schools."

[26]*New York.* Original teaching certificates are extended to other fields.

[27]*North Dakota.* Eighteen months of successful teaching experience in North Dakota required after issuance of professional certificate.

[28]*North Dakota.* Only major and minors shown. Also elementary or secondary fields.

[29]*Ohio.* Sixty-four months of teaching and master's degree or 30 semester hours of graduate credit.

[30]*Ohio.* If holder teaches below seventh grade, must obtain special certificate issued for each field.

[31]*Oklahoma.* Separate certificate may be issued for each field, but not required.

[32]*Oregon.* Life certificates are issued to those teachers who were issued 1-year certificates based on graduation—elementary prior to February 25, 1943, and secondary prior to September 1, 1937 —and who have 30 months of teaching experience.

[33]*Oregon.* For health and physical education, art, music, homemaking, and industrial arts.

[34]*Pennsylvania.* College degree plus 6 graduate credits after 3 years of experience; plus 12 credits on certificates issued on and after October 1, 1959.

[35]*Puerto Rico.* Must have worked satisfactorily in the public or accredited private schools of Puerto Rico for a period of not less than 50 months, 30 months of which must have been in the teaching category for which the life certificate is to be issued.

[36]*Rhode Island.* For teachers—10 years of service in Rhode Island after professional certificate and a master's degree (or its equivalent, i.e., 30 semester hours of graduate study). For administrators, 5 years of service in Rhode Island after professional certification as administrator.

Footnotes to Table 23-5—*cont'd*

[37]*Texas.* Completion of bachelor's degree from institution approved for teacher education and upon recommendation from college preparing the applicant.

[38]*Texas.* Special certificate for vocational agriculture, homemaking, distributive education, trades and industries, and for school nurse, librarian, and special education; all-level certificates issued for special subjects of art, health and physical education, music, and speech and drama.

[39]*Vermont.* If eligible for general teaching certificate, endorsement is made on certificate; otherwise special certificate issued for each field.

[40]*West Virginia.* First-class certificate, master's degree, and 5 years of teaching experience. Also as third renewal of a first-class certificate which means 15 years of experience and 18 hours of college credit after initial certificate.

[41]*Wisconsin.* Proof of at least 3 years of successful teaching in Wisconsin. Must have been fully qualified and a teacher in the public schools and possess a license based on bachelor's degree. State superintendent may extend the probation period in individual cases. (Becomes void after 5 successive years of nonperformance of duty for which licensed. Counselors may not secure life certificates.)

tive teacher should inquire directly of the state education department, division of teacher certification, for exact requirements. To summarize these ten areas and the requirements presently established in the fifty states and the District of Columbia and Puerto Rico, the following information is presented.

1. *Citizenship.* Approximately thirty states, the District of Columbia, and Puerto Rico require United States citizenship or a declaration of intention clause. The teacher must be a citizen of the United States to qualify.

2. *Oath of allegiance of loyalty.* Approximately twenty-four states, the District of Columbia, and Puerto Rico require a loyalty oath for teacher certification. The others usually have a written statement that must be signed.

3. *Age.* The age requirement varies among states. The lowest age limit is 17 years. In general, 18 or 19 years of age is acceptable in states specifying a particular age. Some states have no stipulation in this regard.

4. *Professional preparation.* It is in this area that the greatest differences in state requirements may be found. Several states have specific courses that must be taken by candidates for certification. For example, in Illinois, teachers must have

studied American government and/or history; in Texas, Texan and federal government; in Utah, school health education; in Wyoming, the United States and Wyoming Constitutions. Some of these special state requirements must be complete before the first year of teaching, whereas others may be fulfilled within a certain period of time. For example, a course in Rhode Island education may be completed within three years of the first year of teaching in that state.

5. *Recommendation.* A large majority of the states require a teaching candidate to have a recommendation from college or from the last place of employment.

6. *Fee.* A fee for certification, ranging from $1 to $10, is required in a majority of the states.

7. *Health certificate.* Approximately twenty one states, the District of Columbia, and Puerto Rico require a general health certificate, and twelve states, the District of Columbia, and Puerto Rico require a chest x-ray examination.

8. *Employment.* Candidates from other states may need to have secured employment to become certified within some states.

9. *Course of study.* Besides these general areas of state requirements, there are

basic and minimum regulations regarding the course of study that must be followed to qualify for specific certification in physical education. Again, the states disagree in their differentiation of hours of study necessary within the subject of physical education.

10. *Degrees.* In approximately forty-three states and the District of Columbia the bachelor's degree is required for regular certification of beginning elementary school teachers. In Arizona, California, and the District of Columbia, five years of preparation are required for the regular certification of beginning secondary school teachers.

Because of the differences among states in regard to the ten general areas of certification that have been outlined, a certificate to teach in one state does not necessarily permit a teacher to teach in a different state. Reciprocity among states in the same region of the country is a growing reality, but it is not common at the present time.

A further problem in certification presents itself where localities within a state have specific regulations governing selection of teachers. These are often more rigid than the standards established by the state itself. Detroit, for example, has its own set of qualifications that must be met by its teachers. Local regulations usually involve such factors as teacher preparation or experience. An applicant may also have to pass a written and oral examination for local licensing. Information regarding local teaching requirements may usually be secured by writing to the board of education of the city in question.

Applicants for teaching positions should try to determine state and local regulations far in advance, if possible. In so doing they may guide their courses of study in college to meet the requirements. They should submit their records ahead of time in order to become certified before accepting a position.

## TYPES OF CERTIFICATES

The type and value of certificates issued by the states vary nearly as much as do their regulations. In one state, for example, there may be two categories of certification, permanent and probationary, whereas in another state there may be many variations of certificates. The certificate to teach physical education is generally limited to this special field of work, but its validity may be for one year (probationary) or for life (permanent). Some states grant temporary or emergency certificates to teachers who do not fully meet all requirements, with the understanding that within a certain period of time the candidate will become fully qualified.

The value of the certificate again depends on state regulations. It enables the holder to teach in any public school system within that state, except those where local standards require further qualifications. It may qualify the teacher to teach in neighboring states, depending on reciprocity agreements. It may also permit him or her to teach in private schools within the state, at least in private schools seeking state accreditation.

The prospective teacher or the experienced teacher seeking employment in a different state should not let these differences in state requirements and qualifications become a hindrance. An inquiry to the state or local department of education should provide necessary information in time for certification.

## CERTIFICATION TRENDS

There are trends clearly noticeable throughout the country in the certification of teachers. There is a trend to increase the general education requirement. Approximately one half of the states now have such a requirement, and the trend is more and more in this direction. Many of the states are requiring as many as twenty or more semester hours of work in this area. There is a trend toward requiring a bachelor's degree for the certification of a teacher. Nearly all of the states now specify this requirement. There is a trend toward requiring more work in the field of educational theory. Such work usually includes educational psychology, principles and methods of teaching, and observations and practice teaching. Elementary school teachers usually are required to have more work in the field of education than secondary school teachers. Professional education requirements have been on the increase in many states. Some states require as many as eighteen semester hours in this area. If Conant's recommendations are translated into practice, there may develop a trend toward having the college or university certify teachers that it trains.

The physical education requirement is increasing in many states. Very few states are reducing the requirement. More and more states are requiring twenty-five or more semester hours in specified areas as a requirement to teach physical education.

As previously mentioned the American Association for Health, Physical Education, and Recreation has adopted the prerequisite for new members to have obtained the bachelor's degree in an institution accredited by the National Council for Accreditation of Teacher Education.

The requirements for certification vary in the fifty states. The lowest certification requirements are usually for the rural elementary schools. However, the trend seems to be in the direction of requiring two or three years of preparation even in these areas. Most cities require a minimum of four years of preparation of college work for elementary school teaching and a bachelor's degree and five years of preparation for high school teaching. All prospective teachers should plan to obtain at least a bachelor's degree and, if possible, the master's degree.

There is a trend toward centralization of authority in the state board of education or state school agency. This trend makes possible better administration of the responsibility of certifying teachers, assures higher professional standards, and should result in less discriminatory action among the states. If Conant's recommendations are put into practice these trends may be reversed.

There is a trend toward less discrimination against out-of-state applications. Such a trend makes it possible for qualified candidates to teach in various sections of the country. Furthermore, it makes possible the sharing of educational experiences in school systems that represent various geographical and economic sections. It also permits a qualified candidate to accept a promotion into a better position without being restricted by local requirements.

The trend toward certification reciprocity between the states will allow for the flow of qualified teachers across state boundaries, make for a better balance between supply and demand for teachers, increase a feeling of national unity, contribute to the breaking down of provincialism, and aid in teacher growth. Movements in the direction of certification reciprocity have been made by the Southern Association Study, the Ohio Valley Association, the North Central Association Studies, the Central States Conference, and the Compact of New England States, New York and New Jersey.

The certification requirements for the states of Alabama, Arizona, California, Illinois, Massachusetts, and New York are listed to provide a picture of some of the standards required for teaching.

## Alabama

### Requirements for Class B
### Elementary Professional Certificates

A Class B Elementary Professional Certificate, valid in periods of 8 years, may be issued to a person who presents credentials showing:

1. That he has graduated with a bachelor's degree from a standard institution and has met requirements as prescribed by the State Board of Education for the education of elementary teachers
2. That he has earned prescribed credits as follows:

| Subjects | Semester hours | Quarter hours |
| --- | --- | --- |
| Education | 30 | 45 |
| Psychology | 6–10 | 9–15 |
| Principles and philosophy | 3–6 | 4½–9 |
| Materials and methods | 4–8 | 6–12 |
| Directed teaching | 3–8 | 4½–12 |
| Electives | 0–14 | 0–21 |
| English and literature | 14 | 21 |
| Social studies—Must include courses which have a credit value of at least 3 semester hours in 3 of the following fields: history, economics, political science, sociology, or geography | 18 | 27 |
| Science (biological and physical) | 12 | 18 |
| Health and physical education | 3 | 4½ |
| Music | 3 | 4½ |
| Art | 3 | 4½ |

### Requirements for Class A Elementary Professional Certificates

A Class A Elementary Professional Certificate, valid in periods of 10 years, may be issued to a person who has graduated with a master's degree from a standard institution in a curriculum approved for the education of teachers and who has met all professional and academic requirements for the Class B Elementary Professional Certificate.

### Requirements for Class B Secondary Professional Certificates

A Class B Secondary Professional Certificate, valid in periods of 8 years, may be issued to a person who presents credentials showing:

1. That he has graduated with a bachelor's degree from a standard institution and has met requirements as prescribed by the State Board of Education for the training of secondary teachers
2. That he has earned prescribed credits as follows:

| Subjects | Semester hours | Quarter hours |
| --- | --- | --- |
| Education | 24 | 36 |
| Psychology | 6–10 | 9–15 |
| Principles and philosophy | 3–6 | 4½–9 |
| Materials and methods of teaching major or minor subject in high school | 2–6 | 3–9 |
| Directed teaching of major or minor subject in high school | 3–8 | 4½–12 |
| Electives in the field of secondary education | 0–10 | 0–15 |
| English | 12 | 18 |
| Social studies—Must include courses which have a credit value of at least 3 semester hours in 2 of the following fields: history, economics, political science, sociology, or geography | 12 | 18 |
| Science (biological and physical) | 12 | 18 |

3. That he has to his credit an academic major of 24 semester hours in all areas, except English, social studies, and science. These three areas require 30 semester hours
4. That he has to his credit an academic minor of 18 semester hours in an approved subject

### Requirements for Class A Secondary Professional Certificates

A Class A Secondary Professional Certificate, valid in periods of 10 years, may be issued to a person who has graduated with a master's degree from a standard institution in a curriculum approved for the training of teachers, and who has met all professional and academic requirements for the Class B Secondary Professional Certificate.

## Arizona

### Certification of elementary school teachers

*A. Elementary–temporary certificate*

1. A certificate stamped elementary–temporary may be granted to holders of a bachelor's degree from an elementary teacher education program approved by the State Board of Education.
2. This certificate is granted upon fulfillment of the following conditions:
   a. Specialization in professional education appropriate to elementary school teaching
   b. Completion of a broad program of general studies
   c. Specialization in one or more content fields of interest to the teacher trainee
3. The temporary elementary certificate will entitle the holder to teach in nursery school or kindergarten, and in grades 1–8 inclusive.
4. This certificate shall be valid for 5 years only, and may not be renewed or reissued.

## Certification of secondary school teachers

B. *Secondary–temporary certificate*

1. A temporary secondary certificate may be granted to holders of a bachelor's degree from a secondary teacher education program approved by the State Board of Education.
2. Preparation of the prospective teacher will include:
   a. At least one teaching major as defined by the college or university. He may also elect a teaching minor.
   b. A broad program of general studies.
   c. Professional study including carefully supervised directed teaching.
3. The temporary secondary certificate shall be valid for 5 years only and shall entitle the holder to teach grades 7–12. It may not be renewed or reissued.

## California

### The standard teaching credential with a specialization in secondary teaching (issued for life)

An applicant for the standard teaching credential with a specialization in secondary teaching shall have successfully completed in *approved* institutions a program including the following:

1. A bachelor's degree.
2. A fifth year of college or university postgraduate course work taken at the upper division or graduate level.
3. 45 semester hours of course work in four of the areas listed below as items A through F, including, in every case, the English and the English composition requirement in the humanities area; a maximum of six semester hours of this work

## Majors and minors

This table shows all possible acceptable combinations of majors and minors.

| Majors (professional education is excluded by law) 24 semester hours of upper division or graduate level work required for all majors | Minors (all must be commonly taught in public high schools) |
|---|---|
| A. *Academic subject commonly taught* in public high schools | No minor is required.* |
| B. *Academic subject commonly taught* in public high schools | 1. 20 semester hours in a single academic or nonacademic subject, OR<br>2. 20 semester hours in an academic interdepartmental group, including 12 semester hours in one subject, OR<br>3. An area of specialized preparation. |
| C. *Nonacademic subject commonly taught* in public high schools | 1. 20 semester hours in a single academic subject, including 12 semester hours at the upper division of graduate level, OR<br>2. 20 semester hours in an academic interdepartmental group, including 12 semester hours in one subject of which 6 semester hours must be upper division or graduate level. |
| D. *Academic subject not commonly taught* | Two minors of 20 semester hours each. One must be academic. The other may be nonacademic or an area of specialized preparation. |
| E. *Nonacademic subject not commonly taught* | Two minors of 20 semester hours each are required. Both must be academic. |

*Authorization for service. If the credential lists *both* a major and a minor, the district governing board may by resolution, on a yearly basis, authorize the teaching of any subjects in grades 7 through 12, except in classes for exceptional children.

may be applied toward the requirement for either a major or a minor.

  a. Humanities. Either three semesters (four quarters) of English including a course in composition must be completed, or two semesters (three quarters) of English, and, in addition, the passing of a special examination in English composition (not the college entrance examination) given by an institution.

  b. Social sciences. Two semester hours in course work, or an examination given by any approved institution, on the provisions and principles of the United States Constitution, must be completed before this credential will be issued. If an out-of-state examination is offered it must have been taken after September 17, 1965, to meet this Constitution requirement.

  c. Natural sciences.

  d. Mathematics requiring a knowledge of high school algebra and geometry as prerequisites.

  e. Fine arts.

  f. Foreign languages.

4. One of the combinations of majors and minors in the accompanying table entitled "Majors and Minors."

5. Professional preparation to include:

  a. Both of the following:

    (1) 120 clock hours of actual teaching in a course in student teaching. Successful full-time teaching experience in public schools of equivalent status in California, or elsewhere, may be substituted for course work in student teaching at the rate of one year of teaching for one half of the requirement. At least one half of this requirement shall be completed in any grades 7 through 12.

    (2) 9 semester hours of course work to include:

      (a) The sociological or the historical, or the philosophical foundations of education or any combination of these courses.

      (b) The psychological foundations of education.

      (c) Curriculum and instructional procedures and materials used in teaching in secondary schools.

## Illinois

### Minimum requirements for state certificates effective July 26, 1965

I. *Standard Elementary Certificate*

The Standard Elementary Certificate is valid for 4 years for teaching in kindergarten through grade 9 of the common schools. This certificate may be issued to graduates with a bachelor's degree from a recognized college who presented certified evidence of having earned credits as follows:

| Subjects | | Semester hours |
|---|---|---|
| A. General education* | | **78** |
| 1. Language arts | 8 | |
| 2. Science | 6 | |
| 3. Social science including a course in American history and/or government) | 6 | |
| 4. Humanities (including a minimum of 1 semester hour in music and 1 semester hour in art) | 6 | |
| 5. Mathematics | 4 | |
| 6. Health and physical education | 3 | |
| 7. Additional work in any above fields and/or psychology (except educational psychology) to total | 78 | |
| B. Professional education | | **16** |
| 1. Educational psychology including human growth and development) | 2 | |
| 2. Methods and techniques of teaching at the elementary level | 2 | |
| 3. History and/or philosophy of education | 2 | |
| 4. Methods of teaching reading | 2 | |
| 5. Student teaching grades K–9 | 5 | |
| 6. Electives in professional education may be taken from the above fields and/or guidance, tests and measurements, and instructional materials to total | 16 | |

*Note:* Those who have had 5 semester hours of student teaching above grade 9 and who have had successful teaching experience, are not required to take another student teaching course at the elementary level.

| | | |
|---|---|---|
| C. Electives | | **26** |
| Total | | **120** |

II. *Standard High School Certificate*

The Standard High School Certificate is valid for 4 years for teaching in grades 6 through 12 of the common schools. This certificate may be issued to graduates with a bachelor's degree from a recognized college who present certified evidence of having earned credits as follows:

| Subjects | | Semester hours |
|---|---|---|
| A. General education | | **42** |
| 1. Language arts | 8 | |
| 2. Science and/or mathematics | 6 | |
| 3. Social science (including a course in American history and/or government) | 6 | |

*Each field (except physical education) must have a minimum of 1 additional hour which may be either content and/or methods.

4. Humanities      6
5. Health and physical education      3
6. Additional work in any above fields and/or psychology (except educational psychology) to total      42

B. Professional education      **16**
  1. Educational psychology including human growth and development)      2
  2. Methods and techniques of teaching at the secondary level or in a teaching field      2
  3. History and/or philosophy of education      2
  4. Student teaching grades 6–12      5
  5. Electives in professional education may be taken from the above fields and/or guidance, tests and measurements, methods of teaching reading, and instructional materials to total      16

*Note:* Those who have had 5 semester hours of student teaching below grade 6 and who have had successful teaching experience are not required to take another student teaching course at the secondary level.

C. One major area of specialization,      **32**
  or three minor areas of specialization
  (16–18–20–24) each      **48–72**

*Note:* Courses which are counted as general education may also be counted as part of hours required for major and/or minor areas of specialization.

D. Electives      **30**

               *Total*      **120**

## Massachusetts

### Certification of public school professional personnel

*Requirements under General Laws, Chapter 71, Section 38G*

1. Proof of American citizenship (A birth certificate or a baptismal record or a registrar of voter's certificate, or other valid proof of citizenship should accompany application. In case of change of name, submit a copy of court decree or marriage certificate. Photostatic copy of any document is acceptable.)
2. Proof of good health
3. Proof of sound moral character
4. Proof of possession of a bachelor's earned academic degree, or graduation from a 4-year normal school approved by the Board of Education (Official transcripts of records stamped with college seal must accompany application. Photostatic copies, if legible, will be accepted.)
5. Proof that applicant's preparation included the minimum number of semester hours of undergraduate or graduate credit in courses approved for the certificate requested, as listed below (Education courses must be so listed in catalog or official letters or publications of the col-

lege. In case of question regarding specific courses, applicants should submit evidence to substantiate claim.)

a. Elementary school teacher
(Kindergarten through grade 8)
18 semester hours in education. Not less than 2 semester hours must be in supervised student teaching in the elementary grades. The remaining semester hours must include courses covering 2 or more of the following areas:
(1) Educational psychology, including child growth and development
(2) Philosophy of education
(3) Methods and materials in elementary education
(4) Curriculum development in elementary education

b. Secondary school teacher
(Junior and senior high schools)
12 semester hours in education. Not less than 2 semester hours must be in supervised student teaching in the secondary schools. The remaining semester hours must include courses covering 2 or more of the following areas:
(1) Educational psychology, including adolescent growth and development
(2) Philosophy of education
(3) Methods and materials in secondary education
(4) Curriculum development in secondary education
18 semester hours in major field or fields
9 semester hours in minor subject field or fields

c. Special subject teacher in elementary and secondary grades, including junior high school, e.g., art business subjects, home economics, industrial arts, music, health, physical education, etc.
12 semester hours in education. Not less than 2 semester hours must be in supervised student teaching at the appropriate grade level. The remaining semester hours must include courses covering 2 or more of the following areas:
(1) Educational psychology, including child or adolescent growth and development
(2) Philosophy of education

(3) Methods and materials of teaching special subject field

(4) Curriculum development in special subject field

18 semester hours in the special subject field

## New York

A. Certification requirements for elementary school teaching (permanent certificate)
  1. Bachelor's degree
    a. 36 semester hours in approved courses in the field of education:
      (1) 12–15 semester hours in observation and practice teaching
      (2) 8–12 semester hours in teaching methods and materials
      (3) 6–10 semester hours in psychology
      (4) 2–6 semester hours in history, principles, problems, or philosophy of education
B. Certification requirements for secondary school teaching (permanent certificate)
  1. Bachelor's degree (or equivalent)
    a. 18 semester hours in the field of education
    b. Preparation in major field
  2. 30 semester hours of approved advanced courses
C. Special requirements in the field of physical education (entitle holder to teach on both elementary and secondary levels)
  1. 36 semester hours in the field of physical education
    a. 2–4 semester hours in applied anatomy
    b. 2–4 semester hours in physiology of exercise
    c. 2–4 semester hours in physical inspection
    d. 2–4 semester hours in first aid and safety education
    e. 2–4 semester hours in physical education of atypical children
    f. 2–4 semester hours in physical education tests and measurements
    g. 6–8 semester hours in administration, organization, and supervision (physical education, recreation, and camping)
    h. 14–16 semester hours in physical education skills and applied techniques
  2. Prerequisites—18 semester hours in science—one course in each of the following fields:
    a. Anatomy
    b. Physiology
    c. Biology
    d. Bacteriology
  3. Athletic coaches expected to meet requirements in physical education
D. Temporary certificates issued in the absence of qualified candidates

• • •

One or more majors and minors is a common requirement for secondary school teachers. Departmentalization prevails on the secondary level, and, consequently, candidates must have special preparation in their specialized areas. The requirements vary from state to state and in many cases the state prescribes the number of semester or quarter hours, whereas in other states the teacher-training institution decides what is the adequate amount of preparation.

Most states issue emergency teaching certificates in the absence of qualified candidates. It seems logical that as the supply of teachers grows the qualifications for teachers will be raised and emergency teaching certificates will be abolished.

All states have some type of certification system for teachers. Certificates for teaching are usually issued by the state departments of education or state school agency. It should be kept in mind, however, that although states have established certification requirements, many local school systems require more training than those listed as minimum requirements by the state certifying agency. Certification requirements pertain to teaching in the public schools. In most cases teachers in private schools are not required to meet state certification standards. However, these schools have their own requirements for teaching, which in many cases are similar to those that prevail for the public schools. College teachers are rarely certified. Some junior colleges must meet state certification requirements, which are very similar to secondary school requirements.

In the special certification requirements that prevail for the teaching of physical education, there is considerable difference in nomenclature and qualifications listed. Furthermore, in many states the physical education teacher may teach health education, whereas in others he is limited to the field of physical education. The physical educator who desires to teach in a particular state selects courses that will qualify him for teaching in that particular state. It is practically an impossibility to prepare for the teaching of physical education in all of the fifty states. However, if a physical educator's work is planned with care, the certification requirements for many states may be met with only an additional summer session's training or less. A survey conducted several years ago showed that in order to be certified in all the states a candidate would have the following preparation:

135 semester hours of work in an accredited institution of higher learning
Rank in upper four fifths of class
Bachelor's degree
24 semester hours in the field of education
42 semester hours of prerequisites including biology, anatomy, physiology, personal hygiene, community hygiene, English, American history and government, psychology, sociology, and child growth and development

A minimum of 71 semester hours in physical education work including practice teaching, applied anatomy, applied physiology, kinesiology, correctives, physical inspection, first aid and safety, introduction to physical education, history of physical education, administration and supervision, methods and materials, coaching techniques, nature of play, recreational activities, leadership, and theory and practice of various types of games, rhythms, and dances*

Today a candidate would be required to meet even higher requirements than these that have been listed.

## QUESTIONS AND EXERCISES

1. Why is it essential to have certification requirements?
2. A few educators are advocating national certification standards. What are the advantages and disadvantages of such a proposal?

---

*Morehouse, Laurence E., and Schaaf, Oscar: Research Quarterly, AAHPER **13:**293, Oct., 1942.

3. What are the certification requirements for the state in which you desire to teach? To what extent does your present training program prepare you to meet these standards?
4. What are some of the requirements that are similar for the various states?
5. What are emergency teaching certificates? What are their advantages and disadvantages?
6. What are some of the common characteristics of the certification requirements in the states of Alabama, Arizona, California, Illinois, Massachusetts, and New York?
7. What is the average semester-hour requirement in the specialized area of physical education for the fifty states?
8. What procedure should be followed by the student in order to make sure he understands thoroughly the certification requirements of a particular state?
9. Discuss the trends in regard to the certification of teachers in the various states.
10. Discuss the certification requirements for your state in the light of professional standards discussed in previous chapters.
11. What are J. B. Conant's recommendations in regard to the certification of teachers?

## SELECTED REFERENCES

Armstrong, W. Earl, and Stinnett, T. M.: A manual on certification requirements for school personnel in the United States, Washington, D. C., current issue, National Education Association.

Blesh, T. E.: Evaluative criteria in physical education, Doctoral thesis, New Haven, 1945, Yale University.

Bowers, Harold J.: Reciprocity in teacher certification, Journal of the National Education Association 39:14, Jan., 1950.

Bucher, Charles A.: Administration of school health and physical education programs, St. Louis, 1967, The C. V. Mosby Co.

Bucher, Charles A., Koening, Constance, and Barnhard, Milton: Methods and materials for secondary school physical education, St. Louis, 1961, The C. V. Mosby Co.

Conant, James Bryant: The education of American teachers, New York, 1963, McGraw-Hill Book Co.

Stinnett, T. M., Bowers, Harold J., and Robert, E. B.: Interstate reciprocity in teacher education-certification, Journal of Teacher Education 1:56, March, 1950.

Woellner, Elizabeth H., and Wood, M. Aurilla: Requirements for certification, Chicago, 1965, The University of Chicago Press.

# Chapter 24

# Employment opportunities

Teaching has more members than any other profession in existence today. The number of full-time men and women teachers in the United States is more than 2.4 million. Furthermore, no other profession offers so many employment opportunities for women. There are approximately 1.5 million women teaching today, more than twice as many as in the nursing profession. There are many more women than men teaching in the elementary schools of the nation. However, at the secondary level, in junior and senior high schools, the number of men and women in teaching is about equal. At the college and university level there are more male teachers. Men hold about four fifths of all college and university positions.

Education is America's largest business. More than one out of every four individuals is in school. The high birth rates, proportion of young people getting more schooling, emphasis on quality education, and other factors indicate a bright future for this field of work. Total annual outlays for education are over $40 billion. This sum of money is more than equal to the annual sales of the steel industry.

Educational construction costs approximately $4.5 billion a year. Expenditures on classroom equipment, such as books, audiovisual devices, and desks, amount to $1 billion a year. Certain leading corporations in the United States have linked themselves to the educational business in such areas as copying machines, microfilms, texts and other reading material, programmed instruction, electronics, language laboratories, and learning systems. More than 60% of the antipoverty program in the Economic Opportunity Act is estimated as being allocated directly to education. Job Corps centers rely heavily on educators for help and guidance.

The growth of education during the last few years has been phenomenal. For example, expenditures in 1950 were about $9.3 billion, or 3.5% of our gross national product (the sum of all goods and services). A rise to $50 billion, or 6.1% of the gross national product, has been projected by 1973. Ten years ago, school and college enrollments were under 40 million. The United States Office of Education foresees enrollments of 62 million by 1973. Textbook sales have risen from about $200 million to $600 million annually in the past decade, or an annual growth of about 12%. Two-year college enrollments have jumped from less than 300,000 students in 1954 to nearly one million today.

## PROFESSIONAL ADVANTAGES OFFERED BY TEACHING

Education is on the move. Those who decide to make a career in this field will be involved in one of the greatest adven-

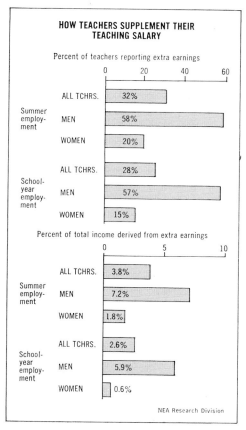

## HOW TEACHERS SUPPLEMENT THEIR TEACHING SALARY

Percent of teachers reporting extra earnings

|  |  |  |
|---|---|---|
| Summer employment | ALL TCHRS. | 32% |
| | MEN | 58% |
| | WOMEN | 20% |
| School-year employment | ALL TCHRS. | 28% |
| | MEN | 57% |
| | WOMEN | 15% |

Percent of total income derived from extra earnings

|  |  |  |
|---|---|---|
| Summer employment | ALL TCHRS. | 3.8% |
| | MEN | 7.2% |
| | WOMEN | 1.8% |
| School-year employment | ALL TCHRS. | 2.6% |
| | MEN | 5.9% |
| | WOMEN | 0.6% |

NEA Research Division

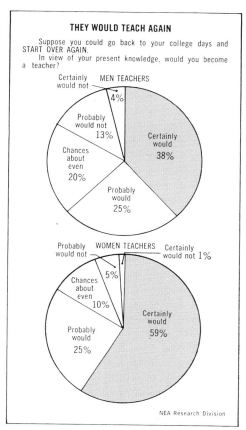

## THEY WOULD TEACH AGAIN

Suppose you could go back to your college days and START OVER AGAIN.
In view of your present knowledge, would you become a teacher?

**MEN TEACHERS**
Certainly would not — 4%
Probably would not 13%
Chances about even 20%
Probably would 25%
Certainly would 38%

**WOMEN TEACHERS**
Certainly would not 1%
Probably would not 5%
Chances about even 10%
Probably would 25%
Certainly would 59%

NEA Research Division

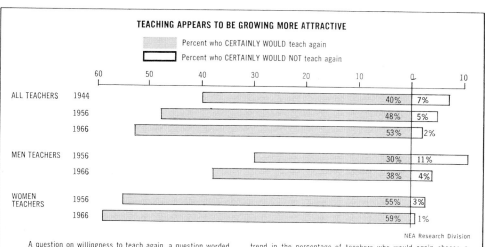

## TEACHING APPEARS TO BE GROWING MORE ATTRACTIVE

Percent who CERTAINLY WOULD teach again
Percent who CERTAINLY WOULD NOT teach again

| | | CERTAINLY WOULD | CERTAINLY WOULD NOT |
|---|---|---|---|
| ALL TEACHERS | 1944 | 40% | 7% |
| | 1956 | 48% | 5% |
| | 1966 | 53% | 2% |
| MEN TEACHERS | 1956 | 30% | 11% |
| | 1966 | 38% | 4% |
| WOMEN TEACHERS | 1956 | 55% | 3% |
| | 1966 | 59% | 1% |

NEA Research Division

A question on willingness to teach again, a question worded exactly as in 1966, has been included in several studies of the NEA Research Division. Replies in 1961, not shown in the graph, are consistent with the others in showing a continuing upward trend in the percentage of teachers who would again choose a teaching career.

The 1966 report includes comparisons with 1956 and 1961 findings on a number of the items in the 1966 survey.

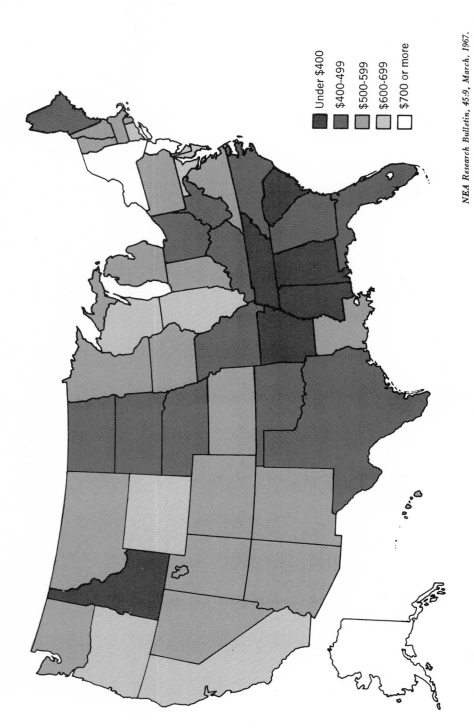

Current expenditure per pupil in average daily attendance, 1966-1967.

*NEA Research Bulletin, 45:9, March, 1967.*

tures that has ever been witnessed in this country. Some of the factors that show the advantages of teaching as a career are teaching salaries, enrollments, teaching vacancies, and additional benefits for teachers.

## Teaching salaries

The average salary for teachers in public elementary schools, according to estimates by the National Education Association, is in excess of $6,000. In the three highest-paying states (California, Connecticut, and New York), teachers' salaries averaged approximately $7,000, and in the six states with the lowest salaries (Arkansas, Mississippi, North Dakota, South Dakota, South Carolina, and West Virginia), it is approximately $4,500.

The average annual salary for teachers in public secondary schools is in excess of $6,500. In California and New York, average salaries exceed $8,000, and in Arkansas and Mississippi the average is approximately $4,500.

The national average salary of instructional staff in the regular public elementary and secondary schools (in 1965–1966 dollars) increased from $4,934 in 1955–1956 to $6,700 in 1965–1966, and is expected to be $8,500 in 1975–1976.

The average annual salaries for teachers in four-year colleges and universities are in excess of $8,500 for nine to ten months' work. The approximate mean annual salaries of full-time faculty members in public and private institutions for nine to ten months' work in institutions of higher education, by academic rank, are as follows: academic deans, $12,500; pro-

---

The following statistics are outlined by the United States Office of Education in a publication that projects the education of the present into the education of the future (1974–1975):

A 71% increase in students getting bachelor's degrees, up from 525,000 to 899,000.

Almost twice as many persons getting master's degrees, from 111,000 to 210,000.

Twice as many persons getting doctoral degrees, from 15,300 to 31,900.

An 89% increase in total spending by colleges and universities, from $11.9 billion to $22.5 billion.

A 74% increase in students seeking degrees at colleges and universities, up from 5 million in the fall of 1964 to 8.7 million in the fall of 1974.

A 13.5% increase in enrollment at public and private elementary and secondary schools, from 48.1 million in 1964 to 54.6 million in 1974.

A 25.9% increase in public and private high school graduates, from 2.7 million to 3.4 million.

An increase of 507,000 public and private elementary and secondary school teachers, from 1.9 million to 2.4 million.

A 47% increase in expenditures for elementary and secondary schools, from $26.1 billion to $38.4 billion in the 1974–1975 school year.

The projections indicate that in 1974 the number of high school students will have more than doubled, and the number of degree-seeking college students will have more than tripled the 1954 totals. A decade from now, an estimated 16.4 million students will be in high school.*

---

*Projections of educational statistics to 1974–1975, Washington, D. C., 1965 edition, U. S. Department of Health, Education and Welfare.

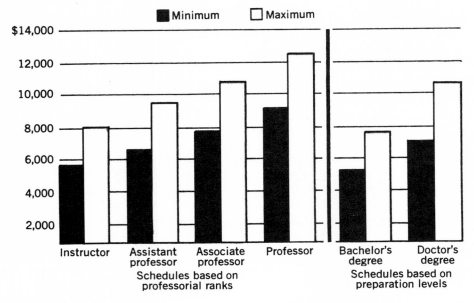

NEA Research Bulletin 44:71, Oct., 1966.

Average scheduled salaries in public junior colleges, 1965-1966.

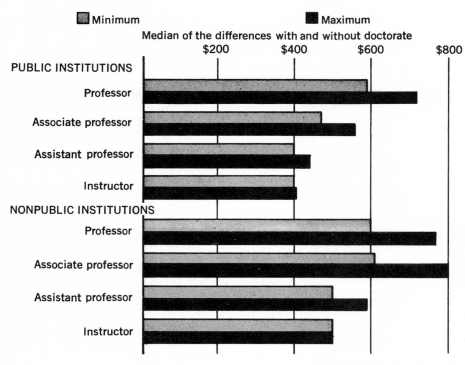

NEA Research Bulletin 44:83, Oct., 1966

Median differences in scheduled faculty salaries.

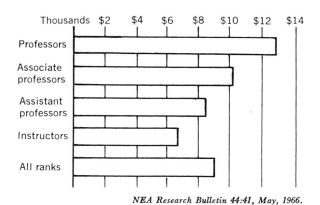

*NEA Research Bulletin 44:41, May, 1966.*

Median salaries paid college teachers, 1956-1966.

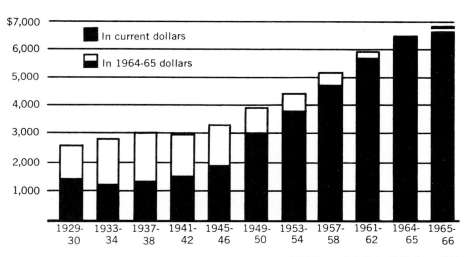

*NEA Research Bulletin 44:36, May, 1966.*

Average annual salaries of instructional staff.

fessors, $12,800; associate professors, $9,900; assistant professors, $8,200; and instructors, $6,700.

### Additional benefits for teachers

Teaching is a profession that has many benefits. It provides the opportunity to render a service in guiding the growth and learning of others, to become a member of a respected and growing profession, to further one's own self-development and personal growth, to travel, and to participate in unlimited exciting experiences with children, youth, and adults. Furthermore, in many school systems it offers tenure, sabbatical leaves, sick leaves, and retirement benefits.

**Tenure.** Many school systems provide tenure for teachers who serve successful probationary periods of two or three years. This means that the teacher who has tenure cannot be dismissed, demoted, or suspended, except as prescribed by law and according to definitely prescribed procedures. This helps to provide security for the teacher.

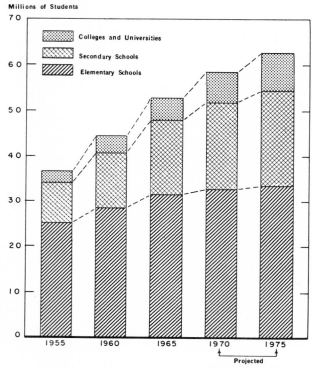

*Employment outlook for teachers, Occupational outlook handbook, 1966, U. S. Department of Labor.*

Total teaching staff will expand by almost a third to over 2½ million during the 1965-1975 period.

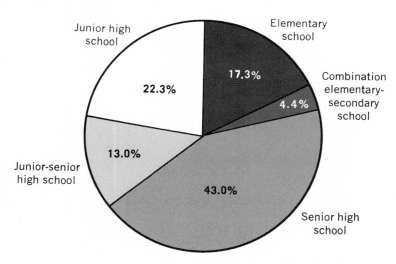

*NEA Research Bulletin 45:14, March, 1967.*

Men teachers by type of teaching assignment, 1965-1966.

**Sabbatical leaves.** More school systems are adopting sabbatical-leave schedules. Teachers, after a period of satisfactory service, say seven years, may take one year or a semester with pay or partial pay to improve themselves, such as pursuing graduate work, travel, or performing research.

**Sick leaves.** Most school systems across the country have sick-leave provisions. The teacher is permitted to take time from his or her job when ill and still draw full salary. School systems usually designate the amount of time that may be used for such a purpose, frequently ten days.

**Retirement benefits.** Most states have some provision for retirement benefits for teachers. After a stipulated period of service, usually from 25 to 35 years, and a minimum age, perhaps 60 or 65 years, the teacher may retire and draw a regular retirement benefit which is usually computed on the amount of salary he or she earned. In addition, about three fourths of all the states are now covered by social security, which gives teachers additional benefits upon retirement.

## SCHOOL AND COLLEGE ENROLLMENTS

The total enrollment in all types of schools and colleges is in excess of 55 million. Increases are expected in most categories. For example, it is expected that in colleges the enrollments will jump to over 8 million by 1975. The growth of the two-year college alone in recent years has been phenomenal. Nearly one million students are enrolled in the more than 720 junior colleges from coast to coast. Furthermore, it is projected that the enrollments will increase nearly 1,100,000 by 1970 and to 1,350,000 by 1974. Enrollments in regular public elementary and secondary schools is expected to be 47.1 million in

**Table 24-1.** *Per cent of school systems granting leaves of absence for professional reasons, 1965–1966\**

| Reason | Group A 25,000 or more enrollment (%) | Group B 3,000–24,999 enrollment (%) | Group C 300–2,999 enrollment (%) | National weighted distribution, all operating systems with 300 or more enrollment (%) |
|---|---|---|---|---|
| Professional study | 85.8 | 60.5 | 31.6 | 38.7 |
| Professional meetings | 87.8 | 95.6 | 94.2 | 94.4 |
| Exchange teaching abroad | 81.8 | 50.0 | 22.0 | 28.9 |
| Professional organization work | 70.9 | 92.5 | 90.4 | 90.6 |
| Visiting other schools | 68.2 | 92.2 | 88.6 | 89.2 |
| Paid sabbatical | 56.7 | 40.8 | 11.7 | 18.7 |
| Professional organization service (extended leave) | 60.8 | 32.7 | 21.6 | 24.6 |
| Department of Defense School | 57.4 | 36.7 | 20.6 | 17.1 |
| Research | 55.4 | 31.6 | 15.5 | 19.5 |
| Travel | 52.7 | 26.2 | 12.7 | 16.2 |
| Exchange teaching in the United States | 54.7 | 36.7 | 20.6 | 24.6 |
| Work experience | 16.9 | 11.6 | 6.5 | 7.8 |
| Number of systems | 148 | 294 | 291 | 12,130 |

*\*Source:* National Education Association, Research Division: Teacher leaves of absence, local practices, 1965–1966.

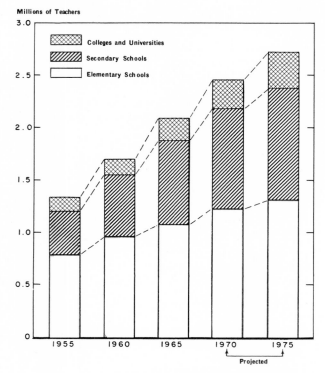

Millions of Teachers

Colleges and Universities
Secondary Schools
Elementary Schools

1955  1960  1965  1970  1975
Projected

*Employment outlook for teachers, Occupational*
*outlook handbook, 1966, U. S. Department of Labor.*

College enrollments will show the fastest growth rate between 1965 and 1975, rising to over 8 million.

1974. Enrollment in kindergarten through eighth grade is expected to be 32.5 million in 1974.

One of the factors affecting enrollments is that the falling birth rates, having leveled off, will now rise slowly to 1974. Enrollment rates at the elementary level will increase slightly, but those at the high school and college levels will continue to increase.

The striking fact about education is that more of the population is going to school and more pupils are staying in school for longer periods of time. More states also have compulsory attendance laws.

**Teaching vacancies**

To staff the new classrooms that need to be provided for the increased number of students, it is estimated that the number of teachers will need to be increased by almost one third, or about 650,000 by 1975. In addition, a much larger number of teachers, approximately 1.8 million, will be needed to replace those who will leave the profession. Furthermore, more new teachers will need to be added to meet the trend of reduced ratios between pupils and teachers.

Teachers planning to teach at the elementary school level will find many vacancies—about 90,000 annually will be needed to replace those who retire, die, or leave the profession for other reasons. In addition, nearly 30,000 annually will be needed to take care of increased enrollments, some improvement of pupil–teacher ratios, and to replace persons not meeting certification requirements. With

# U.S. EDUCATION'S GROWTH—THE PAST AND THE FUTURE

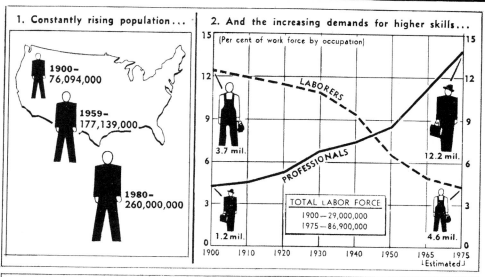

**1. Constantly rising population...**

1900–
76,094,000

1959–
177,139,000

1980–
260,000,000

**2. And the increasing demands for higher skills...**

(Per cent of work force by occupation)

LABORERS

PROFESSIONALS

3.7 mil.

12.2 mil.

1.2 mil.

4.6 mil.

TOTAL LABOR FORCE
1900—29,000,000
1975—86,900,000

1900   1910   1920   1930   1940   1950   1965   1975
⌊Estimated⌋

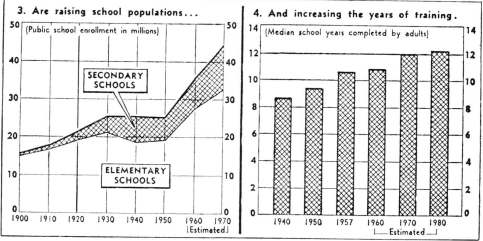

**3. Are raising school populations...**

(Public school enrollment in millions)

SECONDARY
SCHOOLS

ELEMENTARY
SCHOOLS

1900   1910   1920   1930   1940   1950   1960   1970
⌊Estimated⌋

**4. And increasing the years of training.**

(Median school years completed by adults)

1940   1950   1957   1960   1970   1980
⌊—Estimated—⌋

*The New York Times, Aug. 9, 1959.*

Education is America's largest industry.

the passage of the Economic Opportunity Act (1964), the Elementary and Secondary Education Act (1965), and the Higher Education Act (1965), which place special emphasis on aid to pre-schoolers, children in low-income areas, the mentally retarded, and other groups requiring special attention, it is possible that additional kindergarten and elementary teachers may be needed.

There will be a need for approximately 100,000 new teachers each year until 1975 for secondary school teachers to take care of enrollment increases, to reflect some improvement in the pupil-teacher ratio, to replace teachers who retire, marry, or leave the field for other reasons, and to replace persons who do not meet certification requirements. Although some job openings for secondary school teachers will be created by rising enrollments, most of the job openings—about 70% of the total requirements—will come from the need to replace teachers who for various reasons may leave the field. Also, considerable additional demand for teachers may be generated by federal legislation that provides for supplementary educational centers and a National Teachers Corps (federally recruited teachers and teacher-interns for low-income areas). Furthermore, many teachers trained for secondary schools may qualify for junior college positions where demand for teachers is expected to be especially great in the years to come.

College teaching opportunities in the years ahead are especially bright for those persons with doctoral degrees. Furthermore, there will be many opportunities in junior colleges for persons who have master's degrees or have taken further graduate work.

The U. S. Office of Education estimates that the full-time college teaching staff will increase to approximately 337,000 in 1975, an increase of about two thirds. In addition to the teachers needed to take care of the enrollment growth, about 16,000 more teachers may be needed annually up to 1975 to replace those who retire, die, or leave the profession for other reasons. Furthermore, the fact that new degree recipients may be drained from the college teaching ranks by better paying opportunities in industry, government, and nonprofit organizations may increase the critical need to meet the demand in many subject fields through the mid-1970's.

## EMPLOYMENT IN PHYSICAL EDUCATION

Recent events in domestic and world affairs have changed the long-range employment picture in physical education considerably. Although competition for positions will continue, students in training should find jobs more plentiful than those who graduated during the past few years.

Chaotic domestic and world conditions with the demands of the armed forces, industry, and government for manpower; federal legislation; greater enrollments in the schools; the emphasis on fitness; and the increased recognition on the part of the public of the value of physical education are a few of the reasons for this optimism.

The United States is now engaged in a struggle with Communism for world influence. As a result of this struggle, this country is striving to maintain a large potential fighting force and is spending vast amounts of money on rearmament. This in turn has implications for physical education employment prospects. It requires a period of national emergency similar to the one through which this country is now passing to bring to the public a recognition of the need for building up youth physically. Physical education received a great impetus from World Wars I and II and is receiving another impetus from present world conditions. The President's fitness program is having a strong impact on physical education by increasing the emphasis on physical education programs in the nation's schools and other youth-serving agencies. Consequently, there is a demand for more physical educators.

Apart from the international crisis, there are other signs in respect to employment possibilities. Enrollments in elementary and high schools and two- and four-year colleges are increasing, and there are trends in the various states toward less discrimination against out-of-state applicants and toward certification reciprocity. The Economic Opportunity Act and other federal legislation are creating new opportunities for physical educators. These developments make it increasingly possible for qualified candi-

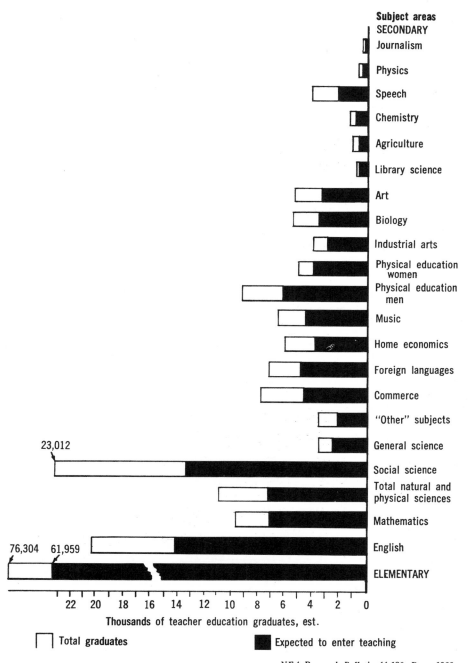

Subject areas
SECONDARY

Journalism

Physics

Speech

Chemistry

Agriculture

Library science

Art

Biology

Industrial arts

Physical education women

Physical education men

Music

Home economics

Foreign languages

Commerce

"Other" subjects

General science

23,012

Social science

Total natural and physical sciences

Mathematics

76,304    61,959

English

ELEMENTARY

22  20  18  16  14  12  10  8  6  4  2  0

**Thousands of teacher education graduates, est.**

☐ Total graduates          ■ Expected to enter teaching

*NEA Research Bulletin 44:120, Dec., 1966.*

Supply of beginning teachers by level and subject. Adjusted trend criterion estimate, 1966.

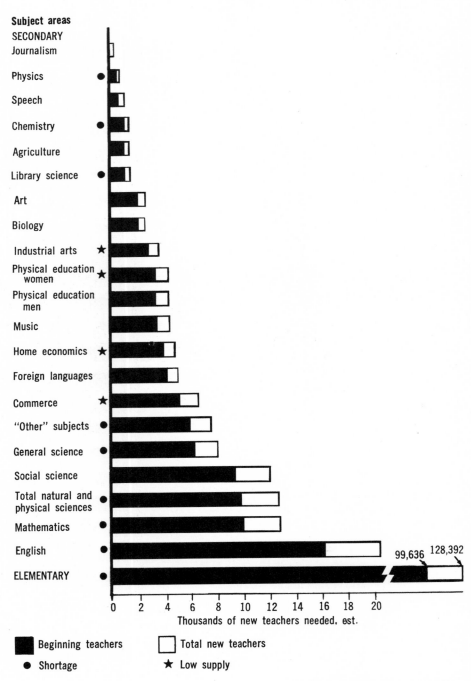

Estimated demand for new teachers by level and subject. Adjusted trend criterion estimate, 1966.

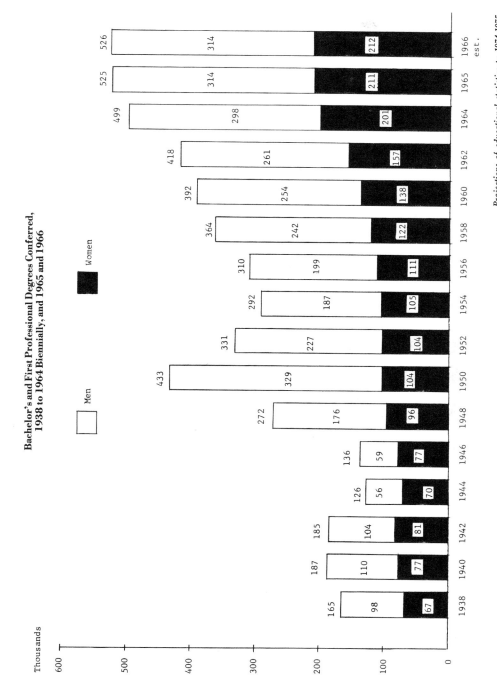

**Bachelor's and First Professional Degrees Conferred, 1938 to 1964 Biennially, and 1965 and 1966**

Men ☐  Women ■

| | 1938 | 1940 | 1942 | 1944 | 1946 | 1948 | 1950 | 1952 | 1954 | 1956 | 1958 | 1960 | 1962 | 1964 | 1965 | 1966 est. |
|---|---|---|---|---|---|---|---|---|---|---|---|---|---|---|---|---|
| Total | 165 | 187 | 185 | 126 | 136 | 272 | 433 | 331 | 292 | 310 | 364 | 392 | 418 | 499 | 525 | 526 |
| Men | 98 | 110 | 104 | 56 | 59 | 176 | 329 | 227 | 187 | 199 | 242 | 254 | 261 | 298 | 314 | 314 |
| Women | 67 | 77 | 81 | 70 | 77 | 96 | 104 | 104 | 105 | 111 | 122 | 138 | 157 | 201 | 211 | 212 |

Thousands

*Projections of educational statistics to 1974-1975, Washington, D. C., 1965, U. S. Office of Education.*

dates to teach in the various elementary schools and high schools throughout the United States in which physical education vacancies exist.

Physical education offers much more than a job and security. It will, in addition, bring a great deal of enjoyment to those who conscientiously prepare for this profession. Through activities such as games, gymnastics, sports, rhythmic activities, and health and safety courses, the physical educator helps in the development of a healthy, happy, alert, and strong America. He or she helps to shape youth for the future; has the opportunity to work in an active type of work, much of which is out-of-doors; renders a service to humanity; and has many opportunities for professional and social contacts.

The physical educator as a teacher has many advantages not characteristic of other professions. He has retirement privileges that promise security in old age. In many states, he has tenure which guarantees that he will not be dismissed from his job at the whim of some politician or cantankerous administrator. He has vacation periods of ample length to provide opportunity for study, rest, relaxation, travel, or work. He has received a college preparation which, with some additional training, may prepare him for work in such areas as health education, adapted physical education, physical therapy, recreation education, camping education, and dance education. He has the prospect of finding employment in public and private schools, colleges and universities, teachers' colleges, camps, playgrounds, youth-serving agencies, and many other places. His is not a blind-alley job. He may be promoted into a supervisory or administrative position, both of which are prevalent in all schools. He may start at a salary of $5,000, $6,000, $7,000, or more a year.

Physical education is rapidly becoming a stable profession. Laws, rules, and regulations are being passed in the various states ensuring physical education a prominent place in the curricula of our schools and providing that all pupils receive the benefits that it offers.

Physical education is a growing profession, having expanded greatly since World War I and World War II, and it is destined to expand much more during the next decade. A statement of a former executive secretary of the American Association for Health, Physical Education, and Recreation has indicated the growth of physical educators in the United States. He pointed out that in 1918 there were approximately 10,000 physical educators who had training in physical education; in 1932 there were 20,000; in 1947 there were 65,000; and today it is estimated there are more than 200,000.

A national survey relating to anticipated job opportunities in physical education, health education, and recreation, and covering twenty-two states, reached the following conclusions in regard to job opportunities in these special fields:

1. An estimated 8,400 new job openings will be available for professional health and physical education teachers from 1967 to 1970.
2. An estimated 9,000 professional job opportunities will be available in the field of recreation from 1967 to 1970.
3. In general, there seems to be an oversupply of high school men physical education teachers.
4. In general, there is a lack of qualified physical education teachers for the elementary schools.
5. There is a shortage of women physical education teachers at all levels.

There is a great amount of variability from state to state regarding the relative maturity of health education and physical education. For example, some states do not have a professional health education program, some states do not provide for adaptive physical education specialists, and some states do not use specialists in physical education in the elementary schools. As the state educational systems mature professionally, it should mean a greater demand for physical educators with specialized skills.

Another survey of selected states indicates a five-year outlook in physical education from 1967 to 1971 (See Table 24-2.)

A survey conducted by the author showed these data when the analysis of the questionnaires was completed:

1. Of the 16 reporting states, 8 were east of the Mississippi River (New York, Maryland, Maine, Massachusetts, Alabama, Delaware, Kentucky, and North Carolina), and 8 were west of the Mississippi River (New Mexico, Oklahoma, Missouri, Minnesota, Louisiana, Kansas, Nevada, and North Dakota).
2. Twelve states indicated increases in the number of positions available in physical education and health education for the projected 10 years (1967–1977).
3. Two states (New York and Maine) had "no idea" of the number of positions available in the projected 10 years.
4. Delaware indicated no increase in positions in the next 10 years.
5. Of all the reporting states, Massachusetts indicated the largest increase in physical education positions: from 1,100 (1967) to 2,500 (1977), and an increase in health education positions from 50 (1967) to 200 (1977).
6. New Mexico and North Carolina listed the smallest increases in physical education positions as 20 (1967) to 40 (1977) and 60 (1967) to 80 (1977), respectively.
7. North Dakota showed the greatest increase in recreation positions as 25 (1967) to 100 (1977).
8. Louisiana indicated the smallest increase in recreation positions as 12 (1967) to 20 (1977).
9. Missouri grouped all three fields together and showed an increase of 368 (1967) to 700 (1977).
10. No report for recreation was submitted by Massachusetts, North Carolina, New York, Kansas, Delaware, Kentucky, Maine, Maryland, and New Mexico.
11. The types of positions available in recreation ranged from directors to coaches.
12. Concerning projected areas of specialization, the listing of elementary school physical education was cited most frequently. Next was preparation to teach an adaptive program and/or a program for the mentally retarded in physical education.
13. The states who replied to the questionnaire required various qualifications, from "specified hours" to a master's degree in the particular field.

## EMPLOYMENT OF PHYSICAL EDUCATORS IN ALLIED AREAS

A significant development during recent years has been the increased emphasis on such allied areas as recreation, health education, camping, and physical therapy. Although these are distinct and separate fields of endeavor from physical education, nevertheless, some aspects of these specialties offer opportunities for physical educators. Furthermore, in some areas of the country shortages of trained personnel force these responsibilities upon physical educators, who in many cases shoulder them reluctantly.

According to the United States Department of Labor, at the present time a serious need exists for persons in the field of recreation. These opportunities are expected to increase rapidly, at least through the mid-1970's. Serious shortages presently exist in all parts of the country for trained recreation workers, particularly in local governments, hospitals, and youth-serving agencies. As a result of this shortage and the great demand for qualified persons, many physical educators will be able to obtain full or part-time employment in these programs.

The Boys' Clubs of America is a rapidly growing national movement with a new Boys' Club being started somewhere in the nation on the average of one every eight days. The Boys' Clubs of America point out that although they have 700 or 800 men available for positions, they still have great need for more people.

**Table 24-2.** *Estimated number of available new job opportunities in physical education for the*

| State | Elementary schools | | | | Junior high schools | | | |
|---|---|---|---|---|---|---|---|---|
| | 1968 | 1969 | 1970 | 1971 | 1968 | 1969 | 1970 | 1971 |
| 1 | 42 | 46 | 47 | 47 | 67 | 69 | 71 | 71 |
| 2 | 5 | 5 | 5 | 5 | 4 | 5 | 5 | 5 |
| 3 | 60 | 70 | 80 | 100 | 30 | 35 | 40 | 45 |
| 4 | 20 | 20 | 20 | 20 | 40 | 50 | 60 | 70 |
| 5 | 25 | 30 | 40 | 40 | 20 | 20 | 20 | 20 |
| 6 | 29 | 35 | 42 | 47 | 17 | 20 | 24 | 30 |
| 7 | 20 | 25 | 30 | 35 | 30 | 40 | 40 | 45 |
| 8 | 700 | 850 | 1,000 | 1,200 | 1,300 | 1,500 | 1,700 | 1,900 |
| 9 | 40 | 50 | 60 | 70 | 55 | 60 | 60 | 65 |
| 10 | 15 | 20 | 20 | 25 | 20 | 25 | 20 | 30 |

*Key: NS* means the figures were not specified by the state.
[a]State 1. Figures were unknown for projected job opportunities in the two-year and four-year colleges.
[b]State 3. Figures were unknown for projected job opportunities in the four-year colleges and univer
[c]State 9. The figure given under junior high schools combines the figures for both the junior and
[d]State 10. The figure given under junior high schools combines the figures for both the junior and

They further point out that they are experiencing a shortage of people for most types of positions at the present time.

The American National Red Cross points out that college graduates with majors in health, physical education, and recreation can find employment with them if they are interested, motivated, have the right type of personality, and possess leadership potential. For example, they cite that they are seeking recreation aides and physical educators for their programs of service in military hospitals and club-mobile programs overseas. They also point out that graduates with a physical education major, who have had teaching experience and possess a knowledge of community organization, may be employed as safety service representatives on the national staff of Red Cross and as directors of safety services in many of the larger chapters.

The preceding represent only a sampling of employment opportunities for physical educators in allied fields. Others that might be explored, depending upon a person's qualifications and interests, are work in such voluntary youth agencies as the young women's and young men's Christian and Hebrew associations, work with the physically handicapped in hospitals and other agencies, camping and outdoor education, churches, resort areas, and the armed forces. Many opportunities are available if one will take time to investigate them thoroughly.

## COMBATING CURRENT DILEMMA

Although the long-range picture for physical education is very bright, some problems still exist. There is an oversupply of men physical educators and a shortage of women physical educators in many parts of the country. One has to be realistic about such problems. Some possible solutions to both of these problems will be discussed.

### Oversupply of men physical educators

Some conditions existing at the present time may radically change the employment for men physical educators in the next few years. Some of these are as follows:

1. *Rising enrollments.* More boys and girls are going to school, and this will mean that more physical educators will

*years 1968–1971 in ten selected states*

| | Senior high schools | | | | Two-year colleges | | | | Four-year colleges and universities | | | |
|---|---|---|---|---|---|---|---|---|---|---|---|---|
| | 1968 | 1969 | 1970 | 1971 | 1968 | 1969 | 1970 | 1971 | 1968 | 1969 | 1970 | 1971 |
| | 59 | 61 | 70 | 70 | — | — | — | —[a] | — | — | — | —[a] |
| | 4 | 5 | 5 | 5 | NS | NS | NS | NS | NS | NS | NS | NS |
| | 25 | 30 | 35 | 40 | 15 | 20 | 25 | 30 | — | — | — | —[b] |
| | 50 | 55 | 60 | 65 | 10 | 15 | 15 | 15 | 40 | 45 | 45 | 45 |
| | 20 | 20 | 30 | 30 | 10 | 10 | 10 | 10 | 12 | 12 | 12 | 12 |
| | 14 | 18 | 23 | 29 | 0 | 0 | 4 | 10 | 10 | 12 | 13 | 14 |
| | 25 | 30 | 35 | 40 | 0 | 6 | 10 | 12 | 7 | 9 | 12 | 18 |
| | 1,100 | 1,200 | 1,300 | 1,400 | 300 | 400 | 500 | 600 | 200 | 215 | 225 | 250 |
| | — | — | — | —[c] | 4 | 6 | 8 | 10 | 6 | 8 | 10 | 12 |
| | — | — | — | —[d] | 4 | 4 | 8 | 10 | 8 | 10 | 12 | 14 |

sities.
senior high schools.
senior high schools.

be needed to satisfy the needs of expanding programs.

2. *The emphasis upon physical fitness.* With federal backing, the country is rapidly becoming fitness conscious. On all sides there is evidence of increased emphasis on physical education in order to enhance the well-being of our youth.

3. *Federal legislation.* The Peace Corps, Economic Opportunity Act, the Elementary and Secondary Education Act, the Higher Education Act, and such innovations as Project Head Start, Job Corps, and the Teacher Corps will increase the need for teachers. These programs place special emphasis on the culturally deprived, the mentally retarded, preschoolers, low-income areas, and other groups of children and adults that need to have greater educational opportunities. This innovation in our culture will mean greater attention to all individuals in our society regardless of intellect, physical condition, economic status, race, and other factors that differentiate human beings. Consequently, this will mean a demand for more teachers of varying specialities in order to provide such programs.

4. *Growth in enrollments in two- and four-year colleges.* The "baby boom" is finally reaching the colleges, and this, together with the fact that more high school graduates are going on to college, means a sharp rise in college enrollment during the next decade. The spectacular rise of the two-year college means there will be many more opportunities for physical education personnel at this level in order to accommodate the many students that will be attending these institutions. Furthermore, surveys show that most two-year colleges are offering physical education service courses for each of the two years, some have started professional programs, and some also include a course in health for all freshmen.

5. *Armed forces.* The increased number of young men being called into the armed forces means fewer college graduates going into teaching in physical education. This could have a critical impact during the years ahead, depending upon the progress of international events.

6. *Lower ratio of teachers to students.* Pressures are being exerted in some sections of the country to have smaller classes per teacher. Physical educators can do a better job with fewer students, as the

English teacher does, and this is a goal that must be accomplished. This will mean that more teachers of physical education will be needed.

7. *Physical education training for coaches.* Another development is to require that coaches receive some training in the field of physical education. Many coaches at present have little or no training in physical education. If such requirements were instituted, it would mean that more physical educators would be needed to work in school athletic programs.

8. *Specialists in elementary schools.* There seems to be increasing recognition that specialists are needed in the elementary schools of the nation, especially in grades 4, 5, and 6. These physical educators may work with classroom teachers or teach the physical education classes themselves. If this practice became nationwide, it would mean many more physical education teachers would be needed. The fact that there are about 84,000 public elementary schools, as contrasted with about 26,000 high schools, supports this premise.

9. *Increased emphasis on allied areas.* Recreation, camping, outdoor education, and health education are allied areas that are expanding. This means that if physical educators take the training needed to participate in these specialized areas, more physical educators will be needed.

10. *Expansion of sports in the American culture.* Sports are playing a more prominent role in the American culture. As a result, more leaders will be needed to teach and guide programs involved with various sports.

11. *Summer school programs.* New York and other states have experimented with summer school programs at the precollege level. The results have been highly satisfactory and should result in the need for more teachers.

### Shortage of women physical educators

1. *Law of supply and demand.* Wherever there is great demand, certain economic and other conditions operate to increase the supply. This is true in the case of women physical educators. Qualified women physical educators have been get-

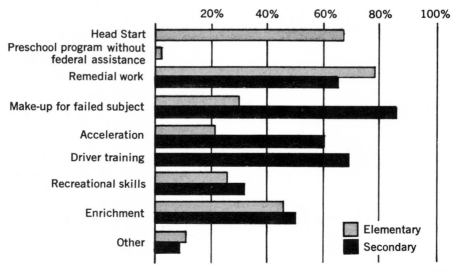

*NEA Research Bulletin 45:20, March, 1967.*

Types of summer school programs offered in systems enrolling 12,000 or more.

ting their choice of positions, high salaries, and other conditions that have attracted more women to this profession.

2. *Stronger recruitment programs.* Leaders in the profession, college admissions officers, and teacher-training institutions are stepping up their recruitment programs for women physical educators. The results of more intensive efforts along this line should result in more women being attracted to the profession.

3. *Education and interpretation.* High school girls are being better oriented in regard to the opportunities available in becoming a teacher of physical education. Young women are recognizing the important place that such programs have in the schools and colleges of our nation, and more women want to become a part of it. They realize that it is not a profession pursued by a super-athletic woman but, instead, is a field of endeavor in which the woman who is interested in developing a healthy, more beautiful, female population has an important role to play. Such areas as dance are attracting many women interested in teaching these physically aesthetic experiences.

4. *Present-day women leaders of physical education are attracting leaders.* Many women have achieved respected positions in schools, colleges, and professional associations. They have received many awards and tributes from the general public as well as their colleagues. They have provided excellent examples of the important role that girls and women can play in the field of physical education. As a result, more girls will try to emulate them.

## TIPS FOR QUALIFIED TEACHER TO FOLLOW IN SECURING A POSITION IN PHYSICAL EDUCATION

Some advice that will help the qualified teacher in landing the right job is incorporated in the following five points:

1. *Start early.* Start looking well in advance of the time you want to start to work. Administrators plan far ahead of their needs. "The early bird catches the worm" may be true in your case. Know what you want and start early to get it.

2. *Know where the jobs are.* Do considerable research to find out what positions are available. Talk with your friends and alumni, register with the placement bureau, write school systems where you would like to work. Write the letter of inquiry with care. Give enough information about yourself to evoke interest, use good English and form, and have the letter typewritten.

3. *Have your credentials up to date.* Select with care and then contact the persons you would like to use for references. Ask if you may use their names. Prepare a list of your qualifications— personal, training, experience, and any other information in which a prospective employer might be interested. Fill out the forms required by the university placement bureau. Register with a commercial agency if you feel it will help, but be selective and use an agency that is particular about its candidates.

Many state education associations and state departments of education also provide placement services for a small fee. Some education associations place non-members as well as members. The American Association for Health, Physical Education, and Recreation maintains a placement service for its members. It sends personal data forms of qualified applicants to employers and then employers make all further contacts directly with applicants. Members of the Association who desire to enroll with this placement service should request personal data forms from the National Office, AAHPER Placement Service. An AAHPER placement booth is also maintained each year at the national convention to assist members who desire to seek new positions. Approximately 2,000 members are registered with the service at the present time.

4. *Write an application letter that will land the job.* In writing a letter of application, use good form, be sincere, appeal to the interest of the employer, offer a service rather than apply for a job, and be specific as to your qualifications.

5. *Leave a favorable impression during the interview.* The interview is the culmination of the search. Dress conservatively, put on a smile, use a firm handshake, be on time, answer questions directly, talk so you can be heard, volunteer any information you feel is important, and listen to what the employer says.

*Good luck!*

## SUMMARY

The old adage that there is always a job for a good person is usually true in the field of physical education. Students who have the essential qualifications for this work and who conscientiously apply themselves should not have any difficulty in finding employment in a setting that will utilize their training and fulfill their ambitions.

The value of physical education to enriched living and its potentialities for building a better society are being increasingly recognized by the public. There is ample room for many qualified young men and women in this growing profession. There is no room for those who cannot meet the professional standards that have been established. Therefore the best advice that can be offered to a student who desires to find employment in physical education is, first, to make sure that he is equipped to do the job. If he is not, then he should seek other fields of endeavor where his talents can be more effectively utilized. If he is qualified, then he should feel confident of the future because he is a member of a profession that is just beginning to realize its potentialities.

## QUESTIONS AND EXERCISES

1. Why should there be more employment opportunities for physical educators during the next decade?
2. What are the implications for the recognition of the value of physical education in times of peace and in times of national emergency?
3. What are some of the advantages the physical education profession offers that other types of work do not offer?
4. Make a list of some laws and rules and regulations that have recently been enacted that point to an emphasis on physical education.
5. How does the number of members in the teaching profession compare to the professions of medicine, law, and clergy?
6. What are the predictions for school enrollments during the next decade?
7. What are the trends in higher education?
8. Make a bar graph that depicts the expected increase in school enrollment over the next five years.
9. Compare the predictions for school enrollments on the elementary school level with those on the secondary school level.
10. What advances have been made during the last ten years in respect to teachers' salaries?
11. What are the professional standards for teachers' salaries that have been established by the National Education Association Commission on Teacher Education and Professional Standards?
12. How do the states in your particular section of the country rank as to the average annual salaries of teachers?

## SELECTED REFERENCES

American Association for Health, Physical Education, and Recreation: Vocational guidance series, No. 3. Physical education, a profession for men, Washington, D. C., 1946, The Association.

American Association for Health, Physical Education, and Recreation: Physical education and coaching as your career, Washington, D. C., The Association.

American Association for Health, Physical Education, and Recreation: Careers in physical education for girls, Washington, D. C., The Association.

American Association for Health, Physical Education, and Recreation: Recreation—A new profession for our time, Washington, D. C., The Association.

American Association for Health, Physical Education, and Recreation: Health education as your career, Washington, D. C., The Association.

Bureau of Labor Statistics, U. S. Department of Labor: Employment outlook for elementary and secondary school teachers, Bulletin No. 972, Washington, D. C., U. S. Government Printing Office.

Clarke, H. Harrison: Select your physical educator with care, Education 68:463, April, 1948.

Conant, James Bryant: The education of American teachers, New York, 1963, McGraw-Hill Book Co.

Marsh, Robert R.: How about recreation, New York, 1966, New York State Recreation Society.

National Education Association Research Division: Teacher supply and demand in universities, colleges, and junior colleges, Washington, D. C., 1965, NEA Publication.

National Education Association: A new look at teachers supply and demand, NEA Research Bulletin, Vol. 44, May, 1966.

National Education Association: Salaries in higher education, NEA Research Bulletin, Vol. 44, May, 1966.

National Education Association: Salary schedule for public junior colleges, NEA Research Bulletin, Vol. 44, October, 1966.

National Education Association Research Division: Teacher supply and demand in public schools, Washington, D. C., 1966, NEA Publication.

Publications of the National Education Association concerned with the future of education.

Publications of the U. S. Office of Education on future school enrollments.

U. S. Department of Labor: 1966–1967 occupational outlook handbook, Washington, D. C., 1967, Department of Labor.

U. S. Office of Education: Teaching as a career, Washington, D. C., 1963, U. S. Government Printing Office.

Wynn, Richard: Careers in education, New York, 1960, McGraw-Hill Book Co.

# Chapter 25

# Challenges facing physical education

Physical education has great promise as an emerging profession if it faces up to the many challenges that are presenting themselves. Whether or not these potentialities are realized will be determined to a great extent by the professional student in teacher-training institutions at the present time. Professional students who have chosen physical education as a career can accept these challenges with firm resolve and strive to meet them, or they can sit idly by and allow their chosen field of endeavor to drift into ineffectiveness and aimlessness. They are the leaders of tomorrow. Upon their shoulders falls the responsibility of establishing their work as a recognized essential to enriched living.

This book has attempted to show what an outstanding field of endeavor physical education is for the student who has a sincere interest in this work. It has attempted to point out such things as an interpretation of the true meaning of physical education, the diversified types of work and settings where it takes place, its need in present-day living, its scientific bases, and the duties and requirements of its leadership. This book has attempted to impress upon the student's mind his or

her part in raising the profession to lofty heights.

A national survey of recognized leaders in the field of physical education identified what are some of the greatest challenges facing physical education today. These include the following:

1. The need to recruit men and women into the field who will gain the respect that physical education needs in modern-day education. These men and women should be scholars, dedicated, enthusiastic professionals, and motivated to help physical education gain greater stature and self-respect.

2. The need to develop programs of physical education that will be meaningful to students while they are in school and will also leave an imprint on their lives after they graduate.

3. The need to develop programs described by the term physical education rather than physical training. The need to develop a program of physical education for each educational level, elementary through college, that is meaningful, progressive, sequential, and identifies basic concepts that guide professionals in their day-to-day work.

4. The need to develop a research program that clarifies and develops a body of knowledge and support for the relationship of physical activity to the psychological, sociological, and intellectual development of human beings. Such knowledge would represent the foundation upon which a professional program is built. Furthermore, there should be more research in rela-

tion to the contribution that physical education can make to the physically handicapped, mentally retarded, and emotionally disturbed.

5. The need to find ways of interpreting to the various publics a more accurate and complete understanding of what physical educators are trying to do.

6. The need to better define the relationship of physical education, health education, and recreation and to determine how all can work together in a manner that helps each area to grow and prosper.

7. The need to bridge the gap between theory and research and practice, so that what has been pioneered through sound scientific research in our colleges and universities and by leaders in the field will be implemented and interpreted at the grass roots level or the action level by our practitioners.

8. The need to place more stress on elementary school physical education, with men and women trained as specialists for this responsibility.

As a closing chapter of this book, the author would like to list and very briefly discuss what he considers to be some of the greatest challenges facing the physical education profession today. It is hoped that the student will keep these in mind and attempt to meet them wherever they may appear in his work. In so doing, physical education can be aided in realizing its potentialities.

In the first chapter, the qualities of leadership that are necessary if physical education is to become a profession in the true sense of the word were pointed out. The trends show us that future leaders in physical education must play certain roles, whether that of a teacher or practitioner, researcher, administrator, professor who specializes in history and philosophy, or some other role. Leaders are needed who are well prepared for their work and are motivated in pursuing excellence in their position, whatever it is. In order to have such leadership, it means that physical education must be selective in the students it admits to such careers. All persons who apply will not be qualified to enter. Furthermore, it means that individuals who use the term "physical educator" for commercial reasons,

*Toledo Public Schools, Toledo, Ohio.*

There is a need to place more stress on elementary school physical education.

such as strength builders, female slenderizers, and so-called physical fitness experts, must be labeled for what they are. There must be a clear identification in the public's mind as to who is and who is not the professionally trained physical education person.

## CHALLENGE OF LEADERSHIP

Physical education desperately needs qualified leadership. This is the key to the realization of many of the potentialities of physical education. Students going into this work as a career should realize that in order to be an asset to this emerging profession they should be enthusiastic and interested in their work; possess the competencies, knowledges, and attitudes necessary to do a good job; and accept the challenges and responsibilities that go with their positions. This type of leadership does not exist in sufficient amount at the present time. Standards must be established that allow only qualified individuals to become members of the profession. This challenge must be met if physical education is to be a respected profession and one in which the public has faith and can place its trust.

### Methods by which more outstanding leaders may be attracted to physical education

1. *Make physical education a respected profession so that the best high school students will want to join the ranks.* A person looks at the law or medical profession and finds respect for an intellectual discipline that has prestige in our society. This respect and prestige were developed only as it became recognized that the leaders in these professions were well-qualified for their positions, guided by high ethical standards, and recognized as rendering an outstanding service to society. We must have scholarly individuals in physical education who possess the physical skills but, at the same time, pos-

sess the mental capacity to understand the psychological, sociological, and biological foundations upon which their field rests.

2. *Raise the standards of admission to the profession.* The American Association for Health, Physical Education, and Recreation's decision to allow only students to enter the profession who graduate from accredited colleges and universities is a very commendable step forward. It will help to raise admission standards in our institutions of higher learning. But it is only a beginning. We must be very selective in our choice of colleagues. Young people who are admitted should be required to struggle and work hard and then feel honored they are permitted to join the ranks.

3. *Initiate a concerted recruitment drive for outstanding students.* Science, business, and other vocations are exerting major pressures to find the best young people in the country. National Merit Scholarship winners are sought after as feverishly as potential All-American football players. Physical education must also seek with all its vigor and strength to interest and recruit the best young people for their field of work. We are not going to get these people by sitting back and wishing. It will be accomplished only through hard work and professional persuasiveness.

4. *Upgrade professional-preparing programs.* Teacher-training institutions represent a key setting for improving the quality of leadership that comes into our professional field. The quality of the staff, number of books in the library, course offerings, facilities for research and laboratory work, and the general education offering are a few of the essentials necessary for an excellent professional-preparing program. Accrediting procedures must ensure that institutions meet acceptable standards and train professional leadership and that those that fail to meet the

standards will not be permitted to offer work in our field.

5. *Aim for more uniformity in certification requirements among the various states.* The degree to which certification requirements vary from state to state is a factor that needs attention. Some states permit teaching of physical education with only a few semester hours of course work. Others require as many as thirty-six semester hours plus prerequisite science. There must be greater uniformity of stringent requirements for teaching physical education. Since education is a state responsibility, this is a difficult task. However, our associations can help considerably in urging our various states to upgrade their requirements in accordance with standards recommended by the profession.

6. *Have each member of the profession become an ambassador.* Each member of the profession must take it upon herself or himself to build an image of physical education that is characterized by respect, scholarly endeavor, and a dedication to serving humanity. As each person attempts to improve his or her own qualities, academicians, educators, and the public in general will realize that physical education is an important phase of total education and deserves their support.

## CHALLENGE OF MAKING ATHLETICS MORE EDUCATIONAL

Educators have lost the battle for a sound sports program in many of our educational institutions. The commercial interests have reaped a bonanza from a gigantic sports boom; the sportswriters have found a gold mine in copy for their newspapers, and radio and television programs; and parents have found pleasure in basking in the limelight of their children's athletic achievements. Educators must assume the leadership role just as they do in other aspects of the school program—in mathematics, history, science, and foreign languages. We need a *New*

*Athletics* in our schools and colleges today—athletics that we can rightfully label educational athletics, as contrasted with the highly competitive spectacular form where athletes are selected and trained to please the rabid customers in the stands, rather than using sports as a means of individual self-improvement.

In other areas and fields of specialization in the schools we seem very much concerned about having a sound educational program that uses the developmental aspects of child growth as guidelines, and we demond progression and sequential development of subject matter. Yet, when it comes to athletics, we become indifferent, bowing to community pressures, and ignoring the way children grow and develop. For example, one can hardly recognize the sequential development of our athletic experiences from the grades to college. They should progress gradually and smoothly from the informal type of activity, the low intensity of competition, and the fundamental skills to the more highly organized activities, higher intensity of competition, and more complex skills. The way the athletic program is conducted in many schools, however, seems to follow an adult formula which is projected downward upon our children and youth, instead of being developmental and progressive in approach.

A coach in California, who says he is traditionally thought of by his students as a rugged, tough, crusty old coach, relates the story of a *boy,* a *hope,* and a *truth.* It happened when Bobby Palacio, a 14½-year-old, ninth-grade Mexican boy, attempted to break a rope-climbing record. There was a question of whether this skinny lad had actually touched the height needed. When the coach, realizing the importance of this teachable moment, asked the boy whether he had succeeded, the class abruptly stopped their cheering, and an oppressive silence settled over the gymnasium. Many boys had trained and dreamed of such an accomplishment; this was a big moment in their lives.

The answer to the coach's question was obvious as the boy, with tears in his eyes, shook his head negatively. But recognizing Bobby's moment of greatness in telling the truth which only he knew, the coach gave him a pat on the back and encouraged him to try again. With the coach and everyone pulling hard for him, he squirmed and struggled up the rope to victory.

Bobby was a champion. But there was still another hero—the coach. His stan-

## AVERAGE P.E. BUDGETS
(NOT INCLUDING INTERSCHOLASTIC ATHLETIC PROGRAM)

| Level | Cost/student | Av'ge cost/District |
|---|---|---|
| ELEMENTARY | $ .67 | $ 6,000.00 |
| JR. HIGH | 2.34 | 6,670.00 |
| HIGH SCHOOL (By District Enrollment) | | |
| under 1000 | 13.70 | 6,610.00 |
| 1000 – 5000 | 10.20 | 11,120.00 |
| over 5000 | 2.40 | 22,200.00 |

## COST - HIGH SCHOOL INTERSCHOLASTIC ATHLETIC PROGRAM

| District Enrollment | Cost/student | Av'ge cost/District |
|---|---|---|
| under 1000 | No. of participants not known | $ 8,585.00 |
| 1000 - 5000 | | 20,900.00 |
| over 5000 | | 95,625.00 |

## DEFICIT SPENDING - HIGH SCHOOL INTERSCHOLASTIC ATHLETIC PROGRAM

| District Enrollment | % of Districts reporting cost of program exceeds gate receipts | Am't of deficit reported by individual schools | |
|---|---|---|---|
| | | Min. | Max. |
| under 1000 | 62% | $ 21.00 | $ 22,296.00 |
| 1000 - 5000 | 43% | 1500.00 | 20,500.00 |
| over 5000 | 37% | 15,652.00 | 164,445.00 |

*From Texas Engineering Experiment Station: Partial shelter for physical education: A study of the feasibility of the use of limited shelters for physical education, College Station, Texas, 1961, Texas A & M University.*

An interpretation of program costs.

dard of values and leadership left an impact for good, not only on the boy but on the entire class and school as well. This man was interested in putting education into sports and athletics.

Do coaches always use the tools of their trade as forces for educational good? Evidently not, if the words of Dr. James Bryant Conant are any indication. The former president of Harvard refers to school sports as the "poison ivy" of education. Unfortunately, there are many educators who agree with him.

What should be our course of action? Should we roll with these lethal punches and refer to such academicians as ivy-towered educators who never had the guts to get in there and win for dear old State? Or should we recognize that at times it is difficult to see the relationship between football, basketball, or baseball and the objectives of education? I think most of us would agree there is some truth in the little verse:

> *Games are evil, games are good;*
> *Oft are games misunderstood.*

Everything virtuous is not found in books; one cannot equate all education with academic attainment. But every once in a while physical educators get a hollow feeling in their stomachs because sports, with their great drive for youth, are not meeting their educational challenge. Students tend to idolize the coach. Youngsters live in the shadows of Mickey Mantle, Joe Namath, and Oscar Robertson. Yet, with all the potential packed into sports, they are not used as a medium of education to the extent they should be. We need to do more than develop such qualities as courage, strength, teamwork, and self-discipline—as important as they are. We must also recognize that education is primarily concerned with the development of the mind and also try to help in exercising the brain as well as the muscle cells.

Each coach has his own ideas as to the place of athletics in the schools and colleges of this nation. He has seen the worth of sports as well as the abuses. And for this reason, those who have glimpsed athletics as an effective medium of education know what can be accomplished.

It should be made clear that physical educators are not for less but for more athletics, not for a de-emphasis but a re-emphasis along educational lines, not for fewer players but more players, and not for insecure coaches but ones who are regular members of the faculty with tenure and all the other privileges enjoyed by full-fledged teachers and professors. These goals can be reached if we make athletics more educational.

I can remember a speech Branch Rickey gave in which he was comparing our school sports to professional athletics. He said in effect:

> The *professional* is in a game where he can scarcely afford to lose.
> *We* are in a game in which we should not engage unless we can afford to lose.
> The *professional* has his eyes on gate receipts.
> *We* have our eyes on the player.
> The *professional* puts a $ sign on muscle.
> *We* should never put a $ sign on muscle.
> The *professional* stresses ideas that will make money.
> *We* should stress ideals that will make men.
> The *professional* fights for individual honors.
> *We* should fight for the educational good that will accrue to all participants.

Ten ways that we might consider in making athletics more educational are as follows:

1. *Give the player more opportunities to think rather than usurping the privilege for ourselves.* Let us reverse the trend that seems to be for the coach to call the plays, plan the strategies, and do the thinking. Today, the coach sends in a substitute to call the pass play, yells from the sidelines for the change to a zone offense, and flashes the signal for the player to keep the bat on his shoulder. The

player is a puppet to be manipulated by the man on the bench. In our desire to sip from the victory cup we may forget that the more thinking that is done by the players, the more educational the activity becomes.

2. *Have shorter practice sessions.* A famous coach once said that what cannot be accomplished in 1 or 1½ hours of practice is not worthwhile. Perhaps if we paid more attention to the organization of practices and carefully evaluated the worth of longer sessions, we might be able to arrange shorter periods. In turn, this would provide many more hours of study for the player. As a result, both the coach and the player would benefit. The student would have a better chance to be a success in his studies, and scholastic ineligibility would be less likely.

3. *Provide for brainstorming sessions.* The coach might be surprised how creative some of his players are in thinking up new plays, new strategies, and new ideas for overwhelming the opposition. A regular brainstorming session would enable the players to get their intellectual machinery into action and the coach and team to be a better ball club.

4. *Furnish tutors out of the athletic treasury for those players who need special help in their studies.* Athletic monies are used to buy drinks for members of the press and better accommodations for the spectators. What better way can such money be used than to help players who are having scholastic difficulties? Tutoring for students who are delinquent in their studies would reap rich rewards.

5. *Develop an attitude of respect for scholarly endeavor.* Young people in school and college are passing through a formative period when attitudes are developed and values are stabilized. The coach is in a position to help shape a boy's outlook by stressing the importance of sports and athletics as a *means to an end—not an end in themselves.* We all

know examples of some coaches who have encouraged their players to enroll in snap courses, sign up for the most lenient professors, and get by as easily as possible in order to stay eligible for varsity competition. In such cases a detrimental imprint is being left upon the boy for the rest of his life. Players should meet the same academic requirements as all students and should recognize that the player who is most valuable to the squad and the team is the one who is a good student.

6. *Make coaches recognized members of the faculty.* Athletics are *a part* of education and not *apart from it.* Similarly, the coach should be a member of the faculty and enjoy all rights and privileges attendant thereto, including tenure and retirement benefits. For such a condition to exist, the coach must assume his responsibility in seeing that athletics contribute to educational goals and that he himself is an active member of the staff. This means playing an active part in faculty meetings and other school activities where policy is formed and educational programs developed.

7. *Keep players on the squad—do not cut.* In our comprehensive system of American education, we do not deny any boy the right to take courses in English or history. Neither should we deny any student the right to engage in athletics. If a boy voluntarily desires to go out for a team and is willing to spend the time and energy involved, then the opportunity should be provided for this experience, even though he may not be highly skilled. The educational potentials are great when there is built-in self-propulsion. We should exploit such opportunities. It may be that the contributions we make to the less-skilled boy are even greater than the ones we make to the gifted athlete. It is said that President Kennedy was not too skilled, but the fact that he was kept on the squad was not without its rewards.

8. *Allow players to take charge at*

*times.* Part of the training at West Point is a requirement that each cadet must coach and organize a team. The military academy has found this experience develops leadership and turns out better graduates. The services of varsity players could be used in junior varsity, intramurals, and sports days at great advantage to both the player and the school. This also enables players to devise their own plays and strategies and then to see how they work under actual game situations.

9. *Hire coaches as much for their educational qualifications as for their win-loss record and file of newspaper clippings.* It is important to have coaches who have been great players themselves and who know sports inside and out. However, since they are in the business of education as much as the teacher or professor of mathematics, it is also important they have a cultural background as well. If they are to be regular members of the faculty, they should meet educational standards required for membership in such a distinguished group.

10. *Emphasize the player rather than the spectator.* The tackle, forward, or first baseman is the one attending school or college—not the rooter in the stands. Rule changes should be designed to improve the player's status instead of helping make the turnstiles click faster. The focus of attention at all times should be that of providing an athletic experience for the player that is safe, free from undesirable pressures, and educational in nature.

## CHALLENGE OF A "SOFT" AMERICA

Some experts say that America's high standard of living is making her citizens "soft." Recent research has suggested that lack of activity is resulting in a weak and physically unfit population. This is a matter of concern to the President of the United States.

The resources of physical education must be mobilized to meet the needs created by this "soft" condition. This country is passing through troubled times, when every profession, organization, and individual must contribute to the welfare and strength of the nation. Physical education, by its very nature, has much to contribute.

In order to contribute to the maximum degree of effectiveness, vigorous physical education programs must be instituted that provide ample opportunities for successful experiences and fun, and that stimulate physical, mental, emotional, and social fitness.

If these goals are to be accomplished, elementary school physical education must be well organized in terms of children's needs, interests, and abilities. Adequate time, facilities, and leadership must be provided to meet these essentials. On the high school level, all pupils should have a daily period of instruction that allows for a vigorous workout, adequate instruction, showers, and the realization of social, emotional, and mental objectives. In schools and agencies where limitations enter the picture, a continuous effort should be made to overcome these difficulties and accomplish the goals. On the college level, activities should be offered that develop sufficient strength, endurance, stamina, and vitality, together with mental and emotional fitness, to withstand the increased stresses of military and civilian life. In the adult population every effort should be put forth to develop individuals who possess total fitness for their duties during the unstable times through which they are passing.

Participants in physical education programs should be classified in such a manner that provision can be made for individual differences and capacities. A well-rounded program should be engaged in by all. Aquatic skill should be emphasized. Athletics for all, through intramural and interscholastic sports, should be an important part of the program. Provision for the handicapped should be made. Boards of education should provide funds for the essentials with which to conduct such programs, nonschool and school resources should be utilized, physical fitness achievement standards should be met, and everything else should be done that will help in establishing a healthier and a more totally fit population.

Physical education should accept this challenge with firm resolve and recognize that this is an opportunity where it can realize many of its potentialities and where it can render a great service to the nation and to the world.

## CHALLENGE PRESENTED BY PUBLIC MISUNDERSTANDING OF PHYSICAL EDUCATION

Physical education is one of the most misunderstood professions in the world today. The average person is not aware of what it can offer to him as an individual or to society as a whole. There is ample evidence that it is still regarded as a "frill," that people think of it as a good means of entertainment but not connected with successful living, and that it is something to be tolerated in education but has no value in realizing educational objectives. In many schools, physical education is the last activity to be scheduled and the first to be canceled for special activities. Credit in physical education is not required for graduation in some schools. Few, if any, colleges require a unit of physical education as an entrance requirement as they do in many of the so-called academic subjects. Insufficient time, space, facilities, and 60 to 100 students in each physical education class are characteristic of many schools. Furthermore, children are not classified homogeneously for classes because of administrative misunderstanding.

These are only a few of the examples that may be listed as evidence of misun-

derstanding on the part of the public. Such a condition must be corrected if physical education is to realize its potentialities. The student should realize that this is one major problem with which he is confronted and should utilize every opportunity to interpret physical education in its true prospective.

## CHALLENGE OF PLACING PHYSICAL EDUCATION IN A DEFENSIBLE POSITION

Physical education is not in a desirable defensible position at the present time. Evidence of this is the lack of answers to the following questions. At what grade or age level should each of the activities that comprise the physical education program be introduced for optimum learning efficiency? What are the individual achievement standards in activities at various age and grade levels? What are the scientific evaluative instruments available for measuring the importance of physical education activities in developing good human relations? How effective is physical education in developing interpretive thinking? Why should physical education be required at all educational levels? What contribution does physical education make to general education? What subject-matter facts and knowledge do we have that justifies physical education's rightful place in education? What is the relationship of physical activity to physical, psychological, and sociological development?

These are a few of the many questions that physical education cannot answer satisfactorily. If the profession is to serve the individual and society in the best way possible and if it is to be interpreted to the public in its correct light, the answers to these and many other questions should be secured. The scientific process of selection, evaluation, and adaptation of activities is the heart of the physical education profession and yet remains largely unsolved. Desired levels of accomplishment in organic skill, knowledge, and adaptation for each age and grade level should be clearly defined. The student who is interested in delving into research will find many opportunities for utilizing his talents. Research in physical education is becoming increasingly important, and students in professional schools today will be the ones to find many of the answers needed to place physical education in a truly defensible position.

## CHALLENGE OF CURRICULUM REVISION

Physical education is being challenged to revise its curriculum. In too many schools the same activities are taught over and over again, there is a lack of organization and progression, and the standards vary from school to school and state to state. Physical education is one of the few areas that has failed to do a major curriculum revision during recent educational history. Although a few leaders are cognizant of this, many of our practitioners have been oblivious to the patterns of curriculum change that are emerging in other areas of the educational curriculum. Examples can be found where schools offer such sports as basketball, volleyball, and softball for as many as six years in a row. If such repetition were practiced in other curriculum areas, it would not be tolerated, and such practices must be seriously questioned for physical education, in light of the many new advances that are taking place in education.

Any curriculum revision must also look carefully at the Movement movement. We must ask the question, "Does physical education have a body of knowledge, and, if so, what is it?" Is it the science of human movement or not? What is the role of movement education as expressed in Chapter 13? If this is our discipline, how can we most effectively communicate a correct view of this subject to all concerned? Physical education has suffered

from lack of identification of an adequate framework of knowledge and role in education. If the Movement movement is the answer, it should be given much more attention by physical educators.

## CHALLENGE OF REEVALUATING THE SCHOOL PROGRAM

The educational system, to a great degree, has failed to accomplish many of the objectives that it has established for itself: health, ethical character, worthy use of leisure, worthy home membership, and citizenship. The increased number of cases of mental illness in this country, the evidence supplied on the extent of crime and immorality in the United States, the quest for material rather than spiritual values, public indifference to public administration, increased divorce rates, and juvenile delinquency are problems that show that the whole educational structure of this country needs reevaluating.

The belief that a knowledge of facts will result in successful living seems to have been the premise upon which the present educational structure rests, and this has proved to be a fallacy. Education should result in changed behavior and in social, physical, mental, and emotional betterment. The evidence, however, does not point to such an accomplishment. Therefore the reevaluation of the whole educational structure should be made to determine what is the best type of education for successful living.

In such a reevaluation it seems that consideration should be given to determining what the physical, mental, emotional, and social needs of individuals are and then to include experiences in the curriculum that will meet these needs. Through such a study it might be discovered that many of the present offerings do not contribute to meeting such needs. Perhaps some of those that are being slighted in many of our schools at the present time would be found to be of much more value than previously determined. Under existing conditions, although health is listed as the first objective, how many schools adequately provide the proper health service, healthful school living, and health instruction for their students? How many schools provide planned instruction in physical activities suited to the sex, grade, ability, and special needs of pupils? How many schools place the same high priority on the physical, mental, emotional, and social health of the individual as they do on his ability to acquire facts in such areas as mathematics, English, Latin, and history?

A thorough reevaluation should bring to light the important role that physical education can play in the educational process. Students should recognize this challenge and aggressively agitate for reevaluation of the educational system. In this way they will be helping physical education to realize its potentialities.

## SUMMARY

Physical education has been effectively contributing to the betterment of society since ancient times. However, it can do a better job; it can be a greater profession; it can contribute more to enriched living for the total population. These achievements will be possible if the professional students of physical education in our schools take up the many challenges that confront their field of endeavor and, after careful thought and deliberation, devise plans that will result in physical education achieving its true potentialities. Physical education is proud of those qualified students now training for this specialized work. It has faith in them to do the job and knows they will accept the challenges facing their field of endeavor. It wishes them the best of success and the most of happiness in a field of endeavor that has no equal for satisfaction derived from conscientious efforts.

### QUESTIONS AND EXERCISES

1. Survey ten leaders in the field of physical education and determine what they believe are the challenges facing the profession of physical education in the next ten years.
2. Survey your own community to determine the challenges facing physical education in your community.
3. Read ten books published on education in the past five years to determine the challenges facing physical education in the years ahead.

### SELECTED REFERENCES

Read all copies of the Journal of Health, Physical Education, and Recreation for the past two years.

# Index

100     60

100
200

200

57

200

43